COLLEGE GEOGRAPHY

CASE · BERGSMARK

COLLEGE
GEOGRAPHY

THIRD EDITION
Revised by

Earl C. Case
UNIVERSITY OF CINCINNATI

New York · JOHN WILEY & SONS, *Inc.*
London · CHAPMAN & HALL, *Limited*

PREFACE
To the Third Edition

The work of the second revision of *College Geography* was interrupted and saddened by the death of Professor Daniel R. Bergsmark. The revision was further delayed during World War II and the immediate postwar period in order to incorporate some of the major problems of human adjustment and maladjustment caused by the war, and also to evaluate some of the geographic problems created by the increasing interests and responsibilities of the United States in other parts of the world.

In revising *College Geography*, I have kept five major purposes in mind, namely: (1) to reweight the subject matter in the light of events that have taken place since 1940 and to expand the textual materials on those areas that have recently become of increasing importance to the United States; (2) to add physiographic diagrams and place and distribution maps which make the textual materials more vivid; (3) to enrich the text in principles and to eliminate any purely descriptive matter; (4) to bring all charts, graphs, and subject matter up to date; and (5) to indicate *trends* in geographic developments in order to avoid any implications that human adjustment to environment is a static condition.

Several areas are treated more fully in the third edition. The most notable example is the Pacific Ocean. A new chapter, "Tropical and Semi-Tropical Islands of the Pacific," has been added. The addition of this chapter is desirable because of our increasing interests and responsibilities in the Pacific where, in 1947, the United States was given the *sole* and *permanent* trusteeship of 623 islands (829 square miles of land now officially named "The Territory of the Pacific Islands") that are spread over an area about the size of the United States.

The textual materials have been expanded on the U.S.S.R., the Orient, western Europe (especially the Ruhr), and the borderlands of the Arctic Ocean. All these areas have become more important to the American people since the book was first written.

Some of the textual materials, especially the chapters entitled "Our Climatic Environment" and "The Geographical Significance of Soils," have been simplified, clarified, and in places expanded.

Place maps, topographic maps, and maps that show the distribution of resources, products, and industries have been added. These maps, such as the one showing the distribution of coal, iron ore, and petroleum resources of the U.S.S.R., together with other maps that show the distribution of other important mineral resources, climatic belts, agricultural belts, ice-filled coastal waters, and distribution of major crops of the U.S.S.R., will help students to understand some of the reasons for Russia's potential strength. They will also help the students to visualize some of Russia's problems and weaknesses.

Wherever statistics of production are provided, the author has either shown the long-time trends or has given, at least in most cases, data of production both for the years prior to World War II and for postwar years. These two sets of data permit a study of the influences of World War II in many fields of activity and in many areas; they also afford numerous examples of new adjustments to the natural environment whenever the more or less normal social order has been disrupted. The two sets of data emphasize the fact that man is often compelled to make a new adjustment to the natural environment to fit, in so far as is possible, changes in the social environment.

EARL C. CASE

January 1949

PREFACE
To the First Edition

College Geography is intended to meet the need of an increasing number of departments of geography in universities, colleges, and normal schools which are emphasizing the regional and economic phases of the subject in their beginning courses, usually designated as world geography, elements of geography, or principles of geography.

Although *College Geography* is intended as a survey of the subject for students in their early years in college, it may be used as a textbook in the latter years of high school, especially if the teachers have had sufficient training in the subject to be able to elucidate the more difficult parts of the text. It should also be a valuable aid as a reference book for high-school teachers and pupils in schools using a more elementary textbook.

Several years of experience in teaching geography to students in the colleges of Education, Commerce and Business, and Applied Arts have convinced the authors that a basic course in the principles of geography is the best foundation for future work in the subject, whether the student expects to major in commerce and perhaps become a marketing expert, or in education and become a teacher. The organization and materials presented in this book are intended to meet the needs for such a basic course in geography. Thus while the book presents a bird's-eye view of geography to the students who do not intend to pursue the subject further, it also lays the foundations for more detailed and advanced study.

The first four chapters treat of the significance of climate, land forms, soils, and space relationship to human activities, and give a working knowledge of the principles of these subjects for future use in the study of economic and regional geography. For example, if one wishes to know something of the effect of climate on human activities one must first know something of the climatic characteristics of the region under consideration. But any attempt to learn the characteristics of a region without first learning a few of the most basic principles of climate is likely to result in unnecessary waste of effort by the mere memorizing of facts that should be understood. On the other hand, if the students understand the principles of monsoon winds, convection, the influence of temperature changes on the capacity of the air to hold moisture, and other fundamentals of climate, the study of the relation of climate to human affairs takes on more meaning and interest. The first four chapters of the book are intended, therefore, to give the student possession of the tools needed for later study of regional and economic geography.

Chapters V to XV are given to a study of regional geography based largely on climatic types. In several textbooks published recently special study has been made of some of these regions, such as the deserts, steppes, tundras, and rainy low latitudes, but, in so far as the authors know, this is the first attempt to give a systematic and geographic treatment of the entire world based on climatic types.

Since certain subjects such as the Mineral Industries, Trade and International Dependence, and Seas and their Economic Products are less closely related to climatic conditions than to other geographic factors, they have been treated separately in Chapters XVI to XXI.

In writing on a subject which has so challenged the attention of eminent scientists for centuries, and which has a relatively rich literature, the authors must naturally owe much to previous writers. Their numbers are so great that we are forced to limit ourselves to a general acknowledgment of our indebtedness. Grateful acknowledgment must be made to members of the Geology and Geography Department of the University of Cincinnati, especially to Dr. Nevin M. Fenneman, Dr. John L. Rich, Dr. Walter H. Bucher, and others, for helpful criticisms and suggestions in the preparation of this work. Special acknowledgment is due Dr. Howard H. Martin, of the University of Washington, Seattle, for contributing the chapter on the northern coniferous forest, and for his critical review of several other chapters. Thanks are due the United States Weather Bureau, the United States Department of Agriculture, and the United States Bureau of Reclamation for permission to use pictures which they had taken. Grateful acknowledgment is also due Mrs. Earl Case and Mrs. Daniel Bergsmark for their constant aid in the preparation of the book.

EARL C. CASE
DANIEL R. BERGSMARK

University of Cincinnati
September 9, 1932

CONTENTS

PART I OUR WORLD ENVIRONMENT

PART II CLIMATIC REGIONS AND HUMAN ACTIVITIES

PART III MINERALS AND MINERAL INDUSTRIES

PART IV   TRADE AND TRANSPORTATION

PART I

OUR WORLD ENVIRONMENT

Chapter 1

THE GEOGRAPHICAL SIGNIFICANCE
OF SPACE RELATIONSHIPS

Among the factors of the geographical environment, the space relationships—location, size, and form—are of fundamental importance. For centuries these factors have commanded the attention of the students of geography, as indicated in the writings of the early Greek geographers as well as those of the modern school. The Greek geographer was concerned mainly with the description of the earth, which must, of necessity, include concepts of the relationship of space. The modern geographer gives much attention to an interpretation of the distribution of land forms, climatic regions, resources, and peoples and their activities.

The advantages of favorable space relationships are clearly reflected in their effect on the national economy of powerful states. The great powers of the present day owe their significance in large part to the possession of favorable location, size, and form. When these factors are found in effective combination, they favor the development of world power, as in the United States—a country located in a temperate climate with easy access by ocean transportation to highly industrialized Europe on the one hand, and to the raw materials and rapidly expanding markets of the South American countries and the Orient on the other. It is, however, impossible to evaluate accurately the importance of America's location in terms of dollars and cents, educational advancement, political and industrial progress, or human happiness; but it is evident that this country is better off in all these respects than she would be with a location similar to that of land-locked U.S.S.R., where every outlet has been from time to time effectively closed by warring neighbors.[1]

[1] It is impossible to isolate entirely one geographic factor from all others while attempting to analyze its importance. The relation of climatic conditions to agricultural development cannot be separated wholly from soil fertility, plant and

LOCATION

In all man's activities—economic, social, and political—location plays a role of vast importance. Ellen Churchill Semple says that the location of a country or people is always the supreme geographical fact in its history.[2] Industry starts and develops in favorable locations; man's social status is modified and influenced by the conditions that exist in the area in which he is located; and the political power of a country or state is markedly affected by a combination of factors arising from its location.

Central versus Peripheral Location. From a geographical point of view, a central location means accessibility to other significant areas, favoring (1) a ready interchange of ideas, (2) the mingling of races, (3) the enrichment of language, (4) the growth of commercial relations, and (5) the expansion of political power. These effects of central location are well illustrated in Great Britain's relation to the lands of the North Atlantic, in Germany's situation in the heart of Europe, and in Italy's position in the Mediterranean. Historically, a central location gave the Magyars a controlling position in the Danube Valley, and the Iroquois tribes, located where the Mohawk Valley opened a way through the Appalachian barrier between the Hudson River and Lake Ontario, occupied a strategic position which gave them power and importance out of all proportion to their numbers.[3]

On the other hand, an area that has a peripheral location is distinctly handicapped in its national economy, since outside influences enter slowly, resulting in a retarded economic and social growth. In general, an area is seriously handicapped economically if it is inaccessible to the chief markets of the world. The paucity of outside influence frequently causes a meager national life and history.[4] In recent years,

animal resources, location, and other geographical factors, since the various geographical factors are so intimately bound together that man's adjustments are nearly always affected by all of them. Yet some one factor, such as isolation, desert climate, or lack of mineral resources, may be of such a dominant character in limiting man's opportunities that it commands special study.

[2] Ellen Churchill Semple, "Geographical Location as a Factor in History," *Bulletin of the American Geographical Society*, Vol. 40, p. 65.

[3] *Op. cit.*, p. 66.

[4] Effects of peripheral location may be seen in Chile, Australia, and New Zealand. Even on the west coast of the United States remarks may be heard about "you back in the States."

however, the ill effects of a marginal (peripheral) location have been mitigated by the development of rapid and cheap transportation.

Given a sufficiently long period of time, an area may actually pass from peripheral to central location. At the time Rome had reached her maximum power, the British Isles were located on the margin of civilization, whereas today Great Britain occupies a central position with reference to commerce and industry, being located on most of the important ocean routes of the world. Similarly, during the early stages of the development of the United States, the Thirteen Colonies occupied a distinctly peripheral location, whereas at present this area is becoming to an ever-increasing extent an important center which radiates its influence in every direction and is sensitive to changes which take place on any side. A famine in China, an earthquake in Japan, a drought in Australia, longer working hours in Russia, or a new medical discovery in Germany are recorded on the stock tape in Wall Street, and are discussed in tariff debates in Washington, in church pulpits, and in colleges and universities all over our land.

Strategic Locations. Throughout historic times, strategic locations or points of military advantage have been eagerly sought by contending powers. Political disputes have been waged and wars have been fought in order to obtain control of places that have strategic advantages. Such areas include straits, isthmuses, mouths of navigable rivers, and islands located on major ocean routes.

In Europe, Copenhagen and Istanbul (Constantinople) owe their importance in large measure to their control of narrow channels and straits. The situation of Copenhagen on the narrow strait or sound connecting the Baltic with the Skattegat, Skaggerak, and North Sea, has been a dominant factor in the city's development (Fig. 1). In controlling the outlet to the lands of the Baltic, Copenhagen was in a position to reap profits from the trade of that region, actually collecting dues on cargoes passing through the sound until the year 1857, when various nations paid her $20,000,000 to relinquish her claims. This strategic location has also subjected the city to attacks by belligerent powers during periods of war. She was attacked several times by the Hanseatic League; besieged by the Swedes in the seventeenth century; bombarded by the English, Dutch, and Swedes in 1700; and suffered grievously through sea fights and bombardments in 1800 and again in 1807. Since 1895, the relative importance of her location has been waning, in large measure because of the construction of the Kiel Canal, with its deeper channel and its more direct route between the Baltic lands and important trade areas adjacent to the North Sea.[5]

The straits of the Bosporus and Dardanelles represent one of the major zones of international strife in the world. These straits are economically, politically, socially, and strategically valuable to Russia as a passageway for her merchant marine and navy. Any powerful nation in control of these straits could, if it so desired, disrupt trade

Fig. 1. The strategic location of Copenhagen (Köbenhavn) on the sound, a narrow waterway that separates Sweden and Denmark.

over some of the most important commercial highways of the world; create political confusion in a part of the world that is politically unstable; and use the neighboring land zone as a military springboard against neighbors that are weak and divided.

The strategical significance of this zone has long been recognized and Istanbul (Constantinople) has been a military stronghold for centuries (Fig. 2). "Napoleon believed that its possession was worth half an empire. Even under the handicap of Turkish rule Constantinople remained a great port. Its position at the crossroads of Europe and Asia enabled it . . . to profit enormously from the trade of southern Russia, Transcaucasia, Persia, and Mesopotamia, and also, in earlier years, from the overland trade of Inner Asia, India, and the Far East. Through it ran a part of the Berlin-Bagdad railway line, by which

---

[5] The narrow strait or sound at Copenhagen is too shallow to permit the passage of the largest merchant vessels and men-of-war.

Germany expected to control the Near East and the road to India." [6]

The United States had military strategy in mind when the Virgin Islands were purchased from Denmark. These islands form a naval base from which protection may be extended to both the Straits of Florida and the Panama Canal. Until the United States bought the islands, there was always the danger that Denmark would sell them to some powerful European nation which might establish a foreign naval base in dangerous proximity to these narrow channels of commerce.

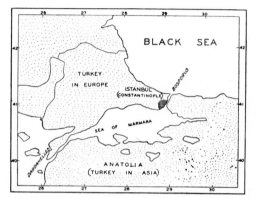

FIG. 2. The location of Istanbul (Constantinople). Napoleon once said that because of its location Constantinople was worth half an empire.

The strategic importance of a narrow land bridge or isthmus is well illustrated at Panama and the Isthmus of Suez. Both areas have arisen to great military importance, especially since canals have been opened through them. These canals—the Suez and Panama—are extraordinarily similar in many details. Both burrow their way through comparatively low necks of land; both are gateways of tremendous commercial importance; and both are controlled by great English-speaking nations.

The importance attached to the control of the Suez Canal by the British Government was clearly indicated when Egypt was granted her independence. One of the four major reservations made was intended to insure the safety of British communications, with special reference to the Suez Canal. This narrow passageway is a strategic link in the shortest route between Great Britain and her valuable possessions (or recent possessions that are still economically and com-

[6] From Isaiah Bowman's *The New World*, Fourth Edition, p. 409, copyright 1928, World Book Company.

mercially important to Great Britain) in East Africa, India, Malaya, the British East Indies, Hong Kong, Australia, New Zealand—a vast empire bordering the Indian Ocean and the western Pacific. Any interruption of trade through the Suez Canal would not only injure the markets of Great Britain but also weaken her control in the Far East.

The Panama Canal holds a key position between the Pacific and Atlantic similar to that which the Suez holds between the Atlantic and Indian oceans. Commercial products and naval vessels may be moved rapidly and economically. Thus it is desirable that the Panama Canal should be well protected in order to keep it open at all times.

The commerce through this narrow land bridge is growing so rapidly that steps are being considered for the construction of another interoceanic canal. Moreover, two water routes in this area would prove a distinct military asset. Under present conditions any obstruction that blocked the Panama Canal would effectually separate the Atlantic and Pacific fleets and seriously injure interoceanic trade.

Navigable rivers sometimes become the subject of international strife. Some rivers flow through or by several countries, tap areas rich in natural resources, and thereby become important arteries of commerce for several nations. A powerful country located athwart or at the mouth of such a river may cause international trouble by tying up the river traffic, especially in times of war, to the detriment of all other nations that wish to use the river.[7]

Not only river arteries but also some ocean routes are controlled from areas that are strategically located. These areas quite commonly consist of islands and headlands that may be used as naval bases and coaling stations on long and commercially important ocean lanes. One such ocean route, the Mediterranean, extends from northwestern Europe through the Mediterranean Sea, the Red Sea, and the Indian Ocean to India and other lands of the Orient. Owing to the great length of this route, steamships from Europe are forced to take on coal several times before the Orient is reached. Great Britain is much concerned over this road to India, formerly the most important of her possessions and still closely linked to her through investments and trade. Consequently Great Britain has secured and fortified a large number of islands and headlands distributed at strategic points along the route. Among these places, Gibraltar, Malta, and Cyprus have played important roles.

---

[7] The Danube River is an excellent example of a navigable stream that flows through several countries. Consequently its control creates from time to time serious international problems.

Geographical Location as a Factor in History. The location of a country or people is always one of the dominant geographical factors in its history. In fact, according to Ellen Churchill Semple, "it outweighs every other single geographical force.[8] All that has been said of Russia's vast area, of her steppes and tundra wastes, of her impotent seaboard on land-locked basins or ice-bound coasts, of her poverty of mountains, and wealth of minerals, fades into the background before her location on the border of Asia. From her defeat by the Tartar hordes in 1224 to her attack upon the Mongolian rulers of the Bosporus in 1877, and her more recent struggle[s] with Japan [Russo-Japanese War of 1904–1905, and again in World War II, 1945], most of her wars have been waged against Asiatics. Location made her the bulwark against Asiatic invasion and the Apostle of Western civilization to the heart of Asia. If this position on the outskirts of Europe, remote from its great centers of development, has made Russia only partially accessible to European culture and, furthermore, has subjected her to the retarding ethnic and social influences emanating from her Asiatic neighbors, and if the rough tasks imposed by her frontier situation have hampered her progress, these are all the limitations of her geographical location, limitations which not even the advantage of her vast area has been able to outweigh." [9]

There are many areas in the world where the people find themselves thrust into international affairs and creating world problems that are not of their making but are the result of their location. For example, on May 7, 1945, the date of Germany's unconditional surrender, at least ten strips of territory bordering the western U.S.S.R. and held by the U.S.S.R. either were claimed by other countries or sought independence, whereas nine strips of territory were held by other countries but were claimed by the Soviet Union. Each of these nineteen areas creates a political problem because of its location with respect to various countries, races, language groups, resources, trade routes, or other environmental factors.

A study of any one of these nineteen areas would indicate that the people faced problems that resulted from their location. For example, the location of Latvia between eastern and western Europe is one of the most important facts of its history. It forms part of a buffer zone

[8] Although it is doubtful if geographic forces can be isolated and weighted in the exact manner indicated, nevertheless it is quite evident that many characteristics of Russia's political and economic development are a direct result of her location.

[9] Ellen Churchill Semple, "Geographical Location as a Factor in History," *Bulletin of the American Geographical Society*, Vol. 40, p. 65.

between Nordic and Slavic Europe; it lies athwart one of the best trade routes between the Soviet Republics and the outside world; and it occupies a transitional position between races, nationalities, and cultures. The country is occupied by Letts, Russians, Germans, Poles, and Jews. The *Atlas of World Affairs* (1946) contains two maps that suggest the many problems created by location. The maps show areas that are called "hot spots" of the world and "hot spots" of Europe.[10] Each of these areas contains the germs of international strife because of its location.

Central Location a Factor in Business. The significance of central in comparison with peripheral location is strikingly illustrated in the value of land in the various parts of large cities. Almost every city has its "Loop," or business and financial district, which is usually centrally located and easily accessible to all parts of its respective urban agglomerations. The high value of sites at Wall Street and at 42nd Street in New York City, Fifth and Vine streets in Cincinnati, Seventh Street and Nicollet Avenue in Minneapolis, and Third Street and Wisconsin Avenue in Milwaukee, attest the importance of centrally located urban districts for business and financial transactions. Building sites in such districts are frequently five hundred to a thousand times as high in value as sites in the peripheral areas of these cities. For example, in 1930 several hundred feet of frontage on Vine and Fifth streets in Cincinnati sold at an average price of approximately $35,000 a front foot, whereas land in the marginal parts of this city brought only from $50 to $60 per foot.[11]

CENTRAL LOCATION AS ILLUSTRATED IN NEW YORK CITY. The highest land values in the city of New York are found in the Wall Street and 42nd Street sections. The Wall Street district, filled with high buildings, is dedicated to "finance." [12] The 42nd Street section is devoted primarily to amusements, retailing, and merchandising, although it has recently developed considerable importance as a miscellaneous office center and business center.

In Wall Street the managerial function of coordination is of major importance. This function does not require the transfer of huge quantities of material, but it deals almost exclusively with information.

[10] George H. Macfadden, Henry Madison Kendall, and George F. Deasy, *Atlas of World Affairs,* Thomas Y. Crowell, 1946, pp. 5 and 55.

[11] Data obtained from the Real Estate Board of Cincinnati.

[12] "Finance," as here used, includes the exchanges, the banks, the insurance offices, as well as offices of various professional groups, such as lawyers and accountants.

Here the all-important factor is the transportation of ideas, of intelligence. The mail, the cable, the telegraph, and the telephone bring in its raw material and carry out its finished product. Easy and speedy contact of man with man is essential. Thus such a district must be conveniently accessible and must be at the heart of the system of communication. This financial district is in effect one big structure where the skyscraper facilitates personal contacts in a way never possible before.

Location as a Factor in Industry. Accessibility both to raw materials and to markets is a prime requisite of rapid industrial progress, whereas isolation results in a paucity or stagnation of industrial growth. Regions that possess open and easily accessible routes for peaceful trade and communication and at the same time are readily defended against military aggressions are doubly blessed. This dual advantage of location is well illustrated in the British Isles, located near enough continental Europe to benefit from the advances in civilization that took place there, yet sufficiently removed from that land mass so that a large army has seldom been required to defend these islands against invasion. Men who otherwise would have had to serve in the militia were employed in creating wealth at home and in opening up new resources and markets abroad. This economic growth was a handmaiden of political expansion and world power.

The effect of location on a specific industry is well illustrated in the development of the British textile manufacture. Including the production of almost every variety of textiles, this industry was originally concerned mainly with the manufacture of woolens. In the development of textile manufactures, location with special reference to market and raw materials was a fundamental factor. The market was developed through a demand for woolens because of the cool, humid, marine climate; and the raw materials were present in the form of wool, water power, pure water, and coal. Moreover, isolation gave the British Isles an advantage over the continent proper, where wars were often destructive to the sheep industry and, therefore, to the production of raw wool.

The transition from the manufacture of woolens to the production of cotton textiles was easily effected, since the same general type of machinery is used in both industries.

The significance of location in industrial development is seen also in the United States. During the early history of this country industries were frequently located in many unfavorable places. Factories were sometimes built in a town for no better reason than the fact that the owner happened to live there. Many industrial plants had their beginnings in this way, in locations that now are thought of as having many disadvantages. "Since most factories were formerly located without any prior consideration of the advantages of different locations, some people have accepted the obvious inference that there is no logic in their present distribution; in other words there could be no such thing as a science of industrial geography. But the same conclusion would appear even more justified in agricultural geography, whereas O. E. Baker and others have shown that experience teaches even uneducated farmers to plant, not whatever occurs to them, but those crops which make the most profitable adjustment." [13] Similarly, in manufacturing, iron smelting was started, at one time or another, in every one of the Atlantic States, but, through a process of elimination in the least favorable and development in the most favorable places, the industry shifted to areas where optimum conditions are found.[14]

This shifting of industry is continuous, and it is affected by many factors. The most important of these have been indicated by F. H. Hall, who compiled statistical tables from the Twelfth Census of the United States.[15] Summarizing the results, he suggested seven factors that have a major bearing on industrial localization in this country: (1) proximity to raw materials, (2) nearness to market, (3) nearness to water power, (4) favorable climate, (5) supply of labor, (6) capital available for investment in manufactures, and (7) the momentum of an early start.

The relative importance of each of these factors varies greatly with the type of industry. Proximity to raw materials is an exceedingly important factor in copper smelting, because in most cases more than 96 per cent of the copper ore is waste. For example, in Utah millions of tons of ore are being mined that contain less than 1 per cent copper. The 99 per cent dross must be removed near the mine in order to save freight costs. In many chemical industries the raw materials and finished products are of relatively small bulk although large amounts of power are required in the processes of manufacture. Under such conditions, proximity to power resources may be of major importance.

Climate affects many industries directly. Cotton spinning can be carried on more efficiently in a moist atmosphere than in a dry one;

[13] R. Hartshorne, "Location as a Factor in Geography," *Annals of the Association of American Geographers*, Vol. 17, p. 95.

[14] *Ibid.*

[15] F. H. Hall, *The Localization of Industries*, XII Census, 1900, Part I, p. 190.

the meat-packing industry requires cold-storage places; and some medicines must be made under exacting temperature conditions. In many factories these needed temperature and moisture conditions are now created within the fabricating or processing plants. Man, however, has no control over the general climatic conditions of the world. For example, in the humid and enervating climate of the equatorial zone, the undesirable effects of climate are reflected in the natives' lassitude of body and mind, in their lack of desire for progress, and in the small number of commodities that are required to satisfy their wants and desires. Consequently, in this climatic realm there is a paucity of efficient labor, and, in turn, the market is poor. On the other hand, in the invigorating climates of temperate lands, where man is physically strong and healthy and where his mind is keen and alert, labor is efficient, and there is an ever-increasing desire for more and better goods.

A careful study of any manufacturing industry will show that each of the seven factors previously listed plays a part in efficient production and that the scientific location of each industry requires that it be studied in the light of its peculiar needs with respect to each of these seven factors.

Conclusion on the Geographical Significance of Location. Location is a major factor in relation to the political, economic, and social well-being of all peoples; it is a fundamental factor in the study of geography; and it manifests itself with greatest force in strategic and historic consideration. If nations and states throughout all historic time have fought hard for control of a strategically located land pass, strait, isthmus, group of islands, and if nations in control of such features have had an advantage over their neighbors, then these are all indications of the importance of geographical location.

In industry and trade as well as in history, location is of considerable importance. A business enterprise that is centrally located has a marked advantage over competing plants that have marginal or peripheral locations. The significance of a central location in business is clearly reflected in the high values of sites in the "Loop" districts of most large cities.

In the manufacturing industry a favorable location means accessibility to a variety of factors, of which the most important are raw materials, markets, power, and labor. In some types of industry several of these factors are of almost equal importance in determining the location of a plant, whereas the localization of other industries is dependent almost entirely on a single factor.

SIZE OF AREAS

In interpreting geographical phenomena, we are concerned with areas of different size. They may be political units, such as hamlets, villages, cities, counties, countries, or continents; or they may be geographical units—communities, provinces, regions, and realms.

Small Areas. Almost all the significant centers of early civilization and power were small areas—the narrow strip of land along the Nile, the small plains of Greece, the Roman Campagna, Mesopotamia, Syria, and Palestine. These were centers of population concentration, and, as the population increased, these limited areas fostered close contacts and rapid spread of cultural ideas. Much of the culture came into these small areas from the large expanses of tributary land—a culture that was nurtured and transformed to an even higher plane in these small compact units.

But most small countries are characterized by limited opportunity for economic development as well as by military weakness. The small geographical base generally means a paucity of basic raw materials. With raw materials—the source of great wealth—generally lacking, the small country soon finds itself overcrowded with people, some of whom migrate to areas of greater opportunity.[16]

In times of war the small area has always been more easily surrounded by the invaders, whereas a large area is protected largely by the extensiveness of its land mass. Nations that have invaded Russia have usually found the large size of that country a marked impediment to their military success. Moreover, most small countries are handicapped by having a relatively small population. Ellen Churchill Semple says: "Since there is a general correspondence between size of area and number of inhabitants, where physical conditions and economic development are similar, a small area involves a further handicap of numerical weakness of population. Greece has always suffered from the small size of the peninsula, and the further political dismemberment entailed by its geographic subdivisions. Despite superior civilization and national heroism, it has fallen a victim to almost every invader." [17]

Large Areas. A study of the great powers of the present day shows that they contain or control large areas of land. In this respect the

16 Witness the emigration from the small overcrowded countries of Europe to the New World.

17 Reprinted by permission from *Influences of Geographic Environment*, by Ellen Churchill Semple, Henry Holt & Co., 1911, p. 177.

British Empire, Russia, and the United States are noteworthy. The British Empire alone contains more than one-fifth of the land surface and population of the globe; Soviet Russia extends in a long east-west belt almost across the entire width of two continents.

Although large areas develop slowly in relation to small ones, in general they offer greater possibilities for future expansion and well-rounded development of the activities of their people. The large area affords opportunity for a greater diversity of life, bringing about contrasts in social conditions and, ultimately, a greater breadth of human interests. Not only countries but also continents show the effects of their size. "Consider the different environments found in a vast and varied continent like Eurasia, which extends from the equator far beyond the Arctic Circle, as compared with a small land-mass like Australia, relatively monotonous in its geographic conditions." [18] Observe how much greater the development has been in one than in the other, in point of animal forms, races, and civilization. "If we hold with Moritz Wagner and others that isolation in naturally defined regions, alternating with periods of migration, offers the necessary conditions for rapid development . . . we find that for the development of mankind it is large areas like Eurasia which afford the greatest number and variety of these naturally defined segregated habitats, and at the same time the best opportunity for vast historical movements." [19]

FORM

All areas, whether they are geographical or political units, have a certain form or shape. Some are long and narrow (attenuated), others are compact; still others are partly attenuated and partly compact in form.

The country embracing a compact area possesses various distinct advantages in its political economy.[20] In such areas internal communication is facilitated and railways frequently radiate from a few central points, forming a railway net. The problems of government are lightened, since a compact unit may be more readily held together than an attenuated one. Moreover, a compact country may be easily defended, owing in large part to the advantages of favorable internal communication, whereas the attenuated land, with its long frontiers

[18] Reprinted by permission from *Influences of Geographic Environment*, by Ellen Churchill Semple, Henry Holt & Co., 1927, pp. 169, 170.

[19] *Ibid.*

[20] Important compact areas are the United States, Russia, and France.

and long lines of communication is in danger of being broken up during periods of war.

Canada is an excellent example of an attenuated country. It extends more than 3,000 miles from east to west, and most of its railways lie within the southern part of the country, within a few hundred miles of the United States' border. It is in this southern part that most of Canada's people live. Here all the transcontinental railroads pass through Winnipeg, from which center they branch out both to the east and to the west. Canada has indeed been compared to a huge wasp with its narrow part in the general area of Winnipeg. It has also been suggested that the capture of this city by an enemy would effectively divide eastern (industrial) Canada from the western (agricultural) part of that country.

SPACE RELATIONSHIPS AS SHOWN ON A GLOBE

The Earth Sphere. It is a well-known fact that our earth has the shape of a sphere that is slightly flattened at the poles. It is, therefore, called an oblate spheroid rather than a sphere. The polar diameter is about 27 miles shorter than the equatorial diameter. Yet this distance is only a very small fractional part of the earth's total diameter of about 8,000 miles. This oblateness would cause a shortening of less than a half-inch in the polar diameter of a 12-foot globe, or less than one-third of 1 per cent. If the earth's circumference were shown as a circle, filling as completely as possible the space of the average school blackboard, the thickness of the chalk would be sufficient to show all the earth's departures from true spherical form. Thus, for all practical purposes in our discussion of globes and map projections we may consider the earth as a sphere.

Determining Positions on the Earth. Mankind has long been faced with the problems of determining distances and directions on the earth's surface. Even primitive peoples must be able to locate themselves in respect to various places in and about the areas in which they live. To such peoples knowledge about location becomes a vital necessity. Think of the utter helplessness of the primitive hunters of Borneo and the Congo Basin if they lacked knowledge about landmarks or other points of reference. With the advance of culture, locational knowledge has also advanced.

The records of human progress indicate that man learned very early to orient his directions within the horizon. Observation of the horizon and of the heavenly bodies such as the sun and moon suggested to some of the ancients that the earth was round. However, even the masses of people who then believed that the earth was flat could still find directions and distances. For example, directions could be referred to the rising and setting sun. It is noteworthy that the Latin equivalent for east is *oriens;* for west *occidens;* and for midday it is *meridies.* Later discoveries of the polestar and its position in regard to the North Pole, and the compass in its relation to the magnetic pole, proved a great help to the explorer and the navigator. Distances were commonly determined by means of time. For example, with a knowledge of the rate of travel by foot, boat, or animal caravan, the distance could be reckoned quickly.

The Earth Grid. Latitude and Longitude. If the earth were a flat surface with well-defined borders, points of reference could be determined easily for the mapping of distances and directions. Similarly, if the earth's surface were that of a cone or a cylinder, various definite points could be established. But for the surface of a sphere having no beginning and no ending, points of reference are lacking.

Fortunately, however, astronomical observations have established the facts that the earth rotates on its axis once in 24 hours and that the axis remains parallel at all times. Thus, the earth's axis becomes an imaginary line, with the North Pole as a point at one end and the South Pole at the other. Let us suppose that a plane is passed through the earth at right angles to this axis and midway between the North and South Poles. The circle formed by the intersection of this plane and the earth's surface becomes the equator. With the equator established at latitude 0°, the poles become 90° north and south latitude, since the distance along the earth's circumference from equator to either pole is one-fourth of a circle, or one-fourth of 360°. Suppose that other planes are passed through the earth at right angles to the earth's axis and parallel to the equatorial plane. Where these imaginary planes intersect the earth's surface, still other parallels or lines of latitude are formed. Especially important lines of latitude are the Tropic of Cancer ($23\frac{1}{2}$° north of the equator) and the Tropic of Capricorn ($23\frac{1}{2}$° south of the equator). They are noteworthy because they mark the limits of the belt around the middle of the earth in which the sun, at some period of the year, is directly overhead. Moreover, the polar circles are worthy of mention. The Arctic Circle (latitude $66\frac{1}{2}$° N) and the Antarctic Circle (latitude $66\frac{1}{2}$° S) mark the limits of the regions in which all places have at least one 24-hour period each year during which the sun does not set. These lines are called to our attention again in other parts of this book, especially in the next chapter.

Just as the parallels are imaginary lines that run east-west, so the meridians extend north-south, at right angles to the parallels. These north-south-trending lines converge at the poles and are used to designate longitude. The poles gave us points from which to start in the determination of latitude, but no such convenient points of refer-

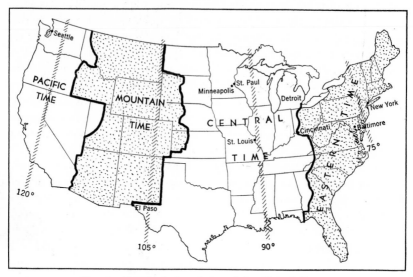

Fig. 3.   Standard time belts of the United States.

ence are found for the determination of longitude. We must, there-fore, decide on the location of some meridian from which the location of others are to be determined. Most countries have chosen the meridian that passes through Greenwich, England, where the British Royal Observatory was established in 1675. That imaginary line is recognized as the prime meridian, or longitude 0°. Beginning at this line, 0°, the first degree east of Greenwich is the meridian of longitude 1° E, and the first degree west is that of longitude 1° W, and so on until 180° have been measured eastward and 180° westward. To-gether with the prime meridian, this meridian of 180° forms a great circle. In traveling between two points located on any given meri-dian, one should follow as closely as possible the course of the meri-dian, since parts of meridians are arcs of great circles, which consti-tute the shortest distances between two points located on a spherical surface. The equator is the only parallel that is a great circle.

Longitude and time. All places along a given meridian have the same average solar time, which is determined by the length of time the earth takes to make a complete rotation on its axis. It is generally reckoned from noon to noon, or from the time of highest sun (zenithal) one day to that of the highest sun the next day. Since the earth rotates 360° in 24 hours, or 15° in 1 hour, or 1° in 4 minutes, sun time is constantly changing. In traveling, we would have to change our watches constantly if every place had sun time. Modern nations, consequently, have established time zones approximately 15° in width (Fig. 3). To the east of the prime meridian the clocks are set ahead of Greenwich time and to the west of the prime meridian they are set back in terms of Greenwich time. For example, in the zone of longitude 7.5° ± E to 22.5° ± E, the clocks are set 1 hour ahead of Greenwich time, whereas, in the zone of 67.5° ± W, to 82.5° ± W, the clocks are set back 5 hours (Fig. 3). Opposite sides of approximately the 180th meridian have a total difference of 24 hours of time. The line is known as the "international date line." The exact location of this line is arbitrarily determined.

Mapping the Earth's Surface on Globes. Long before the time of Christ, globes were fashioned by the Greeks, but their use was narrowly limited. During the period of exploration in the sixteenth and seventeenth centuries many large and costly globes were made. In the eighteenth century some globes were constructed that had a diameter of 12 feet. But the most remarkable of all globes have been made within comparatively recent times. Thus the Paris Exposition of 1937 had a mammoth "globarium" consisting of plastics and steel. Globes should be used in connection with maps, that is, as a supplement to plane-surface presentations of the earth's features, since globes show the various space relationships of the earth's lands and waters with the minimum amount of distortion and the greatest amount of accuracy. But globes are generally quite bulky and are impractical to use for many purposes.

MAPS AND MAP PROJECTIONS

Maps are plans of the earth's surface which show the location and distribution of various phenomena. *Map projections* indicate the methods used in making maps. The nature of a true projection may be illustrated by use of the framework of a globe made of wire which represents meridians, parallels, outlines of continents, and the like. If an electric light were placed in the center of this framework and a cylinder were placed over it tangent to the equator, the shadow of the wire framework would be thrown on the cylinder. In the same way the shadow of the wire could be thrown on a cone that is tangent to some parallel, or on a plane that is tangent to any given point on the globe. By such means the framework of the globe may be projected on a cylinder, a cone, or a plane. The light need not be placed at the center of the globe. It may be placed at some other desired point and still project the shadow of the framework or of some part of it on a cylinder, a cone, or a plane. Maps made in such a manner are true projection maps. In practice, however, most maps are made mathematically by altering true projections.

The chief function of maps is to give a portrayal of location, direction, size, shape, and the differences and similarities in the regional nature of natural environment and human activities. The natural environment may be seen by studying maps showing distribution of climates, land forms, native vegetation, and native animal life. Regional differences in human adjustments may be seen in many of the maps showing distribution of extractive and manufacturing industries, transportation, and trade. Just as maps showing the natural landscape bring out the areal distributions of various features of physical and biological environment, so maps showing cultural landscape reflect the human use of the earth and the extent to which the natural landscape has been altered by man's works. Such maps show distributions of crops, cropping systems, domestic animals, mines, factories, and urban centers. In some densely populated areas human beings have almost completely altered the natural landscape. In other areas, especially the sparsely populated ones, the natural landscape may be nearly or completely unaltered by man's work. Maps help man to understand the forms or patterns of varying cultural landscapes which he has developed in different natural landscapes.

Maps are sometimes misleading, as may be briefly illustrated by the Mercator projection on which Greenland is larger than South America, whereas in reality it is only one-ninth as large as that continent. Since maps are utilized to show so many things by great numbers of agencies —political, industrial, commercial, and academic—it would seem no more than logical to assume that students should know something about the most common map projections. Human affairs are of vital interest to all of us. Thus, maps that show places and help answer questions of "Where in the world is it?" or "Where did it take place?" become essential to a wide range of school subjects and of fundamental importance in a liberal education.

Maps often serve practical everyday functions. Thus, maps help vacationists, tourists, and travelers in general to reach their destinations, whether by road, railroad, or waterway. Maps issued by the Weather Bureau show precipitation, temperatures, and cloudiness. Such maps are carefully studied by great numbers of travelers, farmers, mariners, aviators, and tradespeople. The fruit growers and shippers can often take precautions against destructive frosts if they study and interpret the maps correctly. The extent of their profits may indeed be determined by the degree to which they can understand such maps.

The Ideal Map Projection. The most desirable properties to have in a map are (1) truth of area, (2) truth of shape, (3) exact direction, (4) correct distance or scale, (5) meridians and parallels shown as straight lines, and (6) great circles (shortest distance between two points on the globe) of the sphere shown as straight lines. No map projection can possibly combine all these qualities. For some particular purpose we may have a map projection that fulfils exactly some one condition. For example, if we wish to show the areal extent of some commodity that is produced in higher as well as lower latitudes we would want a map that has truth of area, that is, an equal-area map. But some equal-area maps have poor shape. Thus, if we wish to show the exact shape of some small geographical feature, such as a bay, lake, or cape, we will select projections that preserve shapes of small areas. They are called conformal map projections. Yet such map projections generally do not preserve the shapes of large areas, as compared with the same areas on the globe.

Although maps are often made to fulfil some one condition or to satisfy some particular use, they are more commonly the result of compromise. That is, attempts are made to bring together various desirable features in one map, with as little error as possible.

Map Projections

Characteristic Features of Map Projections. The globe shows the various space relationships of the earth's lands and waters with the minimum amount of distortion and the greatest degree of accuracy. But the globe is not, for most practical purposes, a suitable instrument for the representation of the earth's surface. Hence, the features of the globe are represented on plane surfaces.

In projecting the earth features of the globe onto a plane surface, serious difficulties are encountered, since no part of the surface of a sphere can be spread out in a plane without some distortion. This can be seen by attempting to flatten a part of an orange peel. The outer part will stretch and tear before the central part will come into the plane with it. This is the major difficulty encountered in map making. Thus, a perfect representation of the features of a globe on a plane surface is impossible, but there are many different ways of obtaining approximate results.

In all map projections there is a systematic drawing of lines representing meridians and parallels on a plane surface, either for the whole

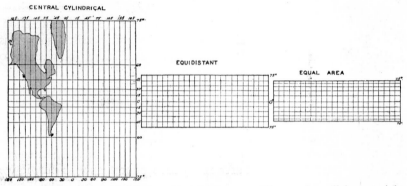

Fig. 4. The various cylindrical projections show meridians and parallels as straight lines and have an advantage over some of the other projections in being easily constructed.

world or some part of it. The shape of the projected parallels and meridians and the shape of areas drawn on the map will depend on the method or type of projection used. An examination of map projections reveals that some of them have straight lines for meridians and parallels, and that others have curved lines; some represent areas with a great amount of distortion in size, whereas others are distorted in shape.

The Cylindrical Projections. Cylindrical projections afford some of the simplest methods of showing the various features of the earth on a plane surface (Fig. 4). The central cylindrical projection may be constructed by placing a cylinder around a globe. Then from the center of the globe project the surface of the globe onto the cylinder. Other cylindrical projections are (1) the equidistant cylindrical projection in which parallels and meridians are spaced equal distances apart, and (2) the equal-area cylindrical projection which is mathematically constructed so that the sizes of areas on the map are to each other as they are on the globe.

Mercator Projection. The Mercator is the best known and most widely used of all the cylindrical projections (Fig. 5). Like the other cylindrical projections, the Mercator contains parallel and equidistant straight lines that represent meridians which are drawn at right angles to the parallels. In all the cylindrical projections there is an increas-

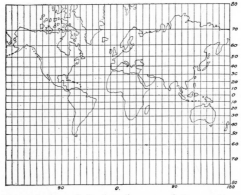

FIG. 5. The Mercator is one of the best known of the map projections. Advantages: (1) Any straight line is a rhumb line; (2) all directions are accurately shown; (3) all parallels cross all meridians at right angles as on a globe. Disadvantages: (1) There is much exaggeration of relative area in high latitudes; (2) the scale of miles varies with latitude; (3) the shortest distance between two points is not a straight line except on the equator or on any given great circles. The Mercator is useful in plotting maps where directions must be featured, as for air or marine navigation and wind directions.

ing distortion of longitude with increasing distances away from the equator, since meridians are shown as parallel lines, in contrast to the converging lines on the globe. For example, on the earth the meridians at 60° north and south latitude are approximately half as far apart as they are at the equator, whereas on all the cylindrical projections meridians are everywhere equidistant. In order to retain the correct shape of any small areas on the map, it becomes necessary, therefore, to increase every degree of latitude toward the pole in exactly the same proportion as the degrees of longitude have been lengthened by the projection. Such proportional adjustment of latitudinal to longitudinal distances has been accomplished in the Mercator projection. This preservation of the constant relationship between the latitudinal and longitudinal lines, as indicated previously, is the chief reason why the Mercator projection was designed for use by mariners. On this projection a course can be laid as a straight line. The latitude and longitude of any place is readily found from its position on the map. In addition, the convenience of plotting points

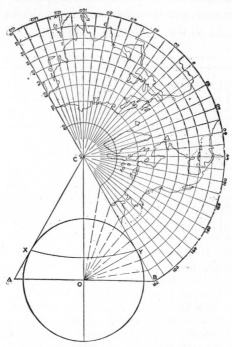

Fig. 6. Conic projection. Advantages: (1) It is easily constructed; (2) it is relatively accurate for small areas at or near the line of tangency; (3) parallels and meridians intersect at right angles. Disadvantages: (1) Inaccuracy increases with distance from the line of tangency; (2) east-west directions are not straight lines. The conic projection is used in mapping states, small countries, or other small areas.

or positions by straightedge across the map from the marginal divisions prevents errors, especially in navigation.

Although the Mercator projection is widely used in the construction of world maps, it has been seriously criticized, the chief objection being the distortion of areas in higher latitudes. Thus, as previously mentioned, on a Mercator map of the world, Greenland appears to be larger than South America, whereas in reality South America is nine times as large as Greenland. At 80° of latitude an area is 36 times as large as one of the same size at the equator, and at 89° an area drawn on the Mercator projection is represented as more than 3,000 times as large as an equal-sized area at the equator. But the polar regions are after all the best places to put the maximum distortion, since our interests are centered mainly between 65° north and 55° south latitude.

Conic Projection. In the making of maps conic projections are widely used. Of these, the simple conic has the advantage of being easily constructed. In its construction a cone may be placed on the

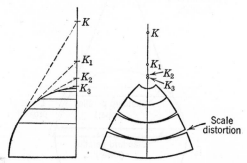

Fig. 7. Polyconic projection. The central meridian of the polyconic projection is straight and vertical. Parallels cross the meridians at true distances from equator and poles. Each parallel is divided truly in proportion to its length on the globe, and the curves connecting the divisions mark the meridians. There is distortion of the scale at the sides of the map as indicated in the right-hand figure. In the actual map these gaps do not appear, but the scale near the margins of the map is enlarged to distribute the error. (Taken by permission from *Geography for Army Training Program*, John L. Rich, Daniel R. Bergsmark, and Urban J. Linehan, mimeographed for use at the University of Cincinnati, 1944.)

globe. From the center of this globe (*O*) straight lines are drawn outward, which project the earth's surface onto the surface of the tangent cone (*A, B, C*). When this projection is made on a cone tangent to the globe at 30°, the unrolled conical map takes the form of a semicircle (Fig. 6).

All distances drawn along the parallel that is tangent (*x, y*) to the cone will correspond exactly with those of the globe; but, with distance away from this line of tangency, distortion increases. The conic map is widely used, therefore, to show small areas and regions that have a considerable longitudinal extent. Thus Europe, stretching east-west through approximately 51° of longitude and only 40° of latitude, is frequently drawn on a conic projection, in which the line of tangency coincides with 55° north latitude. The conic projection is also used to show small areas, these areas being drawn along or near the line of tangency in order that they may be shown with the least amount of distortion.

Polyconic Projection.   One of the major disadvantages of the conic projection is the increasing distortion of areas with increasing dis-

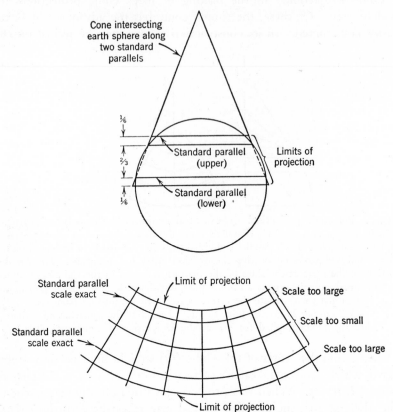

Fig. 8.   Modified conic projection.   Advantages: (1) The scale of the map is correct along two standard parallels; (2) distortion of shapes and sizes is small; (3) meridians and parallels intersect at right angles.   The major disadvantage is slight distortion of shapes and sizes except along the standard parallels.   (Modified from Deats and Adams by John L. Rich, Daniel R. Bergsmark, and Urban J. Linehan, *Geography for Army Training Program,* mimeographed for use at the University of Cincinnati, 1944.)

tances from the line of tangency. It appears, therefore, that a number of lines of tangency would reduce this distortion. This is accomplished in the polyconic projection in which any number of parallels may be used as lines of tangency.

Like the conic projection, the polyconic is used in mapping small areas, and for this purpose it is one of the best of all map projections. It is much better than the conic projection in showing areas that have a considerable latitudinal extent (Fig. 7).

Modified Conic Projection. A conic projection may be constructed with two standard parallels by having the cone cut the earth's surface at two selected parallels. A map made with this projection is accurate along the two parallels of intersection and is relatively accurate throughout its extent, provided it does not cover more than 16° to 20° of latitude (Fig. 8).

Lambert Conformal. This projection is a mathematical modification of the conic projection in which the cone cuts the earth's surface at two selected parallels. Latitudes 33° N and 45° N are commonly used in making a map of the United States. The modifications consist in so spacing the parallels that all quadrangles have the same relative proportions on the map as on the globe. The map is correct along the parallels of intersection, and the distortion is small in other parts of the map, provided the area mapped is no larger than the United States. Any straight line on the map approaches the great-circle route, and the scale is relatively accurate. The map is widely used in American air services.

The Gnomonic Projection. This projection is constructed by projecting the surface of a globe from its center onto a plane touching the globe's surface at a point—the center of the area to be mapped (Fig. 9). A feature of this projection is that any great circle is shown as a straight line. Conversely, any straight line drawn on the map is a projection of an arc of a great circle. Consequently, the route representing the shortest distance between any two points on the map is a straight line connecting them.

In following a great-circle route one does not maintain a constant compass direction unless he is following the equator or a meridian. It is a common practice, therefore, to lay out the great-circle route as a straight line on a gnomonic map. Then the route is transferred to a Mercator map on which are charted all points where the routes cross meridians. These points can then be connected by short straight lines that show true directions on the Mercator map. At each point the compass can be set to the new direction to be followed. By such a method of navigation one follows the great-circle route only approximately.

The Sinusoidal Projection. The sinusoidal is one of the simplest of all projections to construct. Parallels preserve the same distances as

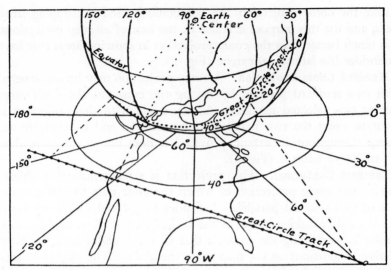

FIG. 9. Gnomonic projection is made from the earth's center onto a plane touching the earth's surface at a single point. Advantages: (1) Any straight line on the projection is part of a great circle; (2) the shortest distance between any two points on the map is a straight line; (3) excellent projection is given for a map of polar regions. Disadvantages: (1) There is distortion of scale towards the border; (2) directions near the edge of the map are likely to be confusing. (From photo of model by Bechtold, taken by permission from *Geography for Army Training Program*, John L. Rich, Daniel R. Bergsmark, and Urban J. Linehan, mimeographed for use at the University of Cincinnati, 1944.)

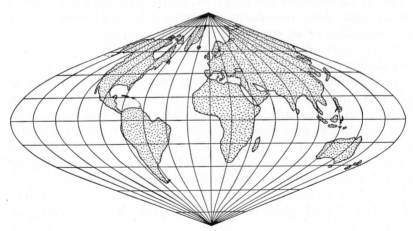

FIG. 10. Sinusoidal projection of the world.

on the surface of the sphere that is being projected. The equator and mid-meridian are drawn at right angles. Parallels are straight lines drawn true to scale, that is, equal in length to the arcs of the parallels of the spherical surface that is being projected. Along any given parallel equidistant points are established for the meridians, which when drawn become cosine curves (Fig. 10).

Although the sinusoidal is an equal-area projection, it does not preserve true shape in all its parts. Near the center and along the equator there is comparatively little distortion, but progressively poleward the

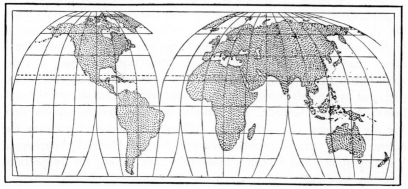

FIG. 11. Showing Goode's interrupted homolographic projection.

distortion of shape increases until the polar areas appear to be considerably pinched together. The sinusoidal projection is therefore widely used in mapping tropical areas, and such continents as South America and Africa. It also constitutes a part (from the equator to 40° N and 40° S) of Goode's homolosine projection.

The Mollweide Homolographic Projection. This projection has been designed to represent the entire surface of the globe without distortion of areas; it shows a proportionality of areas on the sphere with the corresponding areas of the projection.

The homolographic projection possesses several distinct advantages: It represents the whole world on a single complete map; it is equal area; and its parallels and mid-meridian are straight lines. On the other hand, there is one major disadvantage to this type of projection in that areas mapped near its outer border have great angular distortion.

Goode's Interrupted Homolographic Projection. This is a modification of Mollweide's homolographic projection (Fig. 11). On Mollweide's map, areas along the mid-meridian are accurate in shape and size, whereas areas in high latitudes away from the mid-meridian are badly distorted. J. Paul Goode found that a number of mid-meridians could be drawn arbitrarily from one pole to the equator, with each continent centered on a mid-meridian in order to give it the best form —North America around the meridian of 100° W, Eurasia 60° E, South America 60° W, Africa 20° E, and Australia 150° E.

Conclusions. The map projections just described illustrate some of the ways in which the surface of the globe may be shown on a plane surface. Not all these projections, however, may be satisfactory for the same purpose. Thus the Mercator projection is of great service to navigators, since it shows directions in the course of straight lines. On the other hand, this projection greatly exaggerates the size of high-latitude areas. For showing such regions the conic projection is better than the Mercator. The conic projection, however, was devised partly for showing areas that have considerable longitudinal extent, just as the polyconic is used to show regions that stretch through many degrees of latitude. In addition, both projections are excellent for the mapping of small areas. When it is necessary to map the entire world, the sinusoidal, homolographic, Goode's interrupted homolographic, and Goode's homolosine are among the projections that may be used.

Relief Maps

Practically all the nations of the world have either made or are now making topographic or relief maps of their land possessions. In Europe the making of these maps has been largely inspired by military considerations—a desire and necessity for knowing the irregularities and features of the topography in order to facilitate the moving of machinery, the placing of troops, and the digging of trenches. In the United States the main object has been to furnish maps suitable for the economic development of the country—the study of its geological structure and resources and the planning of engineering projects. These maps are widely used in geological work. It is even possible to interpret the age of the land forms, the nature of the soil, behavior of streams and subsurface waters, and the underground structure of many parts of the country from a good, detailed topographic map.[21]

Methods of Showing Relief. Three common methods for showing relief on topographic maps are shading, hachures, and contours. Some-

---

[21] C. L. Dake and J. S. Brown, *Interpretation of Topographic and Geologic Maps,* McGraw-Hill Book Co., 1925.

times merely one method is employed, but frequently a combination
of two or all of these methods is seen on topographic maps. The
European map makers, by their use of contours, hachures, and light
shade effects, have so perfected methods of showing diverse forms

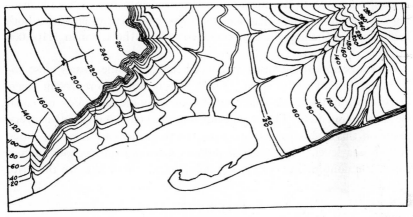

Fig. 12. Showing relief by means of hachures and contours. (U. S. Geologic
Survey.)

of the earth's surface that even on a small-scale map of the Swiss Alps,
for example, we may see before us the wonderful complexity of mountains, deep valleys, snowfalls, and glaciers.[22]

Relief maps designed for the public schools commonly employ a
variety of shades to indicate areas of different elevation. This device

[22] C. C. Adams, "Maps and Map Making," *Bulletin of the American Geographical Society*, Vol. 44, p. 195.

(shading) is particularly advantageous in showing the relief over large areas of land and in giving a generalized impression of the surface features, but where accuracy is required the contour map is employed. On some French maps both contours and various shades are drawn in order to indicate relief.

Hachures are a type of shading in which lines are used. The lines are short and are drawn down slope, that is, they show the direction in which water would flow downhill, and the shape of the hill becomes quite apparent from the lines. The more closely the lines are spaced, the steeper the slope. The hachure method is quite commonly employed in European maps, such as in making the Carte de France and various German and Swiss maps. Hachures are sometimes combined with contours to increase the vividness of expression, as on the British ordnance maps. But maps that show hachures only are less exact than those in which relief is indicated by contours.

"The contour system is used on the U. S. Geological Survey maps, Japanese Government maps, on the German and Swiss 1:25,000 maps, in conjunction with hachures on the English ordnance, and with shading on the new French map and the maps of Norway, and with both hachures and shading on the recent edition of the German 1:100,000 maps." [23]

Contours appear on maps as curved lines, in some places close together and in others far apart. These lines on the map represent imaginary lines at the earth's surface drawn through all points of equal elevation (Fig. 12). Thus a contour line marked 100 means that every point on this line is just 100 feet or meters, as the case may be, above average sea level. The vertical distance between the contour lines is called the contour interval, and it is indicated somewhere on the map.

REFERENCES

ADAMS, C. C., "Maps and Map Sketching," *Bulletin of the American Geographical Society*, Vol. 44.

CHAMBERLIN, WELLMAN, and CHARLES E. RIDDIFORD, *The Round Earth on Flat Paper*, National Geographic Society, 1947.

DAKE, C. L., and J. S. BROWN, *Interpretation of Topographic and Geologic Maps*, McGraw-Hill Book Co., 1925.

DAVIS, W. M., "The Earth as a Globe," *Journal of Geography*, Vol. 29, 1930, pp. 330–333.

FINCH, J. K., *Topographic Maps and Sketch Mapping*, John Wiley & Sons, 1920.

[23] Reprinted by permission from *Topographic Maps and Sketch Mapping*, by J. K. Finch, John Wiley & Sons, 1920, p. 19.

HARTSHORNE, R., "Location as a Factor in Geography," *Annals of the Association of American Geographers*, Vol. 17, pp. 92–99.

PUTNAM, WILLIAM C., *Map Interpretation with Military Applications*, McGraw-Hill Book Co., 1943.

SEMPLE, ELLEN CHURCHILL, "Geographical Location as a Factor in History," *Bulletin of the American Geographical Society*, Vol. 40.

Chapter 2

OUR CLIMATIC ENVIRONMENT

CLIMATIC CONDITIONS AND HUMAN RESPONSES

Weather and Climate. Weather represents the physical conditions of the atmosphere,[1] especially with respect to temperature, moisture conditions, winds, and pressure at any given time or over a short period of time such as a day, a week, or a season. Climate is the composite of weather over a long period of time such as decades, centuries, or millenniums.

Weather and climate affect the actions and well-being of every person every day of his life. Both in work and in play all peoples adjust their actions to climate and weather. Baseball, tennis, swimming, skiing, skating, and other sports are each better suited to some climates and weather conditions than to others. The number and kinds of crops that can be grown in any region are restricted by weather conditions. In fact, a close study of the influences of climate on man reveals that human activities are at all times and in all places closely hedged about by climate and weather.

Climate affects man directly through its influence on his body, mind, and character, and indirectly through its effect on the plants, animals, soil, topography, and even certain mineral resources. Climate not only sets broad limits on the number of people a region can support

[1] The atmosphere is composed of air and its impurities—primarily moisture and dust. Air is a mixture of gases and is not a chemical compound. It consists of 78 per cent nitrogen, 21 per cent oxygen, and 1 per cent made up of several gases of which carbon dioxide is the most important. The average weight of the atmosphere at sea level is 14.7 pounds per square inch. It is equivalent to the weight of 29.92 inches of mercury, or to 1013.2 millibars. Since the atmosphere exerts equal pressure in all directions at any given point, it is common to speak of the force exerted as atmospheric pressure rather than as weight. Since the atmospheric pressure at any elevation is the result of the weight of the atmosphere above that height, the pressure decreases with increase of altitudes. Thus at 18,000 feet the pressure is approximately one-half that at sea level, whereas at 40,000 feet it is approximately one-fifth that at sea level.

but also influences the nature and extent of man's achievements within each region.

The climates of Labrador, the Congo, the Sahara, India, and England are scarcely more diverse than the characteristics of their respective inhabitants. The peoples differ markedly from one region to another in their mental alertness, physical vigor, occupations, customs, manners, homes, food, and clothing. These contrasts result from a combination of many factors, the most potent one being climate. The unifying influences of modern commerce and rapid communication may soften the contrasts but can never entirely break them down. Thus the natives of Labrador can never grow plantain, go practically naked throughout the year, live in flimsily built houses open to the elements on all sides, or do any of a dozen other things that are common in many tropical regions.

The average native of the Labrador coast finds nature niggardly with her gifts. The scant soil left after glaciation is unyielding because of the cold, bleak winds off the ice-chilled current which bathes the eastern shore. Since man cannot make a living from the land he has turned to the sea. Here the prime source of wealth is the fish of the North Atlantic. But the fisherman who would obtain a livelihood from these waters must work hard, brave many dangers, and endure privations in order to secure the bare necessities of life for himself and his family. His little shack of one or two rooms contains none of the luxuries and few of the comforts of the average American home. Yet he should not be condemned for providing so poorly, but rather praised for doing so well. His life is a hard one. Fog, ice, wind, and cold all combine to make fishing a dangerous and difficult task. Courage, resourcefulness, and self-reliance, to an eminent degree, are necessary to wrest a livelihood from the stormy North Atlantic with the meager equipment possessed by the natives.

These harsh living conditions that are experienced along the barren coast of Labrador contrast sharply with the ease of existence in parts of the humid equatorial forests. Within the latter areas, nature is so lavish with her gifts that the native may provide for his simple material wants with a minimum of effort. He requires scant clothing and little fuel; his house is merely a shelter against the rain and can be built quickly and easily from native vegetation; and the harvest season lasting throughout the year makes it unnecessary to provide food for the future. All nature seems to have conspired to discourage thrift.

The natives of many tropical lands see little need for diligent and sustained effort, and, in addition, they are seldom physically fit for more than light and intermittent work. The hot, humid climate is enervating, and the diet is, in general, monotonous and not very nourishing. The terrible plagues of insects—the real "ferocious beasts" of the equatorial forest and the most to be feared—make life miserable most of the time. The heavy, stale humidity and the green gloom of the tropical forests are depressing. The thick roof of foliage shuts out the sunlight, the source of health and good spirits, and, as a result, the native possesses neither physical nor mental vigor. Under such conditions stagnation seems almost inevitable. It is only when invasions from the temperate zones bring new blood and greater vigor into the tropical forests that notable progress is made.

Man's adjustment to the environment of the tropical forest is no more pronounced than it is to the environment of the desert and steppe. The former realm is conducive to mental lassitude; the latter stimulates a spirit of restlessness and alertness. Moreover, the desert nomads have for the most part a wholesome and nourishing diet of milk, meat, barley, dates, and other foods suited to their environment; they live an active out-door life as they follow their flocks and herds or make forays against other tribes. Although the climate is somewhat debilitating, the greatest hindrance to progress is the lack of opportunity for producing and accumulating any considerable amount of wealth through diligent and persistent effort. The degree of prosperity seems to depend more on the uncertain element of rainfall than on the labors of man. When pasture is plentiful and the watering holes numerous, the flocks and herds increase without extra care by the nomads. If the pasture dries up and the water disappears, the animals perish in spite of anything the natives can do. Such conditions afford little encouragement for honest labor.

The tendency has been for the population of the desert and steppe to increase more rapidly than the food supply, causing the nomads, especially during bad years, to resort to robbery, pillage, and conquest in order to survive. Ellen Churchill Semple says: "From time immemorial they [the great deserts and steppes extending across the Old World] have born and bred tribes of wandering herdsmen; they have sent out the invading hordes in successive waves of conquest, have overwhelmed the neighboring river lowlands of Eurasia and Africa. They have given birth in turn to Scythians, Indo-Aryans, Avars, Huns, Saracens, and Turks, as well as to the Tuareg tribes of the Sahara, the Sudanese, and the Bantu folk of the African grasslands."[2] The will to live is strong. Therefore, when the pastures of the desert and the steppe are not sufficient to support the flocks and herds, the very life of the nomad and his family depends on his willingness and ability to pillage, plunder, or conquer. The nomad feels that nature has made these acts necessary; the purpose of the acts—to provide food for the family—is a noble one; and consequently, success in achievement is regarded with pride and not with shame.

The relation between climate and human thought and action is present wherever man goes. The climate best suited to rapid human progress, at least from the material aspect, exists in the humid parts of the upper middle latitudes where the most highly developed civilizations of the world are found. Within these regions nature is neither so lavish with her gifts as within the wet tropics, nor so unyielding as within the deserts and steppes. Millions of men who live in these most temperate lands, after providing for the necessaries and luxuries of life, still find time available for leisure. Since the climate is stimulating, man is too energetic to spend his time idly. Consequently, leisure affords opportunity for progress.

WEATHER THE UNCERTAIN FACTOR OF OUR PHYSICAL ENVIRONMENT

Not only do climatic conditions differ from one place to another, but of equal importance to man is the fact that the weather varies from one year to the next in a very uncertain manner. Other elements of our physical environment, such as soil and water, are just as basic to man's welfare as weather is, but the weather gives man most concern since it is the only factor subject to pronounced variations in short periods of time. One summer is too wet, the next too dry; one spring is late, the next early; one autumn has severe frosts, the next is frost free. Every harvest season brings joy or disappointment, as the case may be, to millions of families whose well-being is closely related to the nature of the season. If the causes of these variations were definitely known and their nature could be forecast, the evil effects could be mitigated. Unfortunately, little progress has been made in this direction. Climatologists, however, are not without hopes of improvement in long-time forecasting. The study of polar climates, upper air currents, sun spots, ocean currents, and other factors that affect our climate may help in the solution of the problem.

[2] Reprinted by permission from *Influences of Geographical Environment*, Ellen Churchill Semple, Henry Holt & Co., 1911, p. 7.

Uncertain weather variations are of far greater consequence in some parts of the world than in others. For example, the rainfall is much more reliable in eastern United States and west-central Europe than in most of Asia, Australia, and South America. It is a well-known fact that in parts of India, China, and Australia years of plenty are followed by years of dearth, owing largely to the variation in rainfall. An extreme example of unreliable rainfall is that of Onslow, in western Australia, where in 1902 the rainfall was only 0.57 inch and the area took on the appearance of a desert; ten years later the precipitation of Onslow was 26.96 inches—sufficient for an excellent crop of wheat. Onslow is not the only part of Australia that suffers because of unreliable precipitation. In fact, the prosperity of the entire continent is bound up with the amount of rain and its seasonal distribution. Griffith Taylor says: "The dread enemy who has ruined thousands is *King Drought*. Frost scarcely affects the country at all; floods are only occasional and their damage is localized; but the fear of drought is always present." [3] The effect of a series of bad seasons is strikingly shown by the fact that the drought of 1901–1902 caused the death of millions of sheep and a loss of more than $600,000,000 to Australia [4] (Fig. 13). The extent of this loss can be better understood when it is realized that it represented more than $500 per family for the entire continent.

In eastern United States, on the other hand, the rainfall is fairly reliable. The annual precipitation seldom departs more than 20 or 30 per cent from the average, and although crops may be injured they are seldom ruined by drought or excessive moisture.

Precipitation is not the only uncertain variable in climate which affects man's well-being. Each region has its own particular weather element which gives the farmer and the business man most cause for worry. Central Florida seldom suffers greatly from droughts or floods, but severe or untimely frosts may bring ruin to thousands of fruit growers and thereby injure business throughout the state as it did in 1892 and 1940. Although frosts never occur in the lowlands of the East and West Indies, these islands are visited by the dreaded hurricane which devastates large areas each year. So it is in almost every part of the world. The oasis tribe dreads the rain; the Kansas farmer fears the drought, frost, hail, and the tornado; the Texas farmer may have his crops destroyed by hot winds; and fog, ice, and winds are

[3] Reprinted by permission from *Australian Meteorology*, Griffith Taylor, The Clarendon Press, 1920, p. 136.

[4] Griffith Taylor, *Australia*, The Clarendon Press, 1919, pp. 140–141.

almost continuously taking their toll along the commerce lines of the
North Atlantic. No region escapes, but the toll exacted by adverse
weather conditions is much greater in some parts of the world than
in others.

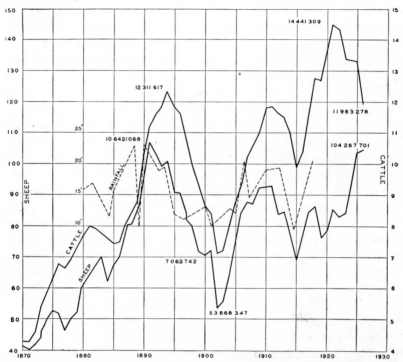

FIG. 13. "King Drought" has ruined thousands of farmers and ranchmen of Australia. The dotted line shows the rainfall for ten Riverina stations. The drought
of 1898–1899 was of short duration, but the droughts culminating in 1902 and
1914 lasted for years and were widespread. That of 1902 was the most disastrous
on record. Millions of cattle and tens of millions of sheep died or had to be
killed because of insufficient pasture and water to support them. (*Géographie
universelle*, Armand Collins, Paris, 1928, Tome X, p. 175, and *Australia in Its
Physiographic and Economic Aspects*, Griffith Taylor, Clarendon Press, 1919,
p. 139.)

In a world of rapidly expanding commercial development, the climate
of any given region is of more than local interest. A season of severe
hurricanes in the West Indies and Florida may increase the price of
bananas in the United States, cause West Indian sugar stocks to de-
preciate in value, injure land values in Florida, and in a dozen other

ways adversely affect business in the United States. A drought in Australia may increase the price of wool and wheat in Europe; unseasonable frosts in Florida may increase the cost of oranges and grapefruit throughout the United States; and a poor season in the American cotton belt may bring about higher prices of cotton goods even in the most remote and isolated parts of the world. The price of wheat in North Dakota is related not only to the amount of local production, but also to the yield in Canada, Australia, India, Argentina, and Russia. A severe drought in Argentina or Australia may add to the prosperity of the North Dakota farmer.

Climatic conditions also affect the problems of distribution of goods. Railroads and highways are difficult to build in hot wet jungles, in deserts, and in the cold polar regions. Snow, hail, sleet, flood, heat, humidity, and wind each creates problems in transportation. The aviator needs an intimate knowledge of the atmosphere through which he flies. In fact, his grasp of the subject should be such as to enable him to derive the greatest possible advantage from every condition of wind and weather along his route.

Since climate affects production and distribution in so many ways, it is essential that the student of economic geography have a general knowledge of the fundamental elements of climate and of their behavior in various parts of the world. He should know the major climatic types of the earth, together with the basic principles that govern the characteristics and general distribution of weather phenomena of each type; he should know the general distribution of production so far as it is related to climatic conditions; and finally, it is very important that he be able to appraise, within reasonable limits, the weather hazards to production, preservation, and distribution of major commercial products in each part of the world.

THE FUNDAMENTAL ELEMENTS OF CLIMATE

The three fundamental elements of climate which all living creatures, plant or animal, persistently demand, and on which their supply of food, directly or indirectly, depends, are heat, light, and moisture. The basic factors in the distribution of these elements are (1) the position of the earth with respect to the sun—the condition that governs the amount and distribution of heat (insolation) received by any part of the earth, and (2) the nature and circulation of the atmosphere.

Temperatures of Atmosphere. Atmospheric temperatures which make life possible on the earth result from insolation—heat from the sun. Part of the heat of the atmosphere is the result of the absorption of heat rays directly from the sun; a larger portion of the heat of the atmosphere is received indirectly from the sun; that is, the short heat rays from the sun are first absorbed by the earth, which, in turn, gives off long heat waves that are more readily absorbed by the atmosphere than are the short solar rays.

The two systems of measuring temperature in common use are represented by the Fahrenheit and the centigrade scales. By the Fahrenheit scale, 180° represent the difference between freezing and boiling (32° and 212°, respectively) whereas, by the centigrade scale, 100° represent the difference between freezing and boiling (0° and 100°, respectively). Thus 100° C. is equal to 180° F. or 1° C. is equal to $\frac{9}{5}$ of 1° F.[5]

Insolation and Its Distribution. The amount of heat received from the sun each year is sufficient to melt a layer of ice 241 feet thick over the entire earth. This energy from the immense powerhouse 92,000,-000 miles away produces, directly or indirectly, all the varied phenomena of weather. It is the prime cause of all the diverse currents of the air, whether they are the gentle breezes and moderate winds so necessary for the distribution of moisture, the destructive hurricanes which sweep across sections of the tropics with such fury, or the terrifying tornado which represents the culmination of violence in air movements.

As indicated by the following study, the amount of heat received from the sun varies greatly from one place to another, and at any given place it varies materially from one time to another.

DAY AND NIGHT. It is common knowledge that in all parts of the world days are warmer than nights. The extent of the diurnal range depends largely on the nature of the atmosphere. If the earth had no atmosphere, the days would be broiling hot, the nights piercing cold, and the diurnal range would be measured in hundreds of degrees. The atmosphere, however, is a moderating influence which acts as a shield against the sun's rays during the day and retards radiation during the night. The tempering influence is especially effective when the air is heavily laden with moisture, as in many places located on windward coasts and in the belt of equatorial calms. Under such conditions the average diurnal range may not exceed 5° to 7° F. On the

[5] To convert a temperature reading from centigrade to Fahrenheit, multiply the centigrade temperature by $\frac{9}{5}$ and add 32°—the freezing point on the Fahrenheit scale. To convert from Fahrenheit to centigrade, subtract 32° from the Fahrenheit temperature and multiply by $\frac{5}{9}$.

other hand, when the atmosphere is clear and relatively free from moisture, as in most parts of tropical deserts, a diurnal range of more than 50° F. is not uncommon.[6]

LATITUDE AND INSOLATION. Latitude is the important factor in determining the distribution of insolation. The more nearly vertical the sun's rays, the more concentrated they are at the earth's surface and the less atmosphere they must penetrate (Fig. 14). As a result, other things being equal, temperatures decrease with increasing latitude. But for the circulation of the atmosphere and ocean waters, with the resultant tendency to equalize temperatures over the earth, the equa-

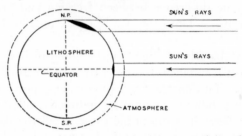

FIG. 14. Latitude is the most important factor in determining the distribution of insolation. The more nearly vertical the sun's rays, the more concentrated they are and the less atmosphere they must penetrate before reaching the earth.

torial regions would be much hotter than they are and the polar regions much colder. If the heat of the equatorial belt were not constantly carried away by the winds and ocean currents, the low latitudes would become too hot for the home of man and also for the existence of most of the plants and animals that thrive there. Likewise, without the influence of ocean currents and winds warmed by the heat of tropical and temperate zones, the polar regions would become much colder than at present.

SEASONS AND EFFECT ON LIFE

Some of the most common and yet most notable experiences of all life are those resulting from changes of season. If the axis of the

[6] The *diurnal range of temperature* represents the difference in temperature between the warmest and the coldest times of day. The *mean* temperature of a day is usually determined by taking the average of the hottest and the coldest temperatures. Greater accuracy may be obtained by taking the average for four or more temperature readings instead of two. The *annual range of temperature* represents the difference between the average temperatures of the warmest and the coldest months.

earth stood perpendicular to the plane of the earth's orbit (the path it describes in its journey around the sun), there would be no seasons, days and nights would be equal everywhere, and very monotonous climatic conditions would ensue. But the earth's axis is inclined about 23° 30' from a perpendicular to the plane of its orbit, and always in the same direction. Accordingly, as the earth moves around the sun, the northern and southern hemispheres are turned towards the sun alternately, and each in turn receives heat and light on more than half of its surface. That is, every place within the hemisphere turned toward the sun receives sunlight more than half the time and the days are longer than the nights. Similarly, when either hemisphere is turned away from the sun, less than half of each parallel receives sunlight at any given time and the nights are longer than the days (Figs. 15 and 16).

Briefly stated, then, seasonal changes are due to (1) the revolution of the earth about the sun, (2) the inclination of the earth's axis, and (3) the parallel positions of the earth's axis at all times.[7]

The two principal causes of seasonal variations in temperature are (1) the ever-changing angle of the sun's rays at any given place on the earth, with effects as previously ex-

[7] Although these three factors alone would result in seasonal changes, the effect of rotation is also necessary to cause seasons such as are experienced on the earth.

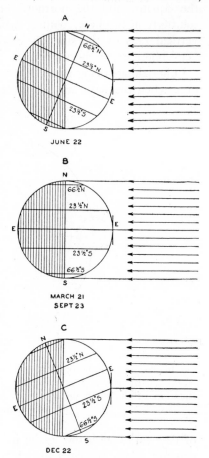

JUNE 22

MARCH 21
SEPT 23

DEC 22

FIG. 15. On March 21 and September 23 the circle of illumination passes through the poles and bisects every parallel. Therefore, the length of day and night is everywhere equal. On June 22 the entire arctic zone is bathed by sunlight and the sun shines on more than half of each parallel north of the equator. The entire antarctic zone is in darkness, and the sun shines on less than half of each parallel south of the equator. (See footnote 8, p. 45.)

plained (p. 43) and (2) the varying length of days and nights. From March 21 to September 23 the vertical rays of the sun fall north of the equator and the northern hemisphere experiences summer, the southern hemisphere, winter; from September 23 to March 21 the vertical rays of the sun fall south of the equator and the southern hemisphere experiences summer.

Other things being equal, it is obvious that a place will receive most heat when the days are longest and the nights shortest. The length

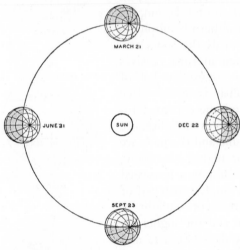

FIG. 16. Seasons are the result of (1) inclination of the earth's axis, (2) parallelism of the earth's axis at all times, and (3) revolution of the earth about the sun. Rotation of the earth on its axis is necessary to produce seasons such as are experienced on earth.

of day varies with the season in all parts of the world except at the equator, where the days and nights are always equal. During the summer six months (March 21 to September 23 in the northern hemisphere and September 23 to March 21 in the southern hemisphere) the days are longer than 12 hours and lengthen with increase in latitude. The mid-summer days of New York are about 16 hours long; in Fairbanks, Alaska, they are 19 hours; in northern Norway the sun does not set during the greater part of May, June, and July; and at the North Pole the sun shines continuously for six months. Figures 15 and 16 indicate that on March 21 and September 23 the circle of illumination passes through the poles and coincides with the meridians. During these times of the year every parallel is bisected by the circle of illumination, and hence days and nights are equal everywhere. On June 21 the sun never sets within the Arctic Circle and never rises within the Antarctic Circle. More than half of every parallel circle in the northern hemisphere lies in the sunlight, and the days are correspondingly longer than the nights; in the southern hemisphere less than half of every parallel circle lies in sunlight, and consequently the days are shorter than the nights.

Characteristics of the Seasons

Low, middle, and high latitudes each have distinctive seasonal characteristics. The distinguishing features of seasons in low latitudes are rhythmic rainfall distribution and variations in the diurnal range of temperature. In middle latitudes, variations in temperature are the dominant seasonal characteristics; in high latitudes, summer and winter are almost synonymous with day and night.

Low-Latitude Seasons. Within the tropics the days and nights are almost equal throughout the year [8] and the sun's rays are never far from perpendicular. As a result, the seasonal variations in temperature are not great. In some places the warmest months are only 2°, 3°, or 4° F. warmer than the coldest—scarcely sufficient to be a distinguishing characteristic.

However, only a few restricted areas within the tropics have a well-distributed rainfall throughout the year. In practically all the densely populated areas, the precipitation is rhythmic, affording an effective basis for dividing the year into seasons.

This seasonal rhythm in precipitation is invariably associated with differences in the extent of the diurnal range. During the wet season (summer) the heavy blanket of moisture which shrouds the land acts

[8] At the equator, days and nights are always equal since the circle of illumination bisects the equator (Figs. 15 and 16), and at the Tropics of Cancer and Capricorn the longest days and nights are but slightly more than 13 hours. The following table indicates that the length of the longest day (hence also of the longest night) increases slowly with increasing latitude up to approximately 50°. In the higher latitudes the lengthening of the longest day is measured by hours, days, or even weeks for each degree of increase.

LENGTH OF LONGEST DAY

Latitude	0°	17°	41°	49°	63°
Duration	12 hr.	13 hr.	15 hr.	16 hr.	20 hr.
Latitude	66½°	67° 21′	69° 51′	78° 11′	90°
Duration	24 hr.	1 mo.	2 mo.	4 mo.	6 mo.

as a shield against the sun's heat during the day and retards radiation from the earth at night. As a result the diurnal range is small—usually only 8° to 15° F. During the dry season (winter), the clear dry atmosphere affords relatively little protection from the vertical rays of the midday sun, while at night the heat of the earth is radiated with remarkable rapidity. Under such conditions the diurnal range frequently exceeds 20°, 30°, or even 40° F.

Middle-Latitude Seasons. In the middle latitudes the year is nominally divided into four seasons—spring, summer, autumn, and winter —as determined by the position of the sun. Spring is commonly regarded as the time between the vernal equinox and the summer solstice; summer, the time between the summer solstice and autumnal equinox, etc.

As related to man's activities and especially to the agricultural industries, a more effective division is that of two seasons—summer and winter. These vary greatly from place to place, both in length and in the time of occurrence. In some areas the winters are mild and the growing season lasts most of the year. Such regions are suited to sugar cane, citrus fruits, and other products that can stand little if any frost; in other places the winters are long, and the growing period is too short even for the hardy cereals to mature with certainty. These areas are given to hardy root crops, vegetables, pasture, forests, or other products that mature quickly or lie dormant during the non-growing period. Lying between those two extremes of the temperate zone are situated many of the best industrial and agricultural areas of the world today. In some places the growing season is cut short by drought; in other places by frost. In some regions, such as the citrus fruit centers of California and Florida, winter is the time of greatest industrial activity; in others, such as the corn belt, summer is the busy season. But in all middle latitudes, variation in temperatures is the most distinguishing characteristic of seasons. A more complete treatment of the influence of seasons on man's activities is given in the study of each climatic type.

High-Latitude Seasons. The seasonal range in temperature is more pronounced in high latitudes than in either middle or low latitudes.[9] The average temperatures for the coldest month may be 20°, 40°, or

[9] In making these comparisons, one must take into consideration the location of places, both in high latitudes and in low latitudes, with respect to land, water, and winds. For example, the windward-western coasts of high latitudes have a small seasonal range, but the windward-eastern coasts of low latitudes have an even smaller one.

even 60° F. below zero; summer temperatures, especially during the heat of the day and over dry land, may be almost as high as in the upper middle latitudes. This extreme seasonal range is favored by long summer days and long winter nights. In latitude 60° the longest day of summer and the longest night of winter are more than 18 hours; at 66.5° latitude, the longest day or night is 24 hours; and at 70° latitude, it is about 2 months. Thus, in these high latitudes, winter becomes somewhat synonymous with night, and summer with day.

EFFECT OF ALTITUDE ON TEMPERATURE

Vertical Thermal Gradient. The temperature of the air decreases 3.3° F., more or less, for each 1,000 feet of increase in elevation. Conversely, the temperature of the air increases about 3.3° F. with each 1,000 feet of decrease in elevation. This change in air temperatures as associated with differences in elevation is known as the *vertical thermal gradient*. It is not a constant. At times the difference in temperature is more than 3.3° F. per 1,000 feet, whereas at other times it is less. In general, however, high altitudes are colder than low ones of the same region because the air is thinner, contains less moisture, and therefore absorbs less heat from the direct rays of the sun and holds less of the heat radiated from the earth below. Thus on the Mexican Plateau (latitude 18° N) the summer temperatures are suited to wheat, barley, potatoes, and other temperate-zone crops, whereas on the lowlands of the eastern coast sugar cane, bananas, and other tropical or subtropical crops thrive. On the still higher plateau of Bolivia (12,000 feet), the temperatures are so low, especially at night, that cereals may not mature. The chief crop is potatoes, but pasture occupies most of the land. The animal life also reflects the low temperatures. The chinchilla and vicuña, both indigenous to this highland, are noted for their heavy fur. The llama, alpaca, and the sheep are the principal domestic animals of the region and the mainstay of the farmers. Similarly, in every part of the world the temperatures of the uplands are lower than those of the neighboring lowlands, with resultant contrasts in life responses.

Yet the temperature of the air over land 10,000 feet high is higher than that of the air 10,000 feet above lowland. This difference is due to the fact that a land surface at a high altitude may be heated quite as much by the sun as one at low altitude, and it then heats the air above it. Isolated elevations like mountain tops are colder than plateaus of the same elevation, because the former are so well exposed to the cooling influence of winds.

Vertical Air Movements and Temperatures. As air rises, the surrounding pressure becomes less and the air expands. When dry air ascends from sea level to an altitude of 17,000 feet the pressure of the air is reduced by approximately one-half, and the air expands to double its volume at sea level. The energy required to effect the movement of the air molecules whereby the double volume is occupied is obtained at the expense of heat, and hence the temperature falls; this change is known as *adiabatic cooling.* Since the pressure falls most rapidly in the densest, that is the lowest, strata of the atmosphere, the cooling by ascent will be most rapid there.[10] Conversely, when air descends it is compressed and becomes warmer.[11] This change is known as *adiabatic heating.* The rate of cooling or heating that results from density changes caused by the vertical movement of dry air is 5.4° F. per 1,000 feet of altitude.[12]

[10] W. G. Kendrew, *A Treatise on the Principles of Weather and Climate,* The Clarendon Press, 1930, p. 127.

[11] The rate of adiabatic change—5.4° F. for each 1,000 feet—may not be the actual rate of change that takes place in the atmosphere as it ascends or descends. The atmosphere contains water vapor, which has required the expenditure of energy to be changed from a liquid form into a vapor or gaseous form. This energy is stored up as latent heat in the vapor. Assume now that convection takes place in an atmosphere that contains an abundance of water vapor. According to the law of adiabatic changes in gases, the air should cool approximately 5.4° F. for each 1,000 feet of ascent. Suppose that in ascending the first 3,000 feet the moisture remains as vapor (a gas), then the temperature of the atmosphere will be lowered 3 × 5.4° F. or 16.2° F. Now suppose that at this level the point of saturation is reached and that any further cooling causes condensation of the moisture (reduces the vapor to a liquid), thus forming clouds and rain. The latent heat stored up in the vapor is now being liberated, and the cooling by further ascent is partly counteracted. The actual rate of cooling may thus be reduced to 2° or 3° F. for each thousand feet. Now suppose that later the air filled with clouds (water in the liquid form) begins to descend. Much of the heat of compression will be used up in evaporating the water particles that form the clouds. Thus, the temperature, instead of increasing 5.4° F. for each 1,000 feet, will increase at a slower rate.

The rate of adiabatic change—5.4° F. per 1,000 feet—should not be confused with the vertical thermal gradient—approximately 3.3° F. for each 1,000 feet of difference in altitude. The former change is due entirely to the expansion or compression of air as it ascends or descends, whereas the latter indicates a more or less permanent difference in the temperature of air strata at different levels.

[12] For a simple discussion of adiabatic heating and cooling see Glen T. Trewartha, *An Introduction to Weather and Climate,* McGraw-Hill Book Co., 1937, pp. 110–113.

ISOTHERMS AND ISOTHERMAL MAPS

A line on which all points have the same average temperature for
any given period of time is called an *isotherm,* and maps showing
such temperatures are called *isothermal maps.* For many meteorological purposes it is better to view the temperatures of any area to be
studied without the complications that result from diverse topography. Hence the temperatures on many isothermal maps are reduced
to sea level. This is usually done by allowing 3.3° F. for each 1,000
feet of elevation. Thus, if the temperature of any given location
having an altitude of 10,000 feet is 32° F., it may be placed on the map as
65° F. (32° + 33°).

Factors Affecting the Trend of Isotherms. If the angle at which
the sun's rays reach the earth were the only factor affecting temperatures, the isotherms would coincide with parallels. However, the
marked deviation of isotherms from the parallels indicates that other
factors are significant.

Water temperatures of any given latitude are more uniform than
those of land, and as a result the isotherms are more regular on the
oceans than on the continents. In latitude 60° of the southern hemisphere, where water entirely encircles the globe, the isotherms extend
almost due east-west; in the higher latitudes of the northern hemisphere where the oceans are separated by land masses the isotherms
depart widely from the parallels (Figs. 17 and 18).

Isotherms are also affected by ocean currents and winds. The influence of these various factors are nicely illustrated by the isothermal
charts. Thus during the summer season the isotherms are deflected
poleward over the warm land and equatorward over the cool water.
During the winter the deflections are in the reverse direction. Wherever isotherms cross cold currents they are deflected equatorward, and
wherever they cross warm currents they are deflected poleward.

A line on which all points have the same barometric pressure for
a given period of time is called an *isobar.* The average weight of air
at sea level is equal to that of a column of mercury 30 inches high.
On maps, the pressure, like the temperatures, is commonly reduced
to sea level. In general, areas with pressures of more than 30 (30
inches of mercury) are designated by meteorologists as high-pressure
areas or belts, especially if the pressure of the surrounding area is
lower than 30; areas with pressures of less than 30 are designated as
low-pressure areas. The difference in pressure is known as *barometric*

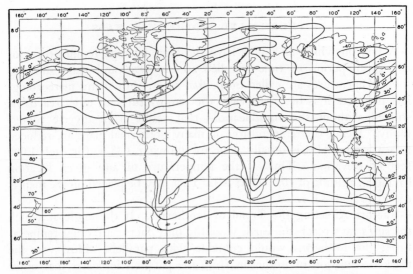

Fig. 17. Isothermal chart for January. (After John Bartholomew, *The Oxford Advanced Atlas*, Oxford University Press, 1942, p. 12.)

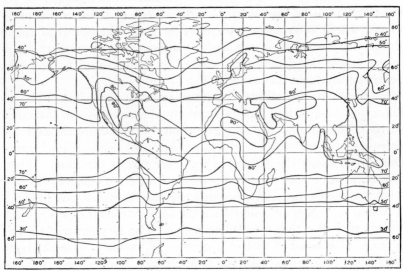

Fig. 18. Isothermal chart for July. (After John Bartholomew, *The Oxford Advanced Atlas*, Oxford University Press, 1942, p. 12.)

gradient. Air flows from high pressure to low pressure, or down the *barometric gradient.* The greater the difference of air pressure between two adjacent areas, the more rapid will be the movement of the atmosphere (the stronger the winds).

The mean annual isobaric map of the southern hemisphere shows a belt of high pressure extending almost around the earth near latitude 35°; the isobaric map of the northern hemisphere is much more

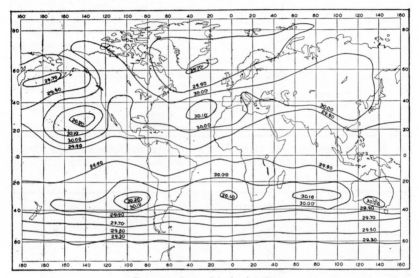

Fɪɢ. 19. Annual isobaric chart.

irregular, but it too shows a high-pressure belt extending around the earth between latitudes 20° and 40° (Fig. 19).

In January the severe cold in the northern continents results in an accumulation of air over these land masses and causes high-pressure systems (hyperbars) to cover much of the land mass. Since air is drawn from the oceans, the low-pressure systems (infrabars) over the North Atlantic and North Pacific have much lower pressure than in summer (Figs. 20 and 21). Thus in the northern hemisphere the isobaric map of July contrasts sharply with that of January.

The unequal distribution of air pressure over the earth's surface is due primarily to (1) the unequal heating of the atmosphere—warm air being lighter than cold air, (2) the general circulation of the atmosphere under the influence of rotation, and (3) the amount of

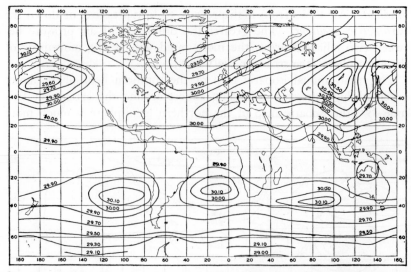

FIG. 20.   Isobaric chart for January.   (After John Bartholomew, *The Oxford Advanced Atlas*, Oxford University Press, 1942, p. 13.)

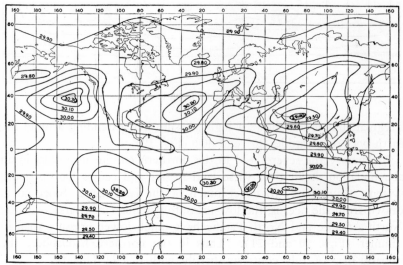

FIG. 21.   Isobaric chart for July.   (After John Bartholomew, *The Oxford Advanced Atlas*, Oxford University Press, 1942, p. 13.)

moisture in the air.[13] The first two of these factors are treated more fully in the section dealing with general circulation of the atmosphere. (Account for the extreme *high* over northern Asia in January; account for the extreme *low* over southern Asia in July.)

THE TEMPERATURES OF LAND AND WATER

Large areas of land are heated by insolation or cooled by radiation several times as rapidly as large bodies of water. The differences in behavior of these two substances, under the influence of insolation or radiation, results from a combination of factors:

1. Much of the energy of insolation that reaches the ocean is spent in evaporating water—changing its state without raising its temperature. On the continents, less heat is lost in this manner. However, if the land is wet throughout the year and especially if it supports a dense growth of vegetation the amount of evaporation may be almost or quite as great as that over the oceans; [14] if the land is relatively dry the amount of heat lost in the process of evaporation is small.

2. A large part of the insolation that falls upon the ocean is reflected and hence has no effect upon the temperature of the water. The amount of reflection depends on the angle of the sun's rays. Near the equator about 60 per cent of the sun's heat is reflected from the ocean's surface; near the poles, more than 95 per cent of the heat is reflected. Land surfaces, on the other hand, are poor reflectors, especially if covered with vegetation. Consequently, more of the heat is absorbed.

3. Most of the insolation that enters the water is transmitted to some depth, and the heat is thereby distributed through many feet of water below the surface. Land is opaque, and hence the heating effect is concentrated at the surface.

4. Waves, currents, and tides keep the water stirred to a considerable depth and thus retard the process of warming the surface.

5. The specific heat of water is much higher than that of land. That is, if equal amounts of heat were received by equal quantities of water and land, the land would be heated about twice as many degrees as the water.

6. Land radiates heat more rapidly than water does.

[13] Other things being equal, moist air is lighter than dry air since the molecules of water are lighter than the air which they displace.

[14] Every leaf of a forest increases the surface from which evaporation takes place.

7. In general, cloudy weather is more common over the oceans than over land. Clouds act as a shield against insolation during the day and retard radiation at night, and consequently tend to keep the temperatures of the ocean more uniform than those of the land.

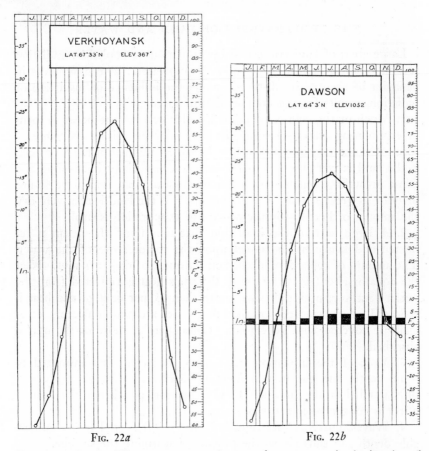

FIG. 22a   FIG. 22b

FIGS. 22a and 22b. The extreme seasonal range of temperature in the interior of large land masses lying in high latitudes is well illustrated at Verkhoyansk, Siberia, and Dawson, Canada. Lines indicate temperatures. Bars show inches of precipitation.)

Oceanic and Continental Climates. Oceanic climate is equable; continental is severe. Owing to the unequal heating and cooling of land and water the largest variation of temperature occurs over the largest land masses. The extremes are experienced in high latitudes where seasonal differences are most effective, and within areas remote from oceanic influence. An absolute maximum range (from highest temperature ever recorded to lowest) of 183° F. has been recorded in northern Siberia. At Verkhoyansk, located within northeastern Siberia in a transition zone between barren tundra and coniferous forest, the mean (average) temperature of the hottest month is 116.8° F. warmer than that of the coldest month. In the interior of North America a

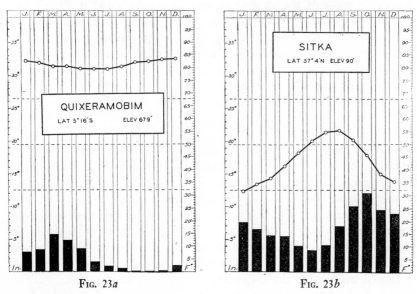

FIG. 23a   FIG. 23b

FIGS. 23a and 23b. The modifying influences of ocean winds and a moist atmosphere are well illustrated by the seasonal range in temperature of Quixeramobim, near the coast of Brazil, and Sitka, Alaska. Compare with Figs. 22a and 22b.

maximum range of more than 120° F. has been recorded over an extensive area, and extreme ranges of 130° F. to 140° F. are not unusual in the north-central part of the United States and the prairie provinces of Canada. At Dawson, on the Yukon River, the average temperature for January is 95.2° F. lower than that for July (Figs. 22a and 22b).

The large temperature range experienced in the interior of the continents contrasts sharply with the small range of the windward coasts situated in the same latitudes. On the western coasts of the continents poleward from latitude 40°, as at Sitka, Alaska, the coldest month is only 16° to 30° colder than the hottest; on the windward (eastern) coasts in lower latitudes, influenced by the steady and reliable trade winds, it is much less—only 3° or 4° in the most favored locations. Thus during the coldest month at Quixeramobim, situated near the coast of Brazil, the temperature is only 4° F. below that of the hottest month (Figs. 23a and 23b).

The diurnal range, like the seasonal, is much greater over land than over water. The results of the *Challenger* expedition show that the diurnal range of air temperatures over the ocean between latitudes 0° and 40° is only 2° to 3° F. The average diurnal range of air temperatures over most of the interior of the continents is 10° to 25° F., but over a few areas it is much greater. At Visalia Station, California, situated within the Great Valley, the average diurnal range for the entire year is 33° F., and during the almost rainless period of July and August, when the relative humidity is exceedingly low, the average diurnal range exceeds 44° F.

MOISTURE DISTRIBUTION

The luxuriant tropical forest of the eastern coast of Central America and the parched sands of the Sahara lie in the same latitude. The former area has been transformed into the most important banana-growing region of the world; the latter lies waste or at best is of little use and, except for the small areas that may be irrigated, will continue so indefinitely. Likewise, the rich corn lands of Iowa lie in the same latitude as the semi-arid pastures of western Nebraska and the desert of Nevada. The difference in the utilization of these lands is caused mainly by the difference of moisture distribution.

Atmosphere as the Medium of Moisture Distribution

Evaporation. We know that, if a pan of water is freely exposed to the air, sooner or later the water will disappear—it will evaporate. In a similar manner, evaporation takes place from bodies of water and moist places everywhere. The rate of evaporation from a free water surface varies materially from one place to another accordingly as it is affected by (1) the temperature of the air, (2) the amount of moisture already in the atmosphere, and (3) the strength of the winds. In low-latitude deserts, where the temperatures are high and where the air contains only a little moisture, the rate of evaporation from a freely exposed body of water may exceed 150 inches annually. In high latitudes, where the temperatures are low, evaporation may not exceed 10 inches a year. In the United States it ranges from 20 to 100 inches.

The ultimate source of all our water supply is the ocean, from which air currents carry the moisture to every part of the globe—even to the driest desert. The amount of moisture that the atmosphere actually contains at any given time is spoken of as the *absolute humidity* and is usually expressed in grams per cubic meter or in grains per cubic foot. The amount of moisture in the atmosphere compared with what it could contain at the same temperature is spoken of as the *relative humidity* and is measured in percentages. The capacity of the air for moisture depends upon the temperature. Air at 90° F. has a capacity for about thirty times as much moisture as at 0° F. (see the following table). Thus the hot, dry winds of the Sahara, which cause the skin to crack and the lips to peel, may actually contain more moisture than exists in the cool, drizzly atmosphere of the western coast of Scotland, but the relative humidity of the latter place is always higher.

MAXIMUM WATER-VAPOR CAPACITY OF 1 CUBIC FOOT OF AIR AT VARYING TEMPERATURES

Degrees Fahrenheit	Grains of moisture	Degrees Fahrenheit	Grains of moisture
−40	0.050	40	2.849
−20	0.166	50	4.076
−10	0.285	60	5.745
0	0.481	70	7.980
10	0.776	80	10.934
20	1.235	90	14.790
30	1.935	100	19.766

Importance of Relative Humidity. The relative humidity of a region affects man both directly and indirectly. It affects his health and comfort and also many of his economic activities. The human body is more sensitive to temperature changes where the relative humidity is high than where it is low. A temperature of 90° F. in the desert of Arizona is not uncomfortably warm, whereas the same temperature along the moist coast of the Gulf of Mexico seems almost insufferably hot and frequently causes sunstrokes and heat prostrations. This contrast in sensible temperatures as compared with actual temperatures is the result of evaporation. When evaporation takes place much heat is utilized in changing the state of the substance from liquid to vapor without changing the temperature. Thus in the hot, dry desert atmosphere much of the heat that strikes the human body is used in evaporating moisture (perspiration), which, in turn, tends to leave the body cooler. On the other hand, the high humidity of the wet tropics checks evaporation from the human body and increases the sensible temperatures during the heat of the day.

Relative humidity not only affects man directly, but indirectly it influences his activities in many ways. High humidity hastens decay and rust and makes the preservation of many products difficult, especially in warm regions. Grains heat and mold, meats and vegetables decay, leather goods, textiles, and paper are likely to become stained, and the utmost care is necessary to keep machinery, wire, and other iron and steel products from being ruined by rust.

Crop production is also affected by the relative humidity. In some areas of moist atmosphere, wheat requires only 8 or 9 inches of rainfall to mature a good yield. However, where the relative humidity is low and evaporation rapid, wheat may need 10, 12, or even 14 inches of water during the growing season.

Condensation and Precipitation. As already stated, when air is cooled its capacity to hold moisture is decreased. When the process is carried far enough the air is compelled to give up part of its water vapor. This cooling may be brought about in various ways: (1) Air may be cooled by convection; that is, as air is pushed into higher altitudes the pressure decreases and consequently the air expands and becomes cooler. (2) Air may be cooled by mixing it with colder air. (3) Air may be cooled by radiation.

The temperature at which air becomes saturated, that is, has a relative humidity of 100 per cent, is influenced by the amount of water vapor in the air. Air containing 5 grains of water per cubic foot will be saturated when the temperature drops to 60° F., but air containing only 2 grains of water per cubic foot must be cooled to 30° F. before the saturation point is reached.

When the temperature at which condensation takes place is above 32° F., the water vapor forms a liquid—dew, fog, cloud, or rain; but when the condensation takes place at temperatures below 32° F., ice is formed, and the result is frost or snow.

Dew and Frost. Very frequently during clear, cool nights the temperature of the surface of the land, roofs of houses, and other objects that radiate heat rapidly, becomes lower than that of the saturation point of the air immediately above these objects. Moisture then condenses on the surface in the form of dew or frost, depending upon the temperature of condensation, that is, whether it is above or below 32° F. Dew is more likely to form (1) on clear nights than on cloudy ones, (2) on open pasture than under trees, (3) in valley bottoms than on hill slopes, and (4) on still nights than on windy ones.[15]

---

[15] Clouds act as a blanket which retards the radiation of heat from the earth and consequently delays the cooling of the atmosphere to the point where the condensation of moisture takes place. Trees influence the temperature changes of the atmosphere in a similar manner. When the atmosphere cools at night

Fog and Cloud. The condensation of water vapor into droplets makes fog if it is near the earth's surface and about the observer; it makes clouds when it is above the observer. Thus the condensation of vapor into droplets about a mountain top results in a fog to the observer who stands on the slope at the elevation of condensation, but the same phenomenon is a cloud to the observer standing at the foot of the mountain. These particles of moisture slowly fall towards the earth unless they are held up by ascending air currents. Many times they evaporate before reaching the earth, and consequently there is no precipitation.

Rain, Snow, Hail, and Sleet. When the products of condensation fall to the earth, rain, snow, hail, or sleet is the result. Sometimes water vapor is condensed rapidly and in large quantities. If the temperature is above 32° F., the tiny droplets, which may be less than 0.001 inch in diameter, are formed in such great numbers that they are bumped together in the air, unite, and form raindrops which may be more than 0.1 inch in diameter. These larger particles fall rapidly towards the earth. Usually the lower strata of the atmosphere have a relative humidity of much less than 100 even during a rain. As the raindrops descend through the lower and drier atmosphere, evaporation takes place. When the drops descend long distances through a relatively dry atmosphere, evaporation is rapid and the raindrops may be dissipated before reaching the ground. In humid regions, however, most of the raindrops reach the earth.

When the condensation takes place at temperatures below freezing, snow is the result. Sometimes moisture condenses at temperatures above freezing, forming drops of water which later pass through strata of air with temperatures below freezing. These processes result in sleet or hail.

The distribution of moisture over the earth's surface is the work of the winds. It is necessary, therefore, to have a general knowledge of air movements before one can understand why nature has given an abundance of moisture to some regions while it has left others parched and dry. It is necessary to know something of the reliability of these winds in order to understand why the farmers of some parts of the world seldom have a crop failure as a result of unexpectedly wet or dry seasons, whereas crop failure is frequent in other parts of the world because the rains failed, came at the wrong time, or perhaps

the cool—heavy—air of the hill slope flows down into the valley and is replaced by warmer air. Thus the atmosphere of the valley may be cooled to the dew point while that on the hill slope is still several degrees above the dew point.

came in superabundance. Since the nature, amount, reliability, and seasonal distribution of precipitation are factors of such vital importance to man, they are discussed somewhat fully later in this chapter and in the regional studies, Chapters 5 to 17, inclusive.

THE MAJOR WIND SYSTEMS

The wind systems of the earth are complicated. Consequently, no complete and at the same time simple explanation of these systems

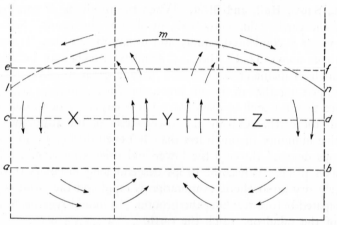

FIG. 24. Diagram illustrating the cause of winds. Explanation given in text.

can be given. However, some very useful concepts of the major wind systems of the earth may be gained by an analysis that proceeds from the simple to the complex. This study begins with simple examples, some of them hypothetical, and adds the complications one at a time until we finally study conditions as they exist on earth.

Causes of Winds. All winds result from the unequal heating of the atmosphere.[16] Air expands when heated and contracts when cooled. These changes set up a circulation that can best be explained by diagram (Fig. 24). Let us assume that the air temperature distribution of the three zones represented by x, y, and z is identical. Then the pressure at given elevations such as a–b, c–d, and e–f will be uniform, and the air will remain motionless. Now assume that the air column y is heated, and consequently expanded, most rapidly towards

[16] The direction in which the air moves is influenced by the rotation of the earth.

the center, while that of columns *x* and *z* are cooled, and as a result contracted, most rapidly towards the outer margins. These movements will cause the upper strata of air to assume positions somewhat as indicated by *l–m–n*. The air from the upper part of column *y* will then overflow, as it were, or will flow down the pressure gradient into columns *x* and *z*, decreasing the weight towards the center and increasing it towards the margins. Unstable equilibrium is then set up in the lower atmosphere, and the heavier air from columns *x* and *z* is forced back into the lighter atmosphere of *y*. This flow will push up the light column of expanded air, and further overflow above will cause further inflow below. These movements will continue as long as unequal heating takes place.

Such convectional movements in the atmosphere may occur on a small scale as witnessed in the bonfire or the thunderstorm, or they may occur on a much larger scale as illustrated by planetary winds.

The Planetary Winds. Let us first consider the wind system of a hypothetical planet that does not rotate and that has a homogeneous surface (all land or all water), of uniform elevation, and with vertical rays always shining at the equator. Under such conditions temperatures would diminish regularly from the equator to the poles. On such a planet the heated air in low latitudes would expand, rise, and flow poleward. In high latitudes it would become cool and heavy and would sink towards the earth's surface, along which it would flow back to low latitudes. The wind systems of such a planet would be exceedingly simple ones (Fig. 25) and would result entirely from unequal heating of the atmosphere.

The planetary wind systems of the earth are not so simple as those of the hypothetical planet since the earth rotates. Ferrell has shown that rotation of the earth causes winds of the northern hemisphere to be deflected to the right and those of the southern hemisphere to the left. Thus the air that flows away from the equator at high altitude is deflected more and more towards the east until in the latitudes of the tropical calms there is a tendency for it to curve equatorward again. This causes the air which has already become cold and dry to pile up and form high-pressure zones from which the air is forced out, both equatorward and poleward, in the lower part of the atmosphere. The air that flows equatorward is, according to Ferrell's law, deflected to the west and forms the *trade winds;* the air that flows poleward is deflected to the east and forms the *westerlies.*

The air that is forced poleward from the tropical high-pressure belt moves spirally towards the poles. The radius of rotation is constantly diminished, so that the velocity of rotation is greatly increased and centrifugal force is developed. This centrifugal force tends to throw the air back away from the poles in much the same manner that water in a circular wash basin is thrown away from the center and upon the sides of the basin when the water is rapidly rotated.

If rotation were the only factor involved, low-pressure areas would be developed at the poles. However, the constant low temperatures

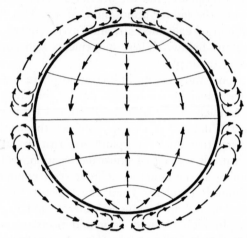

Fig. 25. Diagram showing the simple wind system of a hypothetical planet that does not rotate and that has a homogeneous surface of uniform elevation with the sun's rays always vertical at the equator.

of ice caps or ice-filled waters near the poles offset the influence of the centrifugal force forming highs instead of lows. The low-pressure areas are formed in subarctic regions.

Thus if latitude and rotation were the only factors affecting air movements, that is, if the earth's surface were made of homogeneous materials and were of equal elevation so that all parts of each parallel were heated equally, we would have relatively simple wind systems similar to the ones designated as *planetary winds* (Fig. 26). Under such conditions the isotherms and isobars would coincide with the parallels.

Unfortunately for the student of climate, other factors enter in to make our wind system still more complex. In a world of water, land, snow, and ice, and with elevations ranging through approximately 30,000 feet, the isotherms depart widely from the parallels. As a result of these differences in elevation and in composition of the earth, the departure of temperatures along some parallels may, at times, approximate 100° F. Moreover, because of the changes of seasons the isotherms and isobars are constantly changing their positions. These conditions all combine to give rise to other winds, some of which are scarcely less important than the planetary winds.

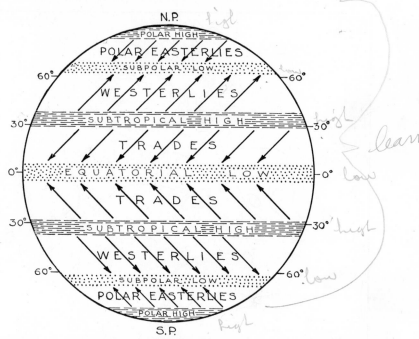

Fig. 26. Diagram showing generalized direction of the planetary winds at the surface of the earth.

Monsoon Winds. [Monsoon, derived from the Arabic word meaning *season*, is an appropriate name since *monsoons* are the chief seasonal winds of the globe.] Since land heats and cools more rapidly than water (see pp. 53 and 54), the continents in summer become much warmer than the surrounding sea, and in winter, much cooler. Asia is the largest land mass and accordingly has the greatest range in temperature, amounting to 183° F. in northern Siberia. In parts of Arabia where the monsoons are well known the maximum annual range of shade temperature sometimes exceeds 85° F. Over most of northwestern India, the temperature for the hottest month is from 20° to 40° F. higher than the average for the coldest, and in parts of the desert the seasonal range is even larger. This wide variation in the temperature on land contrasts sharply with that of the surface waters of the surrounding oceans, which is only 2° to 3° F.

During the hot summer months the air over land expands, and part of it overflows to the surrounding oceans. This movement reduces

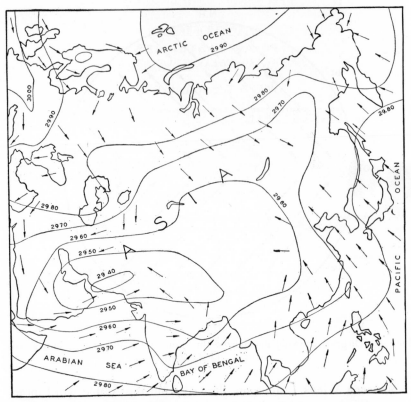

FIG. 27. July pressure and winds of Asia.

the pressure, as is indicated by the fact that the barometric reading over northwestern India in August is only 29.4 inches, whereas southward over the somewhat cooler ocean the pressure rapidly approaches 30 inches (Fig. 27). As a consequence, the air of the lower atmosphere flows down the barometric gradient towards northern India. Owing to the rotation of the earth, these winds are deflected to the right and blow over India from the southwest (Fig. 27). The great quantity of air affected in this manner is indicated by the fact that the summer monsoons are sometimes more than 3 miles in depth.

During the winter the land becomes colder than the sea, the barometric gradient is reversed, and the wind blows from the north or northeast (Fig. 28).

[Monsoon winds are not confined to India but blow over most of the eastern and southern parts of Asia.]

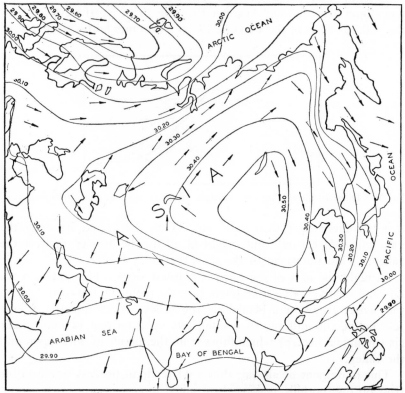

FIG. 28. January pressure and winds of Asia.

Land and Sea Breezes. Land and sea breezes are caused by the differential heating of land and water, just like monsoons. One is seasonal, depending upon the revolution of the earth about the sun; the other is daily, depending upon the rotation of the earth. During sunny summer days, the land becomes warmer than the adjacent lake or sea. As a result, the air over the land heats and expands more rapidly than that over the sea, causing the heavier air from the sea to flow towards the shore. This is the *sea breeze*. It has been shown that the sea breeze has been kept away from the shore for a time because the expanding air over the land pushes outward as well as upward. This outpush diminishes as the rate of increase of temperature over the land diminishes,[17] which undoubtedly accounts for the fact that at times the sea breezes do not begin to blow on shore until after the hottest part of the day.

Mountain and Valley Breezes. During the summer days the mountain slopes become much warmer than the air of equal elevation over the valley. That is, the air (Fig. 29) at *a* becomes hotter than at *a′*, at

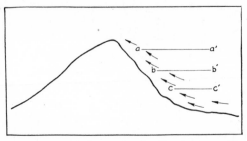

Fig. 29.   Diagram illustrating the principle of valley breezes. Explanation in text.

b it becomes hotter than at *b′*, etc. Thus the heated air along the mountain side expands and is pushed up by the heavier air over the valley. This movement of the air is the valley breeze.

At night the heat of the earth is radiated more readily through the rare and relatively dry atmosphere over the mountain top than through the denser atmosphere blanketing the valley. Consequently, after a few hours, this differential cooling sets up a current of cool, dense air (mountain breeze) which flows from the mountain sides down into the valley.

This movement of air (air drainage) tends to prevent unseasonable frost on the foothills, making them suited to certain crops that cannot be grown successfully in the valley. The coffee plantations of southeastern Brazil are placed on the mountain slopes where they have the greatest protection from frosts. In like manner many of the orchards and vineyards of the middle latitudes are planted on hill slopes to protect them against unseasonable frosts.

Highs and Lows (Cyclones and Anticyclones). In most parts of the United States the dominant factor in weather control is the succession of lows (cyclones) and highs (anticyclones) which are ever passing from west to east across the country. They are the prime

[17] Griffith Taylor, *Australian Meteorology*, The Clarendon Press, 1920, p. 111.

cause of the continuous changes of weather.[18]   The American weather forecasters give more time and attention to these weather phenomena than to all others combined; their positions, which are ever changing, are charted anew each morning by the Weather Bureau as the basis for weather forecasting.

ORIGIN OF HIGHS AND LOWS.   Both theory and observation lead to the conclusion that the succession of highs and lows, which bring the changeable weather of the westerly wind belts, is related to the inter-action of cold air pushing in from high latitudes and of warm air coming in from low latitudes.   An idealized picture of the origin and growth of highs and lows is given in Fig. 30.   When cold polar air and warm, moist tropical air come in contact (Fig. 30A), the warm air, being lighter than cold air, is usually forced to rise over the cold air.   Expansion and cooling take place and precipitation may result.

On the daily weather map a cyclonic storm may be noted first by a slight indentation along a front where the warm air has been forced to rise over the cold air (Fig. 30B).   As the indentation deepens a vast mass of warm air is forced over the body of cold air, and the storm becomes larger and more intense.   That part of the front that lies ahead of the advancing tongue of warm air is called the *warm front* (Fig. 30C).   That part of the front lying behind the body of warm air (where the cold air is pushed under the warm air) is called the *cold front.*

The ascent of warm air at the warm front is usually gradual, and the rainfall is usually relatively steady and covers a broad area.   If, however, the warm air is unstable or potentially unstable, a vast amount of energy may be released in the violent ascent of the air, and violent convective rainfall may result.   At the cold front the forced ascent of warm, moist air is usually strong and intermittent and is frequently accompanied by wind squalls (Fig. 30D).

A high develops as a body of cold air bulges equatorward on the polar front between two lows.

CHARACTERISTICS OF LOWS.   Lows (cyclones) are characterized by large areas of low atmospheric pressure in which the air flows spirally

[18] The term cyclone is sometimes used to designate any low-pressure system of the atmosphere in which the air converges towards the center and at the same time is forced spirally upward. Recently, however, it has become a common practice to reserve the term *cyclone* for that particular type of low-pressure system of middle and upper-middle latitudes which the U. S. Weather Bureau designates as a *low.* This use of the term is the one accepted here. Whenever the cyclonic storm of the tropics is referred to in the text it is always designated as a *tropical cyclone.*

inward and upward. These lows follow one after another in more or less regular order and bring, to regions over which they pass, the successive changes in weather that are so characteristic of much of the middle latitudes. The low atmospheric pressure of a cyclone

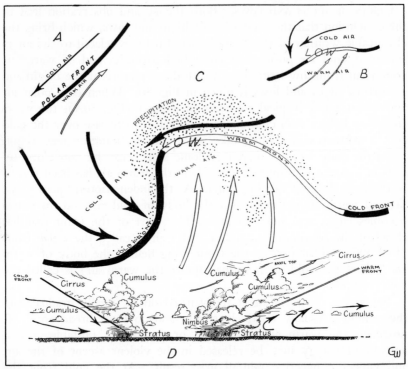

Fig. 30. These highly generalized diagrams *A*, *B*, and *C* together with the textual material indicate the way in which lows (cyclones) are formed. *D* together with textual material indicates something of the nature of the storm. Cumulus clouds are distinguished by their flat bases and their beautiful, towering, cauliflower or anvil tops. Nimbus clouds are dark and are the source of precipitation. Cirrus clouds form at high altitudes (25,000 to 50,000 feet) and are composed of minute ice crystals. Cirrus clouds take various forms, sometimes appearing like a thin light-colored veil over much of the sky. More often they appear like white ringlets or as feathery streamers. Stratus clouds form low-lying and rather uniformly colored (usually a dull grey) sheets across the sky.

results in a great eddy of air 400 to 2,000 miles in diameter. The average size in the United States has been estimated at more than 2,000,000 square miles. Since the depth is 2 to 4 miles, the volume of this moving mass of air is tremendous.

The minimum pressure of a cyclone is found near the center. Thus the outer, heavier air flows towards the center, but because of the rotation of the earth it is deflected to the right in the northern hemisphere (usually at an angle of 20° to 40° across the isobar) and to the left in the southern hemisphere (Figs. 31 and 32).

[The strength of the wind depends on the steepness of the air gradient.] The closer together the isobars are crowded, the stronger the winds are likely to be. The winds usually are light or moderate,

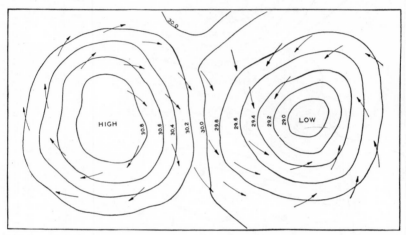

FIG. 31.   Diagram showing generalized wind direction about low- and high-pressure areas in the northern hemisphere.

and seldom do they reach destructive proportions. Other storms which are destructive sometimes develop within a cyclone but they are not a part of it.

Because of the reduced pressure towards the center of the cyclone the air movement is not only inward but also upward. This convectional movement, although very gradual, is an important factor in causing precipitation. Many of the characteristics of a cyclone may be noted during the passage of such a storm. The approach of a cyclone is usually heralded by easterly or southerly winds and by cirrus clouds through which the moon appears pale and upon which it may cast a halo. As the center of the depression comes nearer the clouds get thicker and lower, the air becomes damp and perhaps drizzly in the winter and moist and muggy in the summer. The amount of precipitation, if any, depends upon the degree of humidity of the air and the extent of the convection.

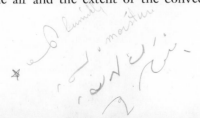

When the center of the low passes, the winds veer to a westerly or northerly direction, the clouds soon break through, and the sky begins to clear. These changes are frequently accompanied or fol-

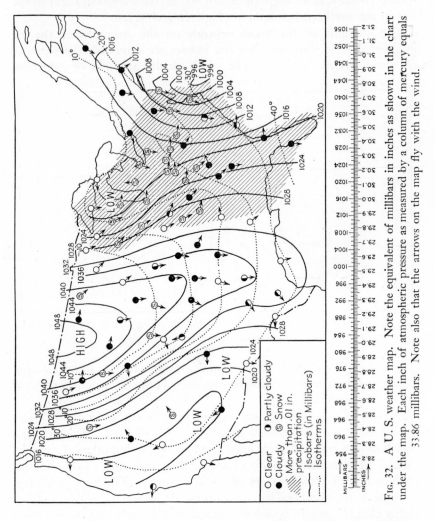

Fig. 32. A U. S. weather map. Note the equivalent of millibars in inches as shown in the chart under the map. Each inch of atmospheric pressure as measured by a column of mercury equals 33.86 millibars. Note also that the arrows on the map fly with the wind.

lowed by a drop in temperature as the cyclone moves on and the anticyclone approaches.

In eastern United States the southeastern quadrant of the cyclone is sometimes called the "rainy quadrant." The wind of this section blows from either the Gulf of Mexico or the Atlantic Ocean, and the

air is laden with moisture. Consequently, as it moves from lower (warmer) latitudes to higher (cooler) latitudes, some of the moisture is condensed.

The frequency of the occurrence of cyclonic storms varies from season to season and from place to place. During the winter from five to eight cross New England each month, whereas during the summer only two or three well-developed cyclones and perhaps another one or two ill-defined ones occur each month. In other parts of the United States these storms are less frequent, depending on the situation with respect to the major tracks of these storms. Normally eight to thirteen of these storms occur somewhere in the United States each month. They usually enter the United States from Canada or the Pacific Ocean, but occasionally they seem to originate or are intensified in the United States. They travel in a general eastward direction, normally at the rate of 500 to 700 miles a day. However, storms occasionally stand almost still for a few days whereas at other times they may travel more than 1,000 miles in 24 hours. Results of numerous studies have shown that the direction and rate of movement of cyclones are approximately those of the upper wind.[19]

CHARACTERISTICS OF ANTICYCLONES. An anticyclone is characterized by a large area of high atmospheric pressure (Fig. 32), in which the air moves out from the center of the high and spirally downward, but the descent is exceedingly slow. The anticyclone usually brings cool weather with little precipitation. Although it frequently brings bright sunny weather, cloudy days during its passage are not uncommon.

Tropical Cyclones. Tropical cyclones, when well developed, are the most destructive of all storms. They are variously named in different parts of the world, being known as *cyclones* in the Indian Ocean, as *hurricanes* in the West Indies, and as *typhoons* in the China Sea. They are not so violent as the tornado but cover a more extensive area, and the loss of life and property is frequently much greater than that recorded for the most destructive tornadoes. They are cyclonic depressions almost circular in shape. The wind frequently has a velocity exceeding 100 miles an hour, and the destructive path is usually from 50 to 150 miles wide.

In many tropical cyclones the wind velocities do not reach destructive proportions. The average maximum, perhaps, does not exceed 40 miles per hour; but in the most violent storms velocities of more

[19] Willis Ray Gregg, *Aeronautical Meteorology*, The Ronald Press, 1930, p. 237.

than 150 miles an hour have been recorded with frightful loss of life. Indeed, if early estimates from India can be trusted, more than 200,000 persons were drowned October 3, 1876, and about 300,000 on October 7, 1737, as the result of cyclone tidal waves in the delta of the Ganges-Brahmaputra rivers, near Calcutta.[20]

A storm at Galveston, Texas, in September 1900, resulted in a loss of 6,000 lives and a damage of property estimated at $30,000,000; a storm which passed along the east coast of Florida in September 1926, resulted in a loss of 242 lives with a property loss which probably exceeded $100,000,000. On September 19, 1947, a hurricane moved inland from the Gulf of Mexico onto the Louisiana and Mississippi coasts, with its center passing directly over the business section of New Orleans. This hurricane took a toll of 51 lives in Louisiana, Mississippi, and Florida, with total property damage estimated at $110,000,000.[21] The loss of life and property in China is even greater than that in America, because in China the cyclones are more numerous and the low coastal plain is one of the most densely populated parts of the earth.

These storms originate within the tropics, generally between 10° and 30° of latitude on each side of the equator. The areas of most frequent occurrence are near the eastern shores of the continents where the oceans are studded with small islands, but they also occur occasionally along the western coasts of Australia and Mexico. They are unknown in the south Atlantic.

Unfortunately the tropical cyclones frequently occur in regions that are densely populated, and, although most cyclones cause little or no loss of life, occasionally the cost in human life is appalling.

The Tornado. Tornadoes are the smallest of our storms and yet the most violent. Few of them exceed 1,000 feet in diameter at the surface of the earth, and many are only a few yards wide. Although they are of small horizontal extent, their air currents attain a velocity far exceeding that of any other storm.

The tornado springs up suddenly and runs its course with great swiftness. Only the briefest warning is given before it strikes. It suddenly appears as a funnel-shaped cloud (Fig. 33), black with moisture and débris which whirls with great rapidity in the ascending air

[20] Stephen S. Visher, "The Cyclones," *Journal of Geography*, December 1930, p. 386.

[21] H. C. Sumner, "North Atlantic Hurricanes and Tropical Disturbances of 1947," *Monthly Weather Review*, December 1947, pp. 251–256.

current. It produces a terrifying, roaring noise and is accompanied by torrential rain and violent lightning and thunder.

The pressure near the center is reduced to perhaps three-fourths normal. Consequently, as a tornado passes a building, the roof, walls, and windows may be blown out as a result of the excessive pressure on the inside of the building as compared with that on the outside.

Because of the narrow path of the tornado and the short distance it travels,[22] the loss of life and property is relatively small. Occasionally,

FIG. 33. Four views of the same storm near Gothenburg, Nebraska. In the first view the funnel-shaped cloud has not yet appeared; in the second, it has not yet touched the ground; in the third, it is just touching the earth; and in the fourth the destructive force of the wind is indicated by the great amount of débris which is being whirled into the air. (Courtesy U. S. Weather Bureau.)

however, a tornado strikes a large city and then the loss may be great. On May 27, 1896, such a storm visited St. Louis and almost instantly destroyed about $12,000,000 worth of property and caused the loss of 250 lives. The Weather Bureau had foreseen the danger of a tornado and had warned all the cities within the central Mississippi Valley. Immediately after the warning was issued the school children of St. Louis were told of the danger and dismissed. Little else could be done in preparing for the disaster. Conditions were favorable for tornadoes but no one could foretell where or when one might strike. Although there is no known method of accurately forecasting the exact time or place of the occurrence of tornadoes, they are usually associated with well-marked lows (cyclones) in which both the temperature and relative humidity are high.

[22] A tornado may travel 300 to 400 miles before it disappears, but more frequently its destructive path is less than 30 miles.

Tornadoes are more common in central and southeastern United States than anywhere else, but they sometimes occur in other parts of the United States, southern Australia, eastern China, northern Argentina, and South Africa.

GENERAL DISTRIBUTION OF PRECIPITATION

The direct cause of precipitation is the cooling of the atmosphere below the saturation point. This cooling is brought about, for the most part, by one or a combination of the following five factors: (1) the ascent of the air, (2) the movement of the air from lower (warmer) latitudes to higher (cooler) latitudes, (3) the movement of air from a warmer to a cooler surface such as results when winds blow over cold currents or ice fields or when they blow from the warm ocean to colder land during the winter season, (4) the mingling of warm moisture-laden air currents with colder ones, and (5) the cooling of the atmosphere by direct radiation. By far the most important of these factors is the first—the ascent of air—brought about by convection or the forced ascent as air passes over highland barriers.

Convection. When the land is heated, the lower air strata are also heated, causing the air to expand and convection to take place. (See p. 60.) When the air ascends as a result of convection it is cooled. Under favorable conditions the air may rise many thousand feet within a few hours or even less, be cooled far below the saturation point, and result in heavy precipitation. This may be called the convectional type of rainfall; it usually occurs during hot seasons and most commonly during the hottest part of the day. Within the tropics, most of the rainfall is convectional and is especially heavy within the belt of equatorial calms. During the summer season, convectional rainfall is common over the land masses of the temperate zone and is the major cause of precipitation in monsoon regions.

Monsoon Winds and Precipitation. We have already learned (pp. 63–65) that, during the hot summer months of the northern hemisphere, the air flows from the Pacific and Indian oceans over eastern and southern Asia. When this vast mass of moist air passes from the oceans to land it is heated. This heating causes the air to expand and rise. As the air rises it is cooled and moisture condenses, causing precipitation known as monsoon rains. The amount of such rainfall depends largely upon (1) the volume of air that flows in from the ocean, (2) the relative humidity of this air, and (3) the extent to which convection and the resultant cooling take place.

During the winter months, the cold heavy air over Asia descends and flows out over the ocean (see pp. 63–65). The temperature of this descending air rises, and its capacity to hold moisture increases. Consequently, the precipitation in those areas affected by winter monsoons is light.

Vortical (Cyclonic) Ascent of Air and Resultant Precipitation. The ascent of air in such storms as cyclones (lows), tropical cyclones, and tornadoes is responsible for much precipitation, and occasionally such storms bring exceedingly rapid condensation and heavy precipitation. The low-pressure systems (lows) of the westerlies are responsible for a large part of the rainfall of these zones.

Forced Ascent of Air. Moist air forced to surmount barriers causes the heavy precipitation received in many highlands. When these highlands are situated on the leeward side of large bodies of water the precipitation may be exceedingly heavy. The Western Ghats of India, standing directly athwart the southwest monsoons, wring from these ocean winds 60 to 120 inches of rainfall within seven months during the summer monsoon season. Similarly as the monsoons flow over Burma and northeast India they drench the highlands of these areas with the heaviest precipitation on earth. All the highlands situated near the windward coasts of continents and islands receive heavy precipitation. This fact is clearly indicated by the heavy rainfall on the eastern coasts of continents and islands located within the trade-wind belts and of the western coasts of land masses lying in the path of the westerlies (Fig. 34).

The Flow of Air from Warm Oceans to Cold Land. During the winter seasons the temperature of the land of middle and upper latitudes is lower than that of water. Consequently, when the moist wind blows from the ocean to land during this season, precipitation is likely to result. This contrast in the temperature of land and water is a major factor in causing the winter precipitation to be heavier than the summer precipitation along the western coasts of land masses lying in the westerly wind belt (Figs. 35 and 36). The condensation of moisture within the westerlies is hastened by the fact that these winds blow poleward (to colder latitudes)—a movement which helps to wring moisture from the atmosphere—and also by the vortical ascent of air within the many cyclones associated with the westerlies.

The Influence of Descending Air Currents and of the Equatorward Movement of the Air. When air descends it is compressed, becomes warmer, and consequently can hold more moisture. Similarly winds that blow equatorward become warmer, and their capacity to hold

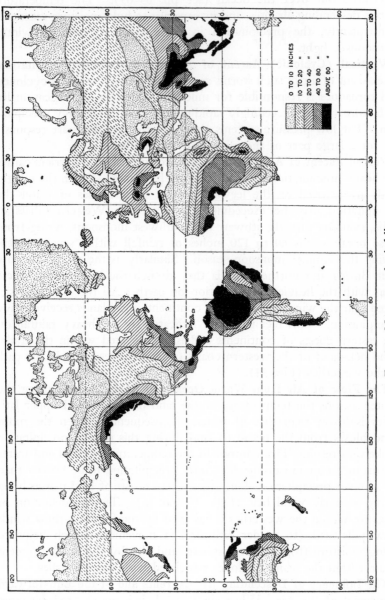

FIG. 34. Mean annual rainfall.

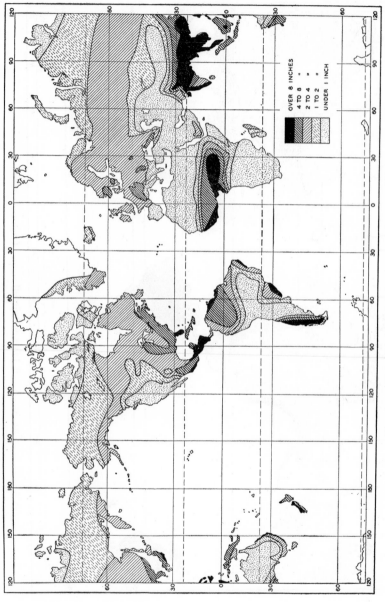

Fig. 35. Mean July rainfall map. (After Kendrew.)

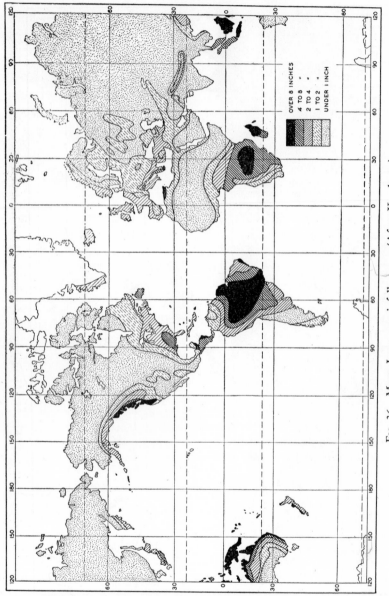

FIG. 36. Mean January rainfall map. (After Kendrew.)

moisture is increased. It is only natural, therefore, that high-pressure areas such as anticyclones, hyperbars, and the tropical calms should be associated with relatively clear skies and light precipitation. Similarly, the trade-wind belts, in which the air moves constantly towards the equator, should be associated with arid or desert conditions except in those highland regions where the air is forced to ascend mountain slopes and is thereby compelled to give up some of its moisture.

The influence of a hyperbar (region of descending air currents) is strikingly illustrated by a comparison of maps of the January and July rainfall of Asia. During January, a hyperbar covers most of this vast land mass, and the rainfall is exceedingly light; during July, it is heavy over a considerable part of the continent. The influence of the trade-wind belts is indicated by the fact that the greatest desert regions of the world are situated within these zones.

This chapter has dealt with some of the more important principles of climate and weather. Since, however, climate and weather are two of the most significant factors affecting the activities of man, the most pertinent facts concerning the distribution and influences of these elements are studied in each of the regional chapters which come later in the text.

REFERENCES

BLAIR, THOMAS A., *Climatology*, Prentice-Hall, 1942.

BOWIE, E. H., and R. H. WHIGHTMAN, "Types of Storms of the United States and Their Average Movements," *Monthly Weather Review*, Supplement No. 1, 1914.

BROOKS, C. E. P., *The Weather*, Ernest Benn, London, 1927; *Why the Weather?*, Harcourt, Brace & Co., 1938.

BRUNT, D., *Meteorology*, Oxford University Press, London, 1928.

CHAPMAN, E. H., *The Study of Weather*, Cambridge University Press, 1919.

GREGG, WILLIS RAY, *Aeronautical Meteorology*, The Ronald Press, 1930.

KENDREW, W. G., *Climate*, The Clarendon Press, Oxford, 1937.

MITCHELL, C. L., "West Indian Hurricanes and Other Tropical Cyclones of the North Atlantic Ocean," *Monthly Weather Review*, Supplement No. 24, 1924.

PETTERSSEN, SVERRE, *Introduction to Meteorology*, McGraw-Hill Book Co., 1941.

PICK, W. H., *A Short Course in Elementary Meteorology*, London Meteorological Office, M. O. 247, 1926.

SUMNER, H. C., "North Atlantic Hurricanes and Tropical Disturbances of 1947," *Monthly Weather Review*, December 1947, pp. 251–256.

TREWARTHA, GLEN T., *An Introduction to Weather and Climate*, McGraw-Hill Book Co., 1937. Part II of the book is given to a study of climatic types and their distribution. The climatic types as outlined by Trewartha have much in common with the climatic realms as outlined in *College Geography*. Consequently, *An Introduction to Weather and Climate* is an excellent aid to any teacher or student who wishes to study the climate of each region in greater detail than is possible in a textbook in geography.

VISHER, STEPHEN S., *Tropical Cyclones of the Pacific*, Honolulu, Bernice P. Bishop Museum, Bulletin 20, 1925.

WARD, R. DEC., *Climate, Considered Especially in Relation to Man*, G. P. Putman's Sons, 1918.

Chapter 3

THE GEOGRAPHICAL SIGNIFICANCE

OF SOILS

The soil is one of man's indispensable assets. It ranks with water as one of the two most necessary of our resources. From it are derived, directly or indirectly, all our food and clothing and much of our shelter—products commonly spoken of as the necessities of life. It is the soil—that more or less loose and friable material in which plants may or do find a foothold—which supplies a seed bed for pastures and crops and constitutes a basic resource for agricultural activities. The importance of the soil is well illustrated in the predominance of agriculture in most parts of the world. The teeming millions of the Orient—an area which contains more than half of the world's population—are mainly agricultural in occupation. Approximately 80 per cent of the Chinese and 72 per cent of India's inhabitants are directly dependent upon agriculture. In the United States the percentage of the total population engaged in agriculture is lower than that of the Orient, yet the value of the agricultural output of our country compares favorably with that of the leading agricultural nations of the world.

The soil may be made to yield indefinitely, but it is by no means indestructible. Thus in parts of China the farmers have cultivated the land for more than forty centuries and the soil is still productive. Parts of the Nile Valley have been farmed for fifty centuries, and because of the rejuvenation of the soil by the sediment deposited by flood waters, together with careful tillage, the yield is probably as high today as it was 5,000 years ago. On the other hand, the Tigris and Euphrates lowland, which in ancient times was one of the earth's gardens, is reported as being a badly depleted land,[1] where areas that

[1] George Wehrwein, "The Land," Part IV, *Conservation of Our Natural Resources,* Van Hise and Havemeyer, The Macmillan Co., 1930, p. 319.

81

formerly supported millions now lie waste. Similarly, in large parts of southern Europe, India, and southern United States tens of millions of acres have been depleted or even made waste by unscientific use. It is an axiom, therefore, that the permanency of agricultural enterprises depends on the skill with which the soil is cultivated.

Soils as Related to Regional Specialization in Agriculture. Before modern transportation facilities were developed, subsistence agriculture was practiced in all parts of the world. Under such a system it was necessary for the farmers of any given district to produce most of the food that they consumed; and, conversely, they consumed most of the food that they produced, since it could not be profitably transported to other areas. Such a system does not lend itself to the cultivation of crops best suited, or in places even well suited, to the soils and climate of a particular district. Civilized man has always craved, and indeed needs, a variety of foods. However, soils that will produce a bumper crop of sweet potatoes may yield but meager returns if given to wheat, corn, apples, or any of a score of other crops. The subsistence farmer, however, does not wish to live wholly on a sweet potato diet; consequently he cultivates other crops even though the yield may be low. In a like manner, the subsistence farmer whose soil (always considered with the climate of the region) will produce bountiful crops of wheat may be ideally suited for but few other food crops. Yet attempts, more or less successful, are made to grow fruits, vegetables, or other food crops in order to satisfy the human cravings for a variety of foods. Thus, under a system of subsistence agriculture, neither the soils nor the climate of a region can be utilized so as to produce the most abundant crop returns and at the same time supply man with the variety of foods which he needs. In other words, the human desires and needs of each district were given major consideration in planting crops, the practical limitations of the soil, of course, always being borne in mind.

Now all this is being rapidly changed in the most progressive parts of the world. The American farmer, for example, no longer gives major thought to local needs when he plants his crops, but to the possibilities of the soil as viewed in the light of world markets. A farmer may now give his entire attention to the growing of any one of a score of crops—celery, apples, potatoes, wheat, etc.—which is marketed hundreds or even thousands of miles away; in return, he buys a great variety of products to satisfy his own needs.

This change from subsistence to commercial agriculture has resulted in a major shifting of crops to those types of soil and climate best suited to their production; changes which have necessitated the elimination, or at least the reduction in acreage, of crops that are poorly suited to the soils and climate of a given area.   Within the United States this movement has been taking place for several decades and has been especially rapid during recent ones.

The excellent adaptation of wheat to the West has promoted indirectly a shift from wheat to corn and other crops in the East, and in turn from corn to cotton in the South.   Raising of hogs accordingly decreased greatly in the South and increased in the North. Dairy production has greatly increased in the North despite a stationary number of cows in the country as a whole.[2]   Similarly an increasing percentage has been realized in the output of several of the most important fruits and vegetables that have been grown in agricultural regions ideally suited to the particular needs of each.   Partly as a result of these shifts of crops to lands better suited to them and partly because of great improvement in agricultural technique, an extraordinary increase in production has been experienced.[3]

This increased acreage yield of crops, resulting largely from a better adjustment of crops to soils and climate, helped to bring about overproduction and resultant low prices—conditions that accelerated the recession of agriculture from the hill lands, the eroded lands, and other depleted or inherently poor soils.

This adjustment which has taken place in the United States cannot be accomplished with equal ease in most other parts of the world. Thus in Europe the many national boundaries retard the easy flow of goods from one country to another and thereby place a premium upon diversification of agriculture within each country regardless of what might otherwise be the best utilization of the soils.   Similarly, the poor transportation facilities of most parts of Asia and Africa retard the shift in the production of crops to the best adaptation to soil types and climatic conditions, which make for greatest output of food value per acre.   However, with the improvement of transportation facilities in all parts of the world, the adjustment of crops to soil types and climates best suited to them will be accelerated, unless the process is retarded by wars, high tariffs, or other man-made obstructions.

Soil and Civilization.   A study of the development of civilization indicates that society has its roots in the soil.   Records of man's early

[2] O. E. Baker, "Regional Shifts in Land Utilization as Shown by the 1930 Census," *Annals of the Association of American Geographers*, March 1932, pp. 46–47.

[3] *Op. cit.*, p. 46.

development show that his progress was considerably accelerated when he began to grow crops and as he changed from the precarious life of the primitive hunter and nomad to the more secure sedentary life of the tiller of the soil. Nomadic kingdoms of the past lacked stability; they were not permanently rooted in the soil. Nomadic peoples contributed comparatively little to existing cultures until they ceased to be nomadic and became tillers of the soil.

The growth of early Egyptian and Babylonian civilizations appears to have been closely associated with the successful development of agriculture in areas of alluvial (river-deposited) soil materials. The civilization of monsoon lands is often called a "vegetable civilization." It is basically agricultural, and the soil is carefully worked so that the millions of natives may secure a livelihood.

World history shows that stable civilizations were associated with long familiarity with a given soil. Such civilizations grow out of the soil and are rooted in it. Thus, the Chinese may be rightfully called "farmers of forty centuries."

Soil and Culture. In many parts of the world the culture of the people is influenced markedly by the nature of the soil. There has been no more distinctive human product of the American soil than that of the most fertile soils of the cotton belt. This is especially true of the black belt of Alabama. Here the climate is much like that of the remainder of the state, but the soil is more fertile than that of most other parts. "Ask almost any Alabaman where the best antebellum architecture of the state is to be found and the answer will surely be, 'in the Black Belt.' Ask in what part of the state the people are most cultured and most highly educated; where the traditions and prejudices of the Old South are strongest, and it will be in the 'Black Belt.' " [4]

The fact that this area was especially suited to the plantation system resulted in the profitable use of slaves, and the proportion of Negroes to whites is the highest in the state.

Perhaps a more striking illustration of the influence of soil in human development is found in Aroostook County, Maine. Here a pocket of glacial soil in a granitic wilderness stands out as an oasis in a desert. The appearance of this clay-soil area suggests prosperity and a high standard of living. Farm buildings are in good repair and the yards are well kept. Ill-kept farms are found only in the hilly, swampy, or

[4] Herdman F. Cleland, "The Black Belt of Alabama," *Geographical Review,* Vol. 10, p. 375.

more gravelly sections of this region, and they are surprisingly few in number. The area has many miles of good roads, many of the farmers own their own automobiles, there are telephones in nine-tenths of the farm houses and electric lights and washing machines in most of them. Here in this garden spot the finest New England traditions are fostered. Almost all the boys and girls graduate from high school; there are good books to read, the churches are well supported, and a lecture course is maintained every winter in the village of Presque Isle.[5]

Surrounding this prosperous agricultural region are thousands of square miles of forest wilderness, with here and there lumber camps, sawmills, and log-choked streams. Within this area are few buildings other than the shacks of the lumber camp occupied mostly by men. Consequently, the contentment and pleasures of home life, everywhere apparent within the clay pocket, are seldom known here. Why the contrast? The answer is found in the contrasting nature of the soil. The Caribou loam of the glacial soil is "ideal potato soil." It is loose, mellow, silty loam, easy to cultivate and on the whole well drained, and the high potash content is especially favorable for potato production. On the other hand, the surrounding wilderness possesses a cold granitic soil—where soil is found—which is relatively infertile and unproductive.[6]

Such illustrations of the importance of soil may easily be multiplied many times. There is scarcely a district within the United States where the diversity of soil conditions has not resulted in more or less marked contrasts in the cultural landscape. The backward pine belt of New Jersey lies on the very border of the greatest industrial and commercial district of the United States, yet most of the land is still covered with pine and brush, and the cultural landscape indicates that the people are classed among the most backward of this prosperous country. Many of the inhabitants dwell in cabins that have neither carpets nor paint; most of the adult population go barefooted in the summer; and the limited agricultural development indicates a shiftlessness which is in sharp contrast to the energy displayed by the farmers who cultivate intensively the well-kept truck farms located on the clay loam soils farther north. The backward conditions of the pine belt have persisted through several centuries largely as a result of the relatively porous, infertile, sandy soil. There is no doubt that, if this

[5] Ella M. Wilson, "The Aroostook Valley," *Geographical Review*, Vol. 16, pp. 197–198.

[6] *Op. cit.*, pp. 197–198.

region, possessing both location and climate well suited to intensive agriculture, were blessed with a fertile soil, the cultural landscape— homes, roads, churches, schools, factories, etc.—would present a marked contrast to its present appearance.

This influence of soil fertility is not confined to the United States but exists in all parts of the world. Note on the population map the contrast between Java and the Amazon Valley (Fig. 47). Java with its 42,000,000 people has much the same climate as the sparsely populated lowlands of northern Brazil. Although the contrast in cultural development is not wholly one of differences in soil fertility, this factor is undoubtedly the major reason why one region is intensively cultivated while the other is largely a vast waste, much of which is still unexplored. Java has a fertile volcanic soil, of relatively recent origin, which yields abundant crops decade after decade; the Amazon lowland has a relatively infertile residual soil that has been robbed of most of its mineral fertilizers by the incessant process of leaching that results from the heavy rainfall of this equatorial zone.

In the hard-rock area of Fenno-Scandia the prosperous agricultural communities are generally found in lowlands where the soil has developed in glacial materials derived from sedimentary rocks, especially limestone. Thus the lowlands adjacent to Oslo, Norway, stand in marked contrast to the rugged soil-depleted highlands of the country. Similarly the lowlands of central Sweden are among the most prosperous agricultural divisions of that country.

Although the influence of soil fertility cannot be summarized in a few pages, some worth-while generalizations concerning soil characteristics and the importance of soil groups can be drawn.

MAJOR SOIL CHARACTERISTICS

Soil Components. Soil consists of disintegrated and chemically altered rock materials mixed with organic materials, liquids, and gases. Pulverized rock is not soil. It must be chemically altered and mixed with materials mentioned above before it can support plant life. The solid portion of the soil is partly inorganic, derived from rocks, and partly organic, derived from living things such as plants, animals, and bacteria. By far the greater part of most soils consists of earth minerals. The minerals in turn are derived from rocks such as igneous, sedimentary, and metamorphic rocks.

Born of parent rock, soil develops slowly under the influence chiefly of climate, vegetation, and relief. Differences in these forces bring about major differences in the great soil groups of the world, as we shall see later.

Chemical Composition of Soils. Just as rocks are aggregates of minerals, so minerals are composed of elements. Although many elements are present in most soils, the great bulk of the inorganic material consists of a relatively small number of elements, notably oxygen, silicon, aluminum, and iron. However, not all these elements are required for plant growth. It was formerly believed that ten elements were essential to plant growth. Of these, carbon, oxygen, and hydrogen are obtained from the air and water. One class of plants—the legumes—may under appropriate conditions obtain nitrogen from the air as well as from the soil. Phosphorus, sulphur, potassium, calcium, iron, and magnesium are obtained by the plant from the soil. Modern science has added several other minerals that appear essential to a well-balanced plant growth. These include manganese, copper, zinc, and boron. But the great majority of our agricultural soils contain large quantities of the essential elements, with the exception of nitrogen, phosphorus, potassium, and calcium. These elements are used in large quantities by plants and yet are likely to be deficient in the soil. Hence they are commonly called the "critical soil elements."

Soil Color. Color is the most obvious characteristic of the soil. In itself color is of minor importance, yet it generally serves as a valuable indicator of other important soil characteristics. In our study of major soil groups we will have occasion to consider black, chestnut-brown, brown, gray-brown, red, yellow, and gray-colored soils.

In general, black and dark-brown soils are regarded as the most fertile. This relationship of dark color and productivity is well founded, but it does not always hold. Black or brown color in soils is generally due to a high humus content and is commonly associated with an adequate supply of chemicals and a favorable soil structure. Yet there are exceptions. Black color is sometimes due to a high content of a certain mineral or to inadequate drainage in humid regions.

Red or reddish-brown soils are generally less fertile than black or dark-brown soils. They are widely distributed in semi-tropical and tropical regions. The red color indicates the presence of iron compounds known as iron oxides that have developed in areas of good drainage.[7]

[7] Technically these iron compounds are unhydrated iron oxides.

Yellow soils, on the other hand, are believed to be due to hydrated iron oxides. Since hydration implies the chemical union of water with the iron oxide, these soils would appear to develop in areas that have imperfect drainage or that were formerly handicapped by poor drainage conditions. In general, the yellow soils have a low inherent productiveness.

Light-colored soils, whether they are yellow, gray, or white, are generally regarded as unfavorable for farming, except for special crops. A gray color may be due to lack of sufficient oxygen or to low content of organic matter and iron. In cool, humid regions, such as the vast expanses of the northern forest of Canada and Siberia, the iron compounds and organic matter have been thoroughly leached, thereby causing a gray color in the soil. The paucity of organic matter in desert areas gives rise to light-colored soils. Accumulations of calcium carbonate and other salts ("alkali") may even impart a white color to the soil. White soils are considered the least fertile.[8]

Soil Texture. By texture we mean the mixture of soil particles of different size. Individual particles range in size from stones, cobbles, and gravel, through the various classes of sand (coarse, medium, fine, and very fine), to the silts and clays. According to the United States Bureau of Chemistry and Soils, the size in each of these texture classes ranges between certain limits, which have been arbitrarily fixed at diameters of more than 2 millimeters for stones, cobbles, and gravel; 2 to 0.05 millimeter for sand; 0.05 to 0.002 millimeter for silt; and less than 0.002 millimeter for clay.[9] But a given soil seldom consists of only one of the above texture classes. There is generally an intermixture of different sizes. The varying proportions of these sizes determines the texture classes of soils. The chief classes in the order of the increasing content of silt and clay are as follows: sand, loamy sand, sandy loam, silt loam, clay loam, and clay. Clay includes the finest particles that can be seen even with a microscope. However, still smaller particles exist—inorganic colloids, or colloidal clays. Fine soils have a total surface area larger than that of coarse-textured soils. A pound of colloids spread out on a flat surface would cover an area of about 5 acres. It is from the surface of soil particles that plant roots draw much of their nourishment. Consequently, fine soils provide larger feeding areas for plant roots and, in general, yield more abundantly than do coarse-textured soils (Fig. 37).

[8] "Soils and Men," *Yearbook of Agriculture,* 1938, U. S. Government Printing Office, pp. 892, 893.
[9] *Op. cit.,* p. 893.

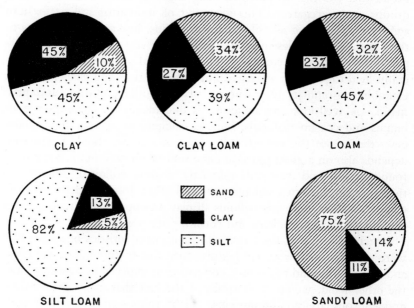

Fig. 37. Proportionate amounts of sand, clay, and silt in major texture classes of soil. (Bureau of Chemistry and Soils, U. S. Department of Agriculture.)

Crumb   Granular   Fragmentary   Angular Nut

Fig. 38. Some examples of soil structure. (U. S. Department of Agriculture.)

Soil Structure. You have perhaps picked up a handful of soil and found that the various particles cling together in very small clusters, groups, or aggregates. This grouping of individual soil grains into aggregates is known as soil structure. Thus, just as texture refers to the size of soil particles and the proportion of various sizes, so structure pertains to their arrangement. The individual grains of soil are generally held together in aggregates of different sizes and shapes, such as crumblike, granular, fragmentary, platy, shotlike, nutlike, and prismatic. A well-knit soil structure is due mainly to the presence of humus and certain materials, such as calcium, potassium, and manganese, that cause the various soil grains to cohere. Such a structure depends also on a good physical condition of the soil and is commonly found in silts and clay soils that have a good colloidal content. It therefore appears that calcium, mineral plant foods, humus, and organic as well as inorganic colloids all play an important part in causing the soil particles to cohere and form a good soil structure.

Structure is one of the most important characteristics of soils. If it were simply a matter of soil texture, then fine-textured soils like clays and silts would tend to become compact and impervious to water. On the other hand, we are well aware of the fact that many of our fine-grained soils are not impervious. Plant roots penetrate them with ease. They admit water and soil air, and they present a good physical condition for the development of plant roots. When we examine such soils we find that the grains or particles are grouped to form aggregates or granules, which behave as individuals, with air spaces between them. These aggregates in turn are sometimes arranged into still larger masses separated by even larger air spaces (see Fig. 38). Under such conditions a fine-textured soil becomes well aerated and in this respect acts much as though it consisted of coarse-textured particles like sand.

It is now known that structure plays an important part in the productivity of different kinds of soils, and that it is just as important to maintain good structure as to maintain a good chemical balance. Recently the farmers of the Great Plains have been faced with the problem of maintaining a rough, finely clodded surface on their soils so that blowing may be prevented. In humid regions the presence of a fine-textured, impervious clay soil located on slope land results in serious erosion which would not occur if the soil had a good nutlike or granular structure that would be readily penetrated by water. Instead the impervious soil does not absorb the water, but rather causes it to run off the surface so rapidly that much soil is eroded.

Granular and crumblike structures are the most important for crop plants. Such types of structure commonly develop under grass or other close-growing vegetation, but crumb structure is sometimes also found in forested areas, especially where there is a considerable undergrowth or a dense ground cover of vegetation. By the growing of grasses and legumes, and by the application of lime and fertilizers, the farmer can help in the development and maintenance of a favorable soil structure.

Organic Substances and Bacteria in Soils. In addition to the various chemical and physical characteristics of soils, there are biological ones. Living things ultimately return to the soil, where they are broken down by untold numbers of microscopic organisms and become humus, which is the well-decomposed part of the organic matter. Like the colloids, this decomposed organic material is gradually released as the humus is further decomposed into simple mineral salts, carbon dioxide, and water. In addition humus has a great deal to do with the development and the maintenance of good soil structure. Hence a permanent and productive agriculture calls for adequate supplies of organic matter such as legumes and grasses, so that the humus content of the soil may be maintained.

Soils teem with microscopic life—bacteria, fungi, algae, protozoans—as well as with various larger organisms. Each of these has its effects on the soil. The microscopic organisms especially are busy bringing about chemical and physical changes of enormous importance to man's use of the soil. Among other things they break down complex organic substances into simpler forms; they furnish nitrogen for plant growth. There is no true soil without organic matter.

Some bacteria known as *Azotobacter* can use the nitrogen of the air in building up proteins within their bodies and thus by continued growth and death can increase the nitrogen content of the soil.

The beneficial effects of legumes is due to the nodules in their roots. These are caused by bacteria that penetrate the rootlets and stimulate the plant to produce a growth at that point. The bacteria grow and reproduce inside the nodule, getting their carbohydrate and mineral food from the plant and their nitrogen from the air to form proteins that are released to the plant. Legumes, therefore, are able to grow normally in soil poor in nitrogen, provided that other conditions such as soil reactions and available minerals are favorable.

The living microscopic organisms that swarm in the soil are the agencies that break down raw material into humus, and this again into simpler elements. They do this in the process of getting food for themselves and building up their own bodies. They in turn die by uncounted billions, to add to the organic matter of the soil. Bacteria are not the only microorganisms that carry on the processes of decomposition. Fungi are numerous and active especially under forest conditions.

Soil Depth. In a state of nature two processes are always at work on the soil. One is constructive; the other is destructive. Soil is being formed continuously by the alteration of the underlying materials; at the same time, soil is being removed at or near the surface by erosion and by leaching (dissolving by percolating water). If soil formation exceeds soil removal the soil increases in thickness; if soil removal exceeds soil formation the thickness of the soil decreases. Thus in large level areas such as those found in parts of the Great Plains of the United States and in the level plains of southern Russia, the residual soils may range between 20 inches and 6 feet or more in depth over wide areas.[10] In many rugged areas the soil may be destroyed almost as fast as it is formed, and thus it may remain very thin. In extreme cases the soil may completely disappear, leaving solid rock at the surface.

Ideally, the old soil at or near the surface should be removed at about the same rate as the formation of new soil. The gradual removal of the top soil is often beneficial. This removal is especially desirable in the wet tropics where heat and moisture combine to hasten chemical weathering so that the surface layers of the soil soon become old and depleted of their mineral and vegetable plant foods. However, erosion of soil that greatly exceeds the rate of formation is always objectionable and usually indicates misuse of the land.

Fertility of Soils. Although we may consider one soil more fertile than another, the value of a soil depends mainly on the use to which it is put, and, in a broader sense, every soil is fertile. Soils that are suitable for certain kinds of crops may prove a failure as a seed bed for other crops. Some crops give best returns on sands; others on clays. Moisture-tolerant plants will often yield large returns in poorly drained soils, whereas drought-tolerant plants would require a much drier seed bed. Some plants give good returns only on soils that are well supplied with lime (either naturally or artificially); other crops appear to be acid-tolerant. Moreover, when a soil is called "fertile" or "infertile," reference is generally made to crop plants, though as a matter

[10] *Atlas of American Agriculture;* Part III, U. S. Department of Agriculture, p. 72, 1935.

of fact every soil is fertile to some plant. Also, many wild grasses grow on steppelands, where the soils are dark-colored and durable, possess a good structure, and contain an excellent balance of mineral plant foods. Yet despite the high quality of the steppeland soils, the steppe regions have a low and uncertain precipitation. Hence, the chief grain-producing areas of the world at present are the humid lands. Nevertheless, it is attempted to make the humid-land soils as much like the soils of the steppe as possible.

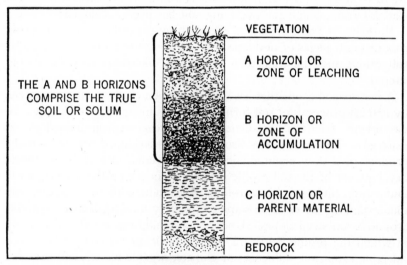

Fig. 39. The soil profile, showing the horizons. Note that the soil or solum comprises topsoil plus subsoil, or, more specifically, the A and B horizons. (U. S. Department of Agriculture.)

But in the last analysis not all land is fertile, because not all land has soil. For example, the earth's surface contains extensive areas of bare rock, which must be broken by weathering. The weathered material is made into soil by living organisms, especially microorganisms. Moreover, soils and plants develop together, each influencing the other.

The Soil Profile. The broad differences in soils may be readily seen where the soil layers are exposed, as along road cuts and excavations. These layers, known as soil horizons, in mature soils include the upper or A horizon, an intermediate or B horizon, and a lower or C horizon (Fig. 39). These make up the soil profile. The surface layer or A horizon generally contains an abundance of organic material and microscopic organisms. This is the horizon of cultivated crops. In most soils of humid regions the A horizon is one of leaching and eluviation (fine particles being washed out of it), and it generally differs in texture, structure, and color from the underlying B horizon. In most soils of humid regions the B horizon receives the finer particles that are washed into it from the overlying soil. In some places the amount of such material has been so great that this horizon has become quite compact and impervious. Together, the A and B horizons are the true soil or solum, below which we find the C horizon or parent material from which the overlying soil has been developed.

Maturity of Soil Formation. It has been generally known that soils pass through stages of development. Some are old, others are mature, still others may be immature or young, and some may be simply altered.

A mature soil is one that has well-developed characteristics produced by natural processes of soil formation and is in equilibrium with its environment. Such soils are generally produced on well-drained parent materials. The mature soil also has a well-developed profile; it is the product of a slow evolution in its natural environment. The fullest development of the soil profile is likely to occur on the smooth, level, undulating, and, in places, rolling lands where there is neither too much standing water as on some of the very level lands nor too active erosion as on steep slopes. Under such conditions a soil will develop in which the profile is mature, and its horizons will reflect to a considerable extent the influences of climate, organic matter, and bacterial action of the natural environment. The soil profile cannot develop to the fullest extent if the soil-making forces are interfered with.

On the other hand, a soil cannot be fully developed if the land is either too level and waterlogged or too steep and rapidly eroded. Moreover, there cannot be well-developed soil profiles in areas that receive constant renewal of new materials, such as flood plains receiving a steady renewal of alluvium.

These soils have a profile, but generally either the parent material or the slope of the land has produced an effect that overbalances the important soil-making forces (climate and vegetation). Such soils are often called intrazonal. They are found scattered here and there in various areas among the mature or zonal soils of the world. A good example of these immature soils may be seen in Java, a humid tropical island in which one would expect to find laterite. However, Java has youthful volcanic soils on many of her slope lands. The slope soils are removed before they can express fully the forces of climatic and vegetative environment. In the valleys alluvial materials are found. Such materials are renewed from time to time by the overflow of the rivers and streams.

MAJOR CLASSES OF SOILS

Methods of Classification

Prior to the beginning of the present century, soil classification was based largely on the types of parent materials from which the soils

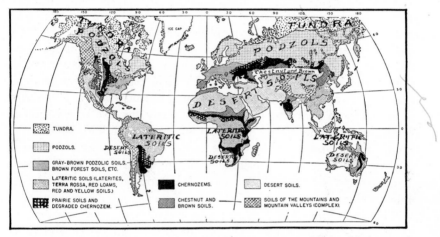

FIG. 40. The major soil groups of the world, according to Glinka, Marbut, and others. (U. S. Department of Agriculture.)

were derived. They were called residual, alluvial, glacial, or volcanic according to the parent materials. Later studies, and even previous studies, indicated that the types of soils were influenced not only by parent materials, but also by climate, vegetation, age, and the slope of the land (land forms).

The present classification used by agricultural experts is too complicated to be grasped quickly. No general and simple classification can account for many of the details of soil conditions and soil distribution in any specific area. This brief discussion deals, therefore, with some of the general principles that determine the broad classification of soils, together with the general location of major types (Fig. 40).

Major Mature Soil Groups

X The mature or zonal soils may be divided into two major divisions: soils of humid regions or non-lime-accumulating soils, and soils of subhumid grasslands and deserts or lime-accumulating soils. The lime-accumulating soils are characterized by the presence of a zone rich in lime, usually in the subsoil, whereas the other major soil division contains no zone of lime accumulation but gives an acid reaction throughout both soil and subsoil. The presence or absence of lime is directly related to the climatic conditions under which the soil developed. Hence soils reaching maturity in areas of aridity to semi-aridity are lime-accumulating, whereas soils developing in areas with abundant precipitation are generally deficient in lime. Moreover, the native vegetation shows a close relationship to these major divisions, the non-lime-accumulating soils developing largely under a cover of forest, the lime-accumulating soils chiefly in regions of grassland.

The presence of an abundance of lime in soils bears a very direct relationship to agricultural production, partly because lime is needed by most crops and partly because the presence of lime indicates an abundance of some or all of the other essential mineral fertilizers. Although there are acid-tolerant plants, most farm crops give maximum returns only when the soil is well supplied with lime. Leguminous plants (clover, alfalfa, beans, peas) usually require an abundance of lime, and some of these plants do not grow well where acid conditions exist. This is particularly true of alfalfa, red clover, and sweet clover.[11] Moreover, certain weeds are much more troublesome on acid soils than on soils well supplied with lime. Among these plants are sheep sorrel, corn spurry, and horsetail rush. In parts of the United States it not infrequently happens that land which is acid is so thoroughly infested with sheep sorrel or horsetail rush that an application of lime is profitable for the eradication of the weeds alone.

SOILS OF HUMID REGIONS: NON-LIME-ACCUMULATING SOILS

Since soils of humid regions are developed under relatively heavy rainfall, they are, as a whole, much leached. They are not only lacking in a zone of lime accumulation, but they are also commonly low

---

[11] Four tons of cured alfalfa remove twenty times as much lime from the soil as the straw and grain of a 30-bushel wheat crop. A ton of alfalfa hay contains 100 pounds of lime. R. A. Moore, *Alfalfa in Wisconsin*, Wisconsin Agricultural Experiment Station, Bulletin 308, 1919, p. 11.

in potash, phosphates, and nitrates—mineral ingredients essential to maximum production. Since they have normally developed under a natural vegetation of forest, the organic matter is either incorporated in the soil slowly, or as is the case in hot, wet lands, the vegetable matter is quickly removed by chemical decomposition and percolating water. As a result, the color of the soil is light. However, both the chemical and mechanical processes of soil formation differ in warm regions from those of cold.

Processes of Soil Making in Humid Areas. The dominant soil-making processes of humid areas are (1) *laterization* in warm areas and (2) *podzolization* in cool or cold areas. Laterization is the dominant soil-making process of warm moist climates and soils made by this process are known as lateritic soils. Since warm humid conditions favor rapid chemical reaction, the organic materials of the soils decay rapidly and are quickly leached out. Likewise because of an abundance of percolating ground water in moist regions, the readily soluble minerals are rapidly lost by leaching. Even much of the silica is dissolved. The ultimate stage of this process results in a soil made primarily of hydroxides of aluminum and iron and is called *laterite*.[12] However, this final stage of soil development is seldom reached.

The dominant process of soil making of cool or cold humid regions is *podzolization*. In the subarctic forests, owing to cold climates, the processes of soil making are unlike those of laterization. Organic matter decays slowly, and consequently it accumulates on the surface. This layer of pine needles and other forest débris absorbs water, remains wet most of the time, and becomes acid. This acid-bearing water percolates through the upper soil leaching out the iron and aluminum compounds, leaving the remaining materials high in silica. In the subsoil there is an accumulation of partly decayed organic matter, iron, aluminum compounds, and other minerals. The final product is a relatively unproductive, acid soil called "podzol."

Soil Belts of Humid Regions. Soil belts of humid lands are closely related to the temperatures of various parts of the world. In the hot, wet tropics most of the soils have undergone laterization and may be classified as lateritic soils. Yet few of them are true laterites. Similarly in the cold or cool regions of high latitudes, most of the soils have undergone podzolization and are podzolic types. Yet few of them are true podzols. Between these two zones of lateritic and

---

[12] Soils weathered from rock rich in iron have a red or brown color or even a dark-red color. Some are rich enough in iron oxide to be used as iron ore. Other soils, especially the lower horizons, may consist largely of hydrous oxides of aluminum ores (bauxite).

podzolic types, intermediate types exist. Since these types are related to temperature conditions of the humid parts of the earth, they form rude belts or zones of soil (Fig. 40). Moreover these soils have a very definite relation to human activities and well-being as indicated by a general survey of the following soil types.

Lateritic Soils. Mature soils of warm, moist climates are developed largely by lateritic decomposition of the rocks (p. 97), yet they are not alike. The parent rock differs greatly from one area to another; the slope of the land varies materially from region to region; there are various degrees of laterization; and, finally, some areas of laterized soils have been influenced more or less by podzolization.

LATERITIC SOILS OF WARM WET LANDS. Most lowlands near the equator are warm and moist throughout the year and support broad-leaved evergreen tropical rain forests. The soil group of this area possesses certain characteristics which make it distinctive among non-lime-accumulating soils. It is generally red in color as a result of the high residue of iron left after excessive leaching. It quite commonly possesses an open, honeycombed structure that makes it poorly suited to cultivation. In addition, because of excessive leaching which results from heavy tropical rainfall, this soil is low in phosphates, potash, and nitrates, and the alkaline earths such as calcium and magnesium are almost completely absent.

In many parts of these tropical regions the animal life is also a factor of marked importance in the decomposition and disintegration of organic matter and in the development of soils. "According to the work of Keller the activity of earthworms is, in the tropics, very important, one species, *Geophagus darwinii*, a Madagascar worm attaining a length of more than three feet and a diameter of more than three-quarters of an inch. Within a half hour's time such a worm will discharge 100 grams of moist earth from its body. . . . No less important is the work of ants (termites), which destroy tree trunks and reduce them to fine powder." [13] The immediate result of the work of these worms is to improve the soil by making it more porous, but the ultimate result is to impoverish the soil since the pulverized material is quickly leached away in these areas of abundant precipitation.

Deficient in lime and humus and containing little of the mineral plant foods, laterites are generally considered poor soils. But this

[13] Reprinted by permission from *The Great Soil Groups of the World and Their Development*, by K. D. Glinka, translated by C. F. Marbut, Edwards Brothers, 1927, p. 50.

infertility is partly offset by favorable climatic conditions for plant growth, and these soils constitute a valuable resource for the production of plantation crops such as bananas, cacao, oil palms, spices, and rubber. However, a large percentage of the lateritic soil is still under forests in which small patches of land have been cleared and are given mainly to the production of food for the native peoples. But in these tropical lands the abundant precipitation and high temperatures combine to cause rapid chemical weathering, and the soils in the small clearings therefore become quickly depleted of mineral plant foods essential to profitable agricultural production. Thus, in areas where such native cultures are found, the inhabitants move from place to place in the tropical forests as the cultivated soils are reduced in fertility. New clearings are made in the forests, and a luxuriant vegetation once more occupies the abandoned cultivated land.

LATERITIC SOILS OF TROPICAL AND HUMID-SUBTROPICAL REGIONS OF REDERTHS AND YELLOWERTHS. The rederths and yellowerths, developed largely by lateritic processes, are situated poleward of the tropical rain forests in areas where the rainfall is less uniform and the temperatures, for part of the year at least, are lower than those of the tropical rain forest. They reach their widest distribution in the humid subtropical and low-latitude wet-and-dry climates to be discussed later. Like the laterites, the non-lime-accumulating red and yellow soils are low in humus, phosphates, potash, and nitrates. But they are not so thoroughly leached as most of the lateritic soils of the tropical rain forest. Nevertheless, fertilizers are usually needed for continuous crop production on these soils, especially on the red and yellow soils of our cotton belt. Where fertilizers are not used, it frequently becomes necessary to abandon the cultivated land and seek new clearings when the crop yields decline—a common practice among many peoples living in the low-latitude regions. Thus on many plantations in the West Indies, especially in Cuba, new land is cleared for sugar cane as the cultivated soils are depleted in fertility by continuous cropping. But such utilization of the land is possible only where the population is relatively sparse and agricultural land abundant. In the rederth and other laterized areas of China, where a dense population presses upon the bands of subsistence, all fertilizing ingredients are highly treasured and carefully conveyed to the intensively cultivated fields.[14]

[14] The Chinese rederths are generally more youthful and fertile than those of the North American cotton belt, which accounts in part for their greater durability.

Podzolic Soils of Cool or Cold Wet Land. Mature soils of cool, moist climates are developed largely by the process of podzolization. Yet, as is true of lateritic soils, they are not all alike. Parent materials, degree of slope, amount of vegetation, rapidity of podzolization, and modification of the soils by laterization all have their effect. (During the short, hot summer, some laterization takes place in regions where the main process of soil formation is podzolization.) The two most important groups of podzolic soils are (1) the gray forest soils, and (2) the gray-brown soils.

1. THE GRAY FOREST SOILS.[15] These soils cover a more extensive area than any other podzolized soil. They occur in the northern forested region of Europe, Asia, and North America (Fig. 40). The floor of these forests—primarily pine—are covered with forest débris (resinous pine needles, twigs, etc.). The low temperatures of these regions retard bacterial action and permit the accumulation of a thick covering of half-decomposed, moisture-retentive organic matter on the forest floor.

Because of the relatively high moisture content of these soils, they are subjected to the influence of abundant percolating waters which carry acid from the fermenting vegetable covering down into the soils. These percolating waters also prevent the accumulation of lime carbonates and even remove in a relatively short time any of that material that may have been present originally in the parent rock. Thus the surface horizon is leached of iron and alumina and has a low content of soluble mineral salts.

One of the best known of all the gray forest soils is the podzol, which covers large areas of land in the northern coniferous forest of Eurasia (p. 95) and North America. In North America podzol extends northward from the upper lake region of the United States through the extensive forested region of northern Canada (Fig. 40). The top soil of the podzol is extremely low in black humus and soluble mineral salts. Moreover, in the development of the podzol, bleaching of the surface soil has been very marked, forming an ash-colored surface. In fact, podzol is the Russian term for "soils the color of ashes." Below this ash-colored topsoil lies a coffee-brown horizon which is generally high in slightly decomposed organic matter. In some places this horizon is indurated to a hardpan by materials (iron, alumina, and some alkaline earths) obtained from the surface soil.[16]

---

[15] The gray forest soils are indicated as podzols in Figure 40.

[16] H. L. Shantz and C. F. Marbut, *Vegetation and Soils of Africa*, American Geographical Society Research Series, No. 13, p. 121.

The long winters and short summers of most parts of this area are not conducive to great agricultural development. Where given to crops, the typical podzol is generally found to be acid and deficient in organic matter. Farmers who cultivate this type of soil frequently make heavy applications of lime and plow under leguminous crops

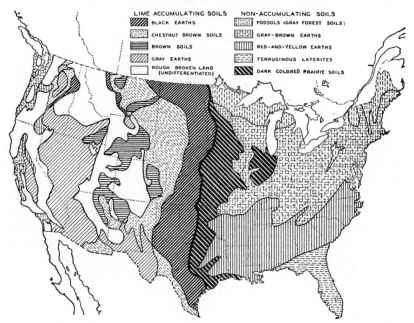

Fig. 41. The major soil groups of the United States. The heavy black line divides the non-lime-accumulating soil division of the humid East from the lime-accumulating soils of the arid and semi-arid West. (After the U. S. Bureau of Chemistry and Soils, and L. A. Wolfanger.)

and manure. The most common legumes grown for this purpose are alsike and red clover. Hardy cereals and vegetables are also grown, but the greater part of these northern regions is still covered with forests. It has been estimated that forests still cover more than 65 per cent of the podzol soils of European Russia, and in America the forest still retains its hold on practically all podzol soils.

2. THE GRAY-BROWN SOILS. These soils are podzolic soils but they are not fully developed podzols. In North America they extend from the red and yellow earths of the cotton belt northward to the podzols of the upper lake region, and eastward from the black prairie earths of the corn belt to the Atlantic Ocean (Fig. 41). They also cover

large areas of land in western (marine) North America and north-western Europe. In all probability more complete soil surveys will disclose a widespread occurrence of these soils in other forested parts of the world.

From the standpoint of fertility, the gray-brown soils command a relatively high place among non-lime-accumulating soils. They are generally less leached of mineral plant foods and humus than the laterites, rederths, and podzols, and, in addition, their structure is generally superior.

SOILS OF SUBHUMID GRASSLANDS AND DESERTS: LIME-ACCUMULATING SOILS

In many parts of the world both within the tropics and within the temperate zones, the climate is too dry to support forests but moist enough to support grass or other vegetation. Under such conditions the types of soils are more closely related to the amount of rainfall and to the nature of the vegetative covering than to temperatures.

Black and Dark-Brown Grassland Soils. In many subhumid regions the climate is moist enough to support a heavy stand of grass and perhaps a few trees here and there in favorable locations, but too dry to support a forest. Under such conditions, the accumulation of dead grass and grass roots supplies an abundance of organic matter (humus) to the soil. Since this accumulation takes place under conditions of low or moderate moisture supply, the humus does not become acid.

Prairie Soils. Prairie soils are intermediate soils which do not fit clearly into the subdivisions of either lime-accumulating or non-lime-accumulating soils. They have no horizon of lime accumulation except in the drier borders; yet they are neutral rather than acid. The dark prairie soils reach their maximum development in the western hemisphere and are narrowly limited in distribution in Eurasia. The United States contains a large north-south-trending belt of black and dark-brown prairie soils—an area that includes the western two-thirds of the corn belt. The prairie soils of the United States constitute the westernmost group as well as the most fertile group of non-lime-accumulating soils (Fig. 41).

These soils developed under a grass cover in a region where the precipitation ranges from 20 to 40 inches. The precipitation, however, is not sufficiently great to cause excessive mechanical weathering, and the average prairie soil is well supplied with mineral plant foods and generally contains a well-knit, granular structure which facilitates cultivation. In addition, the topsoil is deep and rich in humus, having developed under a grass cover, and, therefore, constitutes an excellent seed bed for crop production.

The agricultural value of the dark prairie soils is reflected in the cultural landscape of the North American corn belt, which is the largest area of fertile, well-drained agricultural land in the United States.

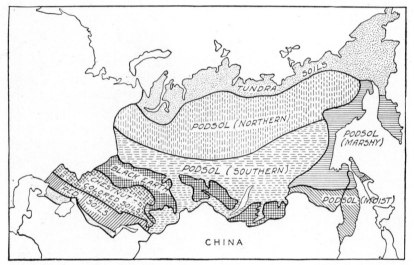

FIG. 42. The major soil groups of Asiatic U.S.S.R. (After Shultz.)

Black Soils of the Extensive Grass-Covered Plains. In the extensive grass-covered plains of middle latitudes are found some of the most fertile and durable soils known to man. Lying west of the black prairie soils of North America is a long north-south-trending belt of black earth. The soils of this belt occupy the eastern part of the Great Plains (p. 101) and correspond in many respects to the black soils (chernozems) of the Soviet Union, which occupy a region that stretches from east to west, with minor interruptions across the southern part of the country (Fig. 42).

Like the dark-colored prairie soils, the blackerths of the Great Plains have a good structure and an abundance of humus, and they contain a large supply of mineral plant foods and lime. These soil characteristics have developed not because of a certain remarkable type of parent material or rock formation, since blackerths are found on many different kinds of rocks, but rather because of the conditions of climate and native vegetation in their areas of occurrence. They have developed in the presence of a quantity of moisture (approximately 15 to 20 inches), which, though sufficient for a rapid and energetic decomposition of the organic substances, is nevertheless insufficient to carry them away in large quantities. Hence, humus accumulates,

FIG. 43. Plowing black, lime-accumulating soil in western Canada. These blackerths of the Great Plains of North America possess an excellent structure and are among the most durable soils in the world.

and the typical topsoil of the blackerths is well supplied with humus. In addition, since the rainfall is relatively low, it does not leach away the lime and essential plant foods.

For crop production, these soils constitute a deep, rich seed bed, and agricultural operations are facilitated in this mellow earth (Fig. 43). These soils are handicapped, however, by being located in relatively dry regions, where the rainfall sets narrow limits to the type and variety of crops which may be produced. The chief crop is wheat. In Russia, the east-west-trending blackerth belt is the major wheat-producing region of that country. It is the region in which attempts to increase production are being carried on with great energy. There seems to be no doubt that total wheat production can be greatly increased if the natural capacity of the region is fully or even only moderately utilized. The area is large and well adapted to low-cost, large-scale production of high-quality wheat.[17]

Light-Colored Soils of Subhumid and Desert Areas. These soils occupy areas in which the rainfall is less plentiful and the cover of native grasses is less luxuriant than in the regions where the black and dark-brown soils predominate. Since the soil contains relatively little vegetable matter it is light in color.

THE CHESTNUT-BROWN AND BROWN SOILS. In the Great Plains of North America the chestnut-brown soils are found in a long north-south-trending belt which lies immediately west of the blackerth belt. In the still drier region located west of the chestnut-brown soils, the surface soils are lighter, being chiefly brown and light brown in color. In Russia a large belt of chestnut-brown soils borders the blackerth belt on the south, whereas still further south the brown and light-brown soils predominate. These soil belts, unlike their corresponding regions in America, extend from east to west.

The chestnut-brown and brown soils, though lower in humus content than the black soils located along their more humid margins, possess a good soil structure and are relatively well supplied with essential mineral plant foods and lime; yet they are used mainly for grazing, crop production being of secondary importance. Wheat is still the grain crop best adapted to these areas, yet failures mainly because of drought are relatively frequent. On the chestnut-brown soils of Russia a failure of three or four crops in ten is not considered excessive.[18]

The Gray Desert Soils. In arid lands, because of the meager rainfall and sparse vegetation, chemical weathering is at a minimum. On the other hand, mechanical disintegration, which in desert regions is caused mainly by extremes in temperature and by the action of frost, is sufficient to bring about a development of a shallow top horizon of fine-grained earthy material. In these regions of scant vegetation, the humus content of the soil is low, and there is essentially nothing to bind the soil and to prevent it from being blown about by strong desert winds.

Grazing constitutes the most widespread economic activity in desert lands. Here vast stretches of soil are utilized by migrating bands of nomads who frequently travel great distances in search of the scanty

[17] C. F. Marbut, "Agriculture in the United States and Russia," *Geographical Review*, Vol. 21, 1931, p. 609.

[18] *Ibid.*

pasturage covering these regions.   Soils utilized for crops are confined to the oases (pp. 285–290).

SOIL CONSERVATION

People who settle in a new country give little thought as a rule to conservation problems, since such people may easily acquire additional lands when their original holdings "run down" and are abandoned. But when a country loses its characteristics of youth, and when the population increases and spreads into the marginal areas, then the problems of soil erosion, crop rotation, and proper fertilization become increasingly important.

The Soil Erosion Hazard.   The most important factor in soil erosion is running water.   As soon as the rocks decay, rain water begins to pick up particles of the residual product and carry them away in the direction of the oceans.   There will always be erosion as long as there are any slopes down which water will flow.   But "the effectiveness of the process from place to place will vary with a number of natural and artificial variants.   Man is doing much to accentuate the process and with a degree of efficiency that has brought about some conspicuous examples of earth spoliation, and effected the impairment of vast areas of farm and grazing lands." [19]

The tremendous magnitude of soil waste is generally overlooked. In the United States alone about 513,000,000 tons of silt and 270,000,000 tons of dissolved matter are discharged annually to the sea by the rivers of this country.   This erosional débris contains approximately 126 billion pounds of plant food—potash, phosphate, nitrogen, lime, and magnesia.   The total loss of these minerals exceeds, by approximately twenty-one times, [20] the annual net loss of plant food removed in crops.

Probably not less than 10,000,000 acres of upland in this country, once of medium to good value for agriculture, have been permanently destroyed or made temporarily unfit for cultivation by soil wash; and in addition about 3,000,000 acres of rich stream alluvium have been seriously damaged or ruined by overwash of sand and gravel and by increasing swampiness resulting from clogged stream channels and

---

[19] Reprinted by permission from *Mimeographed Material on Soil Erosion and Flood Control*, by H. H. Bennett, Graduate School, U. S. Department of Agriculture, 1928, p. 1.

[20] *Op. cit.*, pp. 2 and 3.

consequent increased overflows.[21] This is enough land to support a nation; it exceeds the total land area of either Denmark or Belgium and almost reaches the figure for the total tillable area of Japan.[22]

The Missouri Agricultural Experiment Station showed by actual measurement that, within 24 years, erosion has removed 7 inches of the surface soil from an important type of Missouri farm land, which is plowed regularly to a depth of 4 inches. In bluegrass sod, on the other hand, the same type of soil erodes at the rate of only 7 inches in 3,547 years.

Methods of Preventing Erosion. If all the rain water were absorbed by the ground upon which it falls, soil erosion would be reduced to a minimum. It is obvious, therefore, that in order to prevent or reduce erosive action the soil must receive treatment that is conducive to the admission and the storage of large quantities of rain water; and methods must be employed to reduce the velocity, and thereby the transporting power, of the runoff water.

Since the capacity of a soil in storing water depends upon its porosity, any treatment that results in an increased porosity of the soil will materially reduce erosion. This porous condition usually is obtained by deep plowing and by a thorough incorporation of organic matter in the soil. The treatment of cover, such as seeding land to pasture, growing timber, and planting cover crops in winter, also tends to check and diminish erosion greatly (Fig. 44). Other methods that retard the flow of the water and conduct the excess runoff from the field with a reduced amount of erosion are contour plowing, hillside ditching, and terracing.

Crop Rotation and Soil Conservation. Crop rotation—the growing of different crops in recurring succession on the same land—was recognized as advantageous by early agricultural scientists and was made the foundation of the improvements in agriculture which took place in England, in large parts of continental Europe, and in the United States during the last part of the eighteenth and especially during the nineteenth century. The benefits to be derived from the growing of leguminous crops in alternation with the cereals were distinctly recognized by the ancient Romans; and the benefits of growing intertilled turnips or root crops in rotation with barley, clover, and wheat were

[21] *Op. cit.*, p. 12.

[22] The total of this waste land amounts to about 13,000,000 acres. The total land area of Belgium is approximately 7,000,000 acres; of Denmark about 10,600,-000 acres; whereas the total tillable land area of Japan covers little more than 14,000,000 acres.

Fig. 44. Erosion in gully arrested by vegetation, after two years' growth. (Courtesy Soil Conservation Service, U. S. Department of Agriculture.)

color of soil — mineral content — vegetation

discovered about 1730 in England. The farmer of ancient Rome understood that crops following beans, peas, and vetches were usually better than those following wheat or barley, but it was not until the last quarter of the nineteenth century that people learned that the legumes with the aid of associated bacteria have the power of feeding on the free nitrogen of the air, while the non-leguminous plants can draw only on the nitrogen supply stored in the soil.

The effects of crop rotation on yields are manifold: Rotation aids in controlling weeds and certain crop pests and diseases. It may render manure and chemical fertilizers more effective. It increases the soil supply of organic matter and nitrogen, improves tilth, and conserves the soil reserve of plant nutrients; and the different crops in themselves may exert beneficial effects on those that follow.

Much has been written about the increase in nitrogen when legumes are grown. It must be remembered in this connection that legumes do not increase the nitrogen when the entire crop is harvested and permanently removed from the soil. But when the legumes are plowed under, a large increase in this mineral constituent may result, depending upon the quantity of legume growth plowed under. Scientific agricultural experiments show that 3 tons of alfalfa contain 150 pounds of nitrogen or the equivalent of nitrogen found in the grain and straw of 75 bushels of wheat.[23]

A study of the long-continued soil fertility experiments of the United States and of England, made by the Department of Agriculture, has disclosed the following facts about crop rotation in its relation to soil productivity: (1) In general, crop rotation has been found to be practically 95 per cent as effective as farm manure and complete commercial fertilizers in maintaining the yields of wheat, corn, and oats, and about 90 per cent as effective as these fertilizers in increasing the yields of these major crops. (2) The favorable effects of crop rotation do not impair the benefits derived from the use of fertilizers, so that when these two farm practices are combined the one practice adds to the benefits of the other. (3) In comparison with the effectiveness of manure and commercial fertilizers, the relative value of crop rotation is practically 20 per cent higher on soils sufficiently supplied with lime as compared with soils that are acid.[24]

[23] J. E. Greaves, "Does Crop Rotation Maintain the Fertility of the Soil?" *Scientific Monthly*, Vol. 6, p. 465.

[24] W. W. Weir, "Soil Productivity as Affected by Crop Rotation," *Farmers' Bulletin* 1475, pp. 1–22.

Conservation and Supply of Fertilizers. The great majority of agricultural soils contain large quantities of all the elements essential to plant growth, with the exception of *nitrogen, phosphorus,* and *potassium.* These are used by the growing plant in larger quantities than any of the other elements obtained from the soil, and in the great majority of soils they are the most important constituents in crop production.

NITROGEN. This element, which is vital to the growth of every plant, is depleted more quickly than other plant foods. There is frequently a paucity of nitrogen for plant growth in spite of the fact that air contains about 80 per cent pure nitrogen, since plants cannot use it in that form.[25] It must be taken into the soil through the roots of plants in the form of soluble nitrates. Because it is soluble in water it is more or less rapidly washed away, and a new supply must be added. This is done naturally, but very slowly, by soil bacteria. Since nitrogen enters into every part of all plant organisms, no plant can grow without it. If the supply in the soil is inadequate, growth is stunted. If the supply is exhausted, no growth at all can take place.

Nitrogen can be conserved in the soil by following a rotation of crops which contains a legume, and by plowing under as much as possible of this legume growth. But in some areas it is inadvisable to follow such a practice, and in other sections it is difficult to get legumes to grow. The nitrogen must then be supplied artificially in some form of nitrogenous fertilizer.

Nitrate of soda from the Chilean fields and small deposits of potassium nitrate are the only *natural supplies* of nitrogen in a form available for fertilizers. Other available forms are ammonium sulphate from coke ovens and gas works, cottonseed meal, animal tankage, dried bone from slaughter-houses, fish scraps and non-edible fish, and nitrogen taken from the air through a hydroelectric process.

PHOSPHATES. Phosphorus or soluble phosphate is next in order in the rapidity with which it is exhausted. Although it forms a very small part of any plant, it is so important that the cells of the plant cannot divide if phosphorus is lacking, and therefore growth cannot take place. A sufficient abundance of phosphate hastens the production and maturity of fruit and seeds.

[25] "It must be remembered that the world's stock of nitrogen is not in compounds. It is at least free to make engagements, though not very anxious or even willing to do so. With most substances a divorce is necessary before a new attachment can be made." N. M. Fenneman, "A Classification of Natural Resources," *Science,* Feb. 20, 1925, Vol. 61, No. 1573, p. 191.

Phosphate comprises more than two-thirds of the 7,000,000 tons of
fertilizer used in the United States annually and constitutes our most
important fertilizer material. Fortunately, the United States possesses
the largest known deposits of phosphate rock in the world, making us
entirely independent of foreign sources.

Phosphate fertilizers may be divided into two classes: (1) those in
which the phosphorus is practically insoluble in water but is in such a
form that it can be slowly utilized by plants and (2) those in which
the phosphorus is readily soluble in water. Basic slag, bone meal, bone
ash, bird guano, and finely ground rock phosphate belong to the first
class. Bone meal, bone ash, and bird guano are valuable fertilizers,
but they are produced only in comparatively small quantities. Under
certain conditions of soil and climate good results have been obtained
with finely ground, raw rock phosphate, for example, when it is applied with farmyard manure or green manure.

Our most important phosphate fertilizer is acid phosphate, or superphosphate. It is manufactured by treating phosphate rock with
sulphuric acid, and it contains from 16 to 20 per cent of phosphoric
acid, of which practically all the phosphorus is soluble in water and
can readily be utilized by plants. Double superphosphate is produced
in limited quantities in this country. It contains from 40 to 45 per
cent of water-soluble phosphoric acid.

Practically all the present known supply of phosphate rock is possessed by a few countries, and most of the commercial production is
under the control of the United States and France. The chief deposits
under French control are located in Tunisia, Morocco, and Algeria.
Our southeastern states produce nearly one-half of the world's phosphate rock, Florida supplying about four-fifths of the American output, and Tennessee most of the remainder. The Florida deposits, located near Tampa, consist mainly of stones and pebbles mixed with
sand and clay. They are worked by both steam shovels and dredges.
On the other hand, large reserves of easily mined bedded phosphate
deposits are found in Colorado, Montana, Idaho, Utah, and Wyoming.
But the deposits are situated too far from the principal markets to be
marketed extensively. However, some production takes place, chiefly
at Conda, Idaho, and Garrison, Montana.

POTASH. Potassium, commercially known as potash, is the third element in the order of rapidity with which it is leached from the soil.
This element is directly concerned in the manufacture of sugars and
starches in plants, although it does not form a part of them. Numerous
field tests as well as the experience and observations of farmers have

3

shown clearly the necessity for potash in crop production, not only in the effect it has on crop production, but also in the influence it may have on crop quality.

Containing the most extensive and valuable known deposits of soluble potassium salts, Germany ranks first in the world as a potash producer. Extensive deposits encircle the Harz Mountains, and in the north-central part of the plain near Stassfurt, in Prussia, lays an immense deposit of salt, the upper layers of which contain 2 billion tons of potash. Germany leads not only in production but also in potential reserve of this mineral. Another important producer is France.

After the discovery in Germany of these extensive subterranean deposits of potash and their commercial exploitation, the use of potash as a fertilizer became a matter of common practice in America. Before World War I almost all the potash used by American farmers came from Germany—an unsatisfactory state of affairs, because of the long haul from the German mine to the American farms, and because in the event of war between Germany and other world powers the supplies might be checked or cut off entirely. In 1913, for example, the United States imported about 255,000 tons of potash, 90 to 95 per cent of which was used in agriculture. But during the war period the incoming supply of German potash was gradually cut down until in 1918 less than 300 tons were imported. In order to avert a potash famine, the United States began to produce its own potash. This domestic product is derived principally from Searles Lake, California, as a very pure and high-grade muriate of potash; from the Carlsbad field of New Mexico; and from the waste water of alcohol manufacture at Baltimore, Maryland, as a high-grade mixture of potash salts which may be described as "plant ash." Other possible sources of potash in this country are the giant kelps of the Pacific Ocean, the natural desert brines of California, and the potash minerals like alunite, leucite, and greensand. Large potash deposits have been found in Texas and New Mexico, and commercial production has begun.

CONCLUSION

Soils have developed on a great variety of parent materials, but these materials do not constitute soil. In the soil-making process, these basic materials have been subjected to a number of physical forces, chief of which are climate and native vegetation. Owing to the great range in these two factors from place to place in the world there is a great variety of soil types, which, from the standpoint of soil classification, fall into two main divisions, each containing several major soil groups.

For crop production, the most desirable soils possess a thick surface horizon, are well supplied with humus, and contain a moderate-to-high amount of lime, phosphate, nitrogen, and potash. The soil groups that most nearly meet these conditions are found in middle-latitude grasslands, especially the blackerth regions of the Great Plains and Russia. Among other fertile agricultural soils are the dark prairie soils and the gray-brownerths of middle latitudes. On the other hand, in tropical regions with abundant rainfall, the soils are quickly leached and, therefore, generally have a poor structure and are quickly depleted of their fertility.

The various soils will not last indefinitely if they are handled carelessly, and with increasing intensity the problems of soil conservation are confronting the peoples of many lands. In numerous areas the hill lands are being washed away with a rapidity demanding rapid application of remedial measures. In some areas the soil is beginning to suffer most severely by being depleted of its humus and mineral foods. In order to check this soil waste, crop rotations should be practiced wherever possible, and legumes should be given a prominent place in the farm layout.

REFERENCES

Atlas of American Agriculture: Part III, "Soils of the United States," U. S. Department of Agriculture, 1936.

BENNETT, HUGH HAMMOND, *Soil Conservation*, McGraw-Hill Book Co., 1939.
 "Soil Conservation in a Hungry World," *Geographical Review*, April 1948, pp. 311–318.
 "Adjustment of Agriculture to its Environment," *Annals of the Association of American Geographers*, Vol. 33, 1943, pp. 163–198.

GLINKA, K. D., *The Great Soil Groups of the World and Their Development,* translated by C. F. Marbut, Edwards Brothers, 1927.

HALL, SIR A. L., *The Soil*, J. Murray Publishing Co., 1920.

HILGARD, E. W., *Soils*, The Macmillan Co., 1921.

SHANTZ, H. L., and C. F. MARBUT, *The Vegetation and Soils of Africa*, American Geographical Society Research Series No. 13, 1923.

SHAW, C. F., "The Soil Series Names," *Soil Survey Association Bulletin X*, pp. 85–101.

"Soils and Men," *Yearbook of Agriculture*, U. S. Department of Agriculture, U. S. Government Printing Office, 1938.

WEIR, W. W., "Soil Productivity as Affected by Crop Rotation," *Farmers'*
   Bulletin 1475, U. S. Department of Agriculture, pp. 1–22.
WHITNEY, MILTON, *Soil and Civilization*, D. Van Nostrand Co., 1925.
WOLFANGER, L. A., "Simple Key to Soil Geography," *Journal of Geography*,
   Vol. 30, November 1913.
   The Major Soil Divisions of the United States, John Wiley & Sons, 1930.

Chapter 4

MAJOR LAND FORMS

CLASSIFICATION OF LAND FORMS

Continents and oceans comprise relief features of the first order. Each of these may be further subdivided. Thus within the oceanic areas there are continental shelves and deep seas. The boundaries between these two divisions are not always sharp. Along the margins of the continents the sea floor usually sinks gradually for distances ranging from a few miles to hundreds of miles from shore and then rather abruptly drops to the abyssal depth of the deep sea. These shallow margins which in general extend out from the shore to depths of approximately 100 fathoms (600 feet) are called *continental shelves*. Some authors speak of continental shelves as those portions of the continental land masses that are covered by the sea. The remainder of the ocean with an average depth of approximately 2½ miles is called the *deep sea*. Some areas where the depth of the ocean is exceedingly great are called *deeps*.

The major land forms are plains, plateaus, and mountains. These terms have been rather loosely used by students of earth sciences. In general, however, *plains* are areas of low relief and are usually low-lying with respect to at least part of the surrounding area. Most plains are relatively low in altitude but there are notable exceptions. *Plateaus* are uplands (500 feet to 15,000 feet or more) that usually stand distinctly above part of the surrounding area and that are or have been, prior to erosion, relatively level. Wherever erosion has deeply dissected such an upland and has reduced most of its area to steep slopes, it is known as a dissected plateau. It is then hill-land or, if especially rugged, it may be considered mountainous to the layman. In such a region the summits of the hills or mountains are concordant; that is, the summits over much of the area have about the same elevation, corresponding roughly to the original elevation of the plateau before dissection. *Mountains* are much like hills with ex-

115

tremes of relief. Most mountains have been formed by folding and
faulting of the earth's crust or by volcanic activity. However, as
already explained, mountains may also be carved from high plateaus.

DISTRIBUTION OF MAJOR LAND FORMS

✗   The oceans occupy about 70.8 per cent of the earth's surface; the
land occupies about 29.2 per cent. About 75 per cent of the land is

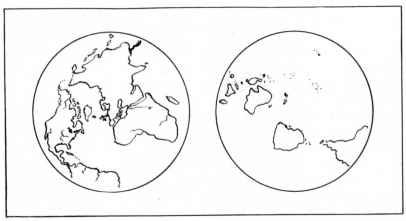

Fig. 45. Land and water hemispheres. The land hemisphere with its pole (center)
situated in the English Channel contains about 83 per cent of the land surface
of the earth. The water hemisphere with its pole near New Zealand contains
only 17 per cent of the surface of the earth. (After John Bartholomew, *The
Oxford Advanced Atlas*, Oxford University Press, 1942, pp. 4, 5.)

situated north of the equator and is grouped about the Arctic Ocean.
The earth may be divided into hemispheres by locating one pole in
the English Channel and the other near New Zealand (Fig. 45). The
northern one contains 83 per cent of the land surface of the earth
and is called the "land hemisphere" in spite of the fact that more than
one-half of it is occupied by oceans. The other hemisphere, "the
water hemisphere," contains only 17 per cent of the land surface of
the earth and is 90.5 per cent water. As travel and transportation by
air increases, a central location in the land hemisphere becomes increasingly important. Such a location would become especially significant if stratosphere flying were highly developed, that is, if passengers and freight were carried above clouds, storms, and other adverse weather conditions.

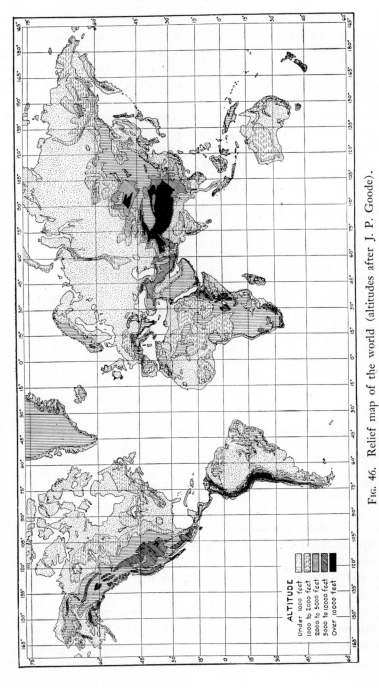

ALTITUDE
Under 1000 feet
1000 to 2000 feet
2000 to 5000 feet
5000 to 10000 feet
Over 10000 feet

FIG. 46.   Relief map of the world (altitudes after J. P. Goode).

A study of the relief map of the world shows that the great agricultural and industrial areas of Europe, North America, South America, and Africa drain into the Atlantic Ocean. Since trade tends to follow gentle gradients, it is only natural that much of the export trade of these continents would gravitate to ports located on the Atlantic Coast for shipment to all parts of the world. Likewise, imports are brought to these same ports for distribution to the interior of each of these continents. Consequently seaports of the Atlantic Ocean handle a large percentage of the world's foreign trade.

LAND FORMS AND POPULATION DISTRIBUTION

A comparison of the relief and population maps of the world (Figs. 46 and 47) indicates forcibly that the nature of the relief is a factor

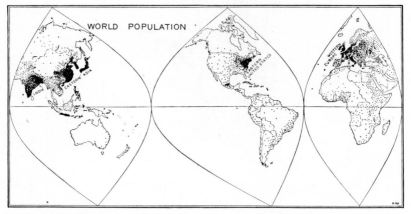

Fig. 47. The distribution of the population of the world. Note the four major concentrations of people, that is, the four great agglomerations. Each dot represents 500,000 people.

of major significance in man's choice of a place in which to live. Perhaps no other factor of the physical environment, except climate, has played such a large part in the distribution of the world's population; and, indeed, the relief of the land affects the climate and also the soil.

The diverse surface of the earth has made a great variety of human adjustments both necessary and possible. The high mountain, the broad plateau, the level plain, all necessitate differences in human activities in order that man may make the best use of his environment.

On mountain slopes where the steepness of the gradient prevents the growing of crops, he keeps flocks of sheep and herds of cattle and exploits both forests and minerals.[1] On the other hand, the fertile, well-watered plains usually afford a suitable environment for extensive as well as intensive agriculture, and their level surface facilitates communication and the growth of trade centers.

The relief map of the world (Fig. 46) shows that all the continents have mountains, plateaus, and plains; but the relative amount of land occupied by each of these relief features differs materially from one continental land mass to another. More than one-half of Europe is below the 600-foot contour, giving this continent the maximum percentage of easily cultivable land. Next in order come South America with two-fifths; North America with one-third; Asia with one-fourth; whereas only one-eighth of Africa is below that level. Much of the remaining seven-eighths of Africa is too rugged for ease of cultivation even if rainfall were well suited for agriculture.

The relative proportion of highland and lowland, however, does not remain the same indefinitely. From a geological standpoint there is no permanency. The following lines of Tennyson admirably express this constant change.

> There rolls the deep where grew the tree
> O earth, what changes hast thou seen!
> There where the long street roars, hath been
> The stillness of the central sea.

> The hills are shadows, and they flow
> From form to form and nothing stands.
> They melt like mists the solid lands,
> Like clouds they shape themselves and go.

The agents of erosion eventually wear down the high mountain, and the lands of the earth are gradually being pushed into the sea. To offset the loss of land that is being washed away, new land is constantly being formed.

LAND FORMS AS RELATED TO CLIMATE

Students of earth sciences have long recognized that land forms, after prolonged exposure to the agencies of weathering, reflect to some degree the nature of the climates to which they have been ex-

---

[1] In certain densely populated areas the great pressure of population upon the bounds of subsistence has induced man to cultivate the steep slopes by building terraces and practicing intensive agriculture.

posed. Any comprehensive discussion of this subject must be left
to the geomorphologists. The purpose here is merely to give a few
of the reasons for a correlation between climatic types and patterns of
land forms. The student should bear in mind that climate is only one
of several factors that influence land forms.

It is a well-known geological fact that rocks are more rapidly decomposed by the chemical action of the atmosphere in a warm climate
than in a cold one. In fact, chemical activity is approximately doubled
with each increase of 10° C. in temperature. Such activity is also
believed to be greater in a climate where there are uniformly high
temperatures than in areas characterized by temperature extremes. In
addition, climate affects land forms indirectly through the vegetation.

Land Forms of Humid Tropical Regions. High temperatures and
abundant moisture and vegetation are found in tropical regions, especially in the tropical rain forests (pp. 169–174). In these regions the
uniformly high temperatures favor chemical weathering of rocks by
decomposition, which is especially marked because of the abundant
moisture. In addition, there is a luxuriant growth of vegetation, the
decay of which supplies the water with organic acids which further
increase the solvent power. Not only does the vegetation aid rock
decay chemically, but also the roots of forest trees are a marked
factor in mechanical weathering.

The above combination of factors favors the decomposition of rocks
to a considerable depth. This deep layer of weathered material, retained by a heavy vegetative cover, tends to develop a distinctly
rounded form even to regions of relatively rugged topography located
in tropical rain forest regions. In addition, the abundant rainfall
finally results in a well-developed drainage system, in which there is
usually a considerable number of large perennial tributaries. These
streams are the major highways of most tropical forests. It is fortunate that nature has provided such a network of commercial arteries,
since the constantly high temperatures and heavy rainfall combined
with the rapid growth of vegetation make railroad building expensive
and the upkeep burdensome. Thus within the great Amazon lowland
—an area larger than the United States—there are only two railroads,
situated thousands of miles apart, and each only a few miles long. The
close network of rivers, however, permits man to penetrate deeply
into the heavy forests in order to exploit its resources.

Similarly, the rivers of central Africa are the main highways, and
until recently only a few railroads were built except around falls or
rapids where they therefore became an aid to river transportation.

Land Forms in Arid Lands. The land forms of arid regions contrast sharply with those of humid tropical lands. The small amount of precipitation in the former is reflected in the general paucity of perennial streams. Interior drainage is common over extensive areas in all the large deserts, the rivers and streams losing themselves in the desert lowlands (Fig. 48). The relatively few perennial streams

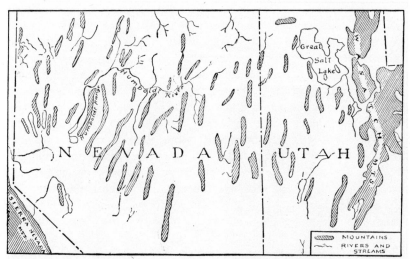

Fig. 48. Interior drainage in the Great Basin of the United States. Note the numerous north-south-trending mountains located within this area.

that cross large desert areas have their source in more humid lands.

In arid regions the small precipitation and sparse vegetation result in but little chemical activity. The topographic features of the desert are consequently angular in character because of the slight rock decay and the relatively sparse vegetation to hold the products of decay (Fig. 49). Steep-sided mesas and canyon walls, and the sharp angles of highlands composed even of relatively weak limestone, are characteristic of the arid environment. Such slopes located in humid lands tend to take a rounded form (Fig. 50).

Mechanical weathering, which in humid tropical lands is caused in large part by the roots of vegetation, results in arid lands mainly from extremes in temperature and from frost and wind-blown sand. In a region of low atmospheric humidity, heating by day and cooling by night are very pronounced, causing expansion, contraction, and breaking of rocks. Thus highland slopes of the desert contain considerable amounts of rock fragments.

The angularity of the topography together with the absence of a vegetative covering permit the coloring of various rock outcrops to stand out in bold relief and add to the charm which the desert holds for many visitors.

Fig. 49. The extremely angular character of desert highlands is well illustrated in the arid lands of Arizona. Although sharp peaks may be found even in humid tropical regions, they are not common in such areas. (Official photograph. U. S. Army Air Corps.)

Land Forms in Regions Having Seasonal Rainfall. Within some parts of the world a period of aridity is followed by a season of abundant precipitation. Such a periodic rainfall regime is characteristic of the low-latitude wet-and-dry realm and the Mediterranean regions (pp. 229–231). In these regions chemical weathering is active during the wet season, and, on slopes that have little vegetation, erosion is rapid. During the dry season, on the other hand, mechanical weathering is active, and many of the streams dry up completely.

In regions of seasonal precipitation, where rainfall is concentrated in a short period of the year, large flood plains and deltas are formed, such as those lying in the valleys of the Tigris, Euphrates, Ganges,

Irrawaddy, Yangtze Kiang, and Hwang Ho. During the dry months the annual plants wither and die, and the fine root systems of these plants which retard erosion are destroyed. Thus the surface materials are prepared for rapid erosion as soon as the heavy rains begin. The flood waters then transport much of this material to the mouth of the stream, where it is deposited.

Fig. 50. A typical Vermont mountain landscape showing the well-rounded forest-covered slopes characteristic of many highlands that have long been exposed to weathering in humid regions. The length of time that an area has been subjected to weathering is, of course, an important factor. (Courtesy Secretary of State's Office, Montpelier, Vermont. Photo by Richardson.)

Land Forms in Higher Latitudes. In some parts of the higher middle latitudes the land forms reflect the effects of continental glaciation. That such glaciation was very widespread at one time is indicated in a number of ways. Wedge-shaped stones, scratches on transported boulders as well as the bedrock, derangement of the drainage system, unassorted débris in some places, water-laid sediments elsewhere—these are among the evidences of continental glaciation.

The large continental glaciers which moved southward even as far as the Ohio River in the United States made a more uniform relief in some areas by wearing away peaks and hilltops and by filling depressions. The drainage pattern was disturbed to a considerable extent. Lakes and swamps were formed, and streams were deranged. In some places the rivers and streams, forced to take new courses because of obstruction of glacial débris, made their way over steep ledges, thereby causing waterfalls.

In regions of hard rocks where the glacier removed the weathered surface material, large stretches of land became unfit for cultivation. Such areas are found on the Laurentian Shield of Canada and on the Fenno-Scandian Shield of Europe.[2]   Thus Norway has only 3.5 per cent of her land area under crops.   In Sweden the cultivated land constitutes 10 per cent and in Finland 4.5 per cent of the land area. Most of the remaining land of these countries is uncultivable because of lack of soil or because of lakes, swamps, muskegs, or other conditions resulting from glaciation.   Noteworthy is the difference in percentage of cultivated land between the thoroughly scoured hard-rock lands of Fenno-Scandia and the areas of softer sedimentary rocks and greater glacial deposition farther south, as in the areas of the Baltic States, Denmark, and Prussia.

Land Forms of Marine Climate.   Bathed by abundant precipitation and swept by the westerly winds, the west coasts of continents in higher middle latitudes are distinctive in climate and reflect a marine influence more pronounced than is found in any other climatic realm. The land forms are also characteristic.   Here weathered surface materials have been removed in large quantities through the process of glaciation.   In the past, vast areas of glacial ice must have accumulated in these regions, because of the abundant precipitation.   Glaciers deepened the valleys and gouged out heads of bays and other indentations. When the glacier ice melted, the submerged areas, if steep-sided, narrow, deep, and long, became fjords (Fig. 51).   Even today, piedmont and valley glaciers are found in the poleward parts of these regions, especially in Alaska, northern Norway, and southern Chile.

Land Forms of Subpolar and Polar Regions.   Located to the poleward of the northern coniferous forest of North America and Eurasia are vast stretches of tundra, where the extreme cold during the long winters results in a deep freezing of the mantle rock.   So deep and thorough is the frost of winter that in many tundra areas the heat during the short summer is not sufficient to cause a thawing of the ground for more than 2 or 3 feet below the surface.   The top soil of the tundra is, therefore, generally waterlogged and acid during at least a part of the summer.   Here the native vegetation consists mainly of grasses, dwarfed willow, sphagnum mosses, and lichens (reindeer

[2] By shield is meant an extensive area of hard rocks, chiefly crystallines, which constitute the remains of a higher mass of land from which erosion has taken place throughout geologic time.

moss) and the chief type of economic adjustment to environment is the grazing of reindeer.

In the polar regions of both hemispheres (northern and southern) glacier ice covers large areas of land, and where the land is bare it reflects the effects of glaciation. As in the deserts, so in polar regions, mechanical weathering is active, and the angular forms in the landscape are due mainly to frost action. In some areas, angular peaks may

FIG. 51. The fjorded coastal area of Norway in the vicinity of Bergen.

be seen projecting even through glacier surfaces. In many of the highland regions one of the major effects of glaciation has been the formation of numerous amphitheater-like structures, commonly called cirques.

PLAINS AS RELATED TO MAN

Population on Plains. ⎡Plains that are located below the 1,500-foot contour occupy less than two-fifths of the earth's surface, but they are the home of more than four-fifths of the people of the world,[3] and approximately 90 per cent of the world's population lives at elevations of less than 2,000 feet.⎤ Most of China's 450,000,000 and India's 350,-

[3] Relief features of all kinds found below the 1,500-foot contour constitute 43 per cent of the land area of the world. Approximately 41 per cent of the world's land is found between the contours of 1,500 and 6,000 feet above sea level. Thus 84 per cent of all our land is below the 6,000-foot contour.

000,000 people live on the coastal plains or on the alluvial plains of the Ganges, the Indus, the Si Kiang, the Yangtze Kiang, and the Hwang Ho. Noteworthy also is the population density of the plains countries of Europe, such as the Soviet Union, Prussia, Denmark, the Netherlands, and Belgium. In North America the advanced status of agriculture, manufacture, and trade in the Mississippi Basin and on the Atlantic, Gulf, and Pacific coastal plains reflects their superior importance as the home of man, and these areas contrast with the sparsely settled and but little developed uplands near by.

Agriculture on Plains. Favored by a small degree of relief, plains contain some of the most productive and extensively cultivated lands of the world. As a rule, plains possess a high percentage of cultivable land; farm machinery may be profitably employed; and the farm pattern may be so arranged that the greatest economy in agricultural operations may be realized.

Communication on Plains. All industries on plains are aided by the ease of transportation by land as well as by water. The gentle gradient results in relatively low construction and operation costs of roads and railroads, and commodities may be transported quickly and cheaply. Plains contain the largest and most important navigable waterways of the world, both natural and artificial. Of major importance are the Mississippi River and its tributaries in North America; the Amazon and Plate river systems of South America; the Ganges, the Indus, the Yangtze river systems of Asia; and the Danube, the Rhine, and the Rhone in Europe. In the densely populated level lands of the Netherlands, Belgium, Prussia, and throughout parts of France, canal construction has reached a high stage of development, partly because of the extensive stretches of low plains in these areas. Rapid and cheap transportation, together with suitable conditions for agriculture, have favored the development of trade and manufactures. These facts help to explain the high population density in most of the plains areas of the world.

Large Plains Unfavorable to Early Development. From the standpoint of history, it is significant that the regions of early civilization were generally relatively small plains protected by some physical barrier, such as the narrow ribbon of land along the Nile surrounded by desert, the small lowlands with their adjacent highlands in Greece, the Roman Campagna, and the valleys of the Tigris and Euphrates. In such small areas man's activities were concentrated, communication was rapid, and ideas were quickly transmitted from one place to another. Moreover, since nature helped to protect these areas from invasion by unfriendly peoples, man could give most of his energies to the development of the arts and industries rather than to military operations. On the other hand, in the early settlement of large plains, man's development through the stages of hunter, pastoral nomad, and farmer was relatively slow. The extensive plains lacked diversity, and the monotonously uniform geographical base tended toward uniformity in man's activities. Their wide extent and absence of barriers postponed the transmission from nomadism to sedentary life, and their lack of contrasting environments and contrasted developments retarded progress. Thus great plains areas have been among the last frontiers to be developed in the temperate zone. It was not until civilization had advanced in the small protected areas and had made considerable progress in methods of transportation, communication, and the art of defense that man began to push boldly into the larger plains.

Tendency to Unification of Adjacent Plains Areas. Not only is transportation easy, but also ready interchange of goods and ideas is facilitated on plains, which results sometimes in a tendency to commercial and political unity of adjacent plains areas. This is well illustrated in the economic and political growth of Russia. After the time of the Tartar invasions, Russia extended her area from the Baltic on the west to the Pacific on the east. The relief of the land, however, limited her possible advance, and she is still confined very largely to the lowlands, the extensive Eurasian plain. Similarly, France expanded from the small plains area of the Paris Basin, spread over the various lowland saddles into the plains of Aquitaine, the Rhone, and the Rhine. The Baltic states (Estonia, Latvia, Lithuania), parts of a plains area that extends eastward into Russia and westward into Prussia, were at one time under the rule of certain orders of the Teutonic or German Knights. These states were later absorbed under the old Russian Empire until the period of World War I, when they became independent.

In contrast with the extensive plain of Eurasia is the rugged topography of western and southern Europe, where mountains, plateaus, and plains interlock. In such a rugged area there are many barriers that have been difficult to overcome and have fostered separation, as manifested by the large numbers of small political units.

Economic Activities on Coastal Plains

Significance of Coastal Location. The location of the coastal plain is a very important feature. Accessibility to the sea on the one hand

and to interior land areas on the other has made it the passageway for lines of communication. As a rule, this type of plain presents a location that favors its inhabitants with a double larder of land and sea, crops and fisheries, together with opportunities for commercial development.

Early Economic Development. Located along the margin of land and sea, coastal plains receive an early stimulus to economic development. Noteworthy in this respect is the Atlantic coastal plain of the United States. Here the first white settlers of this country found a new home, cut down the virgin forest, and cleared land for agricultural purposes. Here they had most direct communication with the Old World, and this at a time when most of the interior of the continent was as yet an unknown wilderness.

Agriculture on Coastal Plains. For the coastal plains of the world as a whole, more people are engaged in agriculture than in any other major economic pursuit. But the agricultural activities differ from one part of the world to another, largely because of differences in climate and stage of economic development.

On many coastal plains located in intermediate latitudes, stock-raising is an important pursuit partly because of the prevalence of wet meadows, which furnish luxuriant pasturage for summer grazing as well as hay for indoor feeding. The livestock industry has reached a high stage of development in the coastal plains of northwest Europe—the plains of Denmark, the Netherlands, and Flanders.

Truck farming is another dominant activity of many coastal plains located in the temperate zone (Fig. 52). Where the soil is sandy, it heats rapidly and provides a warm seed bed in which truck crops grow and ripen in a comparatively short period of time.

In low-latitude coastal plains are found important agricultural areas. Some of these areas are densely populated and produce not only subsistence crops but also commodities that are eagerly sought by peoples living in colder lands. In many low-latitude regions rice is the most important cultivated crop, especially on the Malabar coast of India, the Arakan and Tenasserim coastal regions of Burma, and the coastal plains of Thailand (Siam), French Indo-China, China, and Japan. On the greater part of the coastal plains of the peninsula of Indo-China (Burma, Siam, and French Indo-China) rice covers more than 80 per cent of the cultivated land. Other low-latitude coastal plains areas are devoted to coconut palms, and still others produce sugar cane and starchy tubers.

Transportation on Coastal Plains. The coastal plains are especially favored by ease of transportation. Their level surface permits rapid and cheap construction of roads and railroads; but of even greater importance, especially during the early development of these areas, is water transportation. Thus streams flowing from the interior of land areas give ready access to hinterland and sea; the offshore waters per-

FIG. 52. Potatoes ready for shipment from a truck-farming district of Tidewater, Virginia. The dry sandy soils of the coastal plain heat quickly, and crops grown here mature in a relatively short period of time. (Courtesy Norfolk & Western Railway.)

mit coastwise traffic; and the general flatness of the land favors the construction of artificial waterways. With respect to this factor, the Netherlands has the most commanding position in all northwest Europe. Lying on a coastal plain at the mouth of the Rhine, possessing numerous canals, and commanding a large portion of the trade of northwest Europe, Holland early developed into an important commercial nation.

Drainage of Wet Coastal Lowlands. In many coastal regions the moisture supply is excessive, and in some areas water covers the land throughout the year. Where such coastal lowlands occur in tropical and semi-tropical regions, human progress is handicapped not only by the abundance of moisture, but quite commonly also by unhealthful conditions caused by disease-carrying insects as well as the enervating climate. In all climatic realms extensive coastal marshes and swamps generally constitute a marked barrier to easy contact between the sea and the economically important parts of the land (Fig. 53).

Reclamation of Land in the Netherlands. Although millions of acres of swamp land are being reclaimed in the many coastal districts

Fig. 53. Ancient roots in the general region of Dismal Swamp, near Norfolk, Virginia. Coastal swamps of this type constitute a marked barrier to transportation. (Courtesy Norfolk-Portsmouth Advertising Board.)

where population pressure is great, the most ambitious of all these projects is that of the Netherlands. Approximately three-fifths of the total area of the Netherlands consists of a lowland, a large part of which lies below the level of the sea, in places as much as 15 to 20 feet. Here reclamation of wet land has been in progress for a long period of time, and one after the other of the former swamps and lakes of this region have been converted into agricultural land.

Even as early as the days of Caesar the inhabitants of lowland Netherlands established themselves on low hills which they constructed in this area. The construction of dikes began about A.D. 1000, these being originally designed mainly to shut out the inundation waters of the rivers and the sea.[4] But the works of man were interrupted and in parts of this area ruined during the thirteenth century. At that time a succession of violent storms swept the North Sea. These storms caused huge waves which lashed with fury over the chains of coastal sand dunes, submerged a large part of what had been until then a part of the European mainland, and created the Zuider Zee, the largest indentation found in the coastal area of the Netherlands.

An extensive program is now being gradually completed to reclaim the greater part of the Zuider Zee (Fig. 54). A large dike has been constructed to separate the area of the Zuider Zee from the North Sea. This dike connects Holland with Wieringen (1½ miles) and the latter island with Friesland (19 miles). This enormous structure— 300 feet wide at its base—eliminates the fear of the North Sea storms and the great expenditure caused by extensive floods.[5] Even more important is the fact that the water behind the dike has become fresh water, because of the constant discharge from the Yssel and other rivers. Thus a large reservoir of fresh water has been created in the middle of the country, from which it is possible to draw as much as is wanted even during the driest summers.

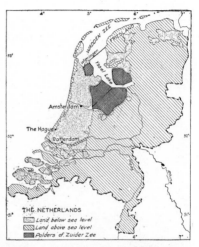

Fig. 54. The Zuider Zee reclamation project. A huge dam has been constructed from North Holland and extends via Wieringen Island to Friesland. Back of this dam four polders and a lake will constitute what was recently an arm of the North Sea.

Whereas in dry summers the surrounding country has a shortage of water, at other times of the year there is often an embarrassing excess. The situation has been improved with the sea behind the dike maintained on a constant low level. Furthermore, the dam is used for railway and road communication between north Holland and Friesland.

[4] See P. Tesch, "Physiographic Regions of the Netherlands," *Geographical Review*, Vol. 13, 1923, pp. 507–517.

[5] In 1915 a large part of the country near Amsterdam was inundated, and drainage involved considerable expenditure.

Flood Plains as Related to Man and His Activities

Importance of Flood Plains. In supplying man with food, flood plains play a role of vast importance (Fig. 55). They also furnish the geographical base for a large part of the world's population, as manifested by the population map (Fig. 47). Note the importance of

Fig. 55. Distribution of cultural features along flood plains of the Rio Grande about 6 miles north of Albuquerque, New Mexico. The foreground is irrigated flood plain on which streams from alluvial piedmont slope at base of Sandia Mountains have built alluvial fans on which villages are located. (Aerial photo by J. L. Rich.)

the Nile, the Tigris, the Po, the Ganges, the Indus, the Hwang Ho, the Rhine, the Rhone, the Mississippi, and many others in furthering the economic, social, and political activities of the countries through which they flow.

The lower part of the Ganges Valley is one of the most densely populated regions of the world. In the alluvial lowlands of eastern Bengal the population density is more than 620 people per square mile, and in some of the districts of this province the density is almost twice that number, as compared with 45 per square mile in the United States as a whole. Similarly the alluvial lands of the Nile Valley support densely populated agricultural communities, the population density being more than 1,500 per square mile in some of the districts (markazes) of the Valley (Fig. 56).[6]

Early Occupancy of Flood Plains. Flood plains, like coastal plains, are usually the first to be occupied in the settlement of a new region both because of their productiveness and because of their accessibility. Containing a variety in types of soil and kinds of vegetation, flood plains provide a diverse geographical base for agricultural development. F. V. Emerson says: "The natural levee is higher and usually better drained than the back lands and this difference often leads to crop differentiation on front and back lands; and, indeed these two divisions are often so clearly marked by crops that the crops map the soil types. Very often the front lands are cleared while the back lands are in forest and here again the vegetation often marks the soils, the line of timber being the boundary line between the front and back lands. Because of this difference in soil, farm boundary lines on flood plains are often roughly perpendicular to the river so that the farm or plantation will include both soil types."[7] Farm buildings are erected on the higher and drier levee lands along the streams, in proximity to transportation lines by land as well as water (Fig. 57).

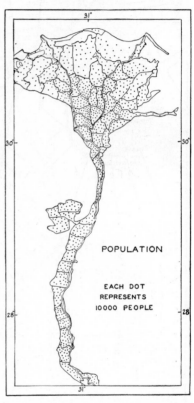

FIG. 56. The Nile Valley is one of the most densely populated agricultural regions in the world—a fertile oasis in the low-latitude desert.

River Floods. Flood plains, however, are not without their handicaps as agricultural regions, since the floods to which they are subject

[6] According to estimates made in 1943, the population density for the lower and middle parts of the Nile Valley is more than 900 per square mile. *The Statesman's Yearbook*, The Macmillan Co., 1946, p. 859.

[7] Reprinted by permission from *Agricultural Geology*, by F. V. Emerson, John Wiley & Sons, 1928, p. 186.

are often disastrous both to life and to property. Flood waters sometimes rush through densely populated valleys, undermining the river banks, cutting new channels, and sweeping away retaining walls,

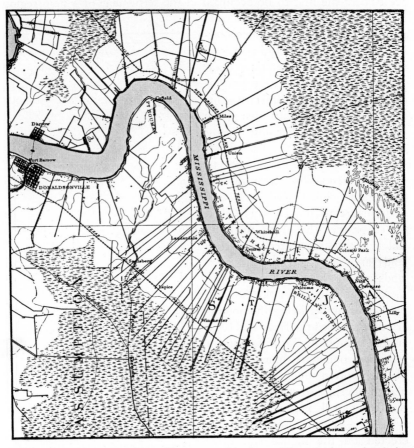

Fig. 57. Part of the Donaldsonville topographic sheet. Note the levees bordering the Mississippi and the swamp lands behind the levees. The main (through) highways tend to follow the very crests of the Mississippi levees, where one also finds a concentration of houses. Secondary roads run at right angles to the main roads and down the levee slopes.

levees, ditches, and even villages. In some of the larger floods the loss of life has been tremendous.

Some of the largest and most destructive of floods known to man have occurred in Asia, especially in the densely populated valleys of China proper and India. In China the valleys of the Hwang Ho, Si

PLAINS AS RELATED TO MAN 135

Kiang, and Yangtze Kiang all have been subject to widespread floods. The Hwang Ho crosses extensive flood plains in its lower part, where it has changed its course several times by flowing alternately north and south of the mountains in Shantung Province, thereby reaching the sea at points as much as 250 miles apart.

These extensive floods of the Hwang Ho are brought about by the marked seasonal precipitation, with a tendency at times for periods of superabundance of rainfall in the middle and upper parts of the river valley. These conditions are further aggravated by the generally forest-denuded slopes and consequently the rapid runoff during periods of abundant rainfall. In addition, vast quantities of soil are washed from the loess-covered hills of western North China and are deposited in the lower part of the valley, thereby further facilitating the change of the river's course.

The Yangtze and Si river valleys of China have also been subject to widespread, destructive floods. Floods in the Yangtze Valley have often inundated the lands from the area of the Wu-Han cities (Hankow, Hanyang, Wuchang) down to the delta, where Shanghai is located. Since this is one of the most important economic and one of the most densely populated areas of China, it suffers tremendous losses during periods of widespread flood. Located south of the Yangtze Valley, the lower part of the Si basin was the scene of especially disastrous floods in 1914, when the waters at Wuchow rose 22 feet in 24 hours.

In the United States, floods have been especially destructive to life and property in the valleys of the Ohio and the lower Mississippi. During March 1913, a very destructive Ohio River flood swept through the river towns, causing great losses of both life and property. The towns on the Miami River (a branch of the Ohio) all but escaped annihilation. The meteorological conditions in the Ohio Valley were especially unfavorable during this period. A heavy southwest storm followed close upon one from the northwest, and both storms came when the ground was already well saturated with moisture. Approximately 8 inches of rain (about 20 per cent of the average annual amount) fell in the Miami Valley within 5 days, resulting in a tremendous runoff. During the latter part of January and the beginning of February 1937, the Ohio Valley experienced the worst flood in its history. At Cincinnati the flood attained the height of 79.99 feet. Throughout the Ohio Valley large areas were inundated, schools were closed, and water and electric supply stations were forced

FIG. 58a. Mound at Arcola, Mississippi, used as refuge for livestock during the flood of 1927. (Courtesy U. S. Weather Bureau.) Ten years later (1937) the Mississippi Valley experienced another widespread and devastating flood, especially in the valley of the Ohio, one of its major tributaries.

FIG. 58b. Flood scene at Onward, Mississippi, during the flood of 1927. (Courtesy U. S. Weather Bureau.)

to discontinue their services. In some places buildings were torn loose from their foundations and were seen floating down the Ohio River. This disastrous flood was due mainly to heavy rains during the winter, when the ground was already saturated and water evaporated slowly. Air currents moved with marked regularity from the Gulf of Mexico and northward across the eastern part of the country. Mild weather prevailed in the East, while the West experienced severe frosts. Georgia peach growers placed ice packs about their trees to prevent premature blossoming while California fruit growers built smudges in order to protect their trees from heavy frost.

The lower Mississippi Valley is affected by flood conditions in the upper part of the Valley as well as by local meteorological factors. Sometimes the rains of the Mississippi Basin are so intense and widely distributed as to produce flooding regardless of antecedent conditions, whereas at other times moderate rains may continue intermittently a week or more with antecedent circumstances favorable to a high runoff. When flood conditions occur the lower part of the Valley frequently suffers from widespread floods (Figs. 58a and 58b). Large areas of alluvial farm lands are sometimes ruined by the amount of coarse sediments poured over them. In this part of the Mississippi Valley the alluvial plains are protected against flood by levees or dykes and by the natural levees being built higher by man. Upon some of these higher, drier lands the inhabitants construct their buildings and roads.

Students working on the flood problem have suggested various schemes for preventing and checking the recurrence of widespread floods. Since floods are associated with rapid runoff, all agencies should be directed to check the rate of runoff. One of the remedial measures consists of planting trees on slopes that have been denuded of natural vegetation. Other schemes include the straightening of river channels by eliminating meanders, and, where practicable, the building of storage reservoirs.

Glacial Plains and Their Economic Significance

Covering vast stretches of land in higher middle latitudes, glacial plains are the result of continental glaciation, chiefly of deposition of earth materials by ice and associated waters. This deposition has created a variety of surface features: in some places sloping sandy plains of glacial outwash; in other areas the hilly belts of terminal moraines; and in still other places the more extensive gently rolling ground moraines or till plains (Fig. 59).

These surface features have developed in conjunction with extensive glaciation during the last era of geologic time. Although glacial action at present is limited to high altitudes and latitudes we are certain that extensive ice caps once covered vast stretches of land in the temperate zone, which are now used for the production of crops. Indeed, geological study in the United States alone shows that glacial ice extended at least as far south as the Ohio River.

FIG. 59. A gently rolling agricultural landscape in glaciated Michigan.

Drainage Conditions in Glaciated Areas. In many glaciated regions drainage is poor. The ice has left many undrained depressions. In its advance the glacier scoured out deep holes, filled valleys with débris, and obstructed drainage in many areas, thereby forming lakes, ponds, and swamps. The state of Minnesota alone boasts of more than ten thousand lakes, and Finland claims about five times as many.

Lakes are eagerly sought by the vacationist, traveler, and pleasure seeker; and thousands of summer resorts are scattered through glacial-lake districts. Noteworthy in this respect are the Lake District of England, the glacial lake regions of Scandinavia, and the upper lake region of North America.

Where lakes are of considerable size, like the Great Lakes of North America, they modify the temperature over the surrounding land areas, and in some localities afford protection to orchards and field crops on the adjacent slopes.

Water Power in Glaciated Areas. Wherever the ancient rivers were obstructed by glacial material they were forced to find new paths around the blocked passageway, and in making the détour they often flowed over uncut ledges. Thus waterfalls were created. The power at such falls is a source of considerable wealth to the manufacturing industry in many glaciated regions. In the New England States the manufacturing industry was attracted at an early date to waterfalls of glacial origin.

HIGHLANDS

Highlands contrast strongly with plains both in environment and in human adjustments. The relief of highlands is greater; the drainage

Fig. 60. Effect of relief upon the utilization of the land reflected in the intensively cultivated plains flanked by bare, uncultivated highlands.

of both the air and the water is more rapid; the climate is colder; and the area of waste land is usually greater than that of the adjacent plains (Fig. 60). Consequently population is usually less dense and social traits are more varied. In addition, highlands frequently stand as barriers to communication. But the highlands themselves, however, offer points of contrast. They consist of both mountains and plateaus, and these provide a diverse geographical base for human activities.

Life on Piedmont Plateaus

The piedmont plateau is intermediate in position between mountains on the one hand and plains on the other. The word piedmont means ✘ "foot of the mountain." Proximity to these two major relief forms—mountains and plains—is reflected in the human adjustments on the piedmont. For example, the cool mountains adjacent to the piedmont

FIG. 61. Apple orchards on well-drained slopes in the piedmont plateau section of Virginia. (Courtesy Norfolk & Western Railway.)

frequently cause an abundance of moisture to be precipitated from passing winds. This water gathers into streams which often fall over ledges, creating sites for water power. Thus along the eastern edge of the piedmont plateau of the United States, where the streams flow from the consolidated rocks of the plateau to the unconsolidated rocks of the coastal plain, important urban centers have developed, such as Baltimore, Richmond, Columbus, and Augusta. Similarly, in the piedmont of northern Italy the hydroelectric power development has been a major factor in the recent industrial growth of the country.

Agriculture on Piedmont Plateaus. In relation to agricultural development the piedmont plateaus are favored by water and silt from the highlands and usually have favorable air and water drainage. Thus piedmont areas frequently escape severe frosts while crops in the adjacent plains suffer. The apple industry of piedmont Virginia has developed in part because of such favorable conditions of drainage (Fig. 61). In some of the more arid piedmont localities the mountain streams are utilized for irrigation purposes.

Commercial Significance of a Piedmont Location. Commercially, the piedmont plateaus command a position of great importance. Routes of travel follow the base of the mountains; but many of these routes branch into or through the mountain fastnesses and serve as outlets for the products of these areas. Thus in some places important trade centers have developed at strategic points on piedmont plateaus, usually in areas convenient to mountain passes. Typical of such centers are Milan (Milano), Zurich, Turin (Torino), Bern, and Denver.

Difficulties of Life in Highly Dissected Plateaus

Some plateaus have been subjected to the agents of erosion for a sufficiently long time to cause them to be badly dissected. Thus, deep valleys surrounding narrow ridges are characteristic of such highlands, and most of the area consists of steep slopes. Typical plateaus of this kind are the "mountains" of Kentucky, the Cumberland Plateau of Tennessee, and the eastern part of the Ozark Highlands. In Europe, Bosnia and Hercegovina are examples.

On the dissected plateau the original land surface has been destroyed, except the narrow ridges which are in large part even-crested. In other words, in viewing the sky line of such a plateau the observer sees the summits of the various hills at approximately the same level.

Agriculture on the Dissected Plateau. The highly dissected land surface and the many steep slopes of the dissected plateau are serious handicaps to the development of agriculture. The little land that is cultivated is confined chiefly to the ridge tops, the flood plains, and the lower slopes of the valleys. In proceeding through the hills of eastern Kentucky and Tennessee, the traveler sees farms that contain small scattered fields of crop land, cheaply constructed farm buildings, and a general lack of social and economic well-being among the inhabitants.

The paucity of good agricultural land in such areas has frequently led to the cultivation of steep slopes. This practice has caused serious erosion in some areas, bringing ruin not only to the crops on the hillsides, but also to the farms on the lower slopes and flood plains of the valleys.

Plateaus That Are but Little Dissected (Undissected Plateaus)

In the undissected plateau or high tableland the greater part of the surface is flat to rolling upland, dissection being most pronounced only along the margins of such plateaus. Among highlands of this type are the Iberian Peninsula, Tibet, and the western portion of the Ozarks.

Unlike the dissected highlands, the generally undissected surface of this type of plateau has permitted a wider distribution of population on the tableland and a relatively small concentration of people in the valleys. Moreover, communication may be well developed because of the generally uniform land surface, whereas in dissected highlands routes of travel follow stream courses or ridge tops, or extend in zig-zag fashion up the steeper slopes.

Mountains

Mountains and Climate. The influence that mountains exert upon man and his activities is one of the most positive of geographical forces. Climatically the mountain influence is very marked. A journey up a mountain side usually takes the traveler through various climatic belts, each with its characteristic types of flora and fauna, and each providing an environment for certain distinctive types of human adjustments. This relationship of climate to highlands is well illustrated in tropical lands, where the life zones of high mountains may be so closely compressed that in places it is but a day's journey from snow fields to low, hot valleys.

In the tropical zone it is necessary to travel more than 15,000 feet up a mountain side before the zone of snow and ice is reached, but on some of the northern slopes in the latitude of Hammerfest, Norway, glaciers extend to sea level. Hence the upper limit of vegetative growth becomes lower with increasing latitude.

Highlands may also give rise to extremes of moisture conditions. High mountains force the passing winds to precipitate most of their moisture on the windward slopes, frequently producing arid lands on the leeward side. The aridity of low-latitude deserts has been intensified from such location (see p. 275), and even in middle latitudes vast stretches of land are made unfit for cultivation owing to their location to the leeward of high mountains.

Mountains in Relation to Irrigation. Many regions which now furnish a home for densely populated agricultural communities would be nothing short of desert or semi-arid waste if their near-by highland areas were removed. Among such lands which owe their life to mountains are the valleys of the Nile, the Tigris, and the Euphrates, and the

FIG. 62. Hoover Dam, the world's highest dam. View shows the upstream face of this gigantic structure just before the waters of the backed-up Colorado River had completely filled the reservoir shown in the foreground of the picture. Note the giant towers through which water will pass to generate electricity. (Courtesy Bureau of Reclamation, Department of the Interior.)

valleys of western Peru. (See pp. 287–290.) Mountains in all parts of the world contain catchment basins, in some of which irrigation waters are stored and released during the growing season to the irrigated farm lands of the adjacent plains (Fig. 62).

Agriculture in Mountains. Containing various climatic and vegetative belts, most mountains also possess suitable environmental conditions for the production of many kinds of crops. Hence in a tropical mountain area the traveler finds a range of crops corresponding to the latitudinal range from the equator to polar regions. (See p. 587.)

In the temperate zone the diversity of agricultural production is equally marked. For example, on the lower slopes of the Swiss Alps, grasses and grains have a conspicuous place in the cultural landscape; farther up the mountain side forests are important; and above the timber line one sees the alpine or mountain pasture, where cattle and sheep are kept during the summer months.[8]

Agriculture in "Mountains" of Eastern Kentucky. The average mountain farmer of the temperate zone is, even today, only in a small way a commercial producer. Subsistence agriculture is usually forced on him mainly because of the paucity of transportation facilities and the difficulty of growing an agricultural product that can stand the cost of export. This is well illustrated in a mountainous region (most of it a highly dissected plateau) like eastern Kentucky—situated almost within sight of great commercial centers, and surrounded by people whose life is inseparably bound up with commerce—the farmer is still content to practice self-sufficiency in his agricultural operations. In consequence of this fact, within the climatic limitations of this area, crops are raised which meet the requirements of the community. By reason of isolation the region still presents the economy of Colonial days, almost unmodified.[9]

Rocky Mountain Agriculture. The early agricultural development of the Rocky Mountains grew out of the need of miners for food. Mining communities far from good roads found the price of bacon, flour, potatoes, and other food high largely as a result of the high cost of transporting these products by train, wagon, and pack mule from distant agricultural centers. Farmers, accordingly, began producing these commodities on small patches of the best land within the region. Under such conditions small Rocky Mountain gardens sometimes brought lucrative returns to their owners. However, as soon as a railroad reached the mining center food could normally be imported more cheaply than it could be grown locally, and immediately agriculture declined. Occasionally the gold, silver, or other mineral was exhausted and the population shifted to other centers; then the farmer had no market, and since he could not export his crop profitably he abandoned the farm. As a consequence, agriculture has never become a very important industry in the rugged Rocky Mountain region. Yet considerable quantities of the hardier vegetables and

---

[8] In Norway this type of highland pasture is called the saeter; in the Alps it is called the alp.

[9] D. H. Davis, *Geography of the Kentucky Mountains*, Kentucky Geological Survey, 1924, p. 60.

cereals, such as potatoes, lettuce, barley, and rye, can be grown within the Rocky Mountain region whenever the population pressure of the United States becomes sufficiently great to warrant the further development of these upland soils.

Dairying and Stock-Raising. In practically all mountain regions of the temperate zone, grazing and stock-raising are important elements

Fig. 63. A shepherd with his flock in the beautiful Rosey Valley near St. Moritz, Switzerland. (Publishers Photo Service.)

in the farm economy of the people. Thus, though the farmer of the Kentucky mountains finds it difficult to export corn over the usually bad roads, he can feed the corn to hogs and cattle and thereby change it into a commodity capable of walking to market. Also he can make corn into whiskey, a concentrated product capable of standing the cost of transportation.

The pastoral industry represents one of the most important uses of the land within a large part of the mountainous section of northeastern United States, and dairy products are important exports. Similarly, cattle and sheep are pastured in most parts of the Rocky Mountain region some time during the year, and animal products represent the major items of the farmer's income.

In the Old World, where the population pressure is greater than in America, mountain pastures are carefully utilized. In south-central Europe many of the mountain slopes are covered with oak or beech forests which supply acorns and nuts—mast—for thousands of swine.

Fig. 64. An Alpine hut in the Bernese Oberland. In the distance are the peaks of Eiger, Monch, and Jungfrau. (Publishers Photo Service.)

This industry is the basis for a large export of pork, since the bacon from mast-fed hogs is highly prized in western Europe.

The high pastures of the Swiss Alps support thousands of cattle during the summer months while the best valley lands are tilled to provide food for the population of the region and winter forage for the stock (Figs. 63 and 64). Here the dairy industry has reached an intensive stage of development, and the Swiss dairy products have become famous for their good quality the world over.

The ability of sheep and goats to subsist on rough mountain pasture and scant summer forage has given them an important place in the agricultural economy of the mountainous parts of Mediterranean Europe. Within many of these areas sheep and goats not only are the chief dairy animals but they also supply wool, hides, and skins as export products. Much of the sheep milk is used in the manufacture of cheese, a part of which is exported; most of the goat milk is consumed fresh.

Intensive Mountain Agriculture in Asia. In mountainous areas where the population pressure is great, even relatively steep slopes are

Fig. 65. Rice terraces on the sides of mountains in the Philippine Islands. (Publishers Photo Service.)

devoted to crops, as is characteristic of many units located in the island fringe of Asia. Thus in Japan proper where a constantly increasing population is straining upon the bands of subsistence and where, because of the preponderance of highland, only 15.6 per cent of the land is under cultivation, the population has spread into the mountainous interior. Here many steep slopes are given to intensive cultivation by means of terraces, which extend upward in the form of giant steps parallel to the plains below. Similarly in other parts of Asia intensive mountain agriculture is practiced. Thus in the Philippines the total length of terrace walls is measured in thousands of miles, the terraces being devoted mainly to the cultivation of rice (Fig. 65).

Mountains as Barriers. High, massive mountains present the most
marked barriers which man meets on the land surface of the earth.
They stand as impediments to the commercial intercourse of people,
to the spread of population, to military campaigns, and to the building
of roads and railroads (Fig. 66). Because of the protection they
afford, mountains are often natural boundary lines between nations.
The statement is frequently made that Africa begins at the Pyrenees,

Fig. 66. Road construction in mountains is difficult. Sometimes roads extending
through such areas are forced to follow relatively narrow ledges. (Photo by
T. J. Hileman.)

and this great highland wall stretching across southern Europe from
the Bay of Biscay to the Black Sea was for centuries an effective barrier separating the culture of central Europe from that of Mediterranean lands.[10]   Similarly, during the early history of the United
States, the Appalachian Mountains stood as a marked obstacle to westward migration and to economic contacts between the Middle West
and the Atlantic seaboard.

Sparsity of Population in Mountains. Mountains are, as a rule,
more sparsely populated than plains—a fact clearly reflected by the
population map of the world. The difficulty of making roads up steep,

---

[10] Ellen Churchill Semple, *Influences of Geographic Environment*, Henry Holt
& Co., 1911, p. 532.

rocky slopes and through forests which sometimes cover their rain-drenched sides is a major handicap to the mountain dweller. But in addition to this the climate is generally rigorous, and there is a paucity of good cultivable land. These forces act as a distinct, positive check to the development of population in most mountainous regions, especially in middle and higher latitudes.

In the tropics, on the other hand, there are exceptions to the general rule. Thus mountains located in arid tropical regions frequently become centers of population, since windward slopes obtain moisture from the passing winds while the adjacent lowlands remain dry. Moreover, mountains in low latitudes are cooler than the surrounding lowlands and offer a more healthful habitat for man. It is significant that more than three-fourths of Ecuador's population is crowded into her highlands. Similarly in Peru, Bolivia, and tropical Africa the mountains constitute the habitat of a large number of people. Even these highlands, however, are not densely populated, since they offer but limited means of subsistence to their native peoples.

Overpopulation and Emigration. For the world at large the obvious and persistent fact of mountain economy is a scanty food supply even when secured by the most intelligent and untiring labor, and consequently there results a fixed tendency to overpopulation. The simplest remedy for this evil is emigration, a fact observed by Malthus. Therefore emigration is an almost universal phenomenon in highland regions.[11] For example, there is an almost constant flow of people from the Italian Alps, many of whom find work in Marseille and other towns of southern France. In some mountains, however, the emigration is seasonal. Thus in autumn, after the field work is over, the Swiss descend from the Jura and Alps in great numbers to cities, seeking positions as servants or factory workers.

Cultural Effects of Isolation. The isolation of mountain life accentuates non-social qualities, as seen in the clannishness of the Scotch mountaineer, the insubordination of the Basques and the tribes of the Caucasus, the Tibetans' dislike of strangers, the lawlessness and family feuds among the southern mountaineers in the Appalachian highlands of America.[12]

Mountain isolation tends to preserve the original language, customs, laws, and ideas. It has been estimated that there are more than 400,000

[11] *Op. cit.,* p. 532.
[12] R. Whitbeck, "Mountains in Their Influence upon Man and His Activities," *Journal of Geography,* Vol. 9, p. 55.

people in the mountains of Wales who cannot speak English, though Wales was joined to England five centuries ago. There are Jewish tribes in the Caucasus who still give their children names in vogue in Israel in the time of the Judges and which have elsewhere been obsolete for 2,500 years.

Mountain isolation retards improvement in living conditions. Thus many areas within the Appalachian Mountains are still difficult of access, even in good weather, and during the winter and spring are virtually cut off from the outside world. Consequently the improvements in living conditions which have taken place in most of the rural sections of the country have not been made here, except to a small degree. Domestic conveniences are still few in number; all the houses of the poorer areas are small and poorly furnished, and much of the furniture is of local manufacture. Many houses are still without screens so necessary to the comfort and health of the occupants, sanitary plumbing is lacking, and the drinking-water supply is, in many places, inadequate and poor in quality.

Mountains and Minerals. Fissures and fractures in the earth's crust and the circulation of mineral-carrying solutions are associated with mountain building. Hence mountains are the natural home of metallic veins and mining. Moreover, in many places the agents of erosion have worn away the overlying rocks, exposing the minerals and facilitating their exploitation.

Mountain Passes. The mountain range presents a challenge to man's energy and endurance; in searching for the lowest dip in the crest by which to cross, men found those natural features, the mountain passes. These constitute the easiest pathway to the country beyond the mountains and become the focus for routes of transportation.

In Europe the Alpine passes are of marked significance. Flanked by the Po, the Rhone, and the Danube valleys, the Alpine passes have been rated among the most significant features of southern Europe. They served as military roads for the passage of armies from the time of Hannibal to that of Napoleon, and later they became thoroughfares for the exchange of products of the subtropical Mediterranean lands and of the Orient, with those of the temperate regions of Europe. Among the important Alpine passes for travel and trade are the Brenner, the Simplon, the St. Gottard, and the Bernard.

Almost every mountain chain has its passes. Unfortunately, some mountain chains such as the Andes, the Pyrenees, and the Himalayas either have no low passes or have passes that are far apart.

LAND FORMS IN RELATION TO VOLCANOES AND EARTHQUAKES

The regions of greatest volcanic and seismic activity are those in which extensive layers of rock of great thickness have been intensively folded, dislocated, and elevated (Figs. 67 and 68). These regions occur in great bands, marking the lines of weakness in the crust, and generally follow the lines of elevation which bound the oceanic basins

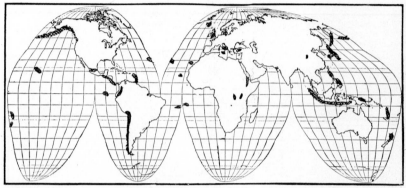

FIG. 67. Major areas of volcanic disturbances. (Mapped on Goode's homolosine projection, copyright University of Chicago Press.)

—regions of recent, or in some cases still continuous, mountain growth.[13]

There are two major earthquake belts in the world: the one along the Mediterranean Sea, and the other following the coastline of the Pacific Ocean, including Japan, Alaska, the California coast, and the western coastline of South America. But there is no region that is absolutely immune from earthquakes, and minor quakes may occur almost anywhere. However, they are seldom serious unless they occur in a vicinity in which the structures are weak.

Volcanoes as Related to Man

Volcanoes afford impressive manifestations of the powerful forces that are still at work on the fashioning of our globe. When active, volcanoes frequently cause considerable destruction to life and property located in proximity to them: in some places through the ashes

[13] E. W. Woolard, "Earthquakes and Volcanoes," *Scientific American*, Vol 129, p. 304.

and stones hurled high into the air later to be dropped in the surrounding area, elsewhere through the burning effects of streams of lava. In still other places, poisonous gases emanate from volcanoes and sweep down their slopes with stifling, deadening effects to plant and animal life. But the greatest destruction from volcanic eruptions is frequently indirect. Thus a violent volcanic explosion may create high tidal waves which sweep over low-lying coasts, drowning thousands of the inhabitants and destroying their homes.

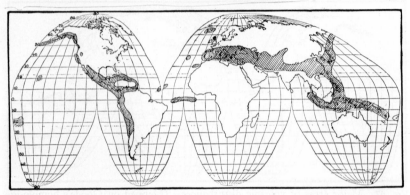

FIG. 68. The earthquake zones of the world. (Mapped on Goode's homolosine projection, copyright University of Chicago Press.)

Destruction by Volcanoes. From the standpoint of rapidity in destroying life and property, volcanoes may be divided into three types —explosive, quiet, and intermediate (Fig. 69). In the explosive type, destruction may be limited to only a few seconds or minutes, typical of which were the eruptive effects of Krakatoa and Mt. Pelée. Volcanoes of the intermediate type usually give warnings for a long time before they erupt, since they are in an active state a large part of the time, then suddenly pour out a portion of their hot interiors. Typical of such volcanoes is the well-known Mt. Vesuvius. The quiet type of volcano usually pours out lava at a moderate rate and with sufficient regularity so that people living in its vicinity may seek places of shelter. To this type belong the volcanoes of the Hawaiian Islands.

Many of the greatest volcanoes on earth appear to be completely extinct, but sometimes a supposedly extinct one erupts. Moreover, in many volcanoes, during a quiescent stage, there appears to be a gradual accumulation of pressure. Lava rises in the conduit, and eventually an eruption begins explosively, great quantities of gases, mingled with dust and stones, being ejected. The pressure is thus relieved, and this phase of volcanism is succeeded by a more quiet one in which lava escapes through rents in the cone. Thus a single volcano may pass through the explosive, intermediate, and quiet stages.

Krakatoa Volcano—A Violent Explosion. One of the most frightful and violent of all volcanic explosions was that of Krakatoa, located in the Straits of Sunda, near Java—a region embracing the greatest concentration of volcanic activity on the globe. In 1883, after pre-

FIG. 69. Scene after a volcanic eruption in the vicinity of a village in Sicily. (Publishers Photo Service.)

monitory outrushes of gas for some time, there suddenly came a series of explosions which blew away more than a cubic mile of the island. The vast dark cloud of dust and ashes rose about 17 miles into the atmosphere, completely hiding the sun over a vast area. This dust was distributed over the entire globe by the upper atmospheric air currents and was responsible for red sunset glows all over the world for many months. The terrific detonations resulting from the explosions broke windows within a radius of 100 miles, and the generated air waves traveled several times around the world, as manifested by barograph records. Sea waves up to 100 feet high rushed along the low-lying coasts of Java and Sumatra, swept far inland, and drowned about 40,000 people. Now the water is 1,200 feet deep where Krakatoa stood.

Volcanoes in the United States. The United States contains many interesting extinct volcanoes—Crater Lake, Oregon, occupies the center

Fig. 70.   Crater Lake, Oregon, occupying the center of one of the numerous extinct volcanoes in the West.   (Courtesy Southern Pacific Co.)

of one—but very few volcanoes have been active within the United States during historic times (Fig. 70). Lassen Peak, California, has exhibited mild activity at frequent intervals since May, 1914.

Extensive Fissure Eruptives in the Past. Wherever volcanism occurs at present it covers but a small surface area, but there have been times even in late geological history when masses of fluid magma were poured out through crustal rifts several miles in length without signs of explosive activity or any restraint upon freedom of crystallization and release of their volatile content. Such conditions gave us the successive flows known as the Deccan traps of India, in which the black cotton soils of that country developed. Similar outflows in the United States covered some 250,000 square miles of land in the Snake River Basin with volcanic material.[14]

The North Atlantic region off Scotland was flooded with lava over an area of at least 250,000 square miles; and recent studies have shown the basaltic plateaus of Argentina and Brazil to have covered 300,000 square miles.

Earthquakes

Distribution of Earthquakes. Seismologists tell us that our globe is trembling somewhere practically all the time. Indeed, an earthquake is felt in some parts of the world on an average of approximately 4,000 times yearly. But fortunately for man and his works, only relatively few of these earth tremors are destructive to life and property.

Although earthquakes may occur in any part of the earth's crust, these disturbances are more pronounced in some parts of the world than others. Through their period of existence, London, Paris, and Berlin have known no severe earthquakes, whereas Tokyo, Yokohama, Valparaiso, and Peiping (Peking) have been shaken violently many times.

Earthquakes occur with greatest frequency along zones that correspond with the deeper parts of the oceans, or that cross the continents where deep seas once divided the lands. One great belt of earthquake disturbances borders the two Americas and extends down the coast of eastern Asia, thus flanking the Pacific. The other belt extends from the East Indies through the Mediterranean Sea and across the West Indies and Central America, where it again meets the Circum-Pacific belt. In these belts the shaking of the ground is more persistent, and, as a rule, more energetic than elsewhere, as manifested by the distribution of the greatest earthquakes known to man.[15]

[14] A. L. Day, "Some Causes of Volcanic Activity," *Annual Report of the Smithsonian Institution*, 1925, p. 269.

[15] R. A. Daly, *Our Mobile Earth*, Charles Scribner's Sons, 1926, p. 6.

Many of the earthquakes occur at sea, under the bottom of the oceans, their general area of occurrence being recorded on seismographs. Such earthquakes sometimes cause great tidal waves which sweep across the ocean, rush inland, and destroy human life and the works of man. Waves caused by earthquakes swept over Lisbon, Portugal, in 1775, causing a loss of approximately 60,000 lives. At times tidal waves have torn ships from their moorings and carried them inland, leaving them high and dry when the waters receded.[16]

Causes of Earthquakes. There are many theories as to the cause of earthquakes, and there is a great divergence of opinion with respect to the basic reason for these crustal vibrations. But it is known that there are breaks in the earth's crust at certain places, and that such breaks have usually resulted from strains. Frequently the strains have continued, and they are relieved only by slipping along the break. When the slip occurs suddenly, an earthquake is almost sure to develop. In other instances the earth's crust does not break, but merely cracks, thereby causing earth tremors.[17]

Destructiveness of Earthquakes. Falling masonry, tidal waves, landslides, and fires are the chief destructive agents after violent earthquakes. Sometimes these destructive forces have caused a loss of human life amounting to more than 100,000 people, especially in densely populated areas located in earthquake zones.

The following table shows that the greatest casualties have occurred in Japan, Italy, China, and Portugal. But there have been tremendous losses from earthquakes that are not recorded in this table. Thus in India in 1737 about 300,000 people are said to have perished, and again in 1897 a stupendous shock was destructive over 150,000 square miles in the northeastern part of that country.

One of the greatest earthquakes of the last few thousand years was that which destroyed Tokyo and Yokohama in September, 1923. Although Japan has suffered grievously from earthquakes and their effects in the past, this earthquake surpassed all previously known disasters. Violently destructive over an area extending 100 miles from north to south and 130 miles from east to west, this earthquake affected a densely populated region containing approximately 7,000,000 people. Here the shaking reached its maximum in about 16 seconds, ruined many thousand houses, and caused the death of more than 140,000 people. In Tokyo most of the deaths occurred from fires which broke

---

[16] W. Bowie, "Earthquakes," *Science*, Vol. 61, pp. 379 and 380.
[17] N. H. Heck, "Earthquakes," *Scientific Monthly*, Vol. 22, p. 141.

out in several parts of the city and were out of control owing to the breaking of the water mains.

CASUALTIES OF INDIVIDUAL EARTHQUAKES *

Region	Persons killed
Lisbon, 1775	60,000
Calabria, 1783	30,000
Naples, 1857	12,300
Argentina, 1861	6,000
Andalusia, 1884	750
Charleston, 1886	27
Riviera, 1887	640
Japan, 1891	9,960
Calabria, 1894	100
Japan, 1896	29,000
India, 1905	20,000
California, 1906	700
Valparaiso, 1906	3,764
Calabria, 1907	175
Jamaica, 1907	1,000
Messina, 1908	100,000
Central Italy, 1915	30,000
Kansu, China, 1920	100,000–200,000
Japan, 1923	142,000–160,000
Khorossan District, Iran, 1929	2,000
North Island, New Zealand, 1931	250
Bihar and Orissa, India, 1934	7,000
Quetta, India, 1935	30,000
Anatolia, 1939	no official figure

* Data up to and including Japanese earthquake of 1923, adapted from R. A. Daly, *Our Mobile Earth*, Charles Scribner's Sons, 1926, p. 3. The remaining data have been obtained from scattered sources.

The earthquake that shook Kansu, China, in 1920 was another of the greatest calamities of recent history. This earthquake occurred in the heart of the loess country of China, and landslides developed on an enormous scale. Apparently water-soaked at the time, this loose material slid rapidly down the hills of this part of China, causing almost complete destruction in some sections. "The most appalling sight of all was the Valley of Death, where seven great slides crashed into a gap in the hills three miles long, killing every living thing in the area except three men and two dogs. The survivors were carried across the valley on the crest of the avalanche, caught in the cross-current of two other slides, whirled in a gigantic vortex, and catapulted to the slope of another hill. With them went house, orchard, and threshing floor, and the farmer has since placidly begun to till the new location to which he was so unceremoniously transported." [18]

America's outstanding earthquake calamity in a large city was the destruction of San Francisco in 1906. Like the Tokyo disaster of Japan, this earthquake severed the water-supply lines, and fire broke out immediately afterwards. Although only about 700 people lost their lives, the property damage amounted to many millions of dollars.

The chief cities of Central America, except those of Honduras and Nicaragua, have repeatedly been destroyed by earthquakes. The principal sufferer has been Guatemala City, which has been practically destroyed more than half a dozen times, and the cities of San Salvador and Cartago have been shaken into ruins on more than one occasion.[19]

In South America the city of Valparaiso, Chile, has suffered from many violent earthquakes. Great damage was inflicted in 1730, 1822, 1839, 1873, and 1906.

In December, 1939, very severe earthquakes were experienced to the east of the Mediterranean Sea. In Anatolia the damage to property was estimated at many millions of dollars, and tens of thousands of people lost their lives. Whole villages were buried under the steep cliffs of the Janik Mountains, which skirt the Black Sea shore on the Turkish-Armenian border.

Building against Earthquakes. Man is unable to stop the waves of an earthquake, but he can erect strong buildings. An example of the worst type of building for an earthquake region is found quite commonly in Japan. Heavy tiles are placed on light structures. This was a cause of serious loss of life in the 1923 earthquake in Tokyo. Moreover, the type of footing material is closely related to the degree of destructiveness during an earthquake. Thus buildings that are erected on unconsolidated earth material are more readily destroyed than structures erected on solid rock. The earthquake vibrations in rock formations are very rapid, but short and relatively harmless. On the other hand, in unconsolidated material the vibrations are longer, stronger, and as a rule, more dangerous.

According to Bailey Willis,[20] various major considerations should be given to the erection of buildings in earthquake zones. Where the ground is of such a nature that vibrations are bound to be dangerous, protection may be afforded by sinking foundations 10 feet or more, by constructing the foundation walls with wide footings, and by

[18] Ashton Close and Elsie McCormick, "Where the Mountains Walked," *National Geographic Magazine*, Vol. 41, p. 449.

[19] "City Toll of Earthquakes," *Science*, Vol. 58, Supplement 14, Oct. 5, 1923.

[20] Bailey Willis was president of the Seismological Society of America.

building the structure on a reinforced slab, so that it will move as a unit. All structures should be framed and braced, whether the frame is of steel, wood, or concrete.

REFERENCES

Bowie, W., "Earthquakes," *Science*, Vol. 61, pp. 379–380.

Daly, R. A., *Our Mobile Earth*, Charles Scribner's Sons, 1926.

Emerson, F. V., *Agricultural Geology*, John Wiley & Sons, 1928, pp. 159–160.

Fenneman, N. M., *Physiography of Western United States*, McGraw-Hill Book Co., 1931.

Physiography of Eastern United States, McGraw-Hill Book Co., 1937.

Jansma, K., "The Drainage of the Zuider Zee," *Geographical Review*, Vol. 21, 1931, pp. 578–579.

Marr, J. E., *The Scientific Study of Scenery*, Methuen & Co., London, 1920.

Russell, I. C., "Volcanic Eruptions on Martinique and St. Vincent," *Annual Report of the Smithsonian Institution for 1902*, 1903, pp. 331–349.

Salisbury, R. D., *Physiography*, Henry Holt & Co., 1919.

Soley, J. C., *Source of Volcanic Energy*, G. P. Putnam's Sons, 1924, pp. 138–139.

Tesch, P., "Physiographic Regions of the Netherlands," *Geographical Review*, Vol. 13, pp. 507–517.

Whitbeck, R., "Mountains in Their Influence upon Man and His Activities," *Journal of Geography*, Vol. 9, p. 55.

PART II

CLIMATIC REGIONS AND
HUMAN ACTIVITIES

Chapter 5

THE RAINY LOW-LATITUDE

REGIONS

MAN IN THE TROPICAL RAIN FOREST

The tropical-forest regions considered here are those low-latitude areas that are sufficiently warm and moist during all seasons for the continuous growth of broad-leaf trees. Since the trees grow during the entire year they do not shed all their leaves at one time and are, consequently, evergreen.

The rainy low latitudes extend over approximately 5,000,000 square miles of land, much of which is still covered with forests or jungles in which human progress has been exceedingly slow. In many respects these vast areas are Mother Earth's greatest paradox. They contain some of the most richly endowed parts of the earth, yet dire poverty exists throughout their extent; they are the world's greatest storehouse of energy,[1] yet within their bounds lassitude of body and mind is man's most common experience; they abound with life, yet death lurks everywhere.

Except for the interruptions of oceans and uplands, the rain forest girdles the earth along its equatorial circumference (Figs. 71 and 72). Throughout this entire realm (all the rainy low-latitude regions) dense vegetation is the dominant characteristic of the landscape. So dense is this rain forest, so thick the mat of vines and creepers which interlace the tall trees, that the sunlight finds its way with difficulty to the earth floor beneath. Midday in the densest equatorial forest is often little brighter than gloomy twilight.

Temptingly rich in economic possibilities, these tropical lands are for the most part lying idle. In the great Amazon Basin vast stretches of land are still unexplored, other extensive areas support no popula-

[1] An acre of land at the equator receives 26 per cent more heat (energy) from the sun each year than an acre situated in latitude 40°.

tion,[2] and even along the main river highways little of the land is fully utilized. In the Congo Basin and in the larger islands of the East Indies most of the scattered tribes live near the rivers and along the better-known forest trails, leaving large areas of the interior almost uninhabited. The native peoples, with their primitive subsistence agriculture, are faced with many problems; in such a welter of heat and humidity that man's energy is sapped, and slow progress can be expected where development is left to the natives alone.

The rainy low latitudes have not escaped the attention of energetic colonizing peoples from middle latitudes who have long been engaged in subduing and settling the productive portions of the earth. Until very recently these would-be colonizers and developers of the rain forest have met with tragic defeat. Determination, resourcefulness, common sense and brawn—the pioneer qualities which have enabled man to spread over the entire temperate zone and make it his home— have not enabled him to master the wet tropics. He might have succeeded in subduing the tangled and quick-growing vegetation had he not been compelled to fight swarms of insects far more dangerous than reptiles or wild animals, and to combat a score of deadly and mysterious tropical diseases. Weakened by disease and forced into inaction by the enervating climate, temperate-zone man usually lost out in the struggle. The decaying remnants of ambitious projects today give mute witness to the hopeless struggle of many people who have settled here.

During the present century we have seen the beginning of a modern "conquest of the tropics" based almost entirely upon science. The work of General Gorgas, Dr. Reed, and scores of other scientists has demonstrated that certain tropical diseases may be eliminated, entirely or in part, by a rigorous program of hygiene and sanitation. General Gorgas banished yellow fever from the Canal Zone, put malaria largely under control, and greatly improved all health conditions. Since Panama has been made livable for the white race, scientific methods of development are being adopted in many other tropical regions. Physicians, nurses, biologists, engineers, meteorologists, geographers, and agronomists are all doing their part in the new development. The East Indies, Malaya, Nigeria, the Gold Coast, and Liberia are among the many places that have thousands of acres in plantations growing tropical products which are especially valued in colder lands. This

---

[2] Theodore Roosevelt traveled several hundred miles down the River of Doubt (River Roosevelt) before he saw any signs of human occupation.

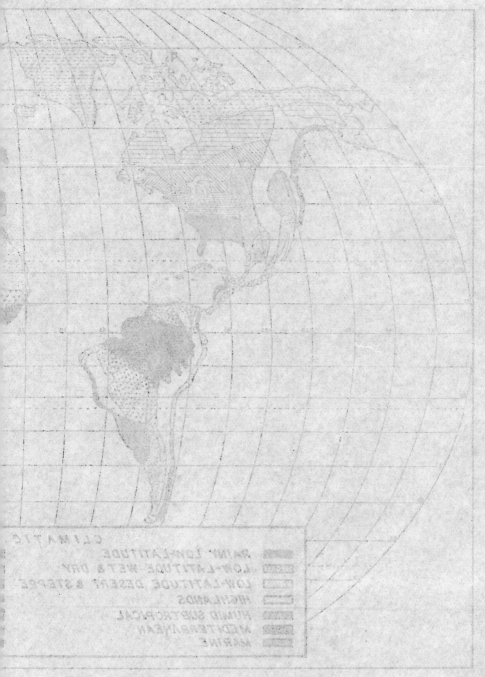

Fig. 71. Climatic regions of the world. (Modification of Jon...

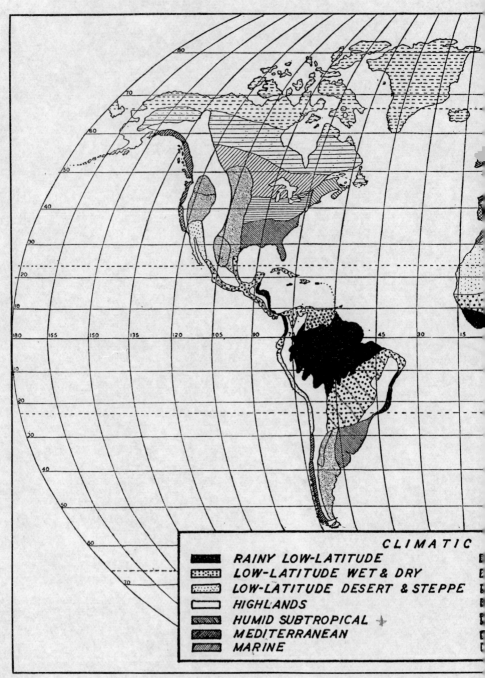

Fig. 71. Climatic regions of the world. (Modification of Jor

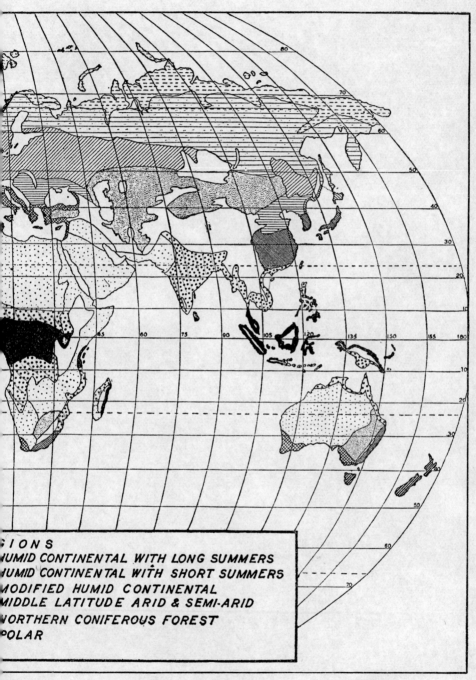

new agriculture has been developed so successfully during the past three decades that plantations of rubber, rice, tropical oil crops, cacao, and various spices are now in a fair way to displace many of the more accessible jungles and forests.   Although a splendid beginning has been made, using efficient, modern methods, the rainy low latitudes are as yet unconquered.   There are enough unsolved disease problems alone to keep the scientists busy for many years to come.

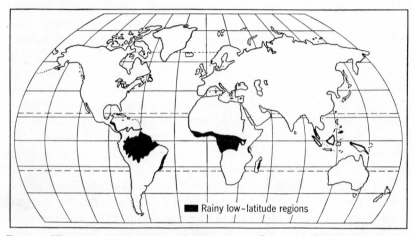

Fig. 72.   The rainy low-latitude regions receive sufficient rainfall in all seasons so that trees grow continuously and the forests are evergreen.   Compare with Fig. 73.   Boundaries of regions drawn by different authors and from different data seldom coincide throughout.   The equatorial and tropical forest areas (Fig. 73) include both the rainy low-latitude forests and the monsoon forests.

Among the more serious tropical problems is that of retaining a degree of mental and physical energy somewhat comparable to that of the temperate zone.   Each region of the tropical rain forest possesses many characteristics that are common to all of them.   The problems and potentialities of the several regions as related to climate, soils, native vegetation, native animal life, diseases, native agriculture, and plantation crops have much in common.   These characteristics, problems, and potentialities that are more or less common to all regions are discussed later in the chapter.

Although the several regions of the tropical rain forest have many characteristics that are common to all, each region also possesses considerable individuality with respect to size, shape, location, soils, peoples, and agricultural potentialities.   These individual qualities can best be portrayed by a brief regional study of each.

REGIONS OF RAINY LOW LATITUDES

The Amazon Valley. The Amazon Valley is a basin that has an east-west extent of approximately 2,000 miles, and a north-south extent of more than 1,200 miles in the zone of maximum width. Although a large part of the region has never been surveyed, a widely used atlas indicates that more than one-half of the Valley is a vast plain that lies below the 600-foot contour.[3] Much of this lowland is flooded in times of high water. In places the flood plain is more than 60 miles wide and the unflooded areas are more or less isolated (Fig. 73).

High temperatures, heavy rainfall, humid atmosphere, rain-leached soil, jungle, heavy forest, insect pests, and diseases may be listed among the major factors that have retarded human progress in the Amazon Valley. Although this region is more than one-half as large as the United States it probably supports less than 2,000,000 people. As late as the 1920's scarcely 100 square miles of this vast area were devoted to any kind of agriculture.[4]

Other Tropical Rain Forest Regions of the Western Hemisphere. Three other tropical rain forest regions are situated in the western hemisphere. Two of them lie in the trade-wind belts and the third lies in the equatorial calm belt west of the Andes Mountains (Fig. 72). Where the trade winds blow against the highlands of eastern Brazil and of eastern Central America and Panama, the rainfall is heavy at all seasons; the temperatures are continuously high; and the tropical forests are evergreen.

The Congo Basin and the Guinea Coast. The tropical rain forest of the Congo Basin has two distinct advantages over the Amazon Valley as the home of man. First, the Congo Basin has considerable elevation above sea level and some areas are slightly cooler than most parts of the lowlands of the Amazon Valley. Second, the rainfall of central Africa is not so heavy as that of the Amazon Basin. Nevertheless the tropical rain forest of the Congo Basin usually receives adequate rainfall at all seasons for native agriculture, whereas most sections of the lowlands of the Amazon Valley receive more precipitation than is desirable.

Guinea Coast. Along the Guinea Coast and its immediate hinterland, the rainfall varies greatly from one place to another depending

---

[3] John Bartholomew, *The Oxford Advanced Atlas*, Oxford University Press, 1942, p. 88.

[4] Preston E. James, *Latin America*, The Odyssey Press, 1942, p. 555.

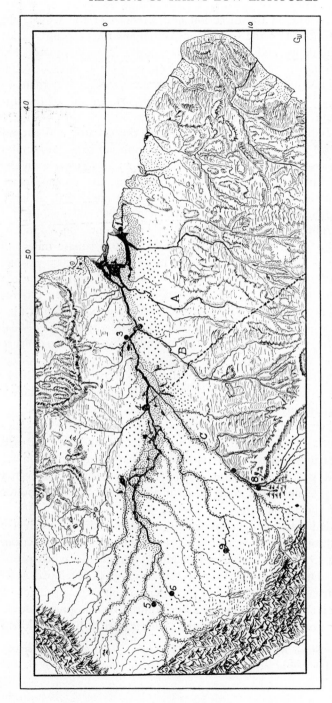

Fig. 73. The Amazon Valley possesses the largest undeveloped tropical forest region of the world. Roads are almost nonexistent and only two short railways have been constructed within the Amazon lowland. An airway with supply stations is now being constructed across the Amazon forest and jungle. Rivers: (A) Xingú, (B) Tapajós, (C) Madeira. Cities: (1) Belém (Pará), (2) Santarem, (3) Obidos, (4) Manaus, (5) Iquitos, (6) Boa Vista, (7) Porto Velho, (8) Villa Bella, (9) Senna Madureiro.

on topography and on the direction and strength of the winds. In the western foothills of the Cameroon Mountains the rainfall exceeds 200 inches annually, and on the higher slopes it approximates 400 inches. Although most of the coastal belt receives from 50 to 100 inches of rainfall, a narrow strip near Accra receives less than 40 inches. This light rainfall may be, at least in part, a result of the up-welling of cold water off this coast.

The East Indies. These islands lie across the equator and extend more than 3,000 miles from east to west and approximately 1,400 miles from north to south. They are scattered over an area larger than the United States but their total land area is approximately 743,000 square miles. Although they are only a little more than one-fourth as large as the United States, they support more than 65,000,000 people.

The East Indies represent great contrasts in economic development. Java and Madoera (Madura) with an area of 51,034 square miles, 40 per cent of which is waste land, support more than 43,000,000 people, or more than 1,500 persons per square mile of utilized land. Yet these people have achieved a relatively high standard of living for the Orient.

For many decades prior to World War II, the Netherlands East Indies constituted one of the most productive and profitable colonial empires in the world. Both plantation and subsistence agriculture prospered, and vast quantities of rubber, copra, palm oil, tea, coffee, cane sugar, tobacco, cassava (tapioca flour), kapok, cinchona bark, and spices were exported. The islands were also important producers of tin and petroleum and were minor producers of nickel.

On the other hand, Borneo and New Guinea are relatively undeveloped. Some of the more rugged sections of the islands are still occupied by backward tribes of natives who have but slight contact with civilized peoples. In some of the most intensively cultivated areas of New Guinea, the tools used in agriculture are little better than those of the Stone Age.[5]

This retarded state of development is not due entirely to adverse natural conditions, but to a lack of proper stimuli for production. In many areas the soil is fertile and produces abundantly when properly tended. During World War II the Americans developed agriculture in parts of the East Indies in order to solve the problem of shipping space that would otherwise be required to transport food to the soldiers. For example, by 1944, an American firm had developed

[5] L. J. Brass, "Stone Age Agriculture in New Guinea," *Geographical Reivew,* October 1941, pp. 55ff.

a 250-acre farm in the Laloki River Valley north of Port Moresby. Planting was regulated so as to assure a steady supply of vegetables to the military forces stationed there. An average acreage yield of 30,000 pounds of lettuce, Chinese cabbage, and silver beets was obtained annually. Squash, radishes, watermelons, carrots, okra, and eggplant each yielded about 20,000 pounds. Production on the farm at times exceeded the demand so that on one occasion it was necessary to dump 100,000 pounds of lettuce into the sea.[6]

The Philippine Islands. The Philippine Islands occupy an area of 115,600 square miles and, in 1940, supported 16,000,313 people. Most of the land is rugged. The mountain systems, although complex, are, in most areas, a succession of north-south-trending folds, fault blocks, or disconnected volcanic ranges.

The soils vary greatly in fertility. In many areas, however, the soils are of volcanic origin or have been weathered from limestone and are fertile. Agriculture is characterized by subsistence rice, corn, bananas, yams, and small quantities of cotton, cassava, and coffee. The major agricultural exports are coconut products, cane sugar, abaca (manila hemp), pineapples, tobacco, and rubber.

CLIMATE OF THE RAINY LOW LATITUDES

Temperature. The rainy low-latitude regions have more uniform temperatures than are found in any other type of climate. As they lie on or near the equator, the noonday sun is always near the zenith, and the days and nights are about equal (on the equator the days and nights are always equal). Within these hot, wet lands the range in temperature depends chiefly on (1) nearness to the sea, especially on the windward side, (2) the amount of moisture in the air, and (3) latitude. The windward coastal margins of these regions, tempered as they are by the sea, have but little change in temperature from month to month. Thus Batavia, located on the windward side of Java, has a mean annual temperature of 78.8° F. and a mean yearly range of only 2° F.

The forested interiors have only a slightly larger mean annual range. Although tempered little by the ocean, these forests give off an abundance of moisture even during the dry season, and the ground is moist

[6] The great potentialities of the Pacific Islands for the development of agriculture are indicated by Robert G. Bowman in "Army Farms and Agricultural Development in the Southwest Pacific," *Geographical Review*, July 1946, pp. 420–446.

and shaded so that it heats and cools slowly. At Manaus, situated in
the interior of Brazil, the mean annual range of temperature is 2.7° F.;

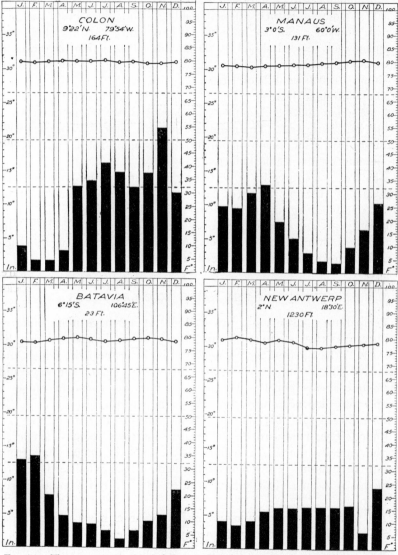

Fɪɢ. 74. Temperature and rainfall records of four rainy low-latitude stations.

and at New Antwerp, located in the forests of west central Africa,
the mean annual range is 3.8° F. (Fig. 74). Even in the uplands the
range is small provided that the humidity is high. Entebbe, situated

near Lake Victoria at an altitude of 3,683 feet, has a mean annual range of only 2.7° F.

Near the cooler margins of the wet equatorial regions, and especially in the interior of a continent, the range from the coldest to the warmest month is larger than at the equator. Thus at Senna Madureira the average temperature range for June is more than 4° F. Beyond the borders of this hot moist realm the annual range increases rapidly, as is indicated by the fact that, at Cuiaba, the coldest month is 12° F. colder than the hottest month, and the monotony of the winter month is broken by alternate cool and warm spells.

Everywhere the diurnal range of temperature is greater than the seasonal range and affords the principal relief from temperatures which, though not exceedingly high, would otherwise be monotonous and debilitating. The diurnal range of temperature is determined largely by the condition of the atmosphere. A heavy and persistent blanket of moisture shields the surface of the earth from the full effects of the tropical sun by day and likewise prevents the rapid loss of heat by night. During the rainy season, especially on the windward coasts, the diurnal range is small and the nights afford little relief. Even in those parts of the interior where the rainy season lasts most of the year, as at Manaus, and in all parts of the realm affected by the tempering winds from the ocean, as at Panama, the diurnal range is small and the nights bring little relief from the heat (Fig. 75).

Even in the most enervating regions there is a winter (cooler and drier) season which is less debilitating than summer. In fact, in some parts of the wet equatorial regions, the winter months are not unpleasantly hot provided that one is not exposed to the direct rays of the midday sun, and during the night one may even suffer from the cold. This is especially true of inland areas situated near the margins of the realm. Thus at Senna Madureira one would scarcely notice the difference from month to month, but he would notice the 27° change from day to night. Night temperatures of 50° F. may cause real suffering to natives who live month after month with the daytime temperature reaching the upper eighties and nineties with fearful persistence.

In Senna Madureira the winter weather is less monotonous than at Manaus and Panama. The variation in weather becomes even more noticeable farther south in the wet-and-dry realm of Brazil.

A study of Fig. 75 indicates that night is the winter of the tropics. The mean temperatures for the coldest month are a little less than the mean for the hottest; moreover, at many stations, high afternoon temperatures are indicated more often in the coolest month than in the hottest. The most significant difference is that the range of temperature, the difference between the maxima and the minima, is greater in

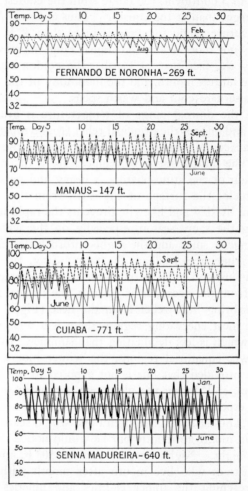

FIG. 75. Everywhere within the rainy low latitudes the diurnal range is greater than the seasonal range. Mark Jefferson, "Actual Temperatures of South America," *Geographical Review*, July 1926, Vol. 16, pp. 443–466.

the cooler month. The cool or winter month has more clear sky; more sunshine falls on the ground to warm it by day; and more radiation through the cloudless air cools it at night. One would scarcely notice the difference in temperature from month to month, but he would notice the 15° to 30° change from day to night. Night, then, affords some relief from the otherwise constantly high temperatures. In some areas the winter nights are sufficiently cool to cause a high mortality from bronchial and pulmonary affections among those who sleep without proper covering.[7]

Rainfall. The rains of the wet equatorial regions come, for the most part, in daily showers, interspersed with much sunshine, and long-continued rains are rare. During even the season of greatest rainfall, almost every day has a clear morning, and the rain comes from thunderstorms in the afternoon. These thunderstorms result from convection currents in the belt of equatorial calms. This distribution of rainfall has a marked effect upon the native people and their activities. In many localities it is common practice to do most of the work in the forenoon, cease all activity by eleven or twelve o'clock, and rest until after the rain is over. In the rubber plantations of the Netherlands East Indies, for instance, the rubber gatherer begins his work before dawn in order to complete it before the heavy rains. In certain localities the rain comes with such marked regularity at a certain hour in the afternoon that social engagements are made for "after the shower."

The seasons of greater and lesser rainfall are determined largely by the position of the sun. When the sun's rays fall vertically and hence have the greatest heating influence upon the earth, convection takes place rapidly and the daily precipitation is heavy. The area of maximum convection which is known as the belt of *equatorial calms*— the zone of daily thunderstorm rains—migrates northward or southward in response to the north-south movement of the sun. The width of the calm belt over land is approximately 8° to 15° of latitude, and it migrates 10° or more.

A few places near the equator have two seasons of heavy rainfall and two of lighter rainfall, but this condition is the exception. For the most part the precipitation of wet equatorial regions consists of one period of abundant rainfall followed by a period of lighter rainfall, the maximum amount occurring when the sun's rays are most powerful. Near the heat equator the season of light rainfall is short, but towards the polar margins of the wet tropics this dry season increases in length with increasing latitude. During the wet season it rains almost every day; during the drier season several days together

[7] The loss of life from bronchial and pulmonary affections was a great handicap in the construction of the Madeira Marmora Railroad in western Brazil.

may pass without rain, but the distribution usually is such as to keep vegetation growing luxuriantly.

Humidity. The relative humidity is high most of the time and the absolute humidity is always high, the highest of any portion of the earth.[8] During the rainy season the atmosphere is so saturated with moisture that it is difficult to keep anything dry. Most food products left in the open spoil quickly; mold forms on clothing, food, books— on almost anything that is not tightly sealed; and metals rust much more rapidly than in the temperate zone. Before the era of refrigerator ships and cars, few products subject to decay could be transported through these regions without excessive loss. The high humidity further added to man's burden by increasing the sensible temperature and thus making the rainy season insufferably hot and enervating.

Soils. Contrary to the widely held idea that tropic soils are invariably rich and promise a never-ending productivity, the soils of most parts of the wet equatorial regions are relatively infertile and easily exhausted when measured by standards in America and Europe. Persistent rainfall and high temperatures break down the original silicate minerals and remove the soluble materials. The soils are thus poor in lime carbonate, potash, and phosphoric acid.[9] Most of the soils have been developed under a cover of arboreal vegetation and consequently contain a relatively small amount of organic matter (see pp. 98–99).

The constantly high temperatures, associated with the heavy tropical rains, have caused the development of lateritic soil types and in places even pure laterite (pp. 95, 98, and 99). The lateritic types are the most extensive.

Though the old soils of the rain forest are relatively infertile, the young soils are often quite productive. These young soils have developed in the relatively recent alluvial deposits found along the streams and in recent lava materials. Since many of the travelers in tropical rain forests have followed stream courses, many of them have emphasized the fertility of these young soils, and the extensive areas of typical mature and infertile lateritic soils have received less attention.

Some of the most notable examples of young soils are well illustrated in Java. This island, widely known for its productive planta-

---

[8] Since air at 90° F. holds, when saturated, about eight times as much moisture as air at freezing, the equatorial belt always carries a large amount of moisture.

[9] Twenty-six samples of soil and subsoil taken from widely separated areas in the Amazon Valley failed to show a trace of lime carbonate or any other carbonate.

tions, supports approximately 42,000,000 people on an area less than the size of New York State, and in addition the Javanese produce an agricultural surplus for export. The exceeding fertility of this island is a gift of its volcanoes, many of which are still active. Layer after layer of fertile volcanic ash has been spread over most of Java, making it the richest garden spot in the wet tropics and one of the most densely populated areas in the world.

NATURAL VEGETATION

The natural vegetation of the rainy low latitudes may be classified in two groups—the jungle and the rain forest. Along streams and ocean shores where sunlight can reach the ground the jungle predominates; in the interior of the forest the canopy of vegetation cuts off the sunlight to such an extent that the smaller plants may be choked out and the ground may be almost bare of undergrowth.

Under the influence of abundant heat and moisture, plant life is more profuse in the jungle of the rainy low latitudes than in any other part of the world. All these lowland regions, watered by daily showers during most of the year, are covered with a dense, broadleaf, evergreen forest which becomes an impenetrable forest jungle along the streams. Crowded in among the trees and sometimes almost concealing them is a riotous profusion of smaller vegetation, including shrubs, flowers, vines, and creepers. Parasitical growth, including many of the multicolored flowers, is especially common, and ferns hang like feathered ribbons from many of the branches. Lianas creep along the ground or climb to the tops of the highest trees, passing from one to another and forming an interlacing network. So intricate is the web of growth that the explorer has difficulty in distinguishing the various parts of a plant, often confusing leaves, flowers, and fruits of different species. Where the lowland jungles are rain-soaked throughout the year, the earth is often smothered by growing vegetation.

The true rain forest, on the other hand, has a thick stand of trees with a dense canopy of leaves that shade the ground. It may, however, be sufficiently free of undergrowth to permit paths to be opened with little effort.

The Amazon Basin contains the most extensive area of rain forest in the world (Fig. 76). From the mouth of the Amazon to the foot of the Andes, and from the upper branches of the Madeira to the forks of the Orinoco, all the country is forested except for occasional breaks

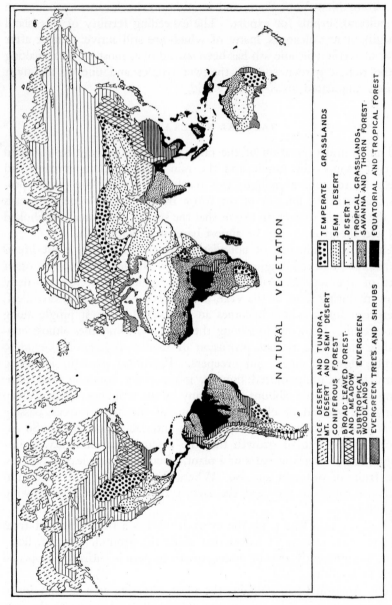

FIG. 76. Distribution of the natural vegetation of the world. (Taken from Philips' wall map, with modifications.)

of low-latitude grassland, such as those of the Venezuelan Campos. On the divides between the tributaries of the lower Amazon the forests give way to this same type of grassland.[10] The Amazon forest as a whole was designated by the Portuguese as the "silva," but it may be divided into three distinct types of forest as follows: (1) the coastal forests, which are for the most part composed of mangrove swamps; (2) the inundated forests, which occur on the alluvial flood plains of the Amazon and the major tributaries from Para to the foothills of the Andes, composed of comparatively few species, most of which are softwoods; and (3) the forests of the uplands (above flood levels), which are very rich in species, predominantly hardwoods which take a high polish.[11]

The silva of the Congo is very similar to that of the Amazon. In places the west African forest extends entirely to the coast, and wherever a river basin provides the proper moisture conditions (where the water table comes close to the surface) the silva also penetrates far back into the Sudanese grasslands. Where the seacoast is bordered with swamps, the tall forest disappears and tangles of mangrove predominate; where the coast is sandy, coconuts and oil palms thrive better than either the mangrove or the silva.

Late explorations indicate that an accurate natural vegetation map of the Congo Basin would probably show, not the wide expanse of uninterrupted forest which appears on some maps, but a series of forest belts along each of the major tributaries—long ribbons of true silvas following the tropical rivers far into the grassland. For a few miles on either side of the river there is a jungle growth, and farther towards the divide the jungle may open out into the typical "campos."

In east Africa, the East Indies, and the Malay Peninsula, the dense jungles and forests are broken in numerous places by plateaus and mountain ranges, the increase in altitude and better drainage producing a variety of vegetation types within a narrow zone. In parts of Java and Sumatra a walk of less than a mile may take one from the densest jungle into the open forest of the mountain side.

Utilization of the Tropical Forest. The rain forests abound in species which are useful to man for their lumber, nuts, fruits, and gums, but their exploitation has too often been difficult and expensive. Such

---

[10] See Vegetation Map of World, *Goode's School Atlas*, Rand McNally & Co., 1923, pp. 6–7.

[11] For a more detailed discussion of the nature of the Amazon forest, see Zon and Sparhawk, *Forest Resources of the World*, McGraw-Hill Book Co., 1923, Vol. II, pp. 692–700.

trees as the *Hevea brasiliensis,* the best wild rubber producer of the Amazon, are usually found deep in the forest, and the gatherer is compelled to open a path through the jungle to each tree. Most of the fruits, nuts, and fibers are obtained with equal difficulty. Since streams are the only traffic routes in most of the tropics, the natives usually limit their forest utilization activities to areas closely bordering the rivers where boats can be used. Paths are opened into the interior only when there is some unusual inducement.

As a source of lumber the wet tropics have been quite unimportant up to the present time. The only woods that have entered to any considerable extent into the export trade have been cabinet woods, dyewoods, and others used for fine interior decorations. These have for the most part been desired because of their extreme hardness, richness of color, fineness of texture, or simply because they are rare. Usually such trees are widely scattered through the forest. This practice of using only a few species, and those among the least abundant, has made logging operations exceedingly difficult and expensive. The problem of developing the forest industries has been further aggravated by inadequate transportation facilities, the lack of suitable beasts of burden, and the scarcity of labor. In addition, many of the cabinet woods are so hard that the felling of the trees and the cutting of the logs constitute laborious tasks, especially in these hot, humid lands where men cannot endure hard labor for any protracted period of time. All these factors, together with others such as mud, floods, insect pests, and unsanitary conditions, have tended to make lumbering costs prohibitive. In the past it has often been a more simple task to import lumber from the temperate zone than to get it from the surrounding forests.

Because of the numerous handicaps to tropical forestry, the idea has prevailed that these great forests can never become an important source of construction timber or other woods which may be substituted in a large way for the hardwoods and softwoods of the northern hemisphere; and that whatever hard timber they produce must inevitably be extremely expensive because of excessive costs of forest operations. Progress is now being made in overcoming many of the difficulties listed above. As a result, lumbering is soon to find an important place among tropical industries. Just as the development of tropical agriculture had to await the aid of science, so progress in the forest industries is likely to be slow until these industries are scientifically conducted. Fortunately, the Philippine Islands afford an excellent laboratory for American study, and the Congo Basin is well suited for similar study by Europeans.

The forest service of the Philippine Islands made a survey of the more accessible forests and found more than 2,500 tree species. It learned, however, that 20 species constituted 80 per cent of the stand. Unfortunately the majority of these 20 species were not popular in the market. The woods were brought to the attention of the local and world markets and within a few years many timber concessions were granted to Americans, British, Filipinos, Chinese, and other nationals for the development of lumber industries.

The development of tropical forestry is encouraged by the rapid depletion of temperate zone forests. Although substitutes for forest products are being found continuously, new uses are also being created, so that the total demand on our forests do not decrease. Already the enormous reserves of the tropics are being carefully studied. According to recent estimates, Brazil alone contains 3,400 billion board feet of standing timber and other regions of the tropical rain forest contain many more billion feet. No other climatic realm has such great forest resources or forest potentialities.

Since some of the valuable softwoods of tropical forests grow very rapidly it is entirely possible that, sometime in the future, softwood plantations may be developed and become of commercial importance. The start has already been made in the "balsa plantations" of Ecuador.

Balsa, the lightest wood known to man, is found almost everywhere in the tropics, but the product of commerce now comes largely from the plantations of Ecuador. The trees grow to heights of 70 or 80 feet with trunks 3 or 4 feet in diameter. The wood, half as heavy as cork, weighs only 5 to 7 pounds to the cubic foot. Imagine a 20-foot timber 12 inches square which weighs only 120 pounds.

The first balsa was brought into the United States in 1911, but the demand for the product was limited as the wood sold for $250 a thousand board feet. Then came World War I with a large demand for balsa regardless of price. Balsa rafts were installed on the crowded army transports in place of lifeboats. Enough balsa rafts to support 450 men could be stowed in the space formerly occupied by one lifeboat, which could carry only 30 or 40 men.

New uses for balsa are being found constantly and the demand for it is increasing. Since balsa is light and strong it is being used in increasing quantities for the manufacture of boxes and crates to be used in shipping expensive goods that must pay high transportation costs per pound. It is also used for the manufacture of life preservers, swimming belts, submarine-mine floats, and pontoons. Balsa is also famous for its insulating properties and is used in the manufacture of refrigerator equipment. Because of its extreme lightness and strength combined with its sound- and vibration-absorbing qualities, the inside walls in the passenger compartments of many commercial planes are made of this wood.[12]

Many other plants of the tropical forest are useful to man for their fibers, gums, spices, fruits, nuts, and oil seeds. The tendency is to cultivate them in plantations rather than seek them in the forest. These tree crops are discussed under plantation agriculture (pp. 191–197).

NATIVE ANIMAL LIFE

Our present limited knowledge of the equatorial forest apparently makes it unsafe to generalize, except in a broad way, concerning the amount of animal, bird, and insect life to be found there. Jungle fauna is far from being uniform throughout these regions, nor is it as abundant as many naturalists have inferred from following one tropical stream while the back forest is left entirely unexplored. One traveler will write at length of the bands of monkeys and the teeming bird life encountered along one of the sluggish low-latitude rivers; the next will comment on the almost entire lack of fauna in an apparently similar region. Many travelers speak of the lonely and oppressive silence of the rain forest—a silence unbroken for long periods except for an occasional splash in the streams or the humming of insects. It will be sufficient to say that in parts of these regions there is no great profusion of animal or bird life.

On the other hand, a considerable fauna does exist throughout the rainy low latitudes as a whole, and several distinct types are common to all these regions. Since grass is almost entirely lacking, grazing animals are rare. Among the species best adapted to the forest are those which subsist mainly upon nuts and fruits; the wild hog, the tapir, and the various members of the monkey family are representatives of this clan. Monkeys, especially, are numerous throughout forested Africa and in certain parts of the Amazon Basin.

The carnivorous group is also represented in the rain forest, the jaguar and the puma being the best examples. They are the particular enemies of the wild hog and the monkey.

[12] Banda C. Francisco, "Balsa Goes to War," *Agriculture in the Americas,* November 1943, pp. 211–214.

Bird life is exceedingly abundant; it varies from the tiny humming-
bird, little larger than a good-sized hornet, to powerful birds of
prey with a wing spread of 6 or 8 feet. Wood pigeons and thrushes
similar to those found in northern lands are among the smaller birds
common to these regions. Macaws with scarlet bodies and blue or
yellow wings, and equally gaudy parrots and paroquets, flit through
the jungle and add to its color and noise. In general, tropical bird
life like tropical flowers tends to unusual variety and brilliance of hue.

The streams contribute their share of tropical life also. During certain seasons, many forest tribes resort to the rivers and with net, trap,
or spear supplement their usual food supply with fish. Along the west
African coast where the swollen rivers run through swamps the natives
hunt the hippopotamus by means of pits or suspended spear traps.
The alligator or the crocodile is found in most equatorial streams, and
in the daytime may be seen along the banks or perched on a log in
the sun. Turtles frequent the African streams and are found to some
degree in the Amazon.[13] Serpent life is abundant, ranging in size
from the tiny water snake to the huge python or boa constrictor which
can quickly crush a large animal.

Insect life is one of the major annoyances of the rainy tropics.
White ants, or termites, swarm in both the eastern and the western
tropics; and the black ants sometimes enter homes or even villages in
such large numbers that the inhabitants are compelled to withdraw.
The multitude of winged insects includes the dangerous tsetse flies,
the mortal enemies of cattle and the cause of sleeping-sickness. There
are also found swarms of night-flying insects such as beetles, fire-
flies, gnats, and a number of rarer insects which are confined almost
wholly to the rainy tropics. The vampire bat is unique among night-
flying fauna. It subsists by sucking blood from the bodies of larger
mammals, including man, usually while the victim is asleep. The
myriads of mosquitoes are probably the most widespread and characteristic of all flying pests; they are also the most troublesome and
dangerous. Since the widespread areas of damp and dripping jungle
afford an ideal breeding place for these disease-carrying insects, they
are difficult to control.

Useful domestic animals have difficulty in surviving the insect pests
and disease germs; moreover, the natural vegetation is unsuitable as
food for most of these animals. Relatively few cattle, horses, and

---

[13] In some sections of the Amazon Valley the turtle is raised for its meat just
as we raise chickens.

sheep are found in the equatorial lowlands, and when imported the breeds usually deteriorate rapidly.[14] The water buffalo is used as a draft animal by the natives of the East Indies and the Malay Peninsula. In places, especially along the east coast of Africa, the mule is used, as he is more resistant to heat and requires less care than the horse. Pigs and chickens are the only other domestic animals which do well in these regions. Roast pork is one of the favorite meat dishes throughout the rainy tropics, and in certain parts of Africa the native feast is incomplete without two or three pigs roasting on spits over the open fire.

NATIVE MAN IN THE WET TROPICS

Each type of civilization has evolved through ages of trial and elimination and is largely the outgrowth of the attempts of a people, either consciously or otherwise, to adjust themselves to environment. The civilization of tropical forest peoples is no exception to this universal rule, and it is in many respects well suited to the living conditions found in the rainy low latitudes. Progress in the sense in which it is known in temperate climates has been retarded, not only by the enervating climate and the unhealthful conditions, but also by the very ease of existence. Life in the tropics is simple from a mere subsistence standpoint, all the actual necessities being obtained with a minimum of physical exertion. This, in turn, slows up the evolution of civilization, since man's advancement results largely from the spur of necessity.

Yet through the centuries those forest peoples have been building up a civilization for which, in the light of the white man's experiences, they deserve much praise. They have been gradually learning to make better use of their resources and to adjust their methods of living to their environment. One of the closest students of jungle peoples, John W. Vandercook, has said that the African jungle dweller of today is the result of just as many eons of steady change and development as the contemporary citizen of Manhattan. At present in

---

[14] "Meat in particular is hard to obtain, for the tsetse flies do not permit cattle raising and were it not for the game there would be nothing. Beween Lake Tanganyika and the mouth of the Congo, a distance of more than two thousand miles, I did not see a single cow—barring a small herd of cattle which the fathers of one of the Catholic Missions have succeeded in raising at their station near Nouvelle Anvers—and only occasionally sheep and goats. Wild pigs are fairly plentiful. . . ." Alexander Powell, *The Map That Is Half Unrolled*, The Century Co., 1925. (Reprinted by permission of publisher.)

the west African interior one finds a society almost as complicated, in its elusive way, as ours. This African culture need not bear any particular resemblance to that of the northlands. It is only natural that there should be many differences in the customs and folkways of peoples who live in entirely different environments and differ racially in so many respects. In the same way that environment has given the equatorial-forest man food, clothing, and shelter which differ markedly from those most common in cool climates, so has it given him a different philosophy of life. A carefree, easy-going existence is valued more in the tropics than in temperate lands.

Tropical Forest Peoples Primarily Farmers

The popular idea of tropical-forest peoples is that they are hunters who live off the fruits, nuts, and game of the forest. It is likely that they have passed through the hunting stage just as the peoples of western Europe have done, but today they are supported primarily by agriculture. Yet there are exceptions to this method of living: in the broad Amazon Basin there still remain Indian tribes that have scarcely reached the agricultural stage, tribes that are ignorant and without ambition. They eke out a scanty living from the food supplies of the streams, from nuts and fruits of the forest, from game animals such as the peccary, monkey, and sloth, and from a few vegetables which require little or no cultivation. This condition is the exception, however, and in both the Amazon and the Congo valleys agriculture is the main support of the natives. They may fish at times, and gather fruit and nuts—primarily to supplement the agricultural products.

The securing of food is a simple matter, and yet it is the most difficult task that the natives have to perform. The other requirements of life—of mere existence—are few: little clothing is needed, houses are quickly and easily built from local materials, and the average native is too debilitated to strive for the luxuries of civilization. Hunger is the prime and constant spur which arouses the native to useful labor. He has learned that the farm (small clearing) affords the largest and safest food return for the effort expended and has, accordingly, developed an agricultural system of the simplest kind—a system requiring the minimum of labor and equipment.

The Milpa System. Milpa agriculture is characterized by the planting of crops in temporary clearings. Instead of keeping the same land under cultivation year after year, new clearings are cut and burned for planting, and clearings of previous years are abandoned to the wild vegetation. Doubtless the utter simplicity of the system has kept it from being recognized as an excellent adaptation of primitive agriculture to tropical-forest soils which are easily exhausted and yield poor crops after a few years' cultivation.[15] The system is found in every rain forest region. It is used by primitive tribes in the cultivation of upland rice in tropical Asia, it is the common method of cultivating many crops in central Africa, and it is the system in most common use among the Indian tribes of the Amazon Valley.

Milpa agriculture is not only well adapted to the soils, but it is also well suited to the needs of a primitive people, since little labor and equipment are needed. The ax or cutlass is the only tool necessary. Tribes that did not have effective cutting implements felled or girdled the trees by building fires around them. Clearing the land is the hardest part of the work. After this, man, or more likely woman, carries on the agriculture in the simplest fashion.

Such a system is best suited to small communities. In the Congo Valley most of the agricultural villages situated between 6° north and 6° south consist of fewer than thirty huts, and settlements of eight or ten are not uncommon. These villages are invariably built along the streams, as no other water-supply systems are known to the natives.

Major Crops

Plantain. The plantain (a kind of banana with fruit larger, less sweet, and more starchy than the ordinary commercial banana) is one of the most important crops of the wet tropics. In some areas it is the chief support of the natives. This fact is well illustrated in southeastern Uganda, where in several provinces plantain occupies more than twice as much land as all other food crops combined. A few years ago its dominance was even greater and in some provinces it occupied more than 85 per cent of the land cultivated in food crops. Still earlier reports indicate that in certain sections it was grown to the exclusion of all other food crops. In writing about this region, Sir Harry Johnson says that many natives never eat anything but plantain pulp.

---

[15] On certain of the volcanic soils of Java, the Spice Islands, and other East Indian islands the soils are rich in mineral fertilizers and yield many crops before they become greatly depleted.

Where the plantain tree bears well it affords a reliable food supply throughout the year with the minimum amount of labor. After the land is cleared and the plants are started, they continue to yield fruit year after year. When a tree begins to grow it soon makes side-shoots which are well developed by the time the fruit of the parent tree is ripe. Thus until the soil becomes depleted the food supply of the family is assured, unless the rains fail or the locusts destroy the crop. During the drier seasons no care is given to the plantain gardens except that of merely cutting the fruit; when the rains come the weeds must be kept down in order that the crops may thrive.[16]

Since the plantain tree yields throughout the entire year, many of the natives make no provision for the future food supply, unless it is to dry a little fruit. As a result, in those areas where the natives depend almost wholly on plantain, any failure of the crop brings on famine. When the dry season lasts more than two months the plantain yield decreases or may fail entirely. Fortunately, the roots of the trees, which contain nourishment, may be eaten by the natives to help tide them over such periods. Yet in certain sections of the Congo Basin, where plantain is the main support of the people, any failure of this crop is disastrous, and the resultant malnutrition and starvation, combined with pestilence, have practically depopulated whole districts.

Cereals. Maize is another excellent agricultural crop for these hot, wet lands. It can be planted in the deadened forests by means of no other implement than a sharpened stick; it will yield a fair crop with little or no care; it may be left standing in the field for a considerable time after it is ripe without excessive deterioration; and the grain keeps fairly well under conditions of heat and moisture.

Another cereal well suited to tropical forest agriculture is rice. It is a hardy cereal and will thrive with little cultivation. In parts of Sierra Leone and the Belgian Congo the crop receives no attention after planting until near harvest time, when the children are required to keep the birds from the fields. The rapid growth and great nutritive value of rice make it pre-eminently suited to cultivation on a small scale. A patch of a few acres will feed a village for a year. Bananas, nuts, and other tree crops require little attention after clearings are once made and the trees planted. No cultivation is necessary, but the other vegetation must be hacked down from time to time.

[16] A more complete discussion of the importance of plantain cultivation is given by John Roscoe in *The Burganda, Their Native Customs and Beliefs*, The Macmillan Co., 1911.

Minor Crops

A score or more of other crops, such as cassava, yams, sweet potatoes, sugar cane, peas, beans, and pumpkins, are of considerable importance, especially in those regions where native agriculture is most
highly developed. In most parts of the wet tropics, however, these
crops are of minor importance as compared with plantain and cereals
—corn and rice.

HOMES OF NATIVE PEOPLES

Throughout the world the house (home) is the most commonplace
and at the same time one of the most significant of man's creations; it
serves as a living place where the family is united, a social center, a
shelter from the elements, and a protection against man and beast.
To the geographer and the sociologist it is doubly significant in that
it often reflects the direct adjustment of man to his environment.

In the temperate zone, for example, a house must be built to retain
warmth; among the wandering nomads of the desert a house must be
light and easily transported from one place to another. Neither of
these functions is important in the forest-covered rainy low latitudes.
In its simplest form the functions of a tropic house are protection
from rain and shelter from the direct rays of the sun. If at the same
time the house is so constructed that it provides for an easy circulation of air, the heat and humidity become more bearable. Thus, the
typical abode of equatorial-forest peoples consists of a light framework
of poles, supporting a heavy thatched roof made of layers of over-
lapping leaves or of broad-bladed grass; the sides of the house may be
open or there may be side walls of loosely woven materials or of poles
daubed with a layer of mud. Such houses are well suited to the region: they are easy to construct, the forest provides an abundance of
building materials, and the thatched roof is an excellent shield from
the sun and a fair protection from the rain (Figs. 77 and 78).

Throughout most of the wet tropical regions the soil is damp, sour,
and unhealthful; in places the natives are troubled by numerous reptiles and wild beasts. In many areas it is a common practice to provide against these unpleasant conditions by placing the houses high
off the ground, on stakes or piles. These elevated houses are situated
not only along the shores of the lakes in Venezuela, near the coasts
of many of the Philippine and East India Islands, and in the lowlands

of the Amazon, Congo, and other river valleys where the floodwaters are common, but they are also found on the uplands of Borneo and the Philippines.

FIG. 77. A typical native shamba of southern Uganda surrounded by fields of plantain, peas, and sweet potatoes. (Courtesy U. S. Department of Agriculture.)

FIG. 78. Note that some of the "modern houses" are being constructed with more light and air space. (Courtesy U. S. Department of Agriculture.)

GOVERNMENT

Practically all the rainy low latitudes are governed by temperate-zone peoples who have not considered the natives capable of governing themselves according to modern standards. Most natives have been submissive peoples who have offered little resistance to the control of the whites. The underlying cause of indolence and ignorance are difficult to dispel in these enervating, disease-ridden regions. The whites, on the other hand, are continuously arriving fresh from invigorating climates with a reserve of physical and mental energy. Under such conditions, their leadership is inevitable.

The whites, unable to appreciate fully the deep-seated causes for the lassitude of the natives, complain of their shiftless habits. Temperate-zone peoples, being capable and aggressive but unwilling to engage in hard manual labor in these hot wet regions, place the drudgery on the natives who produce rubber, hardwoods, oils, and food to help supply the growing needs of an industrial world. The situation as it has existed during the past century has been aptly expressed as follows: "The whites rule; the natives work."

During recent years, however, an increasing number of natives are demanding home rule. The Atlantic Charter, the Dumbarton Oaks Conference, and the United Nations conferences have aroused hopes in the minds of many of these peoples for a higher degree of self-government in the world of tomorrow. The Filipinos have already been given complete freedom, and an increasing degree of self-government is being granted to natives of the Netherlands East Indies. Yet many difficult problems remain to be solved before the guiding hand of temperate-zone peoples can be safely withdrawn from the government of the peoples of the rainy low latitudes.[17]

Conclusion. The natives are still "children of the forest." They are developing, but the progress is slow. After carefully studying their environment one scarcely knows whether they are more deserving of condemnation for their backwardness or of praise for their accomplishments. Man advances and civilization evolves through physical and mental activity; but idleness and dullness are forced upon the natives by the enervating climate; by diseases such as hookworm, malaria, dysentery, and tropical fevers which sap the vitality of the population; and by the ease of obtaining the few necessaries of existence. As a result no masterful peoples nor high degree of civilization has ever been developed in the tropical forest.[18] The natives have,

[17] See John Wesley Coulter, "Impact of the War on South Sea Islands," *Geographical Review*, July 1946, pp. 418–419.

[18] The Maya civilization of Yucatan appears to be an exception, but some students believe that the climate of this region was more invigorating when the great temples of the Maya civilization were built.

however, made many adjustments of living conditions to suit the environment.

PLANTATION AGRICULTURE

The milpa system, well adapted to the needs of native agriculture, is not suited to the large-scale production of high-grade foods and industrial products demanded by peoples of the temperate zone. To meet these newer requirements a modern system of agriculture is being developed in which the unit is the plantation.

In some parts of the rainy low latitudes the plantations are manned by native workers but are owned and directed by more energetic and capable men from the north temperate zone. Such a system of plantation development is especially common in Malaya, the British East Indies, Ecuador, and in parts of Brazil. This dual interest in plantations (native labor and foreign ownership and control) has resulted in much dissatisfaction among the natives. They complain that the foreign landlords are interested primarily in profits rather than in the progress of the natives.

Although the plantation system has been developed with profits in mind, it has brought many blessings to the natives. Tropical peoples are in need of the capital, skill, and science that can best be supplied by the great industrial nations. The plantations, on the other hand, must be manned by willing and capable workers if profits are to be realized. Consequently, most plantation owners look after the simple comforts and the welfare of their laborers. In many parts of the tropics the foreign-owned plantations constitute the only sanitary and wholesome places in which to live. Capable doctors and nurses look after the laborers; engineers create sanitary zones; and hospitals have been erected in areas where but recently witch doctors carried on their pernicious practices while helpless victims died of diseases entirely unrecognized by the natives. Thus the foreign-owned plantations of the tropics have been of benefit both to the natives and to temperate-zone peoples. Their development has resulted in the improvement of health and the standard of living of the natives. At the same time the plantations have supplied industrial nations with rubber, tea, cacao, oils, and other useful products.

Since the early 1920's, native-owned plantations have been developed in great number. In west central Africa and in parts of the East Indies a large percentage of the plantations are owned, directed, and manned by natives. For example, the British have encouraged the natives of Nigeria and of other west African areas to develop their own cacao plantations. At the same time, the Dutch have fostered the development of rubber plantations by the natives of Netherlands East Indies.

The plantation has been developed solely for the production of commercial products. While the fang (milpa farmer) produces a few subsistence crops to satisfy his daily food requirements, the plantation specializes in a wide range of export crops to suit the more varied needs of the industrial world. The crops of the fang are consumed only in the home village, but the foods, fibers, oils, and gums of the plantation have become worldwide in their distribution.

Although the plantation agriculture of the wet tropics has been progressing gradually for more than 200 years, its rapid development is the work of the last few decades. Previous to 1900, Europeans had little knowledge of tropical products for which, as yet, there was little demand; neither had they learned to utilize the wet tropics successfully, and many of their attempts at exploitation had resulted in disaster. Under such conditions, progress was necessarily slow. As recently as 1890 the banana was a curiosity to millions of Americans; rubber was an expensive luxury seldom used by the ordinary man except, perhaps, as erasers; and quinine, chocolate, and coconuts were so expensive that they were purchased sparingly. These and many other products are now being grown cheaply and in abundance on tropical plantations and distributed to the consumers at a small fraction of their former cost. As a result the consumption has increased enormously. Since 1925, except as interrupted by World War II, more than a million tons of these products have been landed annually in American ports, and many of them have become commonplace in every community.

In examining the list of American imports we find that the major portion of the trade grows directly out of climatic differences between the temperate and torrid zones; yet the rapid rise of commerce is inseparably associated with other conditions. Among the most important of these are (1) the rapid growth of population in the north temperate zone, which has created an insatiable land hunger; (2) the discovery of many valuable uses for tropical gums, fibers, and oils, resulting in a tremendous stimulus to their production; (3) an improvement of transportation facilities, which has broadened the possibilities of commerce manyfold; and (4) the improvement of tropical sanitation methods, which has made the tropics more livable for the white man and has multiplied his opportunities for success.

Difference in climate is a fundamental and lasting basis of trade between the wet tropics and the colder regions of the north—a basis which cannot be altered by man. No amount of education or skill can qualify man to grow bananas or cacao on the open plains of the spring wheat belt, or hevea rubber on the fertile farms of the American corn belt which lie wide open to the cold northern blasts. Neither is it likely that the natives of the tropical forest will ever manufacture the great variety of fabricated articles which they now procure from the great industrial centers situated in more stimulating climates. An exchange of products along north-south lines will always be essential in rounding out the development of both the tropical and temperate regions.

The introduction of steam navigation was of major importance in widening the opportunities for tropical development and has been indispensable to the rapid growth of the plantation. The sailing vessel was slow at best, and the time required to pass through the equatorial calms was always uncertain. In the oppressive stillness of the air the sails might idle for days. Only non-perishables could be shipped through the hot, humid calm belt by this uncertain method. Today, subject to interruptions caused by war, the swift and reliable refrigerator ship carries the most perishable plantation products to the distant markets of Europe and America, where they are delivered to the consumer with the minimum of deterioration.[19]

Rubber—The Leading Plantation Crops of the Tropical Rain Forest Realm

Rubber has become indispensable to modern civilization, both in the constructive pursuits of peace and in the destructive pursuits of war. Before the outbreak of World War II, the output of natural rubber exceeded 1,000,000 tons annually, and this elastic product was used in the manufacture of more than 50,000 articles.

Sources of Rubber. Prior to 1910, almost the entire supply of rubber was obtained from the *Hevea brasiliensis*, a tree native to the Amazon Valley. The product was called wild rubber. However, early in the twentieth century it was discovered that the wild rubber

---

[19] Bananas shipped to the World's Fair in Philadelphia in 1876 were carefully wrapped in expensive tinfoil in order to prevent decay, and even then the loss was excessive. Today, by the aid of refrigerator ships and cars, bananas are transported to the most distant American communities, and the percentage of loss is small.

could not supply the rapidly growing demand created by the automobile industry; consequently, rubber plantations were developed in
southeastern Asia and in the East Indies (Fig. 79). These Oriental
plantations supplied 95 to 97 per cent of the world's rubber requirements during the few years before the start of World War II. After
most of these Oriental plantations were taken over by the Japanese
in 1942, the western world was compelled to depend on synthetic

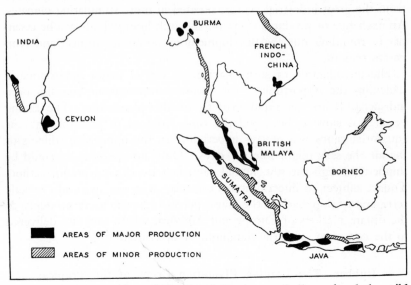

Fig. 79. Plantation rubber of the East has now practically replaced the wild
rubber of Brazil.

products and on scrap as major sources of rubber. With the return
of peace, natural rubber production is once again increasing, with an
estimated output of 790,000 tons in 1946 as compared with a production of 900,000 tons of synthetic rubber during the same year.

Conditions Suitable for Hevea brasiliensis. The tree which yields
most of the rubber of commerce is the *Hevea brasiliensis*. This tree
produces best in areas having high temperatures throughout the year,
a well-distributed rainfall of 60 inches or more annually, and a rich,
deep, loamy soil which is well drained. All attempts to grow *Hevea
brasiliensis* on a commercial scale on the outer margins of the tropical
zone have failed, and practically all the present and projected plantations are within 10° of the equator. The native rubber trees of the

Amazon Valley attain their best development on the uplands drained by the Beni, Madre de Dios, Acre, the upper Jurua, the upper Purus, and parts of the southern tributaries of the Madeira and of the lower Amazon. Likewise, plantations have succeeded better on the uplands than on the flood plains. Fertile land should be chosen for plantations, and even then the soil deteriorates rather rapidly during the years of tapping for latex.

Plantation Rubber versus Wild Rubber. During recent years, practically the entire supply of natural rubber has come from plantations, and the output of wild rubber has been negligible. The transplanting of the rubber tree from the forest to the field made it possible (1) to reduce greatly the labor of gathering the latex, (2) to take advantage of the cheap and abundant labor supply of the more densely populated parts of the tropics, (3) to locate the industry near good transportation facilities, and (4) to provide for scientific development and control of the plantations.

There are no solid stands of rubber trees in the native forests. The rubber gatherer must laboriously open long paths from tree to tree and must trudge for miles each day through mosquito-infested swamps to gather a few pounds of latex. He spends the season in some isolated region where in case of sickness he must be his own physician and depend upon his own limited supplies of medicines. All these adverse conditions have been overcome or mitigated in the plantation. There the trees are planted only a few steps apart, and the gatherer is never far from his base of operation; the foreign owners have taken great pains to improve the health conditions by draining the marshy places and by providing medical attention and hospital care; many of the natives are treated for hookworm and other tropical diseases; and, above all, the laborers who are suffering from malaria are completely isolated from mosquitoes so that the disease may not be transmitted to others. Such operations have paid big dividends by making it easy to secure laborers, by keeping them contented, and by making them physically fit to do a good season's work (Fig. 80).

Fortunately the rainy low latitudes of the Far East not only support a large population, but also they are situated close to the most densely populated parts of the world. When the rubber planter finds it difficult to secure sufficient laborers locally, he can easily bring in workers from the overpopulated lands of India and China. This situation contrasts sharply with labor conditions in the great forests of the Amazon, where some of the best native rubber-growing areas are almost without native peoples and are long distances from a cheap and efficient labor supply suitable for import.

The great rubber plantations of the Orient are conveniently situated near the coast and along one of the world's greatest highways, whereas the best wild rubber sections of both the Congo and the Amazon basins are hundreds or even thousands of miles inland, and some of the districts are remote from safe transportation routes.

Fig. 80. Most of the world's supply of natural rubber is now produced in carefully tended plantations where much attention is given to sanitation. (Courtesy U. S. Department of Agriculture.)

The chief aim of the rubber planter like that of the dairyman is to produce good milkers. The need for improvement along this line is indicated by the fact that in many plantations 75 per cent of the latex is produced from 30 per cent of the trees. Many trees are not paying for their keep and are described as "boarders." To improve this condition the scientist is indispensable. The plant breeder is replacing unprofitable trees with good producers by carefully selecting seed or by budding from choice trees. The pathologist, entomologist, and ecologist are also rendering greater service to the planters in their efforts to increase the acreage yield of latex. None of these scientists can be of much service in improving conditions within the native forests.

In the years preceding World War II, more than 96 per cent of the world's natural rubber output came from the plantations of the Orient (Fig. 81). This emphasis on rubber production in the Orient is based on the abundant labor supply, favorable climatic conditions, fertile soils, good drainage, and excellent commercial location that the region

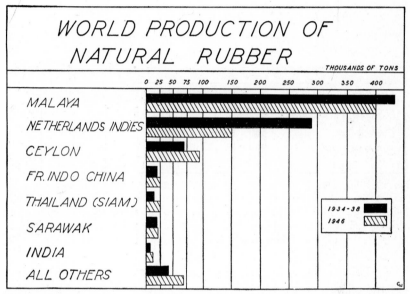

Fig. 81. The export of natural rubber made a quick recovery after the close of World War II. Those countries that were not occupied by the Japanese military forces during World War II have surpassed their prewar exports. Few of the rubber plantations were destroyed and exports of natural rubber will soon surpass the million-ton mark again, provided that there is sufficient demand.

affords. It also depends on the foresight of the British and Dutch planters and on scientific methods of development.

Plantation Rubber versus Synthetic Rubber. Although the United States had produced only a small amount of synthetic rubber prior to 1940, this product became our primary supply of rubber during World War II. Now we manufacture several different kinds of synthetic rubber which have special qualities planned in advance, some of them being far superior to natural rubber for special purposes. Certain types of synthetic rubber are far more resistant than the natural product to oil; others show greater elasticity at low temperatures. Soaked in 100-octane aromatic gasoline, synthetic rubber swells only slightly, whereas natural rubber swells several hundred per cent and loses its usefulness. Inner tubes made of Butyl are as durable as those made of natural rubber and hold air ten times better.[20]

Because of the numerous uses of synthetic rubber, it will be a complement to, and also a competitor of, natural rubber (Figs. 81 and 82).

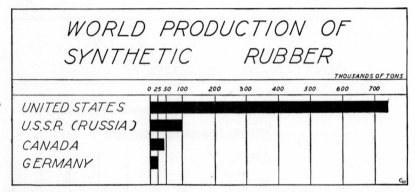

Fɪɢ. 82. The world production of synthetic rubber in 1946 was approximately 900,000 tons and surpassed the world production of natural rubber—approximately 790,000 tons. The relative qualities of the two products, together with competitive and political conditions, will determine the relative amounts of each type of rubber that will be produced in the future.

The relative amounts of each produced yearly will be determined by: (1) the relative cost price, and (2) the relative merits of each product for specific uses.

Outlook for Plantations. The future importance of rubber plantations will depend upon the total world demand for rubber, and also upon the percentage of this demand satisfied by each type of rubber —natural and synthetic. The success of plantation methods in the cultivation of the rubber tree is no longer open to question; plantation rubber ranks high in both quality and quantity. The Orient has a large percentage of land suited to the expansion of plantation agriculture. Consequently, the future of natural rubber is bright in so far as the advantages for production are concerned. Any shortage of supply of this valuable commodity is likely to be temporary, except in times of war.

[20] *Rubber from Oil*, Standard Oil Company of New Jersey, New York City, p. 24.

Cacao

The cacao tree, like the rubber tree, is native of South America. It has been transplanted to other parts of the wet equatorial realm, and like rubber it also has become a profitable plantation crop. From the cacao beans, which grow in pods attached directly to the trunk or larger branches of the tree, are made those very wholesome foods of commerce—cocoa and chocolate. These products have the exceedingly valuable property of keeping for a long time in hot, moist

Fig. 83. Major cacao-producing regions of the world.

climates without becoming rancid. Even the bean after being thoroughly dried will keep indefinitely, and at times it has passed as currency in parts of South and Central America just as did tobacco in Virginia in colonial days.

The cacao tree begins to bear in the fifth or sixth year, but the pods of such young trees are small and scarcely repay the efforts to gather them. The tree does not come into full bearing until it is about twelve years old; it continues near its prime for twenty-five or thirty years, after which the yield begins to decline. Like the acreage of other tree crops that of cacao cannot be adjusted annually to meet the changes in demand. As a result, overproduction and low prices are not uncommon. At such times, many thousand tons of fruit rot on the trees, especially in plantations somewhat remote from good transportation facilities, where the cost of marketing the crop may be prohibitive when the price of cacao is low.

Environmental Requirements Exacting. The cacao tree requires constantly high temperatures and an abundance of moisture. The tree can survive the cool temperatures of the poleward margins of the torrid zone, yet it does not bear well in these higher latitudes, and consequently most of the commercial crop is grown within 12° of the equator. The tree does not flourish where the temperature falls below 60° F., yet it suffers from exposure to the direct rays of the sun, and hence is grown mostly in the shade of other trees. Much moisture and a deep, fertile soil are essential to a good yield. Thus most of the

Fig. 84. Drying cacao at Nsawam, Gold Coast Colony. (Courtesy U. S. Department of Agriculture, photograph by Justus A. C. Holm.)

plantations are on coastal plains or river-bottom land. Desiccating winds reduce the yield, and strong winds injure the pods. It is necessary, as a result, to restrict commercial plantations to the belt of equatorial calms or to valleys which are protected from the winds. Clearings in the tropical forest afford the best situations, as the forest acts as a windbreak (Fig. 83).

Growth of the Industry. Although cacao was introduced into Europe about 1520, its production at that time was a Spanish monopoly, and only the wealthy could afford to use it. As late as 1806, Humboldt estimated the entire European consumption at less than 12,000 tons. By 1935–1939, the average annual world production had reached 701,000 tons. During World War II the production decreased markedly owing to transportation problems and to the fact that much of Europe was cut off from the sources of supply.

In normal times the United States leads the world as a consumer of cacao, with more than 40 per cent of the world's annual crop coming to our shores. The countries of northwest Europe take most of the remainder.

Fig. 85. Loading cacao at the beach, Accra, Gold Coast Colony. Here labor is cheap and abundant. (Courtesy U. S. Department of Agriculture, photograph by Justus A. C. Holm.)

The rapid increase in the use of cacao is due to a number of factors, among the most prominent of which are (1) economic production in plantations, making it possible to reduce the retail price to such an extent that it is within the means of the poorer classes; (2) an increase in the purchasing power of the masses; (3) a more general recognition of the value of cacao as a food; and (4) improvement of methods of preparation by which it is adapted to the wants of the different classes of consumers. The introduction of the cacao tree into west Africa and neighboring islands where labor is plentiful and cheap was another stimulus to the industry (Figs. 84, 85, and 86). The rapid increase in the consumption of cacao products within the United States came with the introduction of the soda fountain in the 1880's.

Fig. 86. Plucking cacao pods from the cocoa trees, Gold Coast Colony. (Courtesy U. S. Department of Agriculture, photograph by Justus A. C. Holm.)

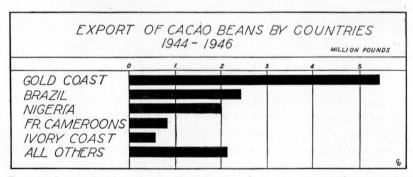

Fig. 87. International trade in cacao dropped from an average of 1,554,000,000 pounds for 1935–1939 to 870,000,000 pounds in 1942. However the cacao plantations were not destroyed and, by 1946, trade in the beans had reached almost the prewar level. The export for 1946 was 1,431,000,000 pounds. (Courtesy U. S. Department of Agriculture.)

Native versus Foreign Plantation. Most of the cacao crop of South America is grown on large plantations owned and managed by foreigners. This condition exists especially in Ecuador, where the ha-

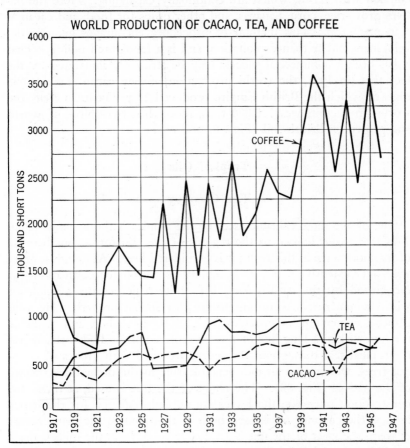

FIG. 88. The production of coffee, which is grown primarily outside the war-ravaged zones of Eurasia, had practically regained its prewar status by 1945. Tea production will recover more slowly.

cienda of 300,000 trees is the ordinary size and there are at least two plantations with more than 2,000,000 trees each. The small plantation owned and operated by the native is the exception. In west Africa the method of production is quite different. There the British have encouraged the natives to develop their own plantations, which vary in size from a fraction of an acre to many acres. The industry has spread to all parts of west Africa that are suited to cacao and that have transportation facilities permitting profitable export. Since the introduction of cacao, the forests of the Gold Coast have been honeycombed with farms, which are continually expanding. Here the natives grow rice, corn, bananas, and other crops for food, and cacao as a money crop. This method of procedure encourages genuine development rather than exploitation, and is a far-sighted policy. That it has been a commercial success may be strikingly illustrated by the fact that, in 1905, the world production of raw cacao was 141,000 tons, of which the British Empire produced 23 per cent; in 1946, the world production was 717,000 tons, more than two-thirds of which was grown on British soil (Figs. 87 and 88).

Tropical Oils

The Coconut

One of the most valuable trees of the tropics is the coconut palm. This tree is not limited to the regions of the rain forest, but because of its importance in this realm it is considered here. Although it grew wild over extensive areas, its suitability as a crop for cultivation was recognized by the natives long before its fruit became a staple of world commerce. According to an East Indian proverb, "He who plants a coconut palm provides food, clothing, shelter, and medicine for himself and a long line of posterity after him." Today the shores of tropical seas throughout the world are lined with groves of coconut trees, which play an indispensable role in the domestic economy of the natives (Fig. 89). The trunk of the tree is used, at times, for construction purposes; the leaves are needed as thatch for the native houses; the coconut oil is used both as food and in the manufacture of soap; the meat of the nut is a valuable food; from the milk is made a wholesome drink, and also an intoxicating one; from the shell are made household utensils such as spoons, bowls, and dishes; and from the fibrous covering surrounding the shell are manufactured rope and mats. Some 10,000,000 gallons of beverages made from coconut milk are consumed annually in the Philippine Islands alone. The local importance of the coconut as a human subsistence crop is indicated by the large consumption in Java. Although the Javanese export from 60,000 to 150,000 tons of copra and coconut oil annually, it is estimated that about as much is used at home—an amount equal to 4 to 10 pounds per capita.

Fig. 89. (a) A coconut plantation; (b) coconuts being cut open and spread in the sun to dry (manufacture of copra); (c) floating coconut rafts to market; and (d) coconut seedlings being grown for transplanting.

The Coconut as a Commercial Crop. About the middle of the last century, when Europeans were beginning to manufacture soap in large quantities, attention was directed to the possibilities of using vegetable oils as well as animal fats. One of the cheapest and most available of these is found in the fruit of the coconut palm growing in relative abundance on tropical shores within easy reach of trading vessels. European traders began to range the tropical seas buying copra—the dried meat of the coconut—from the natives and encouraging the production of additional supplies. The coconut soon became a standard money crop and has held an important position in native plantation agriculture ever since.

Prior to World War II, the total annual production of coconuts in terms of copra probably exceeded 3,000,000 tons. Approximately two-fifths of the crop was consumed within the producing countries. Most of the remainder was exported to Europe and the United States.

The United States normally ranks first among the nations of the world both in the importation and in the use of coconut products. In prosperous peace years, nearly 500,000 tons of copra are required to supply enough coconut oil to meet our needs. Part of this supply is imported in the form of copra and part as oil.

The most important use of coconut oil is in the manufacture of soap. Of almost equal importance is its utilization in the margarine industry. In a number of European countries, where millions of people are too poor to buy butter, coconut oil is the mainstay of this industry, and it is of increasing importance in the manufacture of margarine in the United States. This nutritious and palatable, but cheap, butter substitute finds, therefore, a ready market. The copra cake, which remains after the oil is pressed out, is an excellent feed for dairy cows and other livestock. So important has copra become to the industrial nations of the temperate zone that more than 1,500,000 tons enter commerce annually (Fig. 90).

The most extensive coconut plantations are situated in the Philippine Islands, the East Indies, Malaya, and Ceylon, and these areas supply the major share of the copra which enters world trade. The supremacy of the Far East in coconut growing is largely a result of cheap and efficient labor. Otherwise this area is in no way superior to parts of Africa, South and Central America, and the West Indies, where millions of acres well suited to coconut cultivation now lie idle.

The native coconut industry is now advancing into the manufacturing stage, but, as is common within the tropics, the new development is the result of initiative and energy transferred from the temperate zone. During World War I, fats and oils were greatly needed in Europe. Partly in response to the cheap local labor supply and partly because shipping space was at a premium, a number of oil mills were erected in the leading copra-assembling centers of the Far East. By the end of the war the oil-pressing business was well established, and considerable quantities of coconut oil, soap, glycerine, and other man-

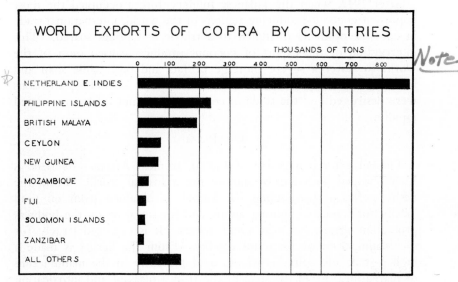

Note:

Fig. 90. Practicálly all the world's commercial copra is produced in southeastern Asia or in neighboring islands. What special advantages has this area for the production of coconuts? (*Vegetable Oils and Oilseeds*, Report of Imperial Economic Committee, His Majesty's Stationery Office, 1938.)

ufactured products are now being exported. These industries have been especially successful in the Philippine Islands, as is indicated by the export of coconut oil. On the other hand, since both the oil and the oil cake are used in the industrial world, there is little or no loss of shipping space by shipping copra instead of oil to the United States and northwest Europe. Moreover, since the manufacturing industries of the world tend to gravitate to regions of invigorating climate it is not surprising that most of the trade is in the semi-raw product, copra, rather than in the manufactured products such as oil, soap, and margarine. The quantity of coconut oil exported from the Netherlands is greater than that exported from the Netherlands East Indies (Fig. 90), but the Netherlands East Indies leads the world in the export of copra.

After World War I there was a revival of the oil-pressing industry in western Europe, and as a result the demand for copra in England, Holland, France, and Germany became so great that many of the mills of the East Indies had to close down. The possibility of successfully promoting manufacturing in the wet tropics, except in a very modest way, is still open to question.

After 1942, when the Japanese military forces occupied the most important coconut-producing regions of the world, international trade in coconut products dwindled to a trickle and prices soared. This interruption of the export of coconut products caused most of the world to suffer a severe shortage of fats and oils, while soap and butter substitutes were scarce. Relatively few coconut plantations were destroyed and the trade in copra and coconut oil has recovered rapidly.

OIL PALM

The oil palm is a native of humid, tropical Africa. Its fruit is highly valued both locally and by the industrial world. From the fleshy pericarp surrounding the kernels is obtained palm oil used locally for food, for lighting lamps, and for smearing on the body as protection against hot winds and insects. It is exported largely for the manufacture of soap and candles. From the kernel is made a higher-grade oil, palm-kernel oil, used primarily in the manufacture of margarine. From the stem of the fruit a pleasant and intoxicating palm wine is extracted. The trunk and leaves are used in building houses; the fiber, left after the oil has been extracted from the fruit, is mixed with clay and used as plaster, and the heart of the tree top furnishes a vegetable appetizing to the European palate.

Distribution of Palm-Oil Production. Until 1920, the entire supply of commercial oil-palm products came from the rain forests of west Africa, and in 1938, Nigeria produced approximately one-half of the world's supply of oil-palm products. The palm-oil belt of Nigeria lies in the region of heavy rainfall (50 to 70 inches), just back of the coastal swamp on well-drained soils.

The oil-palm industry is now developing, just as civilization has done, from the hunting stage to the agricultural, and the latter is decisively winning the palm-oil and palm-kernel trade. The agricultural stage of development was hastened by the recent increase in demands for fats. During World War I the shortage of animal fats accentuated the need for substitutes. The alert Dutch and British planters, just beginning to realize large profits from rubber plantations, seized this opportunity to experiment with the oil palm as a plantation crop. The results were so encouraging that, by January 1938, approximately 203,000 acres had been planted in Java and 72,143 acres in Malaya. In the Far East careful attention had been given to trees that give a high yield of oil rather than of palm kernels. By careful production a high quality of palm oil is prepared which is able to compete in the market for edible oils. Production of palm oil from these plantations rose rapidly so that, by 1937, the Netherlands East Indies ranked first among the palm-oil producing and exporting nations of the world, as shown by the table. The exports of palm

ESTIMATED PALM-OIL AND PALM-KERNEL EXPORTS FROM MAJOR PRIMARY PRODUCING COUNTRIES, 1937

	Millions of pounds		
Country	Palm oil	Palm kernels	Oil content of kernels
Netherlands East Indies	434	91	41
Nigeria	322	753	339
Belgian Congo	152	211	95
Malaya	96	16	7
French West Africa	44	180	81
Others	62	379	171

oil from the Netherlands East Indies and from Malaya were cut off during World War II or were deflected to Japan.

Plantation versus Native Oil-Palm Industry. The conditions under which the oil-palm industry is conducted in west Africa are in sharp contrast to those existing in the plantations of the Orient. The oil-palm industry of west Africa remains largely in the wild state or in small plantations. After a few hundred nuts are gathered they are laboriously transported on the heads of natives to the factories or to neighboring streams to be floated to factories. The oils are extracted by crude processes and sold to local merchants for export. As the oil is accumulated in small quantities from day to day, part of it becomes rancid before a sufficient quantity has been collected for export. Thus conditions in the native forest make for expensive and low-grade oils. In the better plantations, on the other hand, the palms are grown from carefully selected seed and the fruit is correspondingly of a high grade. The plantations are cultivated and kept clean. The palms, thus relieved of the necessity to struggle for light and air with competing vegetation, do not grow to great heights and the fruit is easily gathered. It is then transported by light rail or truck to modern mills where it is utilized while fresh and wholesome. Moreover, a larger percentage of the oil is recovered than by the native mills. Finally, the plantation is under scientific supervision, and an adequate supply of cheap and efficient Chinese labor is available.[21] Under such favorable conditions it seems inevitable that the plantation will sooner or later supplant the forest as the principal source of commercial oil-palm products. These plantations may in the future be largely native owned just as cacao plantations are. In order to encourage native planters the British are preparing to build modern mills at various places in west Africa. At first these mills will need to be supplied with nuts from the forests, but with good and reliable markets close at hand the natives will probably plant trees from year to year. Even though these native plantations be small, many consisting of only a few trees, it is believed that they will soon amount, in the aggregate, to many thousand acres. This is a sound method of development and is growing very rapidly in both Africa and the East Indies.

BANANA

The banana is not wholly a product of the rain forest. Some bananas are grown in the West Indies, along the west coast of India, and in other parts of the low-latitude wet-and-dry realm which is to be studied in Chapter 7. Since, however, more than 90 per cent of the world's banana crop is grown within the rainy low-latitude realm, the industry is studied here.

There are about seventy species of bananas. Some of these are known as plantains and are seldom eaten raw. In general, plantain constitutes one of the chief foods of the natives who live in the humid tropics. To the tropical natives this food is a substitute for the potatoes and bread that are consumed in such great quantities by the peoples of middle-latitude regions. Plantains are not in demand where potatoes are available.

Commercially, the most important of all species of bananas is the *Musa sapientum*, a large, smooth, yellow fruit of excellent flavor. Most of the bananas sold in the United States are produced from one of these species known as "Gros Michel" or "big mike." Another well-known banana is grown from the red Jamaica species.

The use of the banana as a food for man is far older than human history. The earliest home of the banana is presumed to have been

---

[21] The palm-producing districts are infested by the tsetse fly, which, together with the absence of fodder grasses, precludes the use of animals for transport.

in the humid tropical regions of southeastern Asia, where the armies of Alexander the Great found the fruit abundant in 327 B.C. Fortunately, the banana roots may be carried long distances and transplanted successfully even though the roots are left dry and given but little care. This fact made it possible for the slow-moving sailing vessel to carry the plant to all parts of the wet tropics for transplanting.

It is believed that the banana was established on the east coast of Africa by the traders who crossed the Indian Ocean during the first few centuries of the Christian era. With their traffic in ivory and slaves, the Arabs gradually carried the fruit from tribe to tribe across equatorial Africa to the Guinea Coast.

This valuable plant was probably carried across the Atlantic Ocean by a missionary about A.D. 1516, only a few years after the discovery of America. The fruit, in all probability, had never been cultivated in America, as is indicated by the fact that the ancient Indian tribes of the western hemisphere had no word for the fruit, nor did they leave among their records any pictures of it or references to it.

By the end of the sixteenth century the banana was being produced in practically all parts of the wet tropics and becoming one of the staple foods of the natives. The commercial development of the banana industry was delayed for two more centuries because of the perishable nature of the fruit and the slow methods of early transportation.

A few small cargoes of bananas reached the United States during the first half of the nineteenth century, and by 1885 the banana schooner was making frequent trips between Jamaica and Boston. But the large-scale development of the industry had to await the coming of the refrigerated ship.

Commercial Banana Production. The production and marketing of bananas constitute one of the most highly organized industries in the world. First a suitable region for banana culture must be found. Such a region should contain large areas of relatively level land; the soil should be deep and fertile, so that bountiful crops may be grown and removed year after year for a considerable period of time without the addition of commercial fertilizers. The climatic requirements for banana production are exacting. The temperatures should be high both day and night; the atmosphere should be humid; and a heavy rainfall well distributed throughout the year is essential. The location for the development of a banana plantation must also be given careful consideration. Ease of access to a good harbor is an absolute necessity in order that the fruit may be quickly marketed.

The selection of a suitable environment is only one of the many problems that must be solved by the successful commercial banana producer. An area suitable for banana culture may be exceedingly unhealthful for man. As a consequence, all banana-producing companies must struggle continuously to improve sanitary conditions for the laborers. The tasks of clearing the jungle, draining swamps, and controlling diseases keep engineers, doctors, and nurses always on the job.

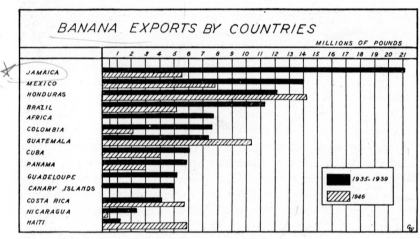

FIG. 91. Most of the world's commercial bananas are normally produced in the countries bordering the Caribbean Sea and in Brazil, tropical west Africa, and the Canary Islands. The industry was disrupted by World War II and in some areas had scarcely revived in 1946.

Since ripe bananas are perishable products they must be marketed quickly. This task necessitates the coordination of every operation of producing, gathering, transporting, and marketing the fruit in order that it may reach the consumer in a good state of preservation.

All things considered, the finest areas in the world for the large-scale commercial production of bananas are found in the lowlands bordering the Caribbean Sea, along the west coast of central Africa, and in the Canary Islands (Fig. 91). The west coast of Africa is relatively close to the European banana market which was growing rapidly prior to World War II. Consequently, African exports jumped from a few thousand bunches in 1934 to approximately 10,000,000 bunches in 1939. World War II practically destroyed this trade and it had not yet recovered to any considerable extent in 1946.

The Brazilian trade in bananas also increased rapidly between the two world wars. In 1924 Brazil exported only 3,879,000 bunches of bananas. However, by 1939 the exports had jumped to more than 12,000,000 bunches. World War II practically destroyed this trade, but improvement in ocean transportation since the war has stimulated the industry once more. By 1946 the exports exceeded 5,000,000

Fig. 92. A close-up view of a banana plantation. (Courtesy United Fruit Co.)

bunches and the acreage given to bananas along the eastern coast of Brazil was increasing rapidly. Bananas are also grown in Queensland, Australia, and some of them are marketed in Sydney and Melbourne. Java ships limited quantities to western Australia, and the Fiji Islands export the fruit in a small way to New Zealand.

Banana plants differ greatly in size and in yield. Those growing in rich river-bottom land, where the rainfall is heavy and the temperatures normally above 75° F., may reach heights of more than 30 feet. Such plants are grown in the best lands along the east coast of Central America. The average height of banana plants grown on the east coast of Central America is from 18 to 25 feet, but in Cuba, with its cooler winters, the normal height of the plant is only 12 to 15 feet. Likewise the heaviest and best fruit comes from Central America; most of the fruit grown in Cuba is lighter and less valuable.

Ideal Conditions for Banana Culture. The Atlantic Coast of Central America has some of the finest land for banana culture to be found anywhere. In this region, extending a few miles back from the Caribbean Sea, lies a fertile coastal strip with an elevation of less than 250 feet. Here both days and nights are hot, the air is humid, and the annual rainfall is 60 to 120 inches or even more. This land, which was once a tropical jungle of the densest kind, has now been transformed into the greatest banana-growing region of the world (Fig. 92).

THE RAINY LOW LATITUDES AS A HOME OF THE WHITE RACE

"The white man in the tropics" is a story filled with tragedy. A French force of 25,000 men in Santo Domingo was reduced to 3,000 in a single year by the ravages of yellow fever; railroad construction in certain of the lowlands of Costa Rica cost a human life for every rail; an English settlement in Sierra Leone was almost annihilated by disease in 1787; and the French were frustrated in their attempt to build a Panama Canal through the toll of life taken by malaria and yellow fever. The list of deaths, failures, and blighted enterprises might be extended indefinitely, but it is sufficient to note that several centuries of effort to colonize the rainy low latitudes have failed to produce a healthy third generation of whites within these regions. Europeans have been able to direct the natives in the exploitation of these hot, wet lands, but they have not succeeded as settlers, capable of carrying on the development by themselves.

Medical science has done much to overcome this terrible situation. Malaria, yellow fever, cholera, dysentery, plague, and beriberi may in time be blotted out, as science has discovered their causes and has provided the means of combating them with success. Malaria still takes a toll, however, of approximately 2,000,000 lives each year. This is only a small part of the loss, for as a rule it does not kill its victims quickly but saps their vitality and reduces their productive capacity. The fight against malaria is difficult and expensive, for the germ is carried by anopheles mosquitoes which are difficult to eradicate.

Tropical dysentery and hookworm, common to warm, hot lands, sap the vitality of the vast majority of the natives. These diseases breed in human filth and impure water and may be avoided through hygienic modes of living. It is difficult to teach the ignorant and careless natives to take these precautions, and disease spreads as much because of neglect as because of climate.

These diseases, though not highly fatal, result in a weakening of the victims which is responsible for the loss of will power, intemperance, and general physical and moral degeneration. It is not uncommon for three-fourths of the laborers of a community to be constantly ill with one of these maladies, and the drain is a frightful handicap to the progress of any community.

Many other handicaps, only indirectly related to climate, such as the abundant multiplication of microorganisms with their attendant evils of disease for both plants and animals, tendencies towards both physical debilitation and moral lapse, the distaste for physical exercise, and difficulty of obtaining a correct and balanced diet make normal and healthy living among the whites in the tropics a difficult problem. Most of these handicaps are subject to correction, yet, like tropical diseases, they are very real problems to white settlers and cannot be lightly dismissed.

If, however, sanitation is made comparable to that of the temperate zone, and if other indirect handicaps are overcome, there still remains the direct influence of tropical sun, heat, and humidity, which acts upon the white man's body and more particularly his nervous system in such a detrimental way as to bring about a debilitated neurasthenic condition. Thus the white man is confronted with difficult problems in every attempt to subdue the rainy low-latitude regions and to make them suitable for his permanent abode.

It appears that if the white man succeeds in making these wet, hot lands suitable as a permanent home he must regulate temperatures as well as sanitation. There is little hope that this can be done on a large scale. However, certain regions have an abundance of water power, and it may not be mere fancy to hope that some day the well-to-do farmer of the tropics may cool his home as easily as the farmer of the intermediate zone heats his. If the farmer could thus provide for himself a place of comfort where he could find relief from the tropical heat for 12 or 15 hours out of every 24 he might be able to endure the climate more successfully. After the several factors are considered, however, there seems to be little hope for a rapid and economic development of the rainy low-latitude regions by the white race. Small areas will undoubtedly be utilized more fully to raise rubber, cacao, palm oil, and other products most urgently needed by the industrial world, but the natives will continue to do the manual labor.

REFERENCES

AHERN, MAJOR G. P., "Tropical Hardwoods," *Bulletin American Union*, Tropical Plant Research Foundation, Washington, D. C., March 1927.

BRASS, L. J., "Stone Age Agriculture in New Guinea," *Geographical Review*, October 1941, pp. 555–569. (Excellent pictures.)

BRYANT, A. F., "Where Copra Is King," *Asia*, Vol. 34, September 1934, pp. 538–543.

CASE, EARL C., and DANIEL R. BERGSMARK, *Modern World Geography*, J. B. Lippincott Co., 1938, pp. 638–683.

COOK, O. F., "Milpa Agriculture," *Smithsonian Institution Report*, 1919, pp. 307–326.

CROWTHER, SAMUEL, *The Romance and Rise of the American Tropics*, Doubleday, Doran & Co., 1929.

DOBBY, E. H. G., "Settlement Patterns in Malaya," *Geographical Review*, April 1942, pp. 211–232. (Excellent pictures of the cultural landscape.)

EMENY, BROOKS, *The Strategy of Raw Materials*, The Macmillan Co., 1934, pp. 132–142 and 158–162.

HANSON, EARL PARKER, *The Amazon—A New Frontier*, Foreign Policy Association, March 1944.

HOSKINS, CARYL P., *The Amazon—The Life History of a Mighty River*, Doubleday, Doran and Co., 1943.

HOTCHKISS, H. S., "The Evolution of the World Rubber Situation," *Harvard Business Review*, January 1924, pp. 129–138.

IMPERIAL ECONOMIC COMMITTEE, *Vegetable Oils and Oilseeds*, His Majesty's Stationery Office, London, 1938.

JAMES, PRESTON E., "Notes on the Geography of Trinidad," *The Journal of Geography*, April 1927, pp. 134–140.

KILLOUGH, HUGH B. and LUCY B., *Raw Materials of Industrialism*, Thomas Y. Crowell Co., 1929, pp. 167–183.

LIPPINCOTT, ISAAC, *Economic Industries and Resources of the World*, D. Appleton & Co., 1929, pp. 405–431.

MANESS, HUBERT, and RUTH G. TUCKER, *World Banana Production and Trade*, U. S. Department of Agriculture, 1946.

MARBUT, C. F., and C. B. MANIFOLD, "The Soils of the Amazon Basin in Relation to Agricultural Possibilities," *Geographical Review*, Vol. 16, 1926, pp. 414–442. "The Topography of the Amazon Valley," *Geographical Review*, 1925, pp. 617–642.

PENDLETON, ROBERT L., "Land Utilization and Agriculture of Mindanao, Philippine Islands," *Geographical Review*, April 1942, pp. 180–210. (Excellent pictures.)

POMFRET, JOHN E., *The Geographic Pattern of Mankind*, D. Appleton-Century Co., 1935, pp. 92–112.

POWELL, ALEXANDER, *The Map That Is Half Unrolled*, The Century Co., 1925.

ROOSEVELT, THEODORE, *Through the Brazilian Wilderness*, Charles Scribner & Sons, 1914.

ROOME, WILLIAM J. W., *Tramping through Africa*, A. & C. Black, London, 1930, pp. 146–200.

SCHURZ, WM. L., "The Distribution of Population in the Amazon Valley," *Geographical Review*, 1925, pp. 206–225.

SHANTZ, H. L., and C. F. MARBUT, *Vegetation and Soils of Africa*, American Geographical Society, 1923.

SMITH, J. RUSSELL, *The World's Food Resources*, Henry Holt & Co., 1919.

Tree Crops, Harcourt, Brace & Co., 1929, pp. 243–249.

TREWARTHA, GLENN T., *An Introduction to Climate and Weather*, McGraw-Hill Book Co., 1937, pp. 198–224.

"Recent Thought on the Problem of White Acclimatization in the Wet Tropics," *Geographical Review*, 1927, pp. 467–478.

TWISS, D. F., "Rubber Latex as a Manufacturing Material," *Royal Society Arts Journal*, Vol. 83, October 1935, pp. 1075–1091.

VISHER, S. S., "Tropical Climates from an Ecological Viewpoint," *Ecology*, Vol. 4, pp. 1–10.

WARD, R. DEC., *Climate Considered Especially in Relation to Man*, G. P. Putnam's Sons, 1918. (See Index.)

WHITFORD, H. W., and A. ANTHONY, "Rubber Production in Africa," *Trade Promotion Series* No. 34, U. S. Department of Commerce, 1926.

WHITFORD, H. W., "The Use of Tropical Lands and Tropical Forests," *Scientific Monthly*, Vol. 17, pp. 135–145.

WILCOX, E. V., *Tropical Agriculture*, D. Appleton & Co., 1916.

Chapter 6

TROPICAL AND SEMI-TROPICAL

ISLANDS OF THE PACIFIC

THE SOUTH SEA ISLANDS AND PEOPLES

When Vasco Nuñez de Balboa first beheld the vast body of water now called the Pacific Ocean, he was looking south from a hilltop in Darien (the Isthmus of Panama), and he called the ocean the South Sea. During the last few decades, the terms "South Sea," "South Sea Islands," and "South Sea Peoples" have been popularized in pictures and in writings by portraying peoples and places located within the tropical and semi-tropical portions of the Pacific Ocean. Today the term "South Sea Islands" is loosely and indefinitely used to connote the thousands of tropical and semi-tropical islands of the Pacific Ocean [1] (Fig. 93). These islands do not all lie within the rainy low latitudes, but throughout the region there is a degree of unity in the ways of life that transcends climatic boundaries.

Climate

The Pacific Islands situated within the tropics have mean annual temperatures ranging between 75° F. and 84° F. Average maximum temperatures above 90° F. are rare. The highest recorded temperature

[1] The East Indies and the Philippine Islands have been discussed in Chapter 5 since the climate of these islands is for the most part that of the rainy low-latitude regions. The climate of many of the other islands of the Pacific do not fit the climatic pattern of the rainy low latitudes. Consequently the authors have chosen to give a separate chapter to those islands. No one has as yet given a satisfactory climatic classification of the islands of the Pacific. Some of the small islands, even those close to the equator, receive less than 10 inches of rainfall during dry years. This certainly represents desert conditions in such a hot region. The same islands may receive almost or quite 100 inches during wet years.

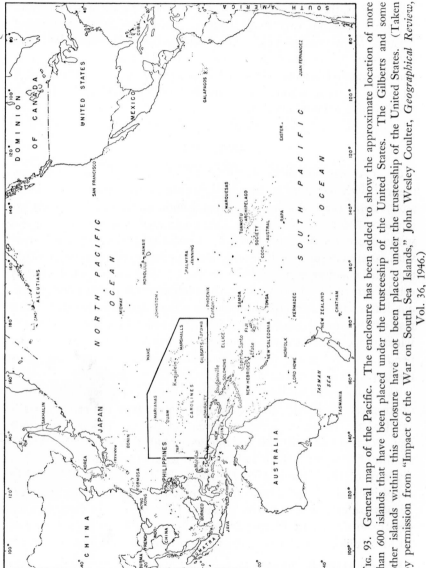

FIG. 93. General map of the Pacific. The enclosure has been added to show the approximate location of more than 600 islands that have been placed under the trusteeship of the United States. The Gilberts and some other islands within this enclosure have not been placed under the trusteeship of the United States. (Taken by permission from "Impact of the War on South Sea Islands," John Wesley Coulter, *Geographical Review*, Vol. 36, 1946.)

is 106° F. on Christmas Island which lies 105 nautical miles north of the equator.

Rainfall is the most variable factor in the climate of this region. Not only does this vary from island to island, but on any one island it varies from year to year. On Fanning Island the annual rainfall varies from 47.4 inches to 208.8 inches; on Malden Island the precipitation has ranged between 3.94 inches and 93.59 inches.[2] The rainfall on other tropical islands, especially the smaller ones without much relief, is exceedingly unreliable.

Land Uses

Coral Atolls. On many of the islands of the South Sea, nature was miserly with her gifts to man.[3] This is especially true of the coral atolls—coral reefs which surround a lagoon and form a ring-shaped island or "necklace of islands." Life on an atoll is a constant struggle with nature for a bare existence. Consisting mainly of solid rock with coral sand on top, the Pacific atoll supports little vegetation other than the coconut and pandanus trees. A few coarse edible tubers can be grown by digging pits in the rock and filling them with coconut leaves and other vegetable matter whose decay makes soil. The rest of the food supply comes from the sea. In years of drought when the coconut supply is less than normal, the natives must depend primarily on the fish they catch, and they live perilously near the border line of starvation.

The inhabitants of the coral atolls suffer many privations because of tropical cyclones. Sometimes the sea sweeps entirely across a small islet. The rushing waters clean out the vegetation, and winds may destroy not only the coconut crop but also the trees. A few stumps of trees mark the location of former coconut plantations.

Many of the lagoons of coral atolls are deep and provide shelter for ships of both the navy and the merchant marine. The Marshall Islands are excellent examples of atolls (Fig. 94). The lagoons vary greatly in size; those of the larger atolls are 20 to 30 miles long and 10 to 20 miles wide. Kwajalein Lagoon measures more than 60 miles

---

[2] Edward H. Bryan, *American Polynesia and the Hawaiian Chain*, Tongg Publishing Co., 1942. This book gives an excellent description of many of the islands of the Pacific.

[3] Coral atolls and coral islands consist of an accumulation of the limy remains of plants and animals (mostly coral polyp) cemented into limestone.

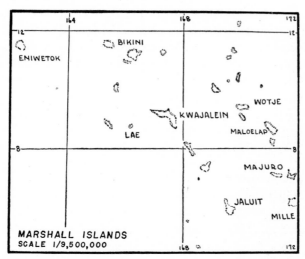

FIG. 94. The Marshall Islands consist of many atolls. The lagoons of many of these islands are deep and afford excellent harbors for ships.

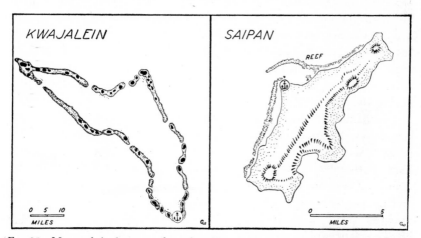

FIG. 95. Many of the lagoons of coral atolls are deep and are capable of providing shelter for ships of both the navy and the merchant marine. Kwajalein Lagoon is more than sixty miles long and could shelter all the navies of the world. Saipan also provides spacious shelter for ships.

in length (Fig. 95), and could shelter all the navies of the world. Although the Marshall Islands are scattered over 375,000 square miles of ocean, their total land area is only 75 square miles.

Coral Islands. Sometimes the lagoons of atolls become filled with coral and form coral islands of considerable size. Land uses on coral islands differ greatly from one to another depending primarily on: (1) the age of the island and the resultant depth to which the rock has weathered into soil; (2) the climate; and (3) the location with respect to other populated areas and the resultant opportunities for trade. On many coral islands soil is almost non-existent and the agricultural development is equally scant; on other islands the coral formation has weathered to considerable depth forming soils of moderate fertility. On many islands the rainfall is too light or unreliable to afford much opportunity for agricultural development; on other islands the rainfall is abundant and fairly reliable.

Okinawa Shima, the largest of the Ryukyu Islands (Fig. 93), represents one of the best of the coral islands for land use when location, soil, and climate are all considered.[4] Okinawa is about 60 miles long and from 3 to 8 miles wide. It is roughly equidistant (350 miles) from Formosa, the coast of China, and the southern coast of Kyushu; and it is located in the midst of hundreds of smaller islands. Its position has encouraged the development of trade which for thousands of years has been carried on with neighboring peoples. The strategic advantages and disadvantages of this island were repeatedly illustrated during the war with Japan.

Approximately one-third of Okinawa has relatively gentle slopes suited to cultivation; the rainfall approximates 80 inches annually and is fairly well distributed throughout the year; and the growing season lasts all the year. Agriculture represents the main industry of the island. The main agricultural crops are sweet potatoes, rice, beans, and many green vegetables. Fruits are not plentiful but a few sour oranges, small bananas, papayas, and peaches are grown. Hogs, chickens, and ducks are found on almost every farm.[5]

Volcanic Islands. Nature has distributed her most bountiful gifts of the South Sea to the volcanic islands. Their fertile soils yield

[4] Okinawa was built by both volcanic and coralline actions but its origin is primarily coralline.

[5] Paul E. Steiner, "Okinawa and Its People," *Scientific Monthly*, March 1947, pp. 233–241. This is an excellent scientific article on the uses of the land in Okinawa.

abundantly. The taro, yam, manioc (cassava), sweet potato, and breadfruit all yield well. Bananas, citrus fruits, pineapples, sugar cane, rice, coffee, cacao, and rubber are produced both for home consumption and also for export wherever climatic conditions permit. Some of the islands are capped with volcanic mountains that are remarkable for their grand and picturesque scenery, for their beautiful forest-clad slopes, and for their fertile mountain-side farms.

The Hawaiian and Fiji islands are representative of volcanic islands at their best. Both groups lie in about the same latitudes—one north latitude, the other south. Both have been built up by the outpourings of volcanic lava on submarine platforms of the Pacific. In the Fiji group, part of the base lies above sea level.

THE TERRITORY OF HAWAII. The Hawaiian Islands have aptly been called "the crossroads of the Pacific." They lie on the most important route of steamers plying between the Orient and the west coast of North and South America. They have also become a major link in the air transport across the Pacific.

The combined area of the Hawaiian Islands is slightly more than 6,000 square miles. The island chain extends about 400 miles in a northwest-southeast direction, and the larger islands—Hawaii, Maui, Oahu, and Kauai—lie within the tropics. Most of these islands possess (1) sandy beaches that make excellent playgrounds and attract tourists; (2) coastal plains, eroded lava plateaus, and hilly lava slopes that make excellent farm land; and (3) high mountains that are noted for their scenic beauty. Mark Twain once said, "The Hawaiian Islands are the loveliest fleet of islands anchored in any ocean."

Both the climate and the soils of Hawaii favor remarkable productivity. The climate of Hawaii is largely a product of its location in a warm tropical sea and in the belt of northeast trades. Freezing temperatures in the lowlands are unknown. The areal distribution of rainfall is largely determined by the degree of exposure of each area to the trade winds. The northeast (windward) slopes receive 100 to 300 inches annually,[6] whereas the southwest (leeward) slopes may receive only 10 to 20 inches (Honolulu receives 25.4 inches).

Most of the soils have been derived from volcanic lavas which weather easily and quickly. The soils are fertile and well suited for agricultural use.

Since the islands have been built up by the outpourings of volcanic

[6] The average annual rainfall at Waialeale, Kauai, is 476 inches.

lavas, the larger islands have a variety of relief features such as sandy beaches, coastal plains, hills, mountains, and plateaus.

Prior to their discovery by Cook in 1778, the Hawaiian Islands were inhabited by Polynesian tribes who lived primarily by agriculture and fishing. Commerce and industry other than hand manufacture played no part in their lives. In 1876 the United States removed all tariff on Hawaiian products after which American capital began to flow into the islands for the development of agriculture, industry, and commerce.

Today the commercial activities of the Hawaiian Islands are dominated by agricultural products together with the manufacture and trade dependent upon them. The agriculture of Hawaii has been almost completely commercialized. The three major crops (sugar cane, pineapples, and coffee), grown almost wholly for export, occupy more than 95 per cent of the cultivated land as indicated by the table.

PRINCIPAL CROPS OF HAWAII *

Product	Acres	Thousands of pounds
Sugar cane	295,900	901,000
Pineapples	48,598	1,228,000
Coffee	4,136	8,547
Corn	1,682	1,632
Taro	622	580
Rice	509	1,901
Potatoes, white	487	1,991
Sweet potatoes, yams	180	927

* Data are for 1940 for all crops except sugar cane and sugar. Data for sugar cane and sugar are for 1945.

Sugar cane, the leading crop, produces abundantly on the rich volcanic soil, chiefly by irrigation. The frost-free climate is suited to sugar cane which requires a growing season of 15 to 24 months, depending on the elevation and, consequently, on the temperatures of the area under cultivation.

The rugged topography of the islands has necessitated extensive engineering construction works in developing plantations, in irrigating and terracing the land, and in providing essential transportation facilities.

Most of the sugar cane is grown on great estates owned by large companies. As a result of the inadequate supply of native workers, many laborers have been imported from various parts of the Orient.

Much of the cane is processed in Hawaii by the use of American-made machinery and with the help of American technicians. The sugar is then shipped duty-free to the United States.

The Hawaiian Islands, chiefly Oahu, rank first among the regions of the world in the production of pineapples. The fruit is grown chiefly on large estates and is canned locally in large canneries. Most

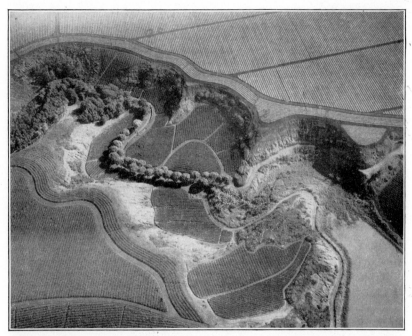

Fɪɢ. 96. Pineapple fields near Wheeler, Oahu. (Permission U. S. Navy.)

of the product is sent to the United States where, like Hawaiian sugar, it is permitted to enter duty-free (Figs. 96 and 97).

Bananas and coffee are also important commercial crops. Rice, taro (a root crop), bananas, guava, and papaya constitute important subsistence crops, and alfalfa is grown as feed for beef and dairy cattle.

Tʜᴇ Fɪᴊɪ Iꜱʟᴀɴᴅꜱ. These islands are a part of the British Empire. The fertile soil, mild climate, and moderate rainfall of approximately 50 inches (heavier on the windward side of highlands) are natural conditions which favor agricultural development. Sugar cane is the dominant crop, but coconuts and a great variety of tropical fruits and vegetables do well on these islands.

Life in the South Pacific Islands is sometimes pictured as one long holiday. This picture no longer fits the facts. The science, skill, worry, and work of the industrial world is being introduced, and the ancient customs, manners, handicrafts, superstitions, and carefree life are being thrust aside.

FIG. 97. Lanai City, Hawaii. This city is surrounded by pineapple fields and is supported by the pineapple industry.

Mineral Production of the South Sea Islands

Phosphate rock derived from guano deposits is widespread. Nauru, a small island of only 5,600 acres, has yielded phosphate for many decades. Ocean Island, one-third as large as Nauru, yields phosphate ore that is 88 per cent pure and is believed to be the richest phosphate ever mined. Several other islands of the South Sea contain large reserves of this valuable mineral plant food. The islands that are formed wholly or in part from the remnants of old continental land masses contain rich metal deposits, such as nickel in New Caledonia and gold in New Guinea and the Fiji group.

Cultures of the South Sea

Incongruity of the ancient and modern cultures existing side by side is apparent almost everywhere in the South Sea Islands today. Natives girt only with loin cloths and smartly tailored natives or Europeans dressed in the latest western fashion are encountered side by side on hundreds of islands. The throw-net fisherman still plies his art in competition with the most modern fishing boats and equipment. The airplane, steamboat, modern canneries, sugar-cane mills, and other factories are being thrust into the very midst of peoples who still practice their traditions, arts, and skills of centuries ago, and whose culture still retains much of the traditional atmosphere of the South Sea as it has been so vividly portrayed in pictures and literature.

The civilization of the Occident and the Orient have come to stay in the South Sea Islands. The peoples of the western world now own much property and many homes in these islands. Basically the American civilization has all but engulfed the native way of life in the Hawaiian Islands. Superficially many signs of the Hawaiian civilization still survive. Some of the customs, manners, and clothing of the Hawaiian civilization are retained as an attraction to tourists. However, the island of Oahu with its great business houses, mills, canneries, and modern agricultural practices is in many respects primarily an extension of the culture of California.[7]

The United States in the Pacific

In 1947, the United Nations gave the United States the sole and permanent trusteeship of more than 600 islands which were formerly Japanese-mandated islands. These islands are spread over a water area about the size of the United States, but the total land area is only 829 square miles (Fig. 93).

These islands possess meager resources, principally phosphorus ores (guano) and coconuts. They are occupied by about 85,000 brown-

[7] The author has had the privilege of reading and making use of an excellent manuscript, not yet published, entitled *South Sea Peoples,* by John Wesley Coulter.

skinned native folks who have no skills except fishing and some wood carving.

Most Americans were unfamiliar with even the names of these islands before World War II. Now the Marianas, Gilbert, Caroline, and Marshall islands are well known to thousands of men and women who obtained firsthand information about these isolated patches of land while in the military service of the United States.

The strategic importance of these islands cannot be accurately evaluated at present. They possess excellent harbors and many airfields, some of which are in disrepair because of being bombed during World War II. Even though the islands are small they will be of value as bases for commercial air fleets, as bases for the Navy, and as way stations for merchant vessels. The network of airfields can be completed to cover the broad expanse of the Pacific Ocean between the United States and Asia.

Guam, an American possession for more than fifty years, is located near the center of these trusteeship islands and now serves as their capital. It has been valued primarily as a permanent naval base.

Truk is a circular atoll that could shelter all the world's navies at one time. It has airfields on 3 of its 89 islands.

Saipan is an island 13 miles long and 5 miles wide with a population in 1946 of 20,000, mostly Japanese. The Japanese developed the cane sugar industry here before World War II.

Kwajalein, an atoll more than 60 miles long, is only 6 feet above sea level at its highest point and has no native population. Nevertheless, it has been developed into a major United States air base.

Yap is a group of four small islands which lie in the western part of the Carolines. The islands are covered with a tropical jungle which supplies mahogany logs for the building of houses. Before World War II, Yap was an important cable station and is likely to become such again.

Taken together these trusteeship islands are valuable primarily as way stations in the Pacific and as future vacation spots. Whether the value of these islands, situated in remote parts of the world, will outweigh the obligations added by their control will be decided by future events.

REFERENCES

BOWMAN, ROBERT G., "Army Farms and Agricultural Development in the Southwest Pacific," *Geographical Review*, July 1946, pp. 420–446.

BRYAN, EDWARD H., *American Polynesia and the Hawaiian Chain*, Tongg Publishing Co., Honolulu, 1942. (This book gives an excellent description of many of the islands of the central Pacific.)

COULTER, JOHN WESLEY, "Impact of the War on South Sea Islands," *Geographical Review*, Vol. 36, 1946, pp. 409–419.

Fiji: Little India of the Pacific, The University of Chicago Press, 1943.

HAAS, WILLIAM H., *The American Empire*, The University of Chicago Press, 1940, pp. 216–304.

SPOEHR, ALEXANDER, "The Marshall Islands and Transpacific Aviation," *Geographical Review*, July 1946, pp. 447–451.

STEINER, PAUL E., "Okinawa and Its People," *Scientific Monthly*, March 1947, pp. 233–241.

SUYDAM, E. H., *Hawaii—Isle of Enchantment*, D. Appleton-Century Co., 1937.

Chapter 7

THE LOW-LATITUDE WET-AND-DRY

REALM

LOCATION AND CLIMATE OF THE REALM

Rhythmic Pattern of Climatic Conditions: Life Responses. As one proceeds away from the equatorial wet lands with their continuous growing season, abundant forest growth, dearth of useful animals, and retarded native civilization, the environment becomes better suited to the progress of native peoples. Here, in the low-latitude wet-and-dry realm, a rhythm of rainfall results in a similar rhythm of life responses; seasons of plenty are followed by seasons of dearth, compelling man to exercise forethought and to save.

The rhythm of seasonal rainfall (summer rain and winter drought) is the distinguishing characteristic of this tropical realm and determines its location (Fig. 98). Many places receive nine-tenths of their rain during the summer half-year. The temperatures are high throughout the year and the growing season is continuous. Yet the regions have a well-marked seasonal rhythm in temperatures as well as in rainfall. Summers with their humid atmosphere are hot both night and day. Winters are cooler, especially at night when the heat of the earth escapes rapidly through a relatively dry atmosphere.

Distribution and Amount of Rainfall. The rainfall of the realm is directly related to (1) the movements of the tropical calm belt, (2) the monsoon winds, (3) convection in the moisture-laden trade winds, and (4) the influence of highlands.

The belt of calms, shifting to the north and to the south of the equator with the apparent movement of the sun in those directions, brings with it summer rainfall and high relative humidity. (See pp. 77–78.) Thus areas located along and near the equator are influenced most by this wind belt; hence, in general the equatorward margins of the realm have higher relative humidity and more abundant rainfall

228

than the poleward areas. Only poleward areas that are favorably exposed to the monsoons or to the moisture-laden trades constitute exceptions to this general rule.

As the trade winds, heavily laden with moisture, pass over the West Indies, the heat of the land in summer sets up convection currents which result in moderate to abundant rainfall, especially on the windward slopes. Thus the slopes that face to the windward of the north-

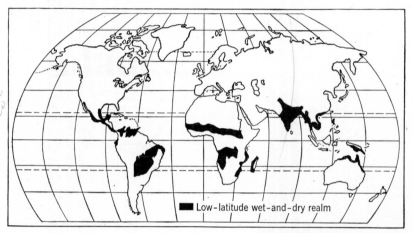

■■ Low-latitude wet-and-dry realm

FIG. 98. The most important climatic characteristic of the low-latitude wet-and-dry realm is the rhythm of rainfall—summer rain and winter drought.

east trades receive rainfall even in winter; the amount in general is greater than that received by land lying to the leeward of highlands. This is well illustrated on the island of Jamaica, where Kingston, located to the leeward of mountains, receives 36 inches (Fig. 99), whereas Port Antonio, a center on the northeast coast, is bathed, during a normal year, in more than 139 inches of rain.

The effect of exposure in relation to amount of rainfall is also indicated in the highlands of northeast India, where the north-south-trending mountain system of Burma meets the Khasi Hills, thereby causing a veritable trap for the moisture-laden winds that blow during the summer from the Bay of Bengal. Here the rainfall is exceedingly heavy. At Cherrapunji, a center located in this area, 458 inches is the mean annual amount, 41 inches of rain having fallen in a single day. Under such conditions erosion is very rapid, the vegetation is rank and luxuriant, and the whole landscape is steaming with hot, humid air.

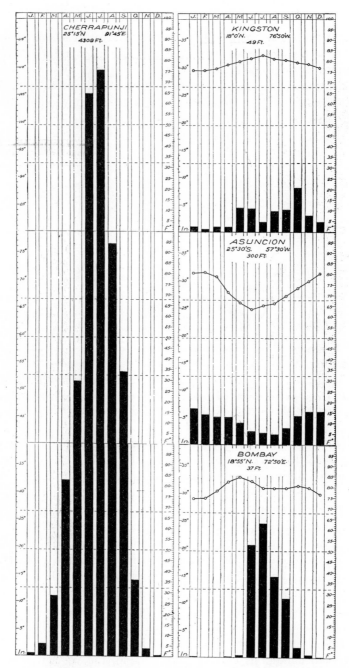

Fig. 99. Climatic graphs of average monthly precipitation and temperatures in low-latitude wet-and-dry areas. All these graphs are on the same scale.

230

Variability of Rainfall. The average rainfall of most parts of this realm is sufficient for agricultural purposes; but unfortunately the deviation from the average is frequent, resulting in either an excess or a deficit of water for crops and pasture. Here rainfall extremes have been recorded, ranging from the heaviest on earth, where from day to day there are incessant downpours during the rainy season, to a low limit which marks the beginning of the steppe, where every drop of rain is quickly absorbed.

The climate of these regions is not conducive to great physical or mental vigor. It is more healthful and less debilitating, however, than that of the tropical rain forest. It also favors the formation of grass rather than forests, and in general the grassland is easier to bring under cultivation, and the yield is larger and more enduring than that of the rain forest.

Temperatures. The temperatures of these regions are high throughout the year. Frosts are unknown except in the uplands, and, where there is sufficient moisture, crops may be grown the year round. Although the regions are warm throughout the year, there is a marked annual as well as diurnal range, which is greatest along the poleward margins, in the interior areas, and in the drier parts of the realm. The average annual temperature range at Lahore, situated in the northwestern part of India, is 40° F.; that of Bombay is only 10.1° F. Kuka, situated along the margin of the steppe in west central Africa, has an average range of 21.6° F.; Wadelai, British East Africa, has a range of only 6.2° F.

Inconvenience Caused by Oppressive Heat. In some of these regions the heat is most oppressive just before the rainy season sets in. Thus in the Indo-Gangetic Plain during April and May, immediately before the wet season, the temperatures range from 85° F. to 95° F.; and along the margins of the steppe readings of 115° F. have been made. Such heat is surpassed only in the desert. Work must be suspended during the hottest hours, and any activity out of doors is dangerous as long as the sun is above the horizon. At such times one should not venture into the open at all without taking the utmost precautions against sunstroke, for the heat and the glare, both direct and reflected, are intense.

The hot season, which in this region begins in March, becomes sufficiently intense by April so that barley and wheat ripen and are harvested. During this season, especially from April until June, there is essentially no rain. It is the period of the year preceding the summer monsoon. An inhabitant of the temperate zone can hardly realize the desiccating, scorching heat of the wind during this season. The temperatures during the daytime frequently soar to more than 120° F., and after 7:00 A.M. no European resident of the Punjab leaves his house unless under the urge of business or other necessary activities. But in such cases he must protect himself from the sun with a sunshade as well as a thick head covering. Houses are generally closed after sunrise, and since only a small door is left open for communication with the outside world, they are more like gloomy prisons than ordinary dwellings. Grass screens are placed in the doorways and continuously sprinkled with water, thereby keeping the rooms somewhat cooler than would otherwise be possible, especially as long as the hot winds blow strongly.

Climate and Human Welfare

The low-latitude wet-and-dry realm contains some of the most densely populated regions of the world and some very sparsely populated areas. The population of India (395,822,250 estimated in 1944) is almost three times that of the United States. Some agricultural sections of India that have abundant rainfall support more than 1,500 people per square mile. Other parts of India are desert and support less than one person to the square mile. The density of population of the various areas and the welfare of the people are closely related to the amount and distribution of the rainfall.

When will it rain, and how much will fall? These are the eternal questions of the realm. With many of the people living here, health, happiness, and even life itself are staked on the answer nature gives. Other physical factors, such as soil, relief, location, and temperatures, all affect man's activities, but the amount and the distribution of rainfall are the factors whose variations have a major influence on man's well-being. They are the ones, therefore, that give man most concern.

In a few parts of the realm, such as the West Indies and the lower Ganges Valley, the rainfall is both sufficiently abundant and reliable for excellent crops; in other parts it is so light and unreliable that the crop and pasture yields are uncertain.

Perhaps no climatic realm has a greater variety of human use zones as related to rainfall. This is well illustrated in the Sudan, where a journey north from the tropical forest takes the traveler through deciduous forests, areas of patch gardening, grain farming, and into the region of semi-nomadic pursuits. In India the Indo-Gangetic Plain alone contains five distinct human use regions.[1]

Rainfall and Famine

Causes of Famines. As previously stated, the chief disadvantage of the rainfall regime of this climatic realm is its uncertainty. Years of abundant rainfall are interspersed with years of drought; years of feast are broken by periods of famine. When the monsoon is normal, crops flourish, and the people have food; but only a slight departure from the normal may cause crop failure. As a result of this monsoonal variation famines occur frequently. They may be caused by an excess of moisture which results in floods, in the rotting of crops, or in the stimulation of insect pests; by a deficit of moisture accompanied by parched ground and dry vegetation; or by irregular distribution which results in crops receiving the moisture at the wrong time.

Rainfall a Critical Factor in Intermediate Areas. The rainfall of this realm is most variable in the drier parts, and it is least variable in areas which receive abundant precipitation. But in both these areas, variations in rainfall are not of much importance. In the drier sections there are few crops that depend upon rainfall; in the areas with greater precipitation the rainfall is usually sufficient for agricultural purposes even during the dry years. The intermediate areas, however, are the critical ones. Here the average rainfall is just sufficient for crop production, and deficiency, irregularity, or superabundance may cause crop failures, frequently resulting in a great loss of life.

Famines in India. In India, where agriculture is the dominant activity, and where the dense population presses upon the means of subsistence, periods of erratic rainfall shake the economic foundation of the entire land, and millions of inhabitants perish. At the present time, however, this conditon is not so critical as it was formerly, since irrigation canals have been built and railways have been extended through many parts of the country. Yet there still remain vast stretches of land lacking irrigation and favorable transportation facilities—land in which a normal rainfall is just sufficient for crop production, and in which a slight deficit may cause starvation.

We have records from the ancient literature of the Hindus that

---

[1] Lower Ganges rice and jute region, the middle Ganges rice region, the upper Ganges wheat region, the Punjab, and the Sind rice and cotton region.

famines have occurred in India from the earliest times.[2]   In the years since Warren Hastings introduced British rule, India has had more than twenty severe famines.   For the period preceding British rule the records have not been so well preserved, but there is ample evidence to show that famine was just as frequent in its incidence and much more deadly in its effects under the native rulers of India.[3]   This is indicated by the Bengal famine of 1769–1770, which occurred shortly after the foundation of British rule, but while the native officials were still in power.   During this famine a third of the population of Bengal, or approximately 10,000,000 people, perished.   Even during the last hundred years India has suffered from more than a dozen severe famines.   In general, however, a famine does not strike all India at one time.   But there are certain localities which suffer more severely than others—localities in which starvation, pestilence, and death hold sway during the famine years.   One of these intense local famines occurred in the province of Madras in 1833.   The northern districts of the province suffered most severely.   In the Gantur district alone 200,000 out of a total population of 500,000 perished.   One of the eye witnesses to this famine stated that the description of the Siege of Corinth of dogs gnawing human skulls is mild compared with the scenes of horror that they were daily forced to witness on their morning and evening rides.   Dogs and horses were greedily devoured by the starving people.[4]

Equally intense and horrifying was the subsequent famine of 1837, which swept northern India.   In the district of Cawnpur a special establishment patrolled the streets and the river to remove the dead bodies.   In many places the dead lay on the roadside until wild animals devoured them.   The mortality due to this famine was estimated at more than 800,000 people.

On some occasions the famine relief work was so successful that there appeared to be no excess death rate during the abnormal periods, especially during the famines of 1874 and 1892 in Bengal.   Occasionally, however, a famine of such wide distribution and intensity may occur that it is almost impossible to check the death rate, even with the present means of transportation.   Thus in 1897 one of the most

---

[2] E. Washburn Hopkins, *India Old and New*, Charles Scribner & Sons, 1902, p. 236.

[3] R. C. Dutt, *Open Letters to Lord Curzon on the Famines of India*, Kegan Paul, Trench, Trübner & Co., London, 1900, p. 1.

[4] R. C. Dutt, *The Economic History of India*, Kegan Paul, Trench, Trübner & Co., London, 1900, p. 70.

widespread and intense famines in the history of India was experienced. On the average, 2,000,000 persons sought help daily, and during the height of the disaster there were weeks together in which more than 6,000,000 persons were given aid. The death toll during this period exceeded that of non-famine years by about 5,000,000.

Famines in Africa. In the low-latitude wet-and-dry regions of Africa fluctuations in rainfall have caused many severe periods of famine. As early as the middle of the nineteenth century, Schweinfurt and other travelers in Africa reported serious periods of drought in the Sudan. In 1872, Nachtigal estimated the population of Wadai at more than 2,000,000, but it has subsequently shrunk to 300,000. The great drought of 1892 threatened the very existence of Abeshir, the capital of Wadai, and local raids and warfare broke out among the tribes. "A. D. Milne reports that the province of Bahr-el-Jebel suffered an acute famine in 1879. Crops everywhere failed to mature except in the rain shadow of a few hills. Entire villages began to move, stealing all the food they could find. Baker Pasha tells of observing other villages where men lay in the streets wailing and putting pieces of dirt into their mouths to show how little they had to eat. L. C. West describes both 1913 and 1914 as famine years in Dongola Province (Anglo-Egyptian Sudan). Cattle and humans died like flies. Hurried relief work by the British Government was the only thing that saved the remnant of the population." [5]

Drought, however, is not the only cause for famine in the African regions; excessive rainfall may bring about the same results. "In 1780, Schweinfurt wrote that almost all the crops of Bahr-el-Ghazal were ruined by excessively heavy rains which lasted for ten days in early summer. In 1914, many districts in northern Anglo-Egyptian Sudan received such violent downpour during July and August that the crops were completely destroyed. During 1916 and 1917 Nigeria suffered from excessive rains, floods occurring all over the country." [6]

The Control of Famines. Thus far we have considered the causes and extent of famines. What is to be done about it? Man is unable to control rainfall, in which either deficiency, irregularity, or superabundance may give rise to these disastrous periods. He can, however, provide measures which reduce the liability of the realm to famine. Chief among these are promotion of railways; extension of irrigation; reclamation of waste land; introduction of agricultural improvements,

[5] G. T. Renner, "The Sudan, A Tropical Famine Area," *Matériaux pour l'étude des calamités*, No. 11, Geneva, pp. 7–8.

[6] *Op. cit.*, pp. 8–9.

such as proper crops and rotations; emigration; and, where necessary, revision of revenue and rent systems. In India railways are being extended rapidly throughout the country; canal, tank, and well irrigation is increasing in importance; and a more reasonable rent system has been realized. It has been found that peanuts yield well even during dry periods, hence they should have a more prominent place in the cropping system in regions visited by drought. But in areas that are subject to an excess of rainfall, moisture-loving plants with a high degree of resistance to insect pests and fungous diseases should be introduced.

NATIVE VEGETATION OF THE REALM: THE PATTERN OF DISTRIBUTION

A Succession of Vegetative Types. Few climatic realms contain such striking contrasts in vegetative types as one may find in these regions. In those parts of the realm where rainfall is most abundant, luxuriant forests have sprung up, being deciduous rather than evergreen—a direct response to the rhythm of rain and drought. The regions of heaviest forest are the wetter (equatorward) margins of the realm and windward slopes of highlands situated in monsoon areas. As one proceeds away from the forested areas, grasslands with park-like timber appear, and these in turn give way to the open savanna and thorn forest along the drier margins.

This banded characteristic of the native vegetation of the realm is well illustrated in Africa. Beyond the tropical rain forest of that continent and forming a broad bank extending from Senegal to Uganda and across the southern Congo and northern Angola is the high-grass low-tree savanna, composed of grass 5 to 12 feet high with scattered bushes and small trees. As one proceeds out from this area tall umbrella-shaped trees make their appearance, and the grasses become shorter and less coarse. Owing to the large size of these trees in comparison with the bushes and small trees of the former area, they are less readily killed by fires which frequently sweep over these grasslands during the dry season.

Forest and Forest Activities

At present the forests of this climatic realm are much less extensive than the grasslands (Fig. 100), yet there is every reason to believe that they formerly had a much wider distribution. "The shrinking of the forested area both north and south of the equatorial zone is a fact which strikes the trained observer. Various types of underbrush in regions which are now treeless, and of aerial lianas which have become half subterranean in order to adapt themselves to new conditions of life, seem to indicate that a part of the immense area now occupied by savannas was formerly forested. At a few degrees dis-

Fig. 100.   Typical savanna grasslands in Africa.   (Courtesy U. S. Department of Agriculture.)

tance from the equator, the forest, driven from plateaus and hillsides, takes refuge in valleys and ravines." [7]   A change in climate alone is not responsible for such retreat; but many remains of the stone age in western Sudan, for example, indicate that man has had his share in clearing land of its forests.[8]

Commercial Species of the Forest—Teak, Sal, and Quebracho

Some of the trees of the forested regions have acquired wide commercial significance, especially teak, sal, and quebracho. Teak and sal are found in widely scattered sections of India, Thailand (French

[7] Reprinted by permission from *Principles of Human Geography*, by P. Vidal de la Blache, Henry Holt & Co., 1926, p. 47.
[8] *Ibid.*

Indo-China) and Java. In eastern Java the teak grows to a maximum height of 75 feet and forms pure stands in which other trees occur merely as subsidiary species. In India and Burma, teak is the most important timber, being used for buildings, furniture, cabinet work, paneling, railroad cars, and agricultural implements. This general utility of the teak is due to the fact that its wood is extremely durable, seasons well without warping or splitting, and is easy to work. Teak is also superior to all other known woods for ship building, since it contains an oily substance which helps to preserve metal that comes in contact with it. Teak timber, however, is heavy, and special methods are frequently required in order to get it out of many of these tropical areas. Thus in Burma, where the timber is extracted from the forests by floating, the trees are girdled three years before felling in order to kill them and render the timber more buoyant.[9]

Sal, a large tree found in solid stands in parts of northern and central India, is widely used for bridge construction, piles, railway ties, and agricultural implements.

The Contribution of Quebracho to Industry. Quebracho holds a position in the New World quite comparable in relative importance to that of teak and sal in southeast Asia. Used chiefly for tanning extract, it has been called "Latin America's greatest contribution to the tanning industry."

Not until the last few decades has the extract of the quebracho tree entered widely in world trade. Prior to 1900, quebracho, as a tanning material, was unknown to the great leather-producing districts of Europe and North America; now it occupies a place in the front rank, essentially the entire world's output of this commodity coming from the Gran Chaco of South America. This rapid development has resulted from the favorable combination of several factors, such as the high percentage of quebracho per unit of timber, purity of the extract, and the abundance as well as accessibility of the timber in the area of production.

LOCALIZATION OF QUEBRACHO. The quebracho forests are situated in a well-defined region, extending from the Argentine province of Santa Fé to the northern limits of Paraguay, or from latitude 21° S to about 31° S. This belt has a maximum width of about 200 miles in the Argentine Chaco, tapering to the south as well as to the north. To the east these forests are bounded by the Parana and Paraguay

[9] Raphael Zon and W. N. Sparhawk, *Forest Resources of the World*, Vol. I, McGraw-Hill Book Co., 1923, pp. 435–436.

rivers, and to the west by areas of deficient rainfall and unfavorable soil conditions.

Quebracho is exacting in its environmental requirements, which accounts for its marked localization in a restricted area.   The optimum conditions for the tree are found where temperatures rarely rise above 105° F. in summer and where they seldom fall below the freezing point in winter.   This tree is particular also in its choice of soil and relief.   The quebracho area embraces a monotonously level lowland, and the tree is seldom found even at elevations of 50 feet above the general land surface of this region.   The drainage must be so slow that the tree receives the necessary amount of moisture, and yet sufficiently rapid so that long and frequent inundations may be obviated. Where quebracho grows on poorly drained, wet land, rot is common, beginning at the heart of the bole and gradually extending upwards, eventually converting the trunk into a mere shell.

CHARACTER OF THE WOOD.   The quebracho tree is extremely hard and heavy, the name quebracho being derived from the Spanish word *quebrar*, to break, and *hacha*, an axe.   Such hard timber requires tools with high-tempered steel in order that it may be successfully transformed into the finished product; and it is with difficulty that the heavy quebracho logs are transported from place to place.

METHODS OF OBTAINING THE TANNING EXTRACT.   Only the heartwood of the trunk and larger branches of the tree are utilized in the manufacture of tanning extract.   After the tree is felled, the first work consists of stripping from the trunk both the bark and the white sapwood, leaving only the red heartwood, which contains about 20 per cent tannin.[10]   The logs, weighing from ½ to 11 tons each, are then hauled in large-wheeled ox-carts or on light railways to the factories, where they are reduced to small chips.   These chips are subsequently conveyed through extractors where they are dissolved in hot water. When its moisture content is about 20 per cent, the quebracho solution is run out into bags where it cools to a dark red solid extract, in which form it is exported.[11]

Other Forest Trees.   The trees of most of the low-latitude wet-and-dry regions, however, do not occur in solid stands, but are widely

---

[10] The bark contains from 5 to 6 per cent tannin; the white sapwood 0 to 4 per cent.

[11] For a detailed discussion of the quebracho industry see "The Quebracho Extract Industry" by H. G. Bennett, the *Leather Trades Year Book*, The Leather-sellers Co., London, 1925, pp. 75–91.

scattered in the sunny, well-aired, and dry grassland. The majority of these trees are of low stature, with a relatively thick stem; the crown is frequently umbrella-shaped and may indeed be flattened like a disk. Umbrella trees figure in all the descriptions of the savannas and open forest formations of the tropics. They constitute an important part of the vegetation in the savannas of Venezuela and east Africa; they occur in the alpine savanna of Java and are conspicuous in the landscape of the Campos of Brazil.[12] In southern India the umbrella-thorn, the crown of which consists of twisted knotty branches, thorns, and finely pinnate leaves, is a conspicuous object in the landscape.

The Grassland

Within the rainy low-latitude regions, grassland is unimportant; only in small areas do grasses appear, owing to local influences. But beyond the rain forest extensive savannas dominate the landscape, in some places containing scattered trees and bushes, in others solid stands of grass (Fig. 100). In accordance with the transition of climate from a wetter to a drier phase, there is also a transition from savanna grasslands in which there is tall grass and many trees to those in which the grass is short and the trees are absent. Thus towards the margins of the steppe, where the period of drought is longer, trees become smaller and much more scattered, and grasses cover almost the entire landscape.[13]

In the Llanos of Venezuela and the Campos of Brazil grass is the dominant type of vegetation, explorers and travelers having described these regions as boundless stretches of land covered with solid stands of grass. But this is contrary to the facts, since in both areas bushes and trees are scattered over the landscape. Grasses are the dominant vegetation, yet in both areas they are richly differentiated, and with scattered trees and bushes give the appearance of a park country.[14]

In Africa, extensive grasslands and areas of parklike vegetation are found to the poleward of the rainy low latitudes. These extensive savannas constitute the natural habitat of a large number of pastoral

[12] A. F. W. Schimper, *Plant Geography*, The Clarendon Press, Oxford, 1922, p. 347.

[13] For a description of the savanna of Africa see H. L. Shantz and C. F. Marbut, *The Vegetation and Soils of Africa*, American Geographical Society, 1923, pp. 50–60.

[14] A. F. W. Schimper, *Plant Geography*, The Clarendon Press, Oxford, 1903, pp. 372, 373.

nomads as well as agricultural peoples. They are also the home of some of the world's largest herbivorous animals.

THE ANIMAL ADAPTATION

Variety of Faunal Groups Correspond to Floral Habitats. The realm contains not only several vegetative formations but also various kinds of animal life. The variety in the habitat from the monsoon forest, through various types of savannas, to the steppe is matched with an equal variety in the faunal groups. In the forests, carnivorous and climbing species predominate, although amphibians and reptiles are abundant along the stream courses, in swamps, and in lagoons. On the other hand, the savannas, with their abundance of grass, support some of the largest herbivorous animals, while in the drier parts of the realm, where the grass is short and where it is necessary to range over larger stretches of land in search for food, the animal is generally long of limb, being built for speed.

In the monsoon forest and along the margin of the rainy low latitude we find such animals as the jaguar, puma, tapir, gray fox, and monkey. In swamps and lagoons alligators are abundant, and lizards of many species add to the variety of creeping forms. Snakes are found everywhere and are of all sizes and all degrees of deadliness. At times millions of mosquitoes cloud the atmosphere. In the Gran Chaco of South America streams of locusts darken the sky for days together. These are the insects which go in vast swarms to the crop lands of the pampa, causing endless destruction to grain and hay. As insect life is abundant, so also will bird life be, since it is almost a corollary of the former. And these areas abound in birds of great variety and brilliancy of plumage.

Throughout the extensive savannas the bushes and trees offer shade and the tall grass provides an abundance of food for the native animals, many of which are of great size, especially the elephant, rhinoceros, and giraffe. But here also are found cattle, deer, kangaroo, bear, wolf, tiger, and panther. Various thin, long-legged animals such as the eland, oryx, and gazelle occupy the drier parts of the realm, regions in which the grass is short and frequently lacking; hence speed is a natural response in the animal structure.

Adaptation of Animals to Climatic Environment. Corresponding to the climatic rhythm of rain and drought is the rhythm of feast and famine in the animal kingdom. The animals of these regions have adapted themselves in various ways in response to these conditions.

In some of these animals the habit of migration is strongly developed, manifesting itself in various kinds of antelopes, elephants, and cattle; it is also very pronounced in birds, which move with the rains into areas where food is most abundant. Still other animals, such as bees, termites, and ants, have developed the habit of saving in order to tide themselves through a period of dearth.

GRAZING ACTIVITIES

Dependence of Man upon Animals in the Open Spaces. This is the realm in which our primitive ancestor received an early opportunity for human evolution. Once out of the forest, he was forced to protect himself in the open spaces against the abundant animal life. He also found animals for domestication—animals to drag his implements and haul his crops, to enlarge his food supply by the addition of meat and milk, and to enrich his apparel, especially by supplying leather and hair.

Grazing versus Agriculture. Agriculture is the dominant activity of most of the people of this realm, yet grazing is widely practiced. This is especially true in the llanos and campos of South America and in the savannas of Africa. Throughout these areas the abundance of grass has afforded a marked impetus to the development of pastoral activities, but in Africa as well as in South America the distance from markets, the poor transportation facilities, and the consequent difficulty of exporting agricultural commodities have hindered the maximum development of this industry.

Grazing Industries of the Llanos of South America. The llanos extend from the inland division of the Carribbean coastal ranges south to the Guiana highlands or to the tropical forests of the lowlands—latitude 6° N to 7° N (Fig. 101). Here is an area two and one-half times the size of England, yet it supports only a few thousand people—approximately one family per square mile.

Throughout this sparsely populated grassland, cattle are the chief means of subsistence but offer a most precarious livelihood to the stock rancher. The lack of good pastures throughout the year, labor shortage, poor transportation facilities, revolutions, distance from market—these are discouraging situations that the rancher must face.

These great cattle plains are not a short-grass country. The natural grasses are large, coarse, and hard when dry. The green shoots at the beginning of the rainy season offer palatable feed for the cattle, but toward the close of the season and the beginning of the dry period the wind and the rain parch the plains, making the grass too coarse and hard for the animals to eat. During the height of the wet season the cattle are forced to move from one high area to another, often wading through vast stretches of swampy land in order to reach these places of refuge where the feed is soon exhausted and the stock begin to suffer. As the waters recede, the cattle follow the drying margins of the flooded areas, eating the green shoots to be found there. The flooded areas, covered with aquatic growth, soon become foul and

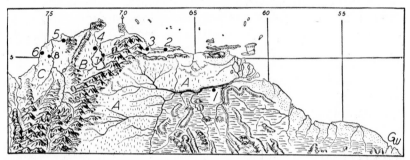

Fig. 101. (A) Llanos, (B) Maracaibo Basin, (C) lower Magdalena and coastal lowlands. (1) Cuidad Bolivar, (2) Caracas, (3) Puerto Cabello, (4) Maracaibo, (5) Santa Marta, (6) Cartagena, (7) Lagunillas, (8) Calamar.

cause diseases to break out which frequently result in disastrous losses.[15]

Owing to the lack of adequate railroad facilities, cattle are driven across the mountains to the coastal markets—usually to Puerto Cabello, the major port of export for the cattle and their products. But pastures in the mountains are usually poor, and great care must be taken so that the cattle retain as much weight as possible. This problem is being worked out at present by means of areas of planted grass, such as Para and Guinea, located at such points that cattle may be brought to the market by easy stages across the plains, being held in those pastures for conditioning. It frequently takes months to drive the stock across the plains and mountains to the outlet near the coast.

The Grazing Industry versus Other Uses of the Land in the Maracaibo Lowlands. The Maracaibo lowlands were formerly given primarily to grazing and agriculture, and mineral resources remained relatively undeveloped. The land is hot and at times the steamy humidity is very uncomfortable. The rainfall in the northern or most

[15] "Venezuela, A Commercial and Industrial Handbook," *Special Agents Series*, No. 212, U. S. Government Printing Office, p. 108.

accessible part of the basin is light and unreliable and supports scrub forest and poor pasture. In the southern part of the lowland, the rainfall is heavier and supports subsistence agriculture together with some plantations of sugar cane, cacao, and patches of coconuts.

The pastoral and agricultural activities of this area now have been overshadowed by the petroleum industry. The largest single producing oil field of all Latin America is situated on the eastern shore of Lake Maracaibo, near the village of Lagunillas (Fig. 101). Oil has transformed the city of Maracaibo. In 1920, it was a village of 15,000 inhabitants, mostly Indians and Negroes. Pavements and sewers were practically unknown and perhaps little desired by these peoples. Today, Maracaibo is a modern industrial and commercial city of 120,000 people, one-fourth being whites.

The Caribbean Coastal Lowland of Colombia. Most of this area is still given to pasture. However, an increasing amount of land is given to agriculture. A region of dense settlement has developed along the railroad from Cartagena to Calamar (Fig. 101). Here subsistence agriculture has been developed and sugar cane and cotton are grown as commercial crops. The land immediately tributary to Barranquilla grows vegetables and fruits for the city market and produces cotton and cane sugar for export. Santa Marta is one of the most important banana-producing ports of the world. South of the port, the United Fruit Company has developed large banana plantations where water for irrigation may be obtained from streams that flow from the Sierra de Santa Marta Mountains.

The Campos. Like the Llanos of Venezuela, the Campos of Brazil are large, sparsely populated grasslands. One may travel for days and days over these gently rolling areas, with their millions of anthills, and scattered scrubby trees and shrubs. The state of Matto Grosso alone covers approximately 532,210 square miles of land, or more than two and one-half times the size of France; yet it has less than 500,000 people. The landscape of this region is vividly portrayed in the following quotation:

> For miles and miles the train runs through the open country, which is covered with coarse, grayish-brown bunch-grass, and perhaps not a tree in sight. In the distance these brown fields look like our own pastures, dried by the August sun. Then suddenly a change comes, and a dense tree cover shades the trek, the forest edge being as sharply marked against the open country as if a man had been at work there with an axe. . . . After the forest may come an immense stretch of grassland with scattering trees and underbrush or stemless palms, and this may be followed by more forest, or

by a wholly treeless region. Thus the day goes on, monotony but variety; a constant repetition of the same landscape, but a constant change.[16]

The agricultural dwellings of this thinly peopled Campos are widely scattered. One may travel long distances without seeing a house or a living being. Then comes an adobe hut, with its thatched roof, a few scattered trees, and a little patch of cultivated ground, with manioc, beans, and sugar cane. In some areas one sees an hacienda, with its outhouses and cattle; and along some trail the wagon of the plains— the clumsy ox-cart, with its solid, spokeless wheels made out of a large tree trunk, the wheels and the axle turning together with a loud cracking sound which may be heard for miles across the open country.

PRODUCTIVE SOIL YET CULTIVATION IS LIMITED. Only in a few places have attempts been made to produce anything but the natural grasses; hence there is a considerable waste of land. Even the natural grasses of the region go to waste, since they are in large part unoccupied by stock. When the soil is plowed and worked it yields good grass for cattle and horses, and great numbers of these animals could be pastured on land which at present is wild. Cereals and vegetables of different kinds thrive under conditions of climate and soil found here. But the region suffers from a serious handicap. It is indeed a striking fact that in this age of mobilization of resources such a large area should be so little known, and even in large part under the control of the Indian, with almost no expanding frontier encroaching. The reason is not a lack of available resources or extremely adverse climatic and physiographic conditions, as might be presumed, but it is chiefly if not wholly the fact that there is no good natural outlet by which the products of the region may reach a world market.[17]

The Savannas of Africa. Throughout a large part of the low-latitude wet-and-dry regions of Africa, grazing is the dominant activity, and it increases in importance with distance towards the steppe, an area of little rainfall and of uncertain crop production. But these drier marginal lands are covered with shorter and finer grass than occurs in regions that lie equatorward. Along these drier margins, then, the native tribes are engaged mainly in pastoral nomadism. Only where irrigation may be practiced is agriculture the dominant economic activity.

[16] Robert De C. Ward, "The Southern Campos of Brazil," *Bulletin of the American Geographical Society*, 1908, pp. 655, 656.

[17] William H. Haas, "Studies in the Geography of Brazil," *Journal of Geography*, Vol. 24, p. 84.

In grazing his stock the rancher is confronted with numerous handicaps and disadvantages. Everywhere, except along the streams and in highland areas—lands which receive more moisture—grass becomes dry and light yellow in color during the period of drought. Frequently fires sweep these areas; at other times they are overgrazed, especially in the North African Sudan, where large numbers of goats and sheep are kept—animals which are capable of sustaining life on a meager supply of water, and on hard, short herbage.

AGRICULTURAL ADJUSTMENTS

In these regions of rain and drought, man was early compelled, owing to the season of dearth, to forethought and saving. It became necessary for him to store away certain commodities for use during the dry season. Meat from domestic as well as from wild animals is abundant throughout the extensive savannas, but it deteriorates rapidly in this tropical climate. Nuts, roots, and seeds, however, are nutritious and keep well. Especially important are the seeds, which in the form of rice, wheat, barley, sorghum, millet, and maize favored the development of agriculture and a sedentary mode of life.

Agricultural Possibilities. In contrast with the desert and the steppe, most parts of this realm may produce crops. Even the grassy savannas contain numerous cultivated fields and large stretches of land awaiting development. The climate which supports the vigorous growth of tall grass is equally favorable to many kinds of cultivated crops. In areas that receive an abundance of rainfall, rice, tea, spices, and even rubber may be produced, and over vast stretches of land in the drier parts of the realm irrigation is practiced. In some places, however, the moisture supply is moderately abundant and irrigation merely supplements the normal rainfall.

Crops

Various Regions and Their Products. Mixed cultures are quite common in most parts of the realm, yet in some areas certain crops are dominant in the rotation. Thus, in the lower Ganges region where water is abundant, rice and jute are the chief crops; in west central India, which receives only a light rainfall, cotton and the grain sorghums are most important. The Punjab is noted for its wheat; Burma for its rice; and Assam for its tea plantations. This dominance of one or a few crops is seen also in the New World—sugar cane in

Cuba, cacao in coastal Ecuador, and maize in the lowlands of Mexico.

This predominance of a crop in a certain place results partly from the advantages of natural environment and partly because of man-controlled factors. Thus water-loving rice has become the most important crop in many of the wet lowlands of these tropical areas, where a dense population has created a strong demand for this commodity. Tea occupies many well-drained, well-watered highlands, but the real progress of commercial tea production was directly related to the large demand coming from middle-latitude lands, and in some places this industry reached its highest stage of development mainly because of European capital and initiative. Sugar cane became Cuba's most important crop not only because the climate, soil, and relief of that island favored production, but also because of Cuba's situation with respect to the United States and the advantages of preferential tariff agreements with that country. Similarly the island of Puerto Rico at present is an important producer of cane sugar mainly because of the benefit of tariff-free access to the United States, the world's greatest sugar market.[18]

Requirements of Commercial Jute Production Exacting. Although jute may be grown in many tropical places, its cultivation is confined almost exclusively to the eastern part of the lower Ganges-Brahmaputra region, especially that area which lies east of the Brahmaputra. (See Fig. 102 and note the insert in the lower left-hand corner.) Here nearly 3½ billion pounds of jute are produced annually on about 2,800,000 acres of land. The successful cultivation of the crop in this place is due to a combination of factors—good soil, an abundance of rain during the growing season, suitable water for retting purposes, and cheap labor. In addition, this area receives a moderately abundant rainfall even before the summer monsoon has developed.

Methods of cultivation as related to jute production. The quality of the fiber and the yield per acre depend in large measure upon the preparation of the soil. The ground should be plowed about four times and all weeds removed. The farming operations, however, are simple when compared with those of our own country, and most of the agricultural implements are of crude construction. Plowing is usually done with wooden implements that have been faced with iron. After plowing, the rough clods are broken with hand mallets or a piece of timber dragged by a pair of bullocks. This working of

[18] R. H. Whitbeck, "The Sugar Industry of Porto Rico," *Journal of Geography*, Vol. 29, 1930, p. 370.

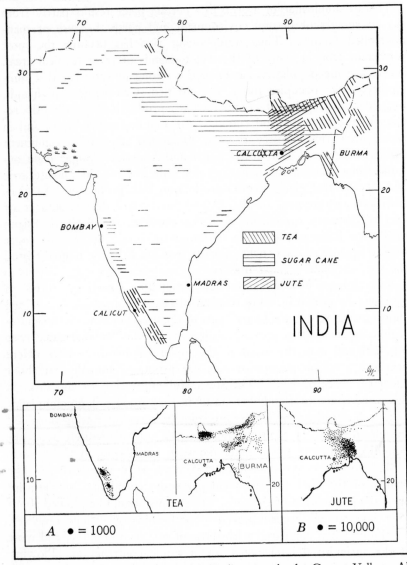

Fig. 102. Most of the sugar cane of India is grown in the Ganges Valley. All the jute is grown in the lower Ganges-Brahmaputra Valley (see insert in lower right-hand corner). Most of the tea is grown in the northeastern and southwestern parts of the country (see inserts at bottom of figure).

Note more done recently in South America.

the land prepares it for the cleaning process, for which bamboos are provided with projecting pins to scratch open the soil and to collect the roots of the previous crop. For fertilizer, farmyard manure, castor cake, and the water hyacinth (a weed) are exclusively used. In this prepared soil the seed is sown by hand, and in a normal season the plant will reach maturity in about 4 months. After the plant is cut, the fiber is separated from the stalk by being immersed in water from 8 to 30 days, the time depending upon the period of the year and upon the district in which the operation is performed. When the ryot (Indian farmer) considers that the bast layers (layers in which the fibers are imbedded) may be separated from the core of the plant with sufficient facility, the work of steeping ceases and the process of stripping commences immediately.

MANUFACTURE OF JUTE. Although practically unknown to Europe and America a hundred years ago, jute fiber has been used in India for centuries in the making of cord, twine, and various coarse fabrics. For an indefinite period these fabrics were produced in India by hand looms. Machine manufacture began in 1822 when some fiber was sent to Dundee, Scotland, now the western home of the jute industry. At that time Dundee was a comparatively important textile center, spinning and weaving flax and hemp; and the same type of plant and equipment could be utilized in the manufacture of this longer and coarser fiber. Dundee exports large quantities of gunny sacks to the coffee districts of Brazil, to the wool-producing areas of Australia, to the sugar fields of Cuba, and to the quebracho area of Gran Chaco, South America.

For a long time India exported raw jute and only a little of the finished product, such as gunny bags and cloth. The British finally directed attention to the possibility of manufacturing jute goods in India, and in the year 1858 a small consignment of machinery was dispatched for Calcutta. Development of the industry, however, was slow because of difficulties encountered in inducing the natives to remain inside the factories during the period of training. In addition, it was difficult to keep the trained operatives constantly employed. In spite of these handicaps, however, the jute industry expanded, and manufactured jute ranks higher in value than raw jute among the exports of India.

Sisal. Unlike jute, which is grown in an area of abundant rainfall and moist soil, henequen, from which the sisal fiber is obtained, is cultivated in some of the drier parts of the realm and is especially important in Yucatan. In this area, climate, drainage, and soil combine to cause dry conditions; but henequen, a desertlike plant, thrives in an arid environment. The average annual rainfall of 35 inches is too scant to supply the moisture needed by most crops grown in this region, chiefly because of rapid evaporation under the intense heat of the tropical sun. In addition, rock and soil make the land even more arid. Water passes rapidly through the thin, stony soil of this area, escaping in numerous underground channels that have been formed in the soft limestone rocks. In some places the roofs of the underground channels have fallen, thereby forming limestone sinks and a karst topography.

From time immemorial the Indians of Yucatan have used the native henequen fiber for making ropes. But its present importance may be said to date from the Spanish-American War, when the export of Manila hemp was temporarily cut off, and today henequen fiber meets almost exclusively the ever-growing demand for binder twine, supplying 80 per cent of the raw fiber used in the manufacture of that commodity in the United States.

There are other areas within the low-latitude wet-and-dry realm in which the natural environment is suitable for the production of henequen, yet Yucatan is the leading producer of this commodity. The proximity of Yucatan to the United States, the largest market for cordage fibers in the world, and the comparatively small cost of production combine with the advantages of the environment in localizing the sisal industry.[19]

Ramie—China Grass. One of the strongest and best of plant fibers is obtained from ramie. It is stronger than any known fiber and almost equals silk in brilliance. In China it is used for clothing, and in many parts of the world it is also manufactured into various articles such as gas mantles, ropes, lines, and canvas.

Ramie grows well in various low-latitude wet-and-dry regions; it is known by various names—ramie in Malay countries, China grass in South China, and rhea in Assam. It is easy to cultivate, and it thrives in almost any soil and in areas where sudden changes of temperature do not occur. Under these conditions two to four crops a season may be secured, each crop yielding about 4 tons of stem per acre. With only two crops per acre and 4 per cent yield of fiber, the resultant fiber would reach nearly one-third of a ton per acre.

Although this plant may be cultivated extensively and yields an abundance of fiber, future development will not be rapid unless some

[19] For an excellent article on the sisal industry see "Sisal Production in Semi-Arid Karst Country of Yucatan," by Alice Foster, *Journal of Geography*, Vol. 29, 1930, pp. 16–25.

device is found whereby the fiber may be quickly separated from the rest of the plant. In China, where labor is abundant and cheap, the fiber is removed by a slow and tedious process of hand labor. Many decorticators have been invented to do this work, but they have not proved successful, since they bruise or otherwise injure the fiber and they do not squeeze out the gum thoroughly. In addition, the problem of producing ramie is handicapped by the varied lengths of the fiber, as spinning is rendered difficult unless the fibers are separated into uniform groups or cut into satisfactory lengths.

Cotton. The low-latitude wet-and-dry realm is second only to the humid subtropical regions in the production of cotton and gives promise of a relatively greater increase in production in the future (Fig. 103). If we examine the environmental complex of this realm in its relation to cotton production, we find a year-round growing season— a distinct advantage over humid subtropical regions because of the possibility of growing perennial varieties of cotton. But many other factors must also be considered. In some parts of the realm, rainfall is either deficient or irregular and irrigation must be provided; elsewhere the soils are poor; in still other areas labor is scarce. There are, however, regions in this realm in which environmental conditions of site and situation so favor production that large quantities of this fiber are grown. India, for example, is one of the major cotton-producing countries of the world; and certain parts of the African Sudan and Brazil are developing rapidly, giving promise of considerable expansion in the future.

COTTON PRODUCTION IN INDIA. Historically there is every reason to believe that India was the original home of the cotton plant—in the eastern hemisphere at least—and there are records of cotton in India as far back as 800 B.C. At the present time, India is surpassed only by the United States in the production of cotton, a relative position that it has held for many years. The greater part of this Indian cotton is grown in the rolling upland of the Deccan, a land of light rainfall and black, fertile soils. The importance of this area as a cotton producer has been a major factor in making Bombay, a center located west of this region, the principal cotton-manufacturing city of India.

The rainfall of the Deccan of India is uncertain. Years of plenty are followed by years of dearth, and drought frequently injures the cotton crop. The solution to this problem in many areas would be to build a more extensive system of irrigation, especially by means of canals. But large parts of the Deccan contain such rugged topography and such deeply imbedded river channels that canal irrigation would

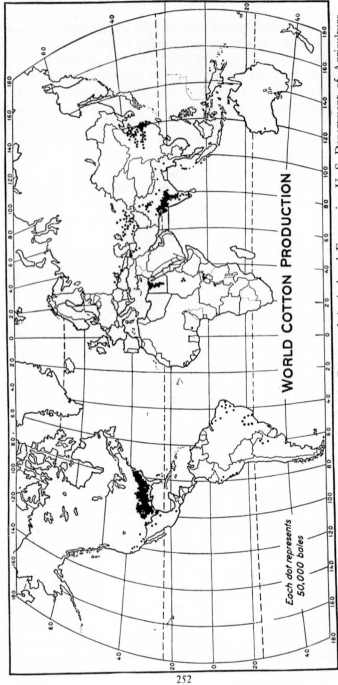

WORLD COTTON PRODUCTION

Each dot represents 50,000 bales

FIG. 103. World cotton production according to the Bureau of Agricultural Economics, U. S. Department of Agriculture.

be an unprofitable enterprise. In some such sections, however, tank irrigation has been developed (Fig. 104).

The rainfall of the Deccan is not only irregular but also concentrated mainly in the summer season. The period of cotton production is therefore narrowly limited, especially where irrigation is practiced little or where it is utilized in the production of other crops. Under

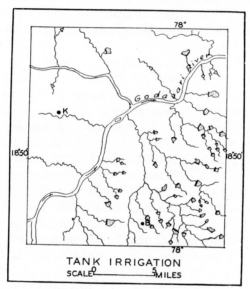

FIG. 104. Tank irrigation in India. (*Géographie universelle*, Armand Collins, Paris, 1929, Tome IX, p. 341.)

such conditions the Indian cotton production has been confined largely to the poorer grades or short-staple varieties, which are better suited than long-staple cotton to the short period of rainfall.

The chief cotton-producing region of India is sometimes called the black-earth belt. The name is derived from the soil color, which has resulted from the decomposition of the basaltic rocks which cover about 200,000 square miles of peninsular India. This black soil is extremely fertile, especially considering its tropical location (pp. 98–99) and remains productive although cropped for hundreds of years. A peculiar characteristic which makes it very valuable in the dry climate of this area is its remarkable tenacity of moisture. Instead of allowing the rain to drain away, it becomes a tenacious mud during the wet season.

The future development of India's cotton industry depends mainly upon the production of more lint per acre and not upon the expansion of the cotton acreage. Although India is the second largest cotton-producing country in the world, its per acre production is extremely low, being only 91 pounds in 1937. Since raw cotton is normally the leading item of India's export trade, an increase in the production of this commodity, especially when the increase is associated with the production at lower cost, would enable the Indian people to obtain from abroad additional economic goods that are lacking within the country.

LARGE POTENTIAL REGION FOR COTTON IN BRAZIL. In normal years Brazil ranks fifth in the world as a producer of cotton, and here there seems to be ample room for rapid expansion. This prospective development is based upon several major favorable conditions in the environment of Brazil: (1) a large potential cotton-growing area, estimated at more than 75,000,000 acres; (2) a climate that is generally favorable; and (3) suitable soil. Credence is lent to the large estimated acreage by the fact that fifteen of the eighteen states of Brazil are already producing cotton in commercial quantities. The existence of suitable soil and climate is evidenced by the high yields—as much as 890 pounds of lint cotton to the acre—and the average yield per acre is more than 130 per cent of that in our own country. Moreover, land is cheaper in Brazil than in the United States; the boll weevil as yet has not spread its ravages; and, owing to the tropical climate, long-staple perennial varieties of cotton may be grown. Yet Brazil's production is only 15 to 20 per cent of that of the United States. No doubt, the intensive interest in coffee plantations, with specialization in production, storing, and marketing of coffee, accounts in large part for the underdeveloped status of cotton growing. Moreover, laborers in general are unskilled and unfamiliar with the cultivation and handling of the crop.

COTTON PRODUCTION DEVELOPED IN AFRICAN REGIONS. Other low-latitude wet-and-dry regions of considerable potentiality in the growing of cotton are found in the Sudan of Africa and territory of Uganda. In Uganda, 1,072,000 acres of long-staple cotton were harvested in 1944–1945. Here climate and soil are favorable, and insect pests cause little loss. In the Anglo-Egyptian Sudan the British have been interested in fostering cotton culture. One of the outstanding and promising fields of operation is the Gezira irrigation project in the Anglo-Egyptian Sudan. During 1940–1946 the Anglo-Egyptian Sudan produced more than 300,000 bales of cotton annually.

Rice. Although the use of rice antedates history so far that we have no knowledge when its cultivation first began, it seems to have originated in this climatic realm, being the only cereal that still grows wild in India. It is the major cereal of the millions of the Far East and the Orient, and these densely populated regions of Asia would indeed be seriously handicapped without it.

The rice production of the world is essentially confined to three major climatic realms—the humid subtropical, the low-latitude wet

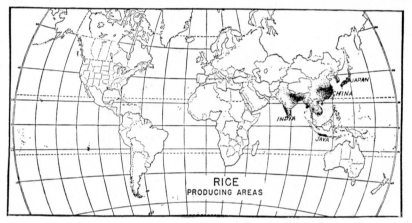

Fig. 105. World rice production. Each dot represents 200,000,000 pounds.

and dry, and the tropical rain forest. Of these the low-latitude wet-and-dry realm is most important (Fig. 105). It contains India, where the average annual production reaches approximately 70 billion pounds of cleaned rice. It also contains the chief rice-exporting countries of southeast Asia.

RICE THE MOST WIDELY CULTIVATED CEREAL IN INDIA. In India, rice is the major crop in the Lower Ganges and Brahmaputra Delta regions, Bihar and Orissa, the west-coast and the east-coast lowlands, and in the Sind (Fig. 106). The practice of growing the rice, however, differs in the various parts of the country, depending largely on the climatic conditions of the various areas. In the Lower Ganges-Brahmaputra Delta, with its abundance of moisture, its low-lying alluvial soils, and its dense agricultural population, two or more crops of rice may be grown annually. Here several varieties are produced, depending on the depth to which the valleys are flooded, some of the larger plants attaining a height of more than 10 feet in the more deeply submerged part of the valleys. In most of the other parts of India rice culture depends largely upon irrigation—well irrigation in the Middle Ganges Plain, tank irrigation in Bihar and Orissa, and canal irrigation in the Upper Ganges Plain.

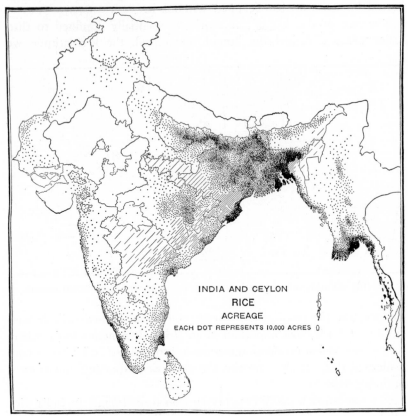

INDIA AND CEYLON
RICE
ACREAGE
EACH DOT REPRESENTS 10,000 ACRES

Fig. 106.   Rice acreage in India and Ceylon.   (U. S. Department of Agriculture.)

RICE PRODUCTION IN CEYLON.   On Ceylon, an island of dense population and intensively cultivated land, rice may be seen growing high up the slopes of the hills and mountains.   In traveling from the seacoast to interior Ceylon, one may see numerous small rice fields, one rising above the other, forming a veritable giant flight of gentle water steps.   Here are evidences of a tremendous amount of hand labor involved in keeping these terraced slopes in the proper condition for rice culture.   Too much water or poorly constructed banks may cause landslides and consequent ruin not only to the terraces that give way, but to the ones below as well; too little water will check maximum yields of the crop.[20]

RICE PRODUCTION IN CHINA. In the wet-and-dry region of south China, rice cultivation flourishes in the valley bottoms and on terraced hillsides. In this densely populated region rice is the most important crop; in some places three crops are produced in a year by reason of the favorable climatic conditions.[21] In this region the rainfall is abundant, falling throughout the year, but principally during the summer monsoon. Along the coast the average rainfall is 80 inches and above, decreasing to less than 40 inches farther inland.

COMMERCIAL PRODUCTION OF RICE. In densely peopled areas rice is consumed at home, very little being exported; in sparsely populated areas rice is an important item in the export trade. Thus the Ganges Plain and south China, though large rice-producing regions, are minor exporters of this cereal. The Lower Ganges Plain, with its population of more than 550 per square mile of land, constitutes one of the major rice-consuming as well as rice-producing regions of the world. In densely populated China rice exportation is usually prohibited. On the other hand, the sparsely populated countries such as Burma, French Indo-China, and Thailand are important in the export trade of this commodity (Fig. 107). In the latter areas tropical jungle covers much of the land, and even upland rice is planted here and there in small, widely scattered clearings in the forest thickets.

Rice is grown also in various other low-latitude wet-and-dry regions of Africa, South America, and Central America; but in none of these regions is it as important as in southeast Asia.

Millet and Sorghum. People living in our latitudes are unable to appreciate the vast importance of millet and sorghum. There are many varieties of these plants, and they are used for many purposes. Some are grown for food, others for forage only, and some for fuel. But in India, South China, and the savanna regions of Africa their most important use is as a food for man.

In India three varieties of millet—jowar, bajra, and ragi—are widely cultivated and constitute the most important cereals in the entire south-central part of the country. Jowar and bajra are grown in the northern part of this area, and ragi in the south. Ragi yields more

---

[20] Ceylon falls into two types of climate—low-latitude wet-and-dry, and rainy low-latitude.

[21] Julean Arnold, "China, A Commercial and Industrial Handbook," *Trade Promotion Series* No. 38, U. S. Department of Commerce, 1926, p. 9.

abundantly than the other two millets on relatively sterile soils; hence it finds a prominent place in the crop rotation of the southern part of the Deccan, an area of generally poor soils derived from crystalline rocks.

Sugar Cane. This is the climatic realm in which the cultivation of sugar cane has reached its maximum development, more than 80 per

Fig. 107.   Rice planting near Rangoon, Burma.   This primitive method of rice planting prevails in the Orient.

cent of the world's crop of cane being grown here.   Such marked development of cane-sugar production attests a favorable combination of environmental conditions.[22]   The year-round growing season, the frequent showers (about 50 to 60 inches of rainfall per year), and the relatively dry harvest season are conditions that bring forth maximum yields.   On the other hand, cool or cloudy weather or drought during the growing season is likely to stunt growth, making short joints in the cane, resulting in a reduced tonnage, an increase in fiber, and a reduction in the sugar content.

CANE SUGAR VERSUS BEET SUGAR.   Sugar cane is the most important raw material used in supplying mankind with sugar, 60 to 70 per cent

[22] *U. S. Department of Agriculture Yearbook,* 1928, pp. 879, 880.

of the sugar of commerce coming from cane and the remainder from sugar beets. The chief increase in cane production came during World War I, at the expense of the output of beet sugar. In the five years just preceding that war, out of an average world production of 18,400,000 short tons of sugar, 8,500,000 tons (46 per cent of world production) were produced from beets. In the five years following the close of the war, only 4,700,000 tons of sugar (25 per cent of world production) were produced from beets.[23] The great falling off in beet-sugar production was due to the fact that Europe, the focus of the war, was also the center of the beet-sugar industry. These countries no longer found an outlet for their surplus sugar and consequently the acreage and production declined. Thus in 1913–1914 Germany produced 2,900,000 tons of beet sugar; but by 1919–1920 her production had fallen to only 800,000 tons.

This decline of the beet-sugar industry stimulated the production of cane sugar, especially in Cuba, where, even before the war, in fact since the reciprocity treaty of 1903, production had increased rapidly,[24] with subsequent heavy investment of American capital in the Cuban sugar industry. In spite of the increased production of beet sugar between the two world wars and the world-wide depression of the 1930's, Cuba still leads the world in the production of sugar for export. Furthermore the island republic is capable of greatly increasing her output if the demand warrants such development.

CUBAN PROSPERITY DEPENDS UPON SUGAR. Sugar cane is a basic factor in the national economy of Cuba. It constitutes the chief source of wealth. From the standpoint of value, raw sugar, refined sugar, and molasses together constitute 80 per cent of all commodities exported. In short, sugar is to Cuba what textiles are to England, coffee to Brazil, and wheat to Canada.

A significant feature of the recent development of the Cuban sugar industry is that it takes place in the eastern part of the island. Although excellent land still exists in the western part, the long period of cultivation has diminished its fertility. On the other hand, the eastern

[23] U. S. Department of Agriculture Yearbook, 1923, pp. 215, 216.
[24] In 1903 a reciprocity treaty was negotiated granting Cuba a preferential tariff rate—20 per cent less than the full duty—on all Cuban products exported to the United States. This concession, so long as full-duty sugar continued to be imported in considerable quantities, operated rather as a bonus to the Cuban producers than as a benefit to American consumers, and therefore stimulated production in Cuba.

section contains virgin soils, and until recently this area has been jungle land, which, when cleared and fitted for cultivation, is extremely fertile and yields large crops at a low cost.

World War II disrupted much of the beet-sugar industry of Europe and once again the world experienced a sugar shortage. Consequently the production of cane sugar was again stimulated. In postwar Europe, the beet-sugar industry is again being encouraged and sooner or later the cane-sugar industry will be depressed.

Cuba's location in the tropics gives her ideal temperature and rainfall for the growing of sugar cane. The environmental conditions are indeed so favorable that the crop is usually a perennial one. When the cane is harvested two courses may be pursued with reference to the next year's crop. If the roots are left in the ground, new shoots or ratoons will spring from them, and a crop may thus be obtained without further planting. Or a certain proportion of the crop of canes may be planted in furrows. Sprouts spring from the joints and provide the next crop. So admirably adapted to the growth of cane are the soil and climate of Cuba that it may often be profitably ratooned for ten or more years. In Louisiana, on the other hand, the cane can grow for only eight or nine months before it is cut because of danger from frost.

In Cuba, sugar cane is produced by large estates which have their own mills, or centrals, from which railways or tramways radiate; but the greater part of the crop is grown under control of tenant planters, called colonos. So much hand labor is involved in harvesting the crop that it is necessary to import laborers from nearby areas. Large numbers of Jamaicans and other West Indian Negroes come for the sugar harvest (Fig. 108); some also come from Spain and the Madeira Islands, but there are never enough. Shortage of labor is the chief problem that has to be faced by the planters.

INDIA'S CANE SUGAR CONFINED MAINLY TO THE GANGETIC PLAIN. India long ranked second only to Cuba in sugar-cane production. But within recent years India has become the world's leading producer of cane sugar because of limitations imposed upon the industry in Cuba.[25] Although the crop is grown throughout most of peninsular India, the chief area of production embraces the middle and upper regions of the Gangetic Plain (Fig. 102). Here the crop is planted during the dry season, usually February to April, irrigated by means of wells

---

[25] Many countries have, at times, placed high import duties or quotas on sugar. These restrictions have made it difficult for Cuba to find markets for as much sugar as she formerly exported.

and canals, and harvested from ten to fifteen months after the time of planting. The fertile alluvial soils, the high temperatures throughout the year, the abundance of rainfall during the summer monsoon, and the dense agricultural population are factors to which the production has adjusted itself in this part of the country. Labor is super-abundant and cheap. Owing to the dense population, most of the

Fig. 108. Hauling sugar cane in a new-style cart in Cuba, which ranks first or second in the production of sugar. (Courtesy United Fruit Company.)

crop is consumed at home in the form of gur, a low grade of soft brown sugar. In spite of the large sugar-cane crop of India, the country does not normally produce enough for her own needs, but imports sugar in large quantities. Since 1937 her exports of this commodity have at times surpassed the imports.

SUGAR PRODUCTION IN JAVA. In Java the cultivation of sugar is a very old industry, and it has been subjected to many vicissitudes. Sugar cane is grown chiefly in the eastern part of the island, since it is here that the climate is the low-latitude wet-and-dry type, the western part being an area of tropical rain forest. Unlike Cuba with a relatively sparse population and extensive cultivation, Java has 42,-000,000 people and practices intensive methods of agriculture. In Cuba, new land is cleared for the sugar crop, whereas in Java a rotation of crops is practiced so that the soil fertility may be maintained and maximum yields obtained, not only of sugar, but also of other food crops. A common practice consists of growing sugar cane one year, then following it with a legume, after which corn and beans are planted.

BRAZIL THE CHIEF SUGAR PRODUCER OF SOUTH AMERICA. In Brazil, sugar cane is produced in the northeast part of the country, where there are excellent natural conditions for the growth of the crop. Here sugar cane has been grown for a long time; in fact, at the time of the early settlement of the United States, the east coast of Brazil was the chief source of supply for the markets of Europe. The crop, however, declined in importance with the discovery of gold and diamonds in the interior, and subsequently with the freeing of the slaves who worked on the plantations. At present, production is handicapped by the lack of intelligent, industrious workers for the plantations as well as the mills. Moreover, the Brazilian planter found it increasingly difficult to compete with the more modern plantations, in Cuba, Hawaii, and other parts of the low-latitude wet-and-dry realm. Brazilian sugar is, therefore, not very important in international trade.

SUGAR-CANE PRODUCTION OF THE HAWAIIAN ISLANDS. Sugar cane was first introduced into the Hawaiian Islands in 1837, after which the industry developed slowly until 1876, when it was greatly stimulated by the reciprocity treaty of 1876, by virtue of which sugar and various other products of Hawaii were admitted to the United States free of duty. This simply resulted in a bonus of about two cents per pound to the Hawaiian producers, which greatly stimulated their industry. Export shipments of sugar increased from 13,000 tons in 1876, the year in which the treaty was made, to 130,000 tons in 1890. This rapid increase was facilitated by the extreme fertility of the volcanic soils of recent origin, together with the regulation of the water supply on some of the plantations by means of irrigation. Scientific agriculture under these favorable conditions has given Hawaii first place among all countries in cane-sugar yield per acre. Here huge irrigation projects have been established, and intensive cultivation and heavy machinery characterize the industry.

PUERTO RICAN SUGAR PRODUCTION AND THE TARIFF. In Puerto Rico the industry may be said to date from 1515, when sugar cane was introduced from the neighboring island of Santo Domingo. Under the encouragement of the Spanish government, which made loans to planters, the industry gradually developed. Since the American occupation, growth has been rapid, old methods of production and manufacture have been discarded, an experiment station has been established, railroads have been built, and an irrigation project for supplying water to the dry southern coastal region of the island has also been put into effect.

Although Cuba has a distinct advantage in producing sugar at lower cost, Puerto Rico is favored in its tariff relations with the United States. The Puerto Rican sugar enters the United States market duty-

Fig. 109. A sugar mill and cane plantation, San José, Calauna, Taguna. (Courtesy U. S. War Department.)

free. In fact, "there is no doubt that the tariff benefit is the greatest single advantage enjoyed by the Porto Rican sugar growers." [26]

CANE SUGAR IN THE PHILIPPINES. Sugar cane has been grown in the Philippine Islands for a long period of time. Indeed, even Magellan reported its presence after his voyage around the world. At present this crop covers approximately 593,000 acres of land, and it is the most valuable export of the islands, about 85 per cent of which is sent to the United States.

For many years the sugar industry suffered severely from backward methods in the technique of sugar production; but conditions in this respect are improving gradually. In 1916 more than 90 per cent of

[26] R. H. Whitbeck, "The Sugar Industry of Porto Rico," *Journal of Geography*, Vol. 29, 1930, p. 370.

the Philippine sugar exports were in the form of muscovado, a crude product like the gur of India. By 1940, modern mills were turning out more than 80 per cent of the total crop as standardized centrifugal sugar (Fig. 109). In cane varieties similar progress has been made. Planters are trying out the best of the Hawaiian and Javanese canes and are developing some excellent varieties of their own.

Fig. 110.   Tea pickers on a vast plantation in the highlands of Ceylon.   (Publishers Photo Service.)

More than 90 per cent of the cane is produced by the tenant system. With few rare exceptions, the mill companies own no cane land but mill the cane for a percentage of the sugar. The tenant or actual grower thus has a detailed contract with the landowners for the use of the land and another with the mill for the grinding of his cane.

Tea—Its Commercial Importance in the Low-Latitude Wet-and-Dry Realm. The tea plant is indigenous to southeast Asia, having originated somewhere in the highlands of South China, Indo-China, or India. The plant, however, has spread out of the realm, poleward into the humid subtropical regions, and equatorward into the rainy low latitudes. "Climatically tea belongs to low latitude areas where high temperatures, long growing season, and heavy, well-distributed rainfall favor a rich, continuous, and rapid growth of new tender shoots. Such conditions are found in southern India, Ceylon (Fig. 110), and the Netherlands East Indies where there is no dormant season for the tea bush and picking continues throughout the entire year." [27]

Tea requires fertile but well-drained soil as well as much moisture, a combination usually furnished best upon hillsides. Given good drainage and a fertile soil, the size of the crop will depend upon the abundance of moisture and uniformity of temperatures throughout the year, since these are conditions which stimulate growth and the development of new tender shoots and consequently govern the number of pickings that may be made during the year.

In the production of tea, China probably ranks first; but in export India leads all others. In South China, tea is grown in family gardens for home use. Its origin seems to have been an attempt to make pleasant the habit of drinking boiled water, a necessity recognized long ago by a population living on a land in which sanitary conditions are greatly affected by density of population and primitive conditions.

Most of the tea acreage of India is in the northeastern part of the country—in northern and eastern Bengal, in the upper Brahmaputra Valley, and in Assam (Fig. 102). In fact, about four-fifths of the tea acreage of India is in this northeastern area, the remaining acreage being in the southern part of the peninsula, in the Nilgiri Hills. The tea districts are situated either on the hills or in the plains. The tea from the hill districts is of a fine flavor, but less is produced per acre than on the plains. In the hills of Assam most of the tea plantations consist of small patches of cleared land in the monsoon forest.

Maté: The Tea of the Plate River Basin. Maté is the name given to the dried leaves of trees that are widely scattered in South America. These leaves resemble the leaves of ordinary tea very closely in chemical composition. In addition, they are prepared in the same general way for use as a beverage, and they have the same effect upon the system as the teas of China, Ceylon, and India.

Although maté trees are found in various parts of South America, the species most suitable for making tea (*Ilex paraguayensis*) is utilized commercially only within a relatively small area. This maté-producing unit embraces the Plate River Basin of Brazil, eastern Paraguay, and northeastern Argentina. In this area maté production is further limited to suitable sites. Thus the maté trees are usually not found

[27] See Glenn T. Trewartha, "The Tea Crop," *Journal of Geography*, Vol. 28, 1929, p. 1.

along the major rivers within a belt which may vary from 10 to 30 miles in width, but rather in depressions in the foothills of mountains.[28]

Although maté is produced in large quantities in Brazil, Paraguay, and Argentina, only the first two countries export the product in noteworthy quantities. In normal years, Brazil produces approximately 200,000 tons of maté and exports 40 per cent of this amount to Argentina, Uruguay, and Chile. Argentina produces approximately 20,000 tons of this commodity annually, but, because of the heavy consumption within the country, imports an additional 100,000 tons of maté a year. Paraguay produces from 12,000 to 15,000 tons of maté annually and exports more than half of this amount to Argentina.[29]

SOCIAL RESPONSES

This tropical realm with its rhythm in rainfall and temperature has had a pronounced effect upon the civilization produced within it. Owing to the high temperatures throughout the year few clothes are necessary, except along the poleward margins of the realm. Yet during the dry season the temperatures become sufficiently cool so that some clothing is essential in order to keep comfortable. Hence the textile art was early developed here, since the raw materials are ever present in the fibers of leaves, husks, and grasses, and in the wool of animals. Materials are also plentiful for shelter, which is constructed in many places from bamboo, the palms, and various woods of the monsoon forest. In the wetter parts of the realm the houses are raised on stilts; in some areas they are constructed in tall trees, affording protection against floods, stagnant air, insect pests, and wild animals. In other regions termites make large buildings of wood unsafe. As a rule, the houses at their best are temporary structures, providing only for the simplest needs of the family.

Owing to the dangers imposed by the abundant animal life of the savannas and forested areas, the family unit has been expanded into the larger social organizations for protection. Within the family unit itself, woman tends toward equality with man, since she is actively concerned with the production of a surplus. She is a farmer, a domesticator of animals, and she also spins and weaves the clothes for the household.

[28] C. R. Cameron, "Maté: An Important Brazilian Product," *Journal of Geography*, Vol. 29, February 1930, p. 56.

[29] *Op. cit.*, p. 68.

POPULATION CONTRASTS

Throughout most of these regions the population density is greater than that of the equatorial forests on the one hand or the desert and steppe on the other, but there are sharp contrasts within the realm itself. A population map of the world (Fig. 47) shows an exceedingly dense distribution of people in some parts of the realm, whereas still other areas have been sparsely settled.

Areas of Dense Population. Regions such as the Indo-Gangetic Plain and South China contain some of the densest agricultural agglomerations on earth. These areas have been subject to human infiltration from the continental interior throughout all historic time. The more advanced peoples, who were the last to descend upon these regions, stamped them with their own social and political institutions. Here human settlements consist of countless little hamlets, the boundaries between which are often difficult to distinguish. "Innumerable little farms, identical in appearance, dozens of mud houses with a few scattered trees, are huddled together. Rarely does one see a larger village." [30]

Also the population increases as one approaches the zones along which different modes of life come in contact. This occurs between the jungle and savanna as well as between savanna and steppe. "Markets, sometimes cities, spring up at these points of contact, or rather of welding, for such zones are bonds between divergent groups." [31]

Sparsely Populated Lands. A dense population, however, is not characteristic of all portions of the realm. The Sudan, the Llanos, the Chaco, Matto Grosso, and northern Australia are among the sparsely populated areas, the environments of which are less favorable for human settlements. All these regions were remote from centers of early civilization, hence they have been subject to slight human infiltration. In some places dense forests, teeming with wild animal life, inhibit human expansion; in others, vast stretches of grassy and scrub-wooded plains interspersed with large bogs or swamps (morichales) offer a precarious subsistence for the sparse population.

The difficult problems resulting from the presence of dense forests are well illustrated in northeast India, in Burma, and in places along the margins of the African Sudan and Amazon Basin, where forests

[30] Rewritten by permission from *Principles of Human Geography*, by P. Vidal de la Blache, Henry Holt & Co., New York, 1924, p. 98.

[31] *Op. cit.*, p. 55.

stand as veritable bulwarks against human expansion. In them clearing of the land is rendered difficult by the rapid growth of trees and brush; in them the danger from insects—the most deadly animals of the tropics—and wild animals is great. Here the lurking tiger, the stampeding elephant, the poisonous snake, and the death-dealing insect all have caused immense loss to the native tribes. One of the greatest obstacles to the cultivation of tea in the cleared patches in the forests of Assam has been the tiger, which, watching an opportunity, pounces upon a lone native and carries him off into the forest thicket.

The landscape of the sparsely populated Llanos is vividly portrayed by a man who traveled from Ciudad Bolivar to Barcelona:

> I chose upstream, and quickly plunged again into another morichale, such a jungle and swamp, filled with the odor of rotting vegetation, as only wild men or lost ones attempt to fight their way through. Plants with shark's teeth, sabre cacti with hook-shaped horns and needle points along the edge, upright sprays of vegetable bayonets, grappled and pierced clothes and skin. Through this mass I waded for perhaps two hours, by no means certain there was an end to it; but finally, with legs and feet a patchwork of cuts and scratches, and my shirt in rags, I came out upon another vast tuft-grass and sandy prairie. On these immense scrub-wooded plains, crisscrossed in every direction by narrow cowpaths, but rarely by human trails, a man might wander until he choked or starved.[32]

In the Llanos of Venezuela, wars and an unstable government have also prevented the population from increasing; in fact, more prosperity was evident there during the 1890's. The money spent, the lives lost, the livestock killed, and crops ruined, all have been detrimental to the llanero, the inhabitant of the Llanos. "Sparse as is the population, it is rather a matter of surprise that the number of inhabitants is so great rather than it is so small. During the period of seventy-five years there have been no fewer than seventy-six revolutions. During sixty of these years the country has seen two armies almost continuously in the field."[33] Under such conditions foreign capital is not attracted to the country for the exploitation of its natural resources; hence land, abundant land, the one great resource of the Llanos, is as yet but slightly developed.

Other causes, such as slavery, pestilence, and famines, have operated to keep a sparse population in many portions of the realm. As pre-

[32] Rewritten by permission from *Working North from Patagonia*, by H. A. Franck, The Century Co., 1921, p. 626.

[33] Rewritten by permission from *Up the Orinoco and Down the Magdalena*, by H. J. Mozans, D. Appleton & Co., 1910, p. 135.

viously stated, famines are common in most of the regions and have decimated whole areas.

CONCLUSIONS

The intermediate location of this realm—except monsoonal south-east Asia—has resulted in less enervating climatic conditions than those of rainy low-latitude regions and more abundant rainfall than in the desert and steppe. The rainfall, however, is frequently irregular in occurrence in many parts of the realm, resulting in years of plenty followed by years of dearth, years of feast followed by spells of famine.

Throughout the realm a seasonal distribution of rainfall is experienced, the rain falling chiefly during the summer, leaving the remainder of the year relatively dry. This marked periodicity in rainfall has been matched by a periodicity in the plant and animal kingdom. Plants spring forth in the rainy season, furnishing feed for animals and food for man. Animals quite frequently store a surplus for the dry season, or they migrate into wetter lands. The farmer plants and cultivates his crops during the rainy period and stores a surplus for the season of dearth.

Some parts of the realm are densely populated and intensively cultivated; others are inhabited only by a few savage tribes. Some parts offer great opportunities for future economic and social progress; others are more or less stagnant when measured with the present-day yardstick. But in general, owing to the year-round growing season, the abundant rainfall in large areas, and the vast expanses of virgin soil almost untouched by man, this realm as a whole is increasing in productivity and is furnishing materials for man locally as well as commodities for export to colder lands. Included within this realm are the densely populated monsoonal areas of the tropics—lands of abundant food.

REFERENCES

BERGSMARK, D. R., "The Geographic Regions of India," *Journal of Geography,* Vol. 28, 1929, pp. 108–122.

BLACHE, P. VIDAL DE LA, *Principles of Human Geography,* Henry Holt & Co., 1926.

DUTT, R. C., *Open Letters to Lord Curzon on the Famines of India,* Kegan Paul, Trench, Trübner & Co., 1900.

The Economic History of India, Kegan Paul, Trench, Trübner & Co., 1900.

FOSTER, ALICE, "Sisal Production in Semi-Arid Karst Country of Yucatan," *Journal of Geography*, Vol. 29, pp. 16–25.

HOPKINS, E. W., *India Old and New*, Charles Scribner & Sons, 1902.

KENDREW, G. W., *The Climates of the Continents*, The Clarendon Press, Oxford, 1922.

MOZANS, H. J., *Up the Orinoco and Down the Magdalena*, D. Appleton & Co., 1910.

RENNER, G. T., "The Sudan, A Tropical Famine Area," *Matériaux pour l'étudie des calamités*, No. 11, Geneva, pp. 7–8.

SCHIMPER, A. F. W., *Plant Geography*, The Clarendon Press, pp. 347, 372, 373.

SHANTZ, H. L., and C. F. MARBUT, *The Vegetation and Soils of Africa*, American Geographical Society, 1923, pp 50–60.

U. S. DEPARTMENT OF COMMERCE, "Venezuela, A Commercial and Industrial Handbook," *Special Agents Series*, No. 212.

WARD, R. DE C., "The Southern Campos of Brazil," *Bulletin of the American Geographical Society*, 1908, pp. 655–656.

WHITBECK, R. H., "The Sugar Industry of Porto Rico," *Journal of Geography*, Vol. 29, pp. 369–370.

ZON, R., and W. N. SPARHAWK, *Forest Resources of the World*, McGraw-Hill Book Co., 1923, pp. 435–436.

Chapter 8

THE LOW-LATITUDE DESERT

AND STEPPE

The population map of the world (Fig. 47) indicates an extremely irregular distribution of people. Conspicuous blots representing human agglomerations stand in sharp contrast to large light-colored patches showing sparsely settled or uninhabited land. Some places are too hot and wet for man to prosper, others are too cold, and still others have excessive heat and drought. In fact, "most of the earth is too something or other" to make a pleasant home for man. This condition is especially true within the tropics, where the area of desert and steppe is vast. More than one-half of all the land lying between the parallels of 15 and 35° latitudes is classified as desert, and much of the remainder receives light or unreliable rainfall. Five thousand miles of desert stretch from northwest India to the west coast of Africa, extending over an area larger than that of the United States. The desert of Australia includes about two-fifths of that continent; and other tropical deserts embrace several hundred thousand square miles of land.

These arid regions, whether uplands or lowlands, are found in their greatest extent in the trade-wind belts, embracing the deserts and steppes of Arabia, Persia, Sudan, Sahara, South Africa, and central Australia (Fig. 111). Wherever they occur they present the same general characteristics of climate, flora, fauna, and even of land surface; and where populated they are inhabited by nomads of pastoral or hunting tribes. In them the movement of peoples reaches its maximum. Here the hunting savage makes the widest sweep in pursuit of his game; here the pastoral nomad follows his systematic wanderings in search of pasture as well as of plunder.[1]

[1] Ellen Churchill Semple, *Influences of Geographic Environment*, Henry Holt & Co., 1911, p. 483.

271

Yet, here and there over these vast stretches of barren rock, sand dunes, and adobe, are scattered small settlements or groups of settlements. In some places these human agglomerations are grouped in circular fashion about a well or depression.[2] Here the presence of water is manifested by the luxuriant growth of vegetation and the carefully cultivated fields. In other places, as in the valley of the Nile and in many of the oases of coastal Peru, northern Chile, northwestern Mexico, and other desert areas, the settlements are strung

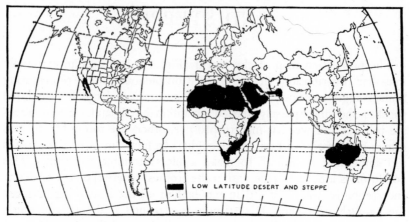

Fig. 111. World distribution of the low-latitude desert and steppe.

in linear fashion along the banks of streams—the life-giving waters which have come from more humid regions.

For hundreds of years the agricultural products of the oases have entered widely into world trade. During the last century, however, the mineral products of the true desert have also taken an important place in the economic life of industrial nations. This is especially true of the sodium nitrates of Chile. These reserves of mineral salts, readily soluble in water, have been preserved for countless centuries owing to the aridity of the region in which they occur. The importance of these deposits is far-reaching, penetrating the economic, social, and political structure of many peoples. Nitrates are used as fertilizers; hence they are essential to food production and to life; and they are an essential ingredient in explosives considered indispensable for national defense. The production of nitrate salts furnishes employment

[2] The houses are built along the outer margins of depressions so that the area within the depression may be devoted to crops.

to thousands of people and has afforded millions in revenue for the Chilean government.

Although sodium nitrate is perhaps the most characteristic mineral product of the desert, the value of the output is less than that of the copper production of arid lands. Still other minerals are of increasing importance, such as potash, salt, borax, and natural soda, products that attest the aridity of these deserts.

The daily life of the desert dweller reflects a nice adjustment to the climatic environment of the realm. His clothes are white so that absorption of heat may be reduced to the minimum. The shelter varies from the sun-dried adobe hut suited to the needs of the sedentary dwellers to the light, easily transported tent adapted to the wandering habits of the nomad. Domestic animals are the desert wanderer's chief means of subsistence, and a shortage of water or pasture is his ever-present fear. The nomad is dependent upon his animals for food, clothing, shelter; in fact, for life itself. When the pastures dry out he faces starvation and death unless he turns to raids and plunder. On the other hand, the sedentary peoples of the oases possess cultivated crops, their water supply although precarious is more reliable than desert rains, and their basis of subsistence is accordingly more secure.

Aridity has thus been an important factor related to almost every human activity of the desert, and it is reflected in the economic, social, and political adjustments of the inhabitants. Thus climate is the dominant factor affecting man's activities here, making possible certain human adjustments and excluding others.

REGIONS OF MAXIMUM HEAT AND ARIDITY

The climate of these deserts is marked by peculiarities and extremes. The steady winds are interrupted by hot sand blasts and whirls, which are extremely trying to both plants and animals. Much of the scanty rainfall comes in the form of cloudbursts, and after a few minutes of torrential downpour the sky may be clear again for weeks together. Changes in temperature are rapid and extreme. The relative humidity rarely exceeds 50 per cent, except in a few coastal areas, and the desiccating winds quickly dry up all tissue not especially adapted to desert conditions. The sunshine is intensely bright from sunrise to sunset, with a truly scorching effect upon the life of the realm.

Rainfall. The amount of precipitation varies from one desert area to another, but in general it is less than 10 inches annually (Fig. 112).

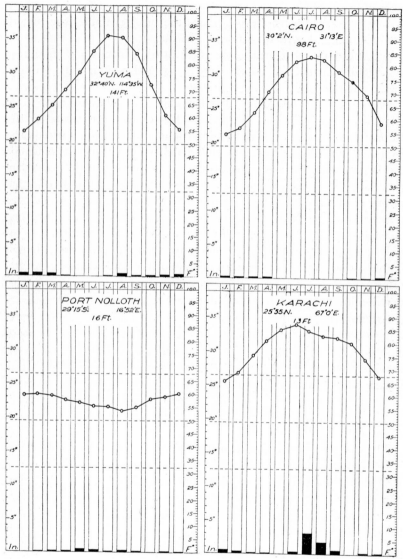

FIG. 112.   Climatic graphs of typical low-latitude desert stations.

This extreme aridity is due primarily to the situation of the several areas with respect to (1) the trade-wind belts, (2) the high-pressure belts (tropical calms or horse latitudes), (3) mountain barriers, and (4) cold ocean currents.

INFLUENCE OF TRADE WINDS AND HIGH-PRESSURE BELTS. In all the low-latitude deserts, with the exception of the Thar of India, the prevailing winds (trade winds) blow toward the equator, in many regions with such persistence that the plants lying within their path are bent in the direction of the wind. The air is thus moving from higher (colder) to lower (warmer) latitudes; hence its capacity to hold water is increased. Such winds evaporate available moisture and leave arid conditions behind.

Along the poleward margins of the desert are situated the high-pressure areas of the world. Here the air is warmed by compression as it settles towards the surface of the earth, and the relative humidity decreases rapidly. Thus in their very origin the trade winds are dry, and as they blow toward the equator this characteristic becomes more pronounced.

INFLUENCE OF MOUNTAIN BARRIERS. Mountain barriers that are situated in the path of the trades receive the maximum amount of precipitation on the windward side, whereas the leeward side remains relatively dry. This is true in the central Andes, where an abundance of moisture is wrung from the trade winds as they are continuously forced up the eastern slopes to higher and cooler altitudes. By the time the air has reached the crest of the mountains it has lost most of its moisture; as it descends the western slopes it becomes warmed by compression, and thus evaporation rather than precipitation is the logical sequence.

The contrast in life responses between the eastern and western sides of the central Andes is as sharp as that of climate. On the lower eastern slopes, the heavy rainfall and high temperatures result in a tangle of trees, vines, and undergrowth so dense that it is difficult for man to make his way through it; the lower western slope is one of the most desolate deserts of the world. On the eastern lowlands the monkeys chatter in the trees and the screams of bright-colored birds are heard in the gloomy rain-soaked forest; on the west coast, at the same altitude and latitude, the cactus, rodents, and reptiles are the most conspicuous forms of life, except where man has entered to exploit the valuable mineral resources of this desert. In the higher altitudes we find just as marked contrasts between these slopes. Similar contrasts exist in Australia, where the southeast trades lose most of their moisture on the eastern highlands, leaving the vast area of the interior, desert and steppe.

COLD CURRENTS AND THEIR EFFECT ON CLIMATE. Where high altitudes act as a barrier to moisture-laden winds on one side, and cold ocean currents shut out most of the moisture from the other side, extremes of aridity are recorded. Such are the conditions off the west coast of Chile and Peru, where the cold, upwelling waters of the Humboldt Current flow along the coast from colder to warmer latitudes. Any winds from the west are therefore relatively dry since they blow from cold water to warm land, and their capacity for moisture is thereby increased.

This region is so extremely arid that for over 500 miles from Copiapo to Pisagua the Loa is the only river of any consequence that reaches the sea, and this only in years of heavy snowfall in the mountains.[3] For a 21-year period Iquique had an average rainfall of only 1.5 centimeter (0.6 inch) and Arica (for a 19-year period) had still less (0.6 millimeter). But the finding of any climatic average for the desert is very nearly a meaningless computation. There is no such thing as normal desert rainfall.[4] Years of absolute drought pass, and when rainfall finally comes it lasts but a few minutes. The cold Benguella Current, flowing off the coast of Kalahari, intensifies the aridity to such an extent that Swakopmund, one of the coastal towns, receives merely 0.7 inch of rain per year.

THE RELATION OF RELIEF TO PRECIPITATION AND TEMPERATURES. The degree of relief is an important factor in relation to desert climates. In the Sahara the mountains are much more favored than the plains both with respect to precipitation and sensible temperatures. The southern groups of Air and Tibetsi receive a considerable rainfall every summer, often in thunderstorms of great violence which cause sudden floods in the neighboring wadis. The unwary, both animals and men, who happen to be in their path, may be quickly swept away. In India the moisture of the summer monsoon condenses when it is carried up the Western Ghats or the highlands of the interior, whereas the lowlands of the northwest remain dry.

The low rainfall in the Thar Desert of India is due to a combination of factors, one of which has already been indicated. During the sum-

[3] Isaiah Bowman, "Regional Population Groups of Atacama," *American Geographical Society Bulletin*, Vol. 41, p. 202.

[4] Isaiah Bowman, *Desert Trails of Atacama*, American Geographical Society, New York, 1924, p. 40.

mer months this desert is a low-pressure center, and winds blow into it from all directions. The air currents that come from the northwest, across the arid plateau of Afghanistan and Baluchistan, become even drier when they descend to the plains of the Sind and can yield no moisture. Air coming from the north, east, and northeast has lost most of its moisture during its passage up the Ganges Valley, and, when this air descends into the basin of the Indus River, it is dried still more by its descent. The Thar Desert, therefore, receives no rain from this quarter. To the west and southwest there seems to be a possible source of moisture. But the air found south of Baluchistan, over the Arabian Sea, has mingled with the drier air currents coming from the highlands and dry lands of the Iranian and Arabian plateaus. Air passing eastward over this northern part of the Arabian Sea, therefore, contains less moisture than it otherwise would, and, as it moves over the plains of the Indus Valley, it crosses lowlands rather than highland areas, and relatively little rain falls.[5]

Relative Humidity and Sunshine. In most of the tropical deserts the absolute humidity is moderately high since the air is warm and hence capable of holding much moisture. The relative humidity, however, is low. Wadi Halfa, Egyptian Sudan, has a mean annual relative humidity of only 32; Cairo, Egypt, 56; Multan, India, 43; and Cassak, Australia, 53. The low relative humidity of these places makes the heat of midday more bearable than it would be otherwise.

There are, however, exceptions to the general rule. Paradoxical though it may seem, in two of the tropical deserts the moist air actually causes discomfort. Isaiah Bowman recognizes a zone, from sea level to 2,000 feet, along the west coast of Peru and Chile, where mists are very frequent and so penetrating as to cause wholesale destruction of carpets, wallpaper, and the like.[6] The mist is a persistent feature of the whole coast and is explained by the contact of the warm winds of the land with the unusually cold waters of the Humboldt Current. Likewise the coast of the Kalahari is an area of high relative humidity, at Walvis Bay amounting to as much as 84 per cent, and that in a region where less than 1 inch of rain falls annually. A dense mist forms over this coastal area during the summer but seldom extends more than 70 miles inland, since the winds from the ocean be-

[5] W. G. Kendrew, *The Climates of the Continents*, Oxford University Press, 1922, pp. 114 and 115.

[6] Isaiah Bowman, "Regional Population Groups of Atacama," *American Geographical Society Bulletin*, Vol. 41, p. 147.

come warmed as they blow over the land.[7] The mist seldom appears during the winter, since air at that time of year is moving out from the minor high-pressure area of the interior and has the effect of a foehn wind as it descends to the coast.

Humidity and Evaporation. Owing to the low relative humidity of most tropical deserts and to the absence of clouds, evaporation from a free water surface is rapid, in some places as much as 150 inches a year. These deserts also receive an excess of light at all times of the year, and light-loving plants such as the date palm and various xerophytic (drought-tolerant) species find a favorable habitat under these cloudless skies.

Temperatures. In general, the tropical deserts are hot by day and cool by night. The diurnal range, which at times exceeds 60° F., is greater than that found in any other type of climate. The dry air and sparse vegetation favor rapid heating by day and active radiation by night. The seasonal range is greatest along the poleward margins of these deserts, especially in those places situated inland and having extreme aridity. In the higher latitudes the summer days are long, and if the air is also dry, conditions are favorable for maximum heating. Thus in Death Valley, California, the extreme shade temperature of 134° F. has been recorded, and the glistening sands become unbearably hot to the traveler. In Baghdad, once a mighty city, the temperature at one time reached 123° F., and temperatures of 115° F. are not uncommon. Many other places experience temperatures of more than 120° F. The annual maximum range, frequently more than 100° F., is greater than that of any other region except those having the continental types of climate. Along the coasts, bathed by cool currents, the range is much smaller than in the interior. Thus Callao, located on the west coast of Peru, has a mean annual range of merely 8.5° F., and Swakopmund, west coast of the Kalahari, about 8.4° F. On the other hand, Wadi Halfa, situated in the interior of the Sahara, has a mean annual range of 31° F. The effect of cold ocean currents upon the mean annual temperatures is strikingly brought out in a comparison of Swakopmund with Wadi Halfa. The former place is located about as far south of the equator as the latter is north of it. Yet the mean annual temperature of Swakopmund is only 59.4° F., whereas that of Wadi Halfa is about 77° F.

Desert Winds and Effects upon Life. Desert winds are frequently of great violence and may sweep up "clouds" of dust visible for miles.

[7] W. G. Kendrew, *The Climates of the Continents*, Oxford University Press, 1922, p. 62.

A single storm may move millions of tons of sand. The simoon of the Sahara has been known to destroy entire caravans, death resulting from suffocation in the dust-laden air. In desert oases that are situated in the low depressions of sand dunes, an incessant struggle is necessary to keep the windblown sand from covering the cultivated areas. This is true in the area of the Suf (N. Sahara).

Prolonged winds are exceedingly trying to both plants and human beings. In eastern Persia, during the summer (June to September), the "Wind of One Hundred and Twenty Days" blows from the north with such violence that in some districts trees cannot grow except under the lee of high walls. Moreover, tourists who have to endure this wind state that it is one of the most trying experiences that they have encountered. It not only renders them irritable but it also deadens their initiative, and they usually seek a shelter of some kind.[8]

The Climate of the Steppe. Along the margins of the desert are regions which receive a greater amount of precipitation. Here the scattered tufts of desert grasses give way to the steppe. The climate of the steppe has a distinct rhythm of rain and drought; but in contrast to the low-latitude wet-and-dry regions, the season of drought is long, with a short period of moderate to scanty rainfall. In general, the average annual precipitation is from 10 inches along the margins of the desert to about 20 inches in the more humid sections.

The climate of the steppe differs greatly from region to region. In Mesopotamia, rainfall is scant, slightly more than 10 inches per annum, whereas the steppe regions of South Africa receive about twice that amount. Furthermore, in some areas winter is the rainy season, and in others the rain falls chiefly during the summer months. In general, winter rain is experienced along the poleward margins of the steppe; it falls chiefly in summer along the equatorward areas. Where the rain falls during the winter, or during that period of the year when evaporation is least rapid, 10 or 12 inches may be sufficient to turn a desert into a steppeland.

SURFACE AND SOILS OF THE DESERT

Many people think of deserts as level areas in which the sand blows more or less continuously throughout the year. This is not so in most deserts; they are neither flat throughout their entire extent nor

[8] Ellsworth Huntington, *Civilization and Climate*, The Yale University Press. New Haven, 1915, pp. 112, 113.

covered in major part by sand. The desert may be divided into three kinds of surfaces—the stony surface, from which loosened waste has been removed; the sandy areas, made of the coarsest waste; and the adobe, made of finer particles. Even in the Sahara, the world's greatest desert, the estimated sand areas do not exceed a third of the surface. When suitably watered, deserts may be transformed into fertile oases, since their soils are often rich in immediately available plant foods which have accumulated during a long period of rest. These soils usually contain an abundance of potash, lime, and other mineral elements essential to plant growth.

THE PLANT RESPONSE TO CLIMATIC CONDITIONS

Adaptation of Plants to Desert Conditions. Desert conditions are extremely harsh for plant life. High temperature and low relative humidity are conducive to excessive transpiration. Not only is water hard to get, but owing to rapid evaporation it is also hard to retain. Plants have adapted themselves in three major ways to meet these conditions: (1) By means of a rapid response to moisture, some plants germinate at the commencement of the rain, ripen their seeds when it terminates, and die forthwith. (2) A large root system, branching out in all directions near the surface of the ground, enables some plants to collect enough moisture during the rainy season to tide them over a period of drought. (3) Finally, there is a group of desert plants which depends upon subterranean sources of water. Their roots are long and penetrate deep into the earth in search of moisture. These plants exhibit a marked xerophilous structure which directly points to the influence of the very dry air.[9]

Transition-Zone Type of Vegetation. Along the margins of the desert the scattered tufts of desert grass gradually give way to more solid stands of steppe vegetation.[10] The grass sward of the steppe is frequently interrupted by bare spaces; yet in places solid stands of grass cover the ground. Such areas are relatively extensive in South Africa. In the steppes of northern Africa there are broad belts which

[9] Absence or very weak development of leaf blades, formation of thorns, succulence, thick cuticle, coatings of wax, and reduced intercellular spaces are xerophilous characteristics. A. F. W. Schimper, *Plant Geography*, Oxford, 1913, p. 614.

[10] Grassland, when hygrophilous or tropophilous, is termed meadow; when xerophilous, steppe.

embrace the well-known halfa grass, which is used in increasing quantities in the manufacture of paper. Along the more humid margins of the steppe, and as one approaches the wet-and-dry type of climate, trees begin to appear. In general these trees are stunted, gnarled, dwarf varieties. But the steppe proper is an area of grassland—and pasture is the one all-important resource.

THE ANIMAL RESPONSE

Adjustment of Animals to Desert Environment. Certain animals have adjusted themselves nicely to meet desert conditions. In some animals this adjustment is reflected in their habit of saving, as in the burrowing spider, most of the bees, the ants which store food in the hills, and rodents and burrowers such as gophers, rats, and prairie dogs. In color also nearly all the desert and steppe animals have responded to their environment. In general they have the dun or tawny color of the surrounding sand and vegetation. That is especially true of rabbits, mice, lizards, quail, coyotes, ostriches, antelopes, lions, and the camels. Even rattlesnakes have protective colorings and markings.

The camel is especially well adapted to harsh desert conditions; he is capable of browsing on the coarse, dried herbage, which he can swallow whole, then at leisure regurgitate for chewing. The stomach walls of the camel are sacculated for storage of an astonishing amount of water. The feet and knees are padded so that the animal may withstand the heat and friction of the bare rock and sand. The nostrils can be closed against the blowing sand and dust, and the hump is a device for storing fat against a time of dearth. Sheep are also well adapted to these arid conditions. They have acquired the power to carry on physiological processes with the minimum of water, often the dew on the grass sufficing for weeks together. Consequently, great numbers of sheep are kept by the desert nomads.

Animals of the Steppe. Owing to the more abundant vegetation, animals are larger and more numerous in the steppe. In certain portions of Africa the large numbers of Herbivora such as the eland, gazelle, zebra, oryx, ostrich, giraffe, and rhinoceros make of the land a paradise for animals like the lion, chetah, jackal, hyena, and hunting dog. Thus the steppe and adjoining grasslands of the tropical highlands and wet and dry realm still constitute the finest big-game areas of the world. (See pp. 240–242.)

THE HUMAN RESPONSE

Human Life in Desert and Steppe. The conditions of the climate and vegetation make the desert one of the harshest human habitats on earth. In its extreme it is a region of death by starvation and thirst. Even the more promising areas afford a most precarious livelihood, except in the fertile oases and the mining districts. In general the population groups of the desert are extremely small and widely scattered and are usually distributed about streams, springs, or wells.

Strangers are usually looked upon with hostility. This is only natural, since they use up part of the scanty water and food supply which the nomads can ill afford to spare. In writing of the Sahara, J. W. Gregory says that single visitors or small parties are suspected of being spies who come to view the land, so that the natural impulse is to slay them at once to prevent their returning as guides of an invading force. This constant struggle with nature has made the people of the Sahara alert and observant. The frequent wars with other tribes have made them strong, active, and reckless in battle. Desert life, with its long, lonely watch over herds and flocks and the silent vigil kept at night to guard against wild beasts or a sudden raid, has tended to make desert peoples emotional and moody. Similar effects result from life on the wide sheep farms of Australia, where the lonely life of the boundary rider often ends in what is called "hut madness." In addition, the desert tends to turn the minds of its people to the spiritual problems of life, rendering them liable to outbreaks of religious excitement which often lead to violence against people of other beliefs.

In the area of the steppe, owing to a more luxuriant vegetation, primitive man found better hunting and better range for his domesticated animals. Much of the area at present is occupied by pastoral tribes who follow their flocks from place to place.

Nomads

In the desert and steppe a nomadic mode of life prevails. The nomad is either a hunter as in Australia or a tender of flocks and herds as in the Sahara. The chief animals—sheep, goats, and camels—can live on the scanty vegetation of the realm, but they must be kept moving from one pasture to another. These pastures have played an important role in human evolution. In fact, the tropical grasslands of the Old World developed historical importance only after the domestication of animals. This step in progress resulted in the evolution of peoples who renounced the precarious subsistence of the chase and who at the same time evaded the drudgery of primitive agriculture, to devote themselves to a pastoral life. This change, however, was possible only where animals suitable for domestication and adapted to these grass-lands were found. Neither Australia nor North America possessed a single animal of this type. Although South America had the llama and alpaca, they were not domesticated in the areas of the desert and steppe. Not until the Spaniards had introduced horses into South America did the pastoral nomad appear on the continent. He is known today as the llanero or gaucho. There still remain, however, a few desert and steppe peoples, both in Africa and Australia, who eke out a precarious existence without the aid of domestic animals.

Nomads Not in Possession of Domestic Animals

The desert and steppe tribes who own no domestic animals are among the most degenerate of all peoples. They were formerly found in parts of the Sonoran and Atacama deserts; they still range over extensive areas in the Australian and Kalahari deserts.

The primitive status of these peoples is clearly reflected in their food, shelter, and clothing. Their diet is a simple one, consisting of seeds, roots, bulbs, locusts, rats, lizards, and snakes.[11] They wear little clothing, and their shelter is crude. In the Australian desert the cloth-ing of these primitive peoples consists merely of a piece of cloth about the loins, and a head dress which is almost indispensable owing to the intensity of the sun's rays. The skins of animals are widely used for clothing. Fortunately, in these arid regions, the skins will dry into usable form and will keep and wear well without tanning. Here also local fibers and grasses afford raw material for the beginnings of a crude textile industry, which supplies the paltry amount of coarse cloth that is worn by the natives. The architecture is as primeval as the clothing. Building materials are scant, but the small "bush" or

[11] David W. Carnegie gives a vivid description of characteristic conditions in the interior of western Australia: "Though feeding, as a rule, only night and morning, these people sit down and cook and eat a rat as soon as it is killed. Everything is eaten in the half-cooked state. The process of preparing a meal is simple in the extreme; the rats are plucked and thrown on the hot ashes with no further preparation, and are greedily devoured red and bloody, and barely warm." D. W. Carnegie, "Explorations in the Interior of Western Australia," *Geographical Journal*, Vol. 11, p. 263.

"shrub" makes possible the construction of a wickiup—a shelter which is patched with grass or plastered with mud. Frequently the house is merely a hole in the ground over which a flimsy roof is constructed.

In recent years scientists have been studying the culture of the Kalahari Desert in search of any tribes that may have preserved the customs of the stone age. In taking the anthropological trail on the fringe of the dark continent, these scientists worked their way backward and down the long tortuous path up which mankind has toiled—through the agricultural, the pastoral, and hunting stages of man's life to the bottom rung of the human ladder, where man possesses only a flint knife, a bow and arrow, a dog, and a wife.

THE PASTORAL NOMAD

The pastoral nomads—those who have domestic animals—have attained a comparatively high state of culture. They are in possession of horses, camels, sheep, and goats—animals which enormously increase the food-producing capacity of the group. Although these nomadic tribes are small, some of them possess large numbers of animals.

These nomadic groups are mobile and far-ranging, as they follow the rains, search for spots that have a little more rainfall than normal and hence more pasture, or travel from one oasis to another. Most of the food is supplied by the flocks and herds. Milk in one form or another constitutes a large part of the diet. Meat is also a valuable food and when dried in the sun will keep indefinitely, even in this hot climate. Yet the nomad is not wholly dependent upon these pastoral products; he is constantly trading with sedentary people of the oases, receiving cereals and dates in exchange for meat, hides, clothing, and blankets.

The pastoral nomad is well supplied with clothing, rugs, and other products made from the wool of sheep and the hair of camels. Spinning and weaving are highly developed, and the manufacture of turbans, clothes, blankets, tents, and rugs constitutes the chief industry other than that of tending the flocks and herds. Some of these people have developed great skill in rug making, and their products are highly valued in many parts of the world.

The constant wandering in search of pasture requires that the human shelter must be light and easily moved. Tents made from skins or cloth meet this requirement and at the same time afford fair protection from the sun's rays and sudden showers. In these tents, rugs are much in evidence, since they are about the only furnishings which can be easily transported.

Most of the stories of desert and steppe life are primarily concerned with two groups of people—the nomads and the sedentary tribes of the oases. Yet there exists an intermediate class, to which the Massaabas of the Sahara belong. These people are in possession of domestic animals as well as palm trees. They have erected storehouses

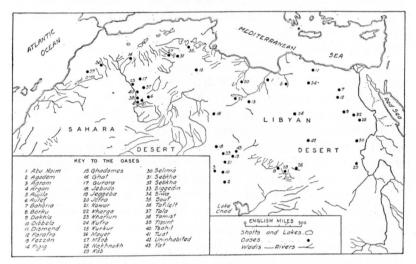

FIG. 113. Oases in the Sahara. (After E. H. Carrier, *The Thirsty Earth*, Christophers, London, 1928.)

of adobe on the borders of the oases of the Suf, camping during the winter in tents or palm-leaf huts in front of the storehouses. Their nomadic characteristics are reflected in the tending of flocks of sheep and goats as well as in their desire to live in tents rather than in substantial adobe houses. Their sedentary tendencies are indicated by their desire to cultivate the date palm for a part of the year.

Oases

An oasis is an area in the desert or steppe where water may be secured for the production of crops. Oases are of various kinds. They may be areas surrounding deep wells, as in the Mzab, situated in the northern portion of the Sahara (Fig. 113); the moist depressions of sand dunes, as in the area of the Suf; or the land watered from perennial streams, such as the Nile, Imperial, Euphrates, and Tigris valleys.

Interdependence of Nomads and Oases Peoples. A close relation exists between the desert and oasis tribes. The true desert people, the pastoral nomads, have much the same relation to the oasis as the country folk have to the cities. The oases, with their reliable water supply, are the only areas within the desert where large numbers of people can assemble for a few days for the purpose of trade—the exchange of the nomads' animals and animal products for dates and grain of the oasis.

Oases in Relation to Highlands. All the large oases of the desert derive their water supply from highlands, sometimes hundreds of miles distant. The floods of the Nile result from the heavy rains in the highlands of central Africa. The lower Indus is watered by the streams which flow from the Himalayas, and the floods of the Tigris and Euphrates are caused by the heavy rainfall in the highlands of Armenia. In the desert and steppe of Peru and Chile numerous streams are found which have their source in the well-watered highlands of the Andes, and parts of the Sonoran Desert are watered by streams which rise in the Sierra Madre Occidental to the east. Many of the highland areas also serve as catchment basins from which the water is carried through porous sandstone formations to distant places where it seeps out on the surface or is tapped by wells.

Oasis Agriculture. Agriculture by irrigation is the dominant economic industry of the oasis. Activities in one, however, may differ widely from those of another. In the area of the Suf (north Sahara), it is necessary to maintain an incessant struggle against the blowing sand, which otherwise would bury the cultivated fields and even the groves of date palms. In the area of the Mzab the underground water is far beneath the surface and can be obtained for irrigation only by digging deep wells and by drawing the water either by man power or by means of camels or donkeys. Water obtained at such cost is treasured very highly, and the natives have contrived ingenious devices to prevent its waste. The small ditches which run from the well to the palm trees are provided with a hard lining so that seepage may be checked, and sometimes they are covered to prevent rapid evaporation.

The Date an Important Oasis Plant. One of the most characteristic plants of oases is the date palm, although the total value of the product is less than that of several other oases crops, notably cotton and corn.

It has been estimated that approximately 90,000,000 date palms are scattered throughout the tropical deserts of the world, of which more than one-half are in the countries bordering the Persian Gulf.

The region of greatest concentration of date palms is the lower Tigris and Euphrates valleys, which probably yields one-third of the world crop. The largest plantations are close to the Persian Gulf, and the little country of Iraq probably supports as many date palms as are

Fig. 114.   Date palms in southern California.   (Courtesy Southern Pacific Co.)

grown in the entire Sahara Desert. The cultivation of the date palm has now spread from the Old World to the New, for a few thousand trees have been planted in the southwestern part of the United States (Fig. 114).

The date palm thrives under conditions of extreme atmospheric aridity and intense sunlight, provided that the roots receive a sufficient amount of moisture. The tree is hardy, long-lived, and yields a large return per acre. Consequently, full-grown trees are frequently valued at more than $150 each.

The Nile Oasis. The Nile oasis is a narrow green ribbon in a vast area of gray, drab sand—a ribbon of land 1,000 miles long and, throughout most of its extent, only 10 to 14 miles wide. One can see it all from the banks of the Nile.

The Nile Valley is an oasis par excellence. For more than sixty centuries this narrow strip of land has been kept fertile and productive by the water and silt of the River Nile. No other nation is so wholly dependent upon a single river as is Egypt, and in no other country are the interests of the people so completely centered in a single resource. Fourteen million people depend upon this stream for food and life. When the Nile is low, Egypt suffers and the people clamor for water. Since the demand is always greater than the supply, the greatest economic problem of the nation is that of using the water of the Nile to the best advantage; the greatest fear of the people is that their water supply may be reduced by excessive withdrawals for irrigating lands farther upstream.

Each year the Nile overflows its banks, providing an abundance of moisture to the otherwise desert soil and a coating of fine silt in which the fellah (Egyptian peasant) plants his crops. It has been estimated that under the ancient system of basin irrigation each acre received approximately 4,000 tons of water and 6 tons of rich alluvial mud each year.[12] By the present system of barrages and dams the water is more effectively used, but much of the silt is lost to the farmer, with the resultant decrease in soil fertility.

The kinds of crops that occupy the land of this oasis vary with the seasons.[13] Cotton, sugar cane, maize, sorghum, and rice are the principal summer crops, the last three being grown primarily as flood crops (Fig. 115). Wheat, barley, beans, and clover are the most important crops of the winter season. Sugar cane, which grows throughout the year, is an important crop above the delta of the Nile. Many parts of the Nile oasis produce two or three crops a year, and the land is sometimes valued at more than $1,000 an acre.

In spite of the great productivity of the Nile Valley the agricultural population is overcrowded. Most of the farms are small, and more

---

[12] Under the basin system of irrigation, which has been practiced in Egypt for thousands of years, the flood water of the Nile is turned into basins which vary in area from 500 to 50,000 acres. Each of these basins is filled with water to a depth of from 3 to 5 feet, and at the end of six weeks the excess water is drained back into the Nile. Crops are then sown upon the mud without previous cultivation. Under this system of irrigation, however, usually but one crop a year is possible.

[13] In dividing the year into seasons the Egyptian peasant has taken account of the high-water stage of the Nile. Three seasons are recognized—summer from April 1 to August 1; the season of flood from August 1 to December 1; and winter from December 1 to April 1.

than a million families eke out a living for themselves on farms that average less than an acre per family.

The farmers live in villages scattered throughout the valley about a mile apart. The houses consist of mud huts made from the only building materials easily available. The walls are adobe, the floors are bare ground, and even the roofs are made of mud. Most of the homes are without a flower or an ornamental shrub. Water is too precious to be used for growing anything but food.

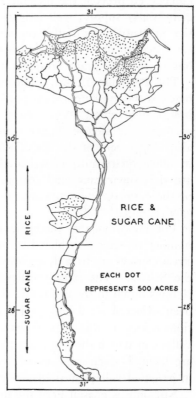

Iraq (Mesopotamia). In ancient times Mesopotamia was the seat of great empires. It was densely populated with progressive agricultural peoples who developed extensive irrigation projects and practiced intensive cultivation of the soil. The early history of this region is one of constant struggle between nations that were contending for this choice bit of land. During succeeding centuries Mesopotamia has been overrun time and again by nomads. As the first of these invaders, the Arabs, pressed forward, the peasants were driven from their lands, the larger irrigation works were neglected, and the rivers, no longer controlled, spread into wide marshes. The depredations which were commenced by the Arabs

Fig. 115. The Nile Valley, a fertile ribbon of irrigated land located in large part in the low-latitude desert of Africa.

were completed by the Turks, Mongols, and Tartars, and one of the most fertile and productive regions of the earth was abandoned to the wasteful practices of pastoral peoples. Since 1918 old irrigation ditches have been reopened, new ones constructed, and pastoral lands have gradually been converted into farms. If political disturbances do not interfere the land may again support a prosperous sedentary population.

The Lower Indus Valley. The lower Indus Valley is the largest oasis in India. This region is cultivated either after the annual inundation or by means of artificial irrigation from the Indus River. The chief crop is rice, with the grain sorghums and millet next in importance. To prevent the possible failure of crops because of an insufficient water supply, well irrigation supplements the inundation practice in many parts of this region. Moreover, as in Egypt, a modern canal system of irrigation has been developed and cotton has become one of the important products of the region.

The Peruvian Desert. The coastal desert of Peru, with its many oases, is the most important portion of the country. Although it embraces only about 10 per cent of the total area of the republic, it accounts for almost 60 per cent of the agricultural income. Here also 55 per cent of the agricultural capital of the country is invested in 1,000 square miles of irrigated land. The chief crops on this land are rice, sugar cane, and cotton, which are the most important ones of the country and represent 50 per cent of the value of Peru's total export trade.[14]

The importance of the agriculture of this coastal strip is due to a number of streams which rise in the Andes to the east. The interstream spaces are bare desert waste, as dry and devoid of vegetation as the Sahara. The stream valleys, however, extend as narrow green ribbons down to the coast, and their flood plains and alluvial fans have been irrigated for a long period of time. In fact, some of the irrigation works of this region were built by the Incas. These are the valleys in which the large sugar estates and cotton plantations of Peru are located—sugar cane in valleys chiefly north of Lima, and cotton in irrigated valleys near that center.

Not only is coastal Peru the most important area agriculturally, but it is here also that most of the cities of the country are located. This region includes all the seaports and Lima, the capital. Here also we find the highest cultural development, the most important oil field in western South America, and the widely known guano deposits.

The Sonoran Desert. Along the desert coast of Sinaloa and Sonora, Mexico, irrigation agriculture is possible owing to numerous streams that head in the highlands to the east. Many of these streams never reach the coast but lose themselves in the dry sands of the coastal plain. On their various fans and flood plains irrigation agriculture is

[14] With a production of 100,000 to 200,000 tons of cane sugar, Peru ranks second only to Brazil as a South American producer of that commodity.

of increasing importance. Corn, an important crop in this area, is grown for local consumption as well as for export. The growing of vegetables is a promising industry owing to proximity and direct rail connection with the United States.

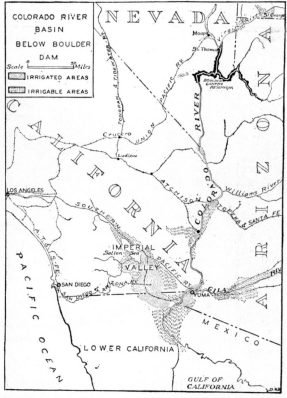

FIG. 116. Showing the Colorado River basin below Hoover Dam. Note the large amount of irrigated land in the Imperial Valley; also the extensive area of irrigable land in Mexico. (After U. S. Bureau of Reclamation.)

The Imperial Valley. The most famed of the American oases is the Imperial Valley. Prior to 1902 this land was part of the large, sterile, desolate waste known as the Colorado Desert and was given over to cactus, rodents, and other desert plants and animals.

The soils of the Imperial Valley are rich silts, washed from seven states and deposited in this lowland by the flood waters of the turbulent, muddy Colorado River. With the application of water the area became one of the most productive to be found anywhere. Silt is still being spread over the land with every application of irrigation water, so that the soil should retain its fertility indefinitely.

Not only is the soil fertile and water abundant, but also the climate is suited to intensive cultivation and bumper crops. The growing season lasts all the year, and the sunshine is continuous and intense.

Fig. 117.   Harvesting cantaloupes in the Imperial Valley of California.   (Courtesy Southern Pacific Co.)

Scarcely a month passes without some crop being harvested and others planted. Alfalfa grows continuously, and each year four or five crops may be harvested from the same land. This legume is excellent cattle feed and the basis of a thriving dairy industry with an output of 8 to 10 million pounds of butter annually.

The valley is even more widely famed for cantaloupes than for alfalfa. It is the greatest cantaloupe-producing center in the world, ten to twenty thousand carloads being grown here each year and shipped by fast express to eastern markets (Figs. 116 and 117). Long-staple cotton, grapes, and head lettuce are among the other important cultivated crops. The large fields of lettuce, which yield handsome profits to the gardeners, afford abundant proof that rapid and efficient transportation facilities connect the valley with large and wealthy markets.

Many of the homes of this area are mere shacks, occupied by tenants who take but little pride in the appearance of the cultural landscape. However, an increasing number of the homes are modern and roomy, surrounded by young shade trees, flower gardens, and attractive shrubbery. It has been the custom of the women and children of the wealthier farmers to leave the valley during the heat of the summer. Now that improved roads have been built over the hills to the mountains back of San Diego—a two- or three-hour drive by automobile— many of the well-to-do families find it convenient to retreat to these highlands for a short period of recreation and rest.

Minor Oases. Besides the large oases, the desert and steppe contain many small areas where water is available for crops. This is especially true in the Sahara, where a large number of small oases are widely scattered (Fig. 113) and during many centuries have been centers of population and cultivation.[15] These oases are watered in various ways—some of them from springs, others from wells. Still others are situated in low, moist depressions of sand dunes.

Human activities vary considerably among these small garden spots of the desert. In some of these areas a variety of crops is cultivated; in others merely the date palm and a few vegetables. In some oases the encroaching sand offers the most critical problem to the natives; in others, the uncertain water supply is the chief issue. In writing about small oases in the northern part of the Sahara, Jean Brunhes brings out some of these contrasts: "In the Mzab the labor to obtain water is regular and constant, and ceases only in time of flood; in the Suf the struggle against the sand is more irregular and intermittent. Likewise the Mozabite certainly works more constantly and energetically while the Soafas are much more inclined to periods of idleness." [16]

In the desert oases of the Sahara the dwellings have the character of towns, not villages. Even that designation, however, may appear overdrawn, by reason of the fact that many oases are no larger than the smallest of villages. But they are found in a natural setting in which the environment is so blank that any "society of dwellings takes on the glamour of urban life." The cultural pattern of these small towns reflects streets that are moderately well laid out, and clay-built houses which are quite compact and complete, some of them

[15] E. F. Gautier, *Le Sahara*, translated by Dorothy Ford Mayhew, Columbia University Press, 1935, pp. 450–453.
[16] Jean Brunhes, *Human Geography*, Rand McNally & Co., 1920, p. 451.

even ornamental. In addition, the market places are characterized by their bazaars and their concentration of people.[17]

MINING ACTIVITIES

Mining in the tropical desert is fraught with difficulties, chief among which are extremely high temperatures, difficulty of transportation, shortage of water, lack of timber, and little or no herbage for beasts of burden. In discussing mining conditions in the nitrate pampa of northern Chile, Isaiah Bowman writes that "at Central Lagunas water is brought in pipe lines from Pigue, 18 miles northeastward; fruit from Pica and Matille, 55 miles in the same direction, and fish from the sea at Iquique, 90 miles by rail. Except for these slender resources locally supplied, all the food and clothing, the building material, machinery, work animals, laborers, everything must be drawn from more favored lands." [18]

Mineral deposits are found in many parts of the realm, and in spite of the difficulties of exploiting these resources many mines are being worked with vast profits, some being famed throughout the world for their richness. This is especially true of the copper mines and the diamond mines at Kimberley, South Africa. Yet the deposits which illustrate a nice relationship to the climatic environment of the realm are the mineral salts and guano.

Mineral Salts. Chief among the mineral salts are the deposits of Chile where, owing to arid conditions, nitrates have accumulated and have been preserved for many centuries. Although sodium nitrate exists in many desert regions, Chile is the only country where workable deposits have been found (Fig. 118).

Various theories have been advanced as to the origin of these deposits. Some authorities believe that the nitrate accumulated in basins filled with salt water, in which guano was deposited. Most of the authors, however, believe that the nitrate deposits have resulted from the accumulation, by means of evaporation, of the minute nitrate content of the underground waters of the region. In other words, they represent a sort of efflorescence of the soluble salts out of the ground water. This accumulation has been made possible through the remarkable relations of ground water and arid climatic conditions existing in the region.

[17] Angus Buchanan, *Sahara*, Appleton-Century Book Co., 1926, p. 188.
[18] Isaiah Bowman, "Regional Population Groups of the Atacama," *American Geographical Society Bulletin*, Vol. 41, p. 153.

The localities where the nitrate deposits occur were in the early days prospected for gold, silver, and copper. Not until the beginning of the nineteenth century was much attention given to the nitrates of the desert, the discovery of which was more or less accidental. Nitrate production began in 1812, and in 1830 about 8,300 tons of the crude product were exported. Subsequently there has been a very rapid growth in the industry. But a vast reserve still remains untouched. In an area of 5,811 square kilometers of nitrate land that has been carefully surveyed by government inspectors the estimated potential reserve is about 240,300,000 tons.

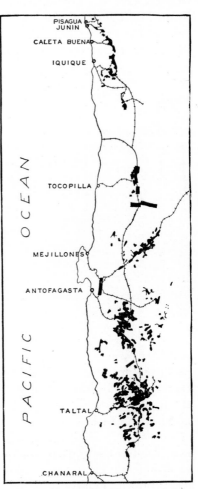

FIG. 118. Distribution of the chief nitrate districts of desert Chile, and the most important ports serving those areas.

Prior to 1920, the methods of mining and processing Chilean nitrate were relatively expensive and wasteful. Holes were dug with iron bars to the base of the deposits. Black powder was then placed in the holes and the beds were blasted. The workmen then sorted the nitrate ore (caliche) by hand, after which the high-grade ore was shipped to the nitrate plant. Here it was crushed and dumped into bins from which it was taken on belt conveyers or in cars to the boiling vats. After being boiled the solution was allowed to cool. At the end of about five days most of the nitrate had been precipitated. The liquid was then pumped off and the nitrate, after being dried, was ready for market. By this crude method of production only the high-grade ores could be used and the product was relatively expensive (Fig. 119).

Recently, owing to increasing competition of other forms of nitrogen, the companies producing Chilean nitrate found that in order to succeed they must improve their methods of mining, handling, and treating caliche. Consequently, power shovels are now being used in mining; improved crushers handle large quantities of ore quickly and economically; and new treating processes, which include the cooling of the nitrate solution to near-freezing temperatures, enable the

FIG. 119.   Huge piles of nitrate of soda in the desert region of Chile.   (Courtesy "The Grace Log.")

producers to recover a larger percentage of the nitrogen than could be recovered by the old process. These improvements have enabled the producers to use low-grade ores and to reduce the cost per unit of labor and fuel.

Two grades of nitrate are marketed, one 95 per cent pure mainly used for fertilizing purposes, and the other 96 per cent pure for use in manufacturing. It is employed in the manufacture of explosives, glass, fireworks, nitric acid, arsenate of soda, and nitrate of potash, as well as in the making of chloride and in the purification of caustic soda. Iodine is a by-product obtained in the refining of nitrate. Nearly the entire world's supply comes from Chile, where it is produced at small cost.

The consumption of commercial nitrogen on a large scale, is a relatively recent development, and has been associated with the increasing need for nitrogen both in the manufacture of explosives and in the production of fertilizers. In 1910, prior to any war on a world-wide scale, Chile, with an output of only 421,000 tons of nitrate of soda, furnished 64 per cent of the world's supply of commercial nitrogen. However, in 1941, Chile exported 1,270,479 tons of nitrate of soda; yet, owing to the competition of synthetic and by-product nitrogen, Chile supplied less than 8 per cent of the nitrogen consumed by the world in that war-torn year. Since the end of World War II the demand for nitrogen has once again decreased, and by 1946 the export of nitrate of soda from Chile had declined to 849,000 tons. Whether a possible future world war would once again greatly increase the demand for nitrogen would depend upon the types of the major munitions of war.

During the next few years the nitrogen industry of Chile is likely to face a crisis brought about by the competition of synthetic and by-product nitrates.

Guano. The first commodity extensively used as a commercial fertilizer was guano, a valuable manure which consists chiefly of the excrement of sea birds in places where rainfall is insufficient to carry away the deposits. The chief habitat of the guano-depositing birds are the Chincha and Lobos islands off the desert coast of Peru. Here, owing to a favorable combination of factors, deposits of great depth have been formed. The cold Humboldt Current provides a suitable habitat for fish, as these tropical waters abound in organisms upon which the fish feed. Fish, in turn, is the chief food of the guano-depositing birds. The cold current intensifies the aridity of the area and causes an environment in which the guano is preserved. In Peru these deposits have been worked since 1842, yielding millions of tons of high-grade fertilizer (Fig. 120). The exploitation of the diminishing reserves is now rigidly regulated by the Peruvian government, and the birds are protected by law in order to provide for the augmentation of the deposits.

Salt. In many desert regions salt is an important mineral product. Along desert coasts it is obtained by evaporating ocean water, where the arid climate facilitates that process. But this source is not so important as that of various desert lakes where the salt solution is more concentrated, or of old lake beds where stores of salt have been left after all the lake water has been evaporated. Even the rock-salt deposits of the earth's crusts were formed under similar arid conditions during remote geological ages of the past.

Borax. Among the other substances associated with salt deposits are borax, soda, and gypsum. Borax exists in many of the alkaline flats of arid regions. Probably the original source of borax is invariably volcanic emanations. These, flowing into the waters of salt lakes, cause borax to accumulate. In some arid regions borax permeates the soil, as does ordinary alkali, in favorable situations forming a crust upon the surface.

FIG. 120. The guanaye, or Peruvian cormorant, inhabits the islands in the Humboldt Current off the coast of Peru. These islands have for a century provided the world with the invaluable fertilizer known as guano. The guanaye is protected by law from any molestation, and until a few years ago no motor vehicle or airplane was permitted on or near its habitation. Caterpillar tractors have been introduced on San Martin and Santa Rosa islands to take the place of the old-fashioned system of hand mining, and the birds have been carefully watched for signs of anxiety. (Courtesy "The Grace Log.")

Borax has many valuable uses. It facilitates welding, since it forms fusible salts with most metallic oxides. It is used in glazing brick and chinaware, and in glossing starched linen in laundry work. It is also an important ingredient of dyes, drugs, and cleansing powders.

COMMUNICATION IN THE DESERT

Large deserts are classed among the world's most pronounced natural barriers to communication. Travel across them is fraught with many difficulties and dangers. Water is scarce and owing to rapid evaporation is hard to retain. Herbage for animals and food for man are even more difficult to obtain in sand-covered areas. The blowing sand and dust may destroy entire caravans, and loose sand renders travel difficult. Violent rainstorms in desert highlands may result in destructive floods which appear suddenly and without warning. When these floods occur in the valleys, such as the wadis (channels of watercourses which are dry except in the rainy season), which are used as highways, entire caravans may be swept away with heavy loss of life.

The construction of railroads is exceedingly difficult owing to the extreme aridity, and, in some places, blowing sand. Furthermore, water and fuel are scarce, and cars must be of special construction in order to withstand the atmospheric conditions. In some areas caterpillar tractors have been introduced. In expeditions across the Sahara from Algeria to Timbuktu and the Niger, caterpillar tractors have made in twenty days the trip which the camel required three months to complete. The camel, however, still remains the "ship of the desert."

SOCIAL AND POLITICAL CONDITIONS

The social and political conditions of the realm differ greatly from place to place. The most backward savage nomad of the desert still lives in a small family group, under primitive conditions. He has almost no concept of religion, his intelligence is low, and his political organization is a tenuous one. On the other hand, the inhabitant of the larger oasis has attained a high state of culture. He lives in a large, intelligent group where religion is well developed and the social bond is strong. Between these two groups is the pastoral nomad who possesses the wandering characteristics of the former and some of the culture of the latter. His ethics, however, are those of the robber, and his morals are formed by circumstances. He has a loose group claim to grazing ground, and a meager concept of definite limitations and private ownership of land. This has led to friction with European powers who wish to draw lines indicating territorial possession.

The family groups vary in size from a small number of individuals, as with the savage, to the larger and stronger family units of the pastoral nomad and oasis dweller. In the small family unit of the desert savage, infant mortality is high; women are about on par with men; and when these people are pressed by hunger and forced to move, decrepit individuals are abandoned to die. The family group of the pastoral nomad is as large as the grazing land will permit. The family, however, is broadened to include the clan, at the head of which is the sheikh (in the Sahara), who may be either the oldest or the most powerful individual. Leaders are essential, since the mode of life of these people is such that many questions must be decided on the spur of the moment. Men are the herders and the warriors; and women, who are inferior in the social scale, keep the tent and care for the children. With strong leadership and authority by the few has also come slavery—a regular institution among these people. In the Sahara, the slaves are secured either from the Guinea Coast, Sudan, or from forays upon neighboring desert groups.

The religion of the realm is closely related to the environment. Most authors agree to the fact that a desert tends to breed monotheism. The sameness of the scene, the unbroken stretches of desolate waste, the many mystical perceptions such as mirages, all tend to strengthen one's belief in some god, and in one, rather than a number of them. An opposite tendency, however, manifests itself in the large oasis. In the Nile Valley with its certainty of crops owing to the regular floods of the Nile, where man is merely a link in the process, a mechanical machine as it were, merely sowing seed and reaping the returns of a plentiful harvest, the natives' dependence upon God naturally becomes less.[19] The religion of the pastoral nomad is the handmaiden of the government, and society is run by the military and ecclesiastic. The mob is kept in control by fear and promise of reward, especially of leisure and luxury in the hereafter.

In some low-latitude desert regions, crime is to a large extent held in check by the influence of the environment. The inhabitants of the sandy desert districts are accustomed to observe and recognize imprints of the feet of men and animals. In fact, in various sandy parts of the Sahara the natives see the tracks of a caravan in the midst of the dunes, and easily make out to what tribe the caravan belongs. Some desert nomads let their camels run free to pasture and when they have need of them they find them by following their tracks over the desert sands. This ability of following tracks in the desert applies with equal force to the finding of human beings. Thus students of the Sahara have recognized the fact that in some of the sandy districts thefts are less numerous than elsewhere, mainly because robbers can be too easily pursued and caught.[20]

[19] G. A. Smith, *Historical Geography of the Holy Land*, Harper and Brothers, London, 1915.

[20] Jean Brunhes, *Human Geography*, Rand McNally & Co., 1920, p. 430.

Individual property in this realm is marked by peculiarities. Among the pastoral nomads property does not consist of land, since there is merely a loose group-claim to grazing ground. Even the herd shows no individual ownership. Property consists of weapons, utensils, equipment for herds, women, and slaves. The Suf and Mzab oases in the northern portion of the Sahara illustrate the exceptional nature of individual property. The surface of the land is not property, for, in the immense areas covered with sand and crossed in all directions by sand dunes, any one may take as much land as he pleases for the planting of date palms or the building of a house. Water is not regarded as constituting property, because it extends in comparatively large sheets under the sands and is within the reach of those who have perseverance enough to tap it. The date palm, however, is regarded as private property. There are often four or five proprietors in a single palm grove, and one person may possess several trees in a number of groves. Possession is based on planting the tree. No one can appropriate the ground in which another has planted; but if a tree dies and its owner does not immediately replace it with another, the first comer is at liberty to plant a tree in that spot. In other words, water and earth are common and not individual possessions, whereas the tree is the initial cause, the limit, and the end in view of individual ownership.

The government of the nomad is military, and the family is the basis of political unity. Here we find only a meager idea of democracy and equality, and authority is in a hierarchy. Fighting is common and is in large part due to the hardships of the desert. When the vegetation withers, the nomad and his flock face starvation. The only thing that occurs to him is to plunder. Thus he makes raids upon neighboring pastoral tribes or oasis peoples.

The laws of the desert differ materially from those of European powers, some of which own large portions of the desert realm. In Europe the laws pertain to the people as well as to the land. Among the desert nomads, however, the laws are associated with them as people, not with the place or territory, since land may be obtained for the mere taking. No one questions the limits of a range since land is free for all.

REFERENCES

BOWMAN, ISAIAH, *Desert Trails of Atacama*, American Geographical Society, 1924.
CARRIER, E. H., *The Thirsty Earth*, Christophers, London, 1928.

HUNTINGTON, ELLSWORTH, Civilization and Climate, Yale University Press, New Haven, 1915.

KENDREW, W. G., The Climates of the Continents, Oxford University Press, 1922.

LEPPAN, H. D., The Agricultural Development of Arid and Semi-Arid Regions, Central News Agency, South Africa, 1928.

MILLER, B. L., and J. F. SINGEWALD, The Mineral Deposits of South America, McGraw-Hill Book Co., New York, 1913.

RICH, JOHN L., "The Nitrate District of Tarapaca, Chile: An Aerial Traverse," Geographical Review, January 1941, pp. 1–22.

ROUSCH, G. A., and A. BUTTS, The Mineral Industry, McGraw-Hill Book Co., 1928, 1929, 1930.

SMITH, G. A., Historical Geography of the Holy Land, Harper and Brothers, London, 1915.

Chapter 9

THE HUMID SUBTROPICAL REGIONS

A Populous Realm. The humid subtropical realm surpasses all others in the number of people it supports. This fact is largely a result of the large population in the humid subtropical regions of the northern hemisphere. Humid subtropical China, Japan, and Korea are all densely populated, and our own Southland supports almost one-half of the agricultural population of the United States. In the southern hemisphere some of the most populous sections of South America, Africa, and Australia are situated in this realm. However, the total population of all humid subtropical regions of the southern hemisphere is not large.

A Realm of Contrasts. No other single climatic realm presents more striking contrasts in human activities from one region to another than the humid subtropical. These contrasts, as we shall see, are found in the nature and the progress of the people, in the standards of living, and in the nature of agriculture, manufacture, and trade. The contrasts are, in part, a result of differences in the natural environment from one region to another, and, in part, a result of differences in the stages of industrial development.

Contrasts in agriculture. Although certain crops such as cotton, sugar cane, and rice are common to all the humid subtropical regions, the percentage of farm land given to each crop differs markedly from one region to another. In southern United States "cotton is king" and corn is also a major crop; in subtropical China and Japan rice fields dominate the cultural landscape; in the South American region alfalfa and pasture are the most important crops, although wheat and corn are widely distributed and exceedingly important; in southeastern Africa sugar cane is the most important commercial crop; and in Australia corn and pasture are the most valuable agricultural products of the area under consideration.

Contrasts in manufacture. With the exception of Japan, none of the humid subtropical regions have as yet developed great manufacturing centers. Since about 1920, the southern United States has made rapid strides in this direction. In so far as manufacturing has developed, no two regions have specialized in the same types of industry. In southeastern United States the manufacture of iron and steel, petroleum products, chemicals, and paper, all associated with major resources of the South, represent some of the larger industries. Ginning of cotton is widespread, while sugar production and refining, rice cleaning, and the manufacture of orange and grapefruit products are important industries and are related to the agriculture of the South. In Japan, the manufacturing industries are diversified, but the production of textiles, chemicals, and iron and steel normally represent the most valuable products. Chinese manufacture is still backward and modern factories are confined to a few of the larger cities. Textile manufacture represents their most modern and valuable industry. In the South American region, meat packing, flour milling, shoe and textile manufacture, wine making, and sugar refining are some of the most important manufactures. In southeastern Africa and in northeastern Australia sugar production ranks high among the manufacturing industries.

This great diversity of human activities from one region to another is closely related to differences in the stages of industrial development and, to a lesser extent, to differences in natural environment. Man's adjustment to each region can be better understood after studying the environmental conditions under which he works.

CLIMATE OF HUMID SUBTROPICAL REGIONS

The regions of a climatic·type, like the people of a physical type, have characteristics common to all; likewise each region has qualities peculiar to itself just as each individual differs from all others. Certain of the common characteristics may be more impressive than the individual traits as shown by the striking similarity in the appearance of people of the Japanese type, or they may be somewhat submerged under the more striking personal qualities and appearances as is repeatedly exemplified in the French type. In the regions thus far studied, climatic likenesses have been more obvious than differences; in the humid subtropical regions the contrasts are quite as pronounced as the similarities. For example, some of these regions are frequently cursed with the most destructive of all storms, the tornado and the tropical cyclone—hurricane or typhoon; others seldom or never experience these terrifying visitants. In China and the United States killing frosts extend over practically all these regions several times each year, constantly menacing the winter fruit and vegetable crops in these populous lands, whereas along the southeast coasts of Africa and Queensland frosts seldom occur. In some regions the rainfall is fairly reliable and well distributed so that the farmer feels quite certain that his labors will be rewarded with something of a harvest whether he plants corn, rice, cotton, sugar cane, or any one of a half-dozen other crops; in some of the other regions the extremely unre-

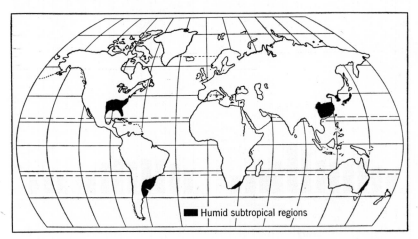

Humid subtropical regions

FIG. 121. The humid subtropical climate occurs on the east margins of continents in lower middle latitudes.

liable rainfall taxes man's wits to the utmost in his efforts to overcome the evil effects of frequent and prolonged drought or of exceedingly heavy and protracted rainfall. Yet the differences in climate from one region to another are not so striking as the likenesses.

Climatic Characteristics Common to All Humid Subtropical Regions

The humid subtropical climate occurs on the eastern margin of continents in about the same latitude as the Mediterranean type of climate on the west coast (Fig. 121). Climatically, however, these two types have little in common except "average annual temperatures" —phenomena which are of little value to any one. All parts of the humid subtropical regions are subject to frost but have a growing season of 200 days or more.[1]

[1] Parts of the narrow coastal region of Africa and Queensland are frost free, but since the uplands immediately back of these coasts are subject to frost it was thought best not to attempt a subdivision here.

Towards the equatorward margins frosts are light and infrequent, but near the poleward margins several hard freezes are expected each

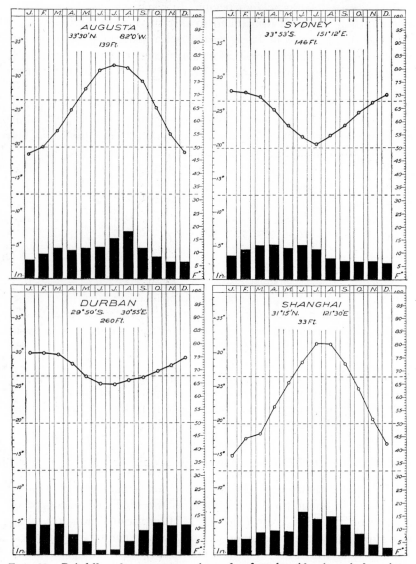

Fig. 122. Rainfall and temperature charts for four humid subtropical stations.

year. The summers are hot, humid, and enervating, there being weeks together every summer when little relief from the heat can be found even at night. The winters are for the most part pleasantly mild, although in southeastern United States and China sudden cold spells are not uncommon.

As suggested by the name, the humid subtropical regions are characterized by moderate to abundant precipitation throughout the year. Fortunately the maximum amount comes in summer, the time of greatest heat and plant growth (Fig. 122). The summer rain is of the local thundershower type interspersed with abundant sunshine. It usually comes in heavy downpours, and not infrequently several inches of water fall within a few hours. The areal distribution is spotty, during some years much more so than during others. As a result one district may have abundant moisture while a few miles away the crops are suffering from drought.[2] The thunderstorms are sometimes accompanied by hail with resultant loss to crops and buildings. Such damage is ordinarily confined to small districts, and the poleward and inland parts of each region are visited more frequently by these storms than the equatorward margins and coastal districts.

The coasts of all humid subtropical regions except that of South America are visited occasionally by tropical cyclones—hurricanes or typhoons—the most destructive of all storms. They result in tremendous losses of life and property, especially on the sea and along the coast, where the fury of the storm is unabated. As the storm passes inland the velocity of the wind decreases, but the accompanying torrential downpour may flood areas which lie hundreds of miles from the shore. The velocity of the wind may reach 130 miles or more an hour, thereby destroying life and property, but the greatest loss is usually the result of tidal waves which flood the coastal lowlands.

Climatic Contrasts from One Region to Another

Rainfall. Although the humid subtropical regions have common climatic characteristics which give them a degree of unity, each one also has certain distinctive qualities which give it individuality. No two regions have the same distribution of rainfall, nor do their winter temperatures fit nicely into the same pattern. Southeastern United States has a relatively uniform and reliable precipitation, the best for any large area belonging to this type; the coastal area of Australia, on the other hand, has one of the most erratic and unreliable rainfall records to be found in the humid portions of the world (Fig. 123). The annual rainfall in eastern United States seldom varies more than

[2] This condition is most common when the region as a whole is suffering from drought.

20 per cent from normal, whereas in Australia it frequently varies 40 to 60 per cent or even more. In addition, the rainfall for any summer month in eastern Queensland may be less than 1 inch or more than

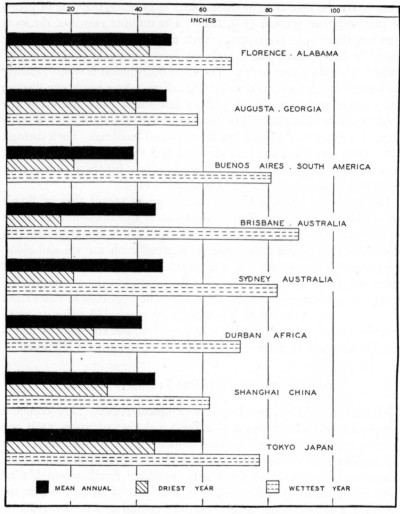

Fig. 123. Rainfall chart for eight humid subtropical stations.

30 inches. In fact, more than 20 inches have been recorded several times in a 24-hour period. These torrential rainstorms occur in all the humid subtropical regions, but Australia and eastern China suffer most in this respect.

The seasonal distribution of rainfall also differs from one region to another. In southeastern United States the precipitation is well distributed throughout the year, about the same amount falling each month. In all the other regions the summer precipitation is decidedly greater than that of winter, the difference being most pronounced in China, where in places the rainfall of the summer six months is more than six times that of the winter half-year. These differences in rainfall are closely related to the differences in the wind systems. The winter rains of all humid subtropical regions are largely a result of cyclones (extra-tropical, see pp. 67–71) which bring the moisture in from the oceans lying to the east and south. Southeastern United States, being visited by cyclones (extra-tropical) more frequently than any other humid subtropical region, receives as a result the heaviest winter rainfall of the entire realm. The lightest winter rainfall occurs in southeastern China, where the dry winter monsoons blow with great regularity from the interior of the continent.

Temperatures. Summer temperatures are similar in all the humid subtropical regions. All have long, hot, humid summers with many days when the maximum temperatures are above 90° F., and occasionally above 100° F. Although the summer temperatures of all humid subtropical regions fall into the same neat pattern, the winter temperatures differ markedly from region to region as determined largely by the amount of land lying to the poleward of each. The southeastern parts of China and the United States are open to the cold winds from the northern interior of Asia and North America respectively. Consequently, destructive frosts sweep down over these areas each year. The 32° isotherm touches its lowest latitude of the whole globe in eastern China, with snow and frost occurring at times as far south as Hong Kong and even at Canton, situated within the low-latitude wet-and-dry realm. This is the only place on record where snowstorms invade the lowlands of the tropics.[3] At Shanghai (in the latitude of southern Georgia) a temperature of 10° F. has been recorded, and lakes have been covered with ice several inches thick. Such low temperatures are caused by cold winds which blow with great regularity from the interior of Asia, where the greatest high-pressure belt of the world is built up during the winter. (See p. 65.) Similarly, southeastern United States lies open to northern winds, and cold waves often reach Florida, bringing frost almost to the extreme south of that state. The "Great Freeze" of 1893 not only

[3] At Hong Kong, situated just inside the tropics, the mean for the coldest month is 58° F., the lowest mean known near the sea level in the latitude. Temperatures of 32° F. have been recorded in this tropical city.

destroyed the orange crop of the state but also killed many of the trees. Other serious frosts have killed much of the fruit from time to time as in 1934–1935 and again in January 1940. Even in the humid subtropical area of South America with a relatively small amount of land lying to the poleward, the dry, cold southwest wind—the pampero—causes suffering among the poorly clad natives of northern Argentina, Uruguay, and southern Brazil. Such sudden cold spells are almost or quite unknown along the coasts of Africa and Australia—areas bathed by warm ocean currents and protected on their poleward margins by thousands of miles of open sea.[4]

The Tropical Cyclone. In one of these regions the desolating winds, tides, and torrential rainstorms of the tropical cyclone are almost or quite unknown, whereas other regions are visited by them ten, twenty, or even thirty times a year as indicated in the table.

AVERAGE ANNUAL FREQUENCY OF RECORDED TROPICAL CYCLONES

Region of occurrence	Number	Region of occurrence	Number
Western North Pacific	30	North Indian Ocean	12
Central North Pacific	8	South Indian Ocean	13
Eastern North Pacific	5	Eastern Australia	13
West Indian Seas	5	West South Pacific	15

The tropical cyclone is the most destructive of all storms. Although the wind is less violent than that of the tornado, it covers a longer path and one several hundred times as broad. A single tropical cyclone which passed over the eastern coast of China took a greater toll of life than has resulted from all the thousands of tornadoes which have been recorded in America since the occupation of this continent by the white man.[5] Such a storm caused the Galveston disaster of September 8, 1900, when 6,000 lives were lost and the property damage was estimated at $30,000,000. The toll of this one storm represents almost twice the loss of life caused by all the tornadoes (about 1,000) which occurred in this country during the ten-year period from 1916 to 1926.[6]

[4] The southeastern coast of Africa is entirely frost free; in Australia light ground frosts occur along the entire coast of New South Wales, but freezing air temperatures have never been recorded north of 30° south latitude. At Sydney, the lowest air temperature ever recorded is 35° F.

[5] It is estimated that at least 50,000 lives were lost in the Swatow typhoon of August 1922. *Monthly Weather Review*, November 1922, p. 436.

[6] The total number of tornadoes reported for the entire country during the ten-year period from 1916 to 1926 was 999, with a loss of 3,158 lives and a property loss estimated at $113,311,000.

The greatest loss of life and property resulting from the tropical cyclone is that caused by the wind and tide along densely populated coasts. Ships are blown onto land or other barriers and wrecked; thousands of people may be caught by tidal waves and drowned; and the foaming tide may weaken foundations of large buildings so that they cannot withstand the tremendous pressure of the wind. Torrential downpours invariably accompany these storms, and the floods may cause tremendous loss of life and property, not merely along the coast but hundreds of miles inland. The passage of a West Indian hurricane over southeastern United States during July 14–15, 1916, caused the greatest floods ever known in the southern Appalachians. At Altapass, North Carolina, 22.22 inches of rain fell in a 24-hour period. The heaviest rainfall ever recorded in a 24-hour period was 46 inches, at Baguio,[7] the summer capital of the Philippine Islands, during the passage of a typhoon.[8] These floods cause vastly more damage each year than that wrought by the terrifying tornado.

Earthquakes and Tropical Cyclones. The coincidence of earthquakes and tropical cyclones has often been noted. Where conditions are ripe for an earthquake the earth's crust is in an unstable condition. It is barely possible, though not yet proved, that the stress accompanying the passage of a severe cyclone may be sufficient to initiate a quake.

It is clear that tropical cyclones subject the earth's crust to an appreciable and relatively sudden strain especially on coasts. A drop of 2 inches in barometric pressure removes a load of about 2 million tons from each square mile of land while over the neighboring sea, a 10-foot rise of water, commonly associated with such a storm, adds about 9 million tons less 2 million tons for reduced air mass or 7 million tons per square mile of sea bottom. Thus when a tropical cyclone passes, a differential pressure of about 9 million tons per square mile between land and sea bottom is created and dissipated within a few hours. A typhoon of such character lay over the Pacific at the time of the Japanese earthquake and the winds made the fires terribly destructive to life and property. Unfortunately the storm center did not come close enough to give rain.[9]

Tornadoes. The tornado is the most violent, least extensive, and most sharply defined of all storms. Like the tropical cyclone it visits some humid subtropical regions but seldom or never occurs in others.

[7] Baguio is situated in the low-latitude wet-and-dry type of climate.

[8] Charles F. Brooks, *Why the Weather*, Harcourt, Brace & Co., 1938, p. 159.

[9] Reprinted by permission from *Why the Weather*, by Charles F. Brooks, Harcourt, Brace & Co., 1938, pp. 153–154.

The "cotton belt" is the only one of these regions where much damage is done by this storm.[10] Moreover, its occurrence is less frequent on the eastern coast than farther west. During an eight-year period only 3 were recorded in Georgia and 6 in Florida, whereas 76 and 68 were recorded during the same period in Arkansas and Texas respectively.

SOILS OF HUMID SUBTROPICAL REGIONS

Because of the relatively heavy rainfall of the humid subtropical regions, practically all the soils are non-lime-accumulating (see pp. 95–99). Within the hottest and wettest parts of the realm, as in Florida, northern Paraguay, and eastern Australia, the soils are largely lateritic and are relatively poor in phosphate, potash, and other valuable mineral plant foods.

Rederths and yellowerths have greater areal extent than any other type of soil found in this realm. They have developed for the most part in areas of 40 to 60 inches of rainfall and are especially common to land that was originally covered with pine forests. These soils cover more than one-half of humid subtropical United States (Fig. 41), and are widespread in southwestern Brazil, Uruguay, and southeastern Paraguay. These rederths and yellowerths, like the lateritic soils, are poor in mineral fertilizers, and as a result crop yields rapidly decline wherever the land is unwisely cultivated. In those areas in the American cotton belt, where cotton and corn are the major crops, large quantities of fertilizers are applied in order to maintain worthwhile crop yield.

Prairyerths are common in the drier and flatter parts of humid subtropical regions. In such areas, leaching is slight for two reasons: first, the rainfall is light, yet high enough for humid crops; and second, the land is flat and drainage is not rapid. The natural vegetation is tall grass as in the pampas of Argentina and in parts of Texas and Louisiana (see p. 176). The prairyerths are relatively rich in mineral fertilizers, and the decay of the vegetation results in the soil's being rich in vegetable matter and, consequently, dark in color. Except for alluvial or volcanic soils, prairyerths are perhaps the most fertile and enduring soils of the humid subtropical realm.

[10] During eight years, 1916 to 1923, the "cotton belt" recorded 278 tornadoes, while the total number recorded in the entire United States was 758.

AGRICULTURE

An enumeration of the crops grown in the various humid subtropical regions indicates about the same variety for each—cotton, sugar cane, rice, corn, wheat, subtropical fruits, vegetables, pasture, and hay. This mere listing of the farm products gives no adequate conception of the agricultural development. Some crops are of major importance in one region and of negligible value in others. In fact, one may travel through large sections of subtropical Asia, southern Brazil, and southeastern United States without suspecting from the crop culture that the climates of all three areas are commonly classified under one type. In the United States cotton is the major crop, and millions of farmers have never seen a field of rice; in Japan and China the paddy fields are the very source of subsistence, and natives everywhere are plodding about in the mud, planting and tending the crops with the most minute care. In parts of Brazil men think in terms of coffee,[11] and the light green of the coffee tree is the most conspicuous part of the cultural landscape. And so the contrast continues from one of these regions to another. In southeastern Australia maize and grass are the staple crops; in southeastern Africa a prominent place is given to sugar cane; in Argentina and Uruguay, corn, wheat, alfalfa, and pasture each predominate in one or more sections. These differences in agriculture, it will be seen from the following study, are closely adjusted to differences in climate, land forms, soil, density of population, and other factors of the natural and cultural environment.

Cotton Culture

Among the civilized peoples of the world, clothing is considered one of the necessaries of life, and an extraordinary amount of energy is spent in satisfying this need. Highly civilized peoples require changes of clothing for summer, for winter, for work, for play, and for social functions—clothing suited to the modifications of both the physical and social atmosphere. Cotton is an ideal fiber for much of this clothing, especially in hot weather. Well over half of the total

[11] The coffee-growing industry of Brazil will be discussed in the chapter "Highlands and Man," but the coffee-growing region of Brazil fits nicely into the humid subtropical realm.

population of the world live in warm climates (tropical or subtropical), and most of the remainder live where the weather is hot part of the year. However, many of the people within the tropics and not a few in the temperate zones are very imperfectly clad. If we add to these facts the tendency of all peoples to possess more clothing as they advance in the scale of civilization, we realize that there is a vast potential market for fibers well suited to this demand.

Cotton is also the principal textile for the manufacture of household fabrics, and cloth for automobile tires, and a considerable quantity is consumed in the preparation of explosives. This extensive use of cotton in all parts of the world, together with the fact that it is grown in restricted areas, has given it first place among the staples in international trade. Cotton textiles normally hold the same rank among the products of the factory.

Cotton is grown in all humid subtropical regions, but it is the major crop in only one of them—the cotton belt of the United States. In all the other regions cotton culture has been handicapped to such an extent that development has been slow. Parts of the realm, particularly in China, are so densely populated that the land is sorely needed for growing food; other parts, especially in South America and Australia, are so sparsely settled that good potential cotton land still lies as waste or is used only for pasture; while still other parts are poorly suited to cotton culture because of adverse physical conditions. In some places the heavy rainfall and moist atmosphere during the picking season cause the fiber to be discolored and of poor quality; in other places the rainfall is so light and uncertain that the fiber is short, the yield small, and the quality poor. High export duties, inefficient labor, the high cost of agricultural machinery, the depredations of insect pests, and the keen competition of other commercial crops have also presented serious obstacles to cotton culture in various parts of the realm.

A study of the cotton culture in each of the humid subtropical regions indicates that in some of them the factors which have retarded development are of a fundamental nature, based on adverse physical conditions which cannot be easily overcome; in other regions the handicaps are merely those associated with frontier conditions, that is, handicaps of the cultural environment such as labor shortage, inadequate knowledge of cotton culture, poor transportation facilities, and unstable government—disadvantages which are being gradually overcome with the industrial growth of the various countries.

Cotton Culture in the United States

Cotton is the most valuable product of the South, and its importance is reflected in many of the economic, political, and social problems. In the cotton belt, it is the basis for most of man's commercial transactions, and the size of the crop and the price of the fiber are matters of the utmost concern not only to the farmer but also to the banker, merchant, and manufacturer. About it frequently hinge tariff issues, labor problems, and banking laws. Cotton is to the South what sugar is to Cuba, coffee to São Paulo, and rubber to Malaya. It ranks third or fourth in value among the crops of the United States, and occupies fifth place in acreage. It is normally the most important commercial crop of the country, and within the cotton belt its value exceeds that of all other crops combined.[12] Under such conditions, it is not surprising that to the South "cotton is king." But some countries have deposed their kings. Similarly the South has been urged from time to time to reduce the rank of "King Cotton" and to give more attention to diversified agriculture, especially to those crops that build up the soil.

Soil Conditions and Cotton Culture. Cotton is grown in practically all types of well-drained soils, but the density of acreage and the yield per acre differ greatly from one type to another. Most of the residual soils of the cotton belt are relatively infertile, and they deteriorate under poor cropping systems much more rapidly than the more fertile glacial and alluvial soils of the upper Mississippi Basin. The average residual soil of the South would be considered mediocre or even poor in the corn belt and spring-wheat region. This contrast has resulted in part from climatic differences and in part from differences in methods of soil formation. In the South the heavy rainfall and the lack of protracted frost subject the soil to excessive leaching during the entire year. Furthermore, over most of the area the rock strata are formed from sediment deposited by water which carries away the most soluble mineral plant foods, leaving an excess of infertile sand. In places, such as the "black belt of Alabama" and the cane and sugar districts of Louisiana and Texas, an abundance of lime (shells or fossil beds) was deposited which weathered into dark calcareous soils, more fertile than most parts of the coastal plain.

[12] The best brief discussion of the cotton-growing industry of the United States is contained in the *Atlas of American Agriculture*, Part V, Section A, U. S. Government Printing Office, Washington, D. C., 1918, pp. 1–28.

Though most of the residual soils of the South are relatively infertile, some of the alluvial soils are exceedingly rich and productive.
The flood plains of the Mississippi, Arkansas, and Red rivers contain
some of the finest farm land of the entire nation. Much of the lowlands called "river bottoms" has an alluvial soil of great depth and
enduring fertility.[18]

Cotton Culture and Soil Depletion. The type of agriculture in the
South has been such that even the efficient farmer finds it difficult to

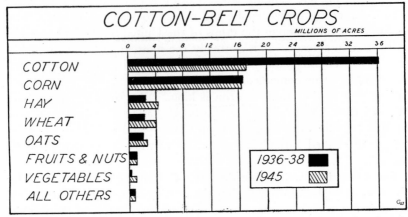

Fig. 124. The acreage given to cotton has greatly decreased during the last decade,
while that given to hay, wheat, oats, and vegetables has increased. Cotton and
corn are, however, still the dominant crops.

retain the soil, and the careless farmer is assiduously helping nature
deplete it. The farmers formerly grew primarily cotton and corn—
crops that require intensive cultivation and keep the surface ever
ready to be washed away by every rain. Although crops less favorable to soil erosion are increasing, corn and cotton are still the major
crops (Fig. 124). As a result, the cotton belt has suffered more from
erosion than any other large section of the United States. Many
millions of acres, once good farm land, now lie waste; other millions
require heavy application of fertilizers in order to make agriculture
profitable.

The farmers of the cotton-belt states utilized in 1945 approximately
45 per cent of the fertilizers consumed in the United States, and fertilizers were applied to more than 90 per cent of the cotton land of

[18] An excellent summary of the soils of the South is given by Almon E. Parkins,
The South, John Wiley & Sons, 1938, pp. 57–63 and 70–77.

North Carolina, South Carolina, Georgia, and Alabama. In spite of this fact, much of the land is deteriorating. The middle and upper coastal plains, composed mostly of sandy loam soils, are easily exhausted. Already a large acreage has been abandoned, and the yield on much of the remaining land is low. The soil fertility of the Piedmont Plateau is also difficult to retain. The region is hilly, and the soils are red clay which erode easily. The alluvial bottoms of the Mississippi and other river valleys are the only parts of the cotton belt on which the one-crop system of agriculture can be practiced for any protracted period of time without rapid deterioration of the soil.

Climate and Cotton Culture. Most of the cotton in the United States is grown in areas having an average summer temperature of 77° or more, and a frost-free season of at least 185 days. The best weather conditions for cotton are found in areas where a mild spring, with light but frequent showers, merges into moderately moist summer weather, warm both day and night, followed by a dry, cool, and prolonged autumn. A cool wet spring retards growth or causes the seed to rot rather than to germinate. The ideal summer rainfall is the thunderstorm type with several days of bright warm weather between rains. The large daily range of temperature in a dry fall favors the maturing crop, as it checks vegetation growth and induces fruiting. Early frost in the fall kills the "top crop" on the upper branches of the plant, or causes the bolls to open prematurely, seriously reducing the yield. As the cotton matures and the bolls begin to open in the latter part of August, rainy weather retards maturity, interferes with picking, and discolors or damages the exposed fibers. The east and south coastal lowland is poorly suited to cotton culture because of the heavy autumn rains and the extensive tracts of poorly drained land.

MAJOR COTTON-PRODUCING AREAS OF THE UNITED STATES

The shaded areas shown in Fig. 125 are designated as the United States cotton belt. However, agricultural and economic conditions differ markedly from one section of this region to another. The proportion of farm acreage in cotton and the yield per acre vary widely from one area to another, as do also the grades of cotton grown, the sizes of the farm, the scale of operations, and the cultural practices. Most of the laborers in some areas are distressingly poor; many of them are illiterate tenants. In other sections most of the farmers own their land and are relatively prosperous. Finally, some parts of the

cotton belt are owned and operated almost exclusively by white farmers, whereas other parts of the region are farmed largely by Negroes.

Although the physical and economic conditions within the Cotton Belt are
not similar throughout, the economic conditions are everywhere built around
the production and marketing of cotton. Almost one-half of the rural population of the United States lives in the Cotton Belt. Consequently one of the
outstanding problems of this country is related to the income and welfare of
the cotton farmer. The following is a brief regional treatment of the important
cotton-growing areas of the United States.

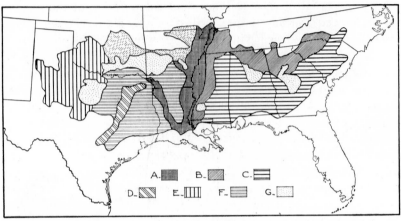

Fig. 125. The United States cotton belt. Within the heavily shaded areas (A,
B, C, D, E, F) cotton is more important than any other crop. (Reprinted by
permission from Case and Bergsmark, *Modern World Geography*, J. B. Lippincott Co., 1938, p. 111.)

Flood Plains of the Mississippi-Arkansas-Red Rivers. The flood plains
of the Mississippi-Arkansas-Red river valleys (designated as "A" in the map
of the Cotton Belt) contain some of the finest cotton land of the entire Cotton
Belt. This is a land of wet flats, low ridges, cypress swamps, and canebrakes
(a thicket of tall, slender, hollow, woody vegetation). Much of it is called
"river bottoms" and has an alluvial soil (sediment laid down by running water)
of great depth and enduring fertility. Most of the "first river bottoms" (lower
flood plains) are flooded each year unless protected by dykes. Other areas
called "second river bottoms" lie above the ordinary flood waters.

Much of the land has been brought under cultivation, and everywhere cotton is the most important crop. In many of the counties 60 to 85 per cent of
the cultivated land is given to this useful fiber. In fact, throughout extensive
areas cotton is grown to the exclusion of all other crops except corn and the
minor crops grown for work animals and home consumption.

Fertile Farms and Poor People. These flood plains are almost unsurpassed for their fertility, and they produce exceptionally large yields (250 to

350 pounds per acre) of long and strong fiber; yet most of the farmers are poor and backward, and many of them are illiterate. Indeed, very few of them can be properly classified as prosperous. Those who live on the land own very little of it. Absentee landlords possess the land, while the actual labor is performed by Negro and white tenants [who live on farms that average 20 to 30 acres].

The area has a large percentage of Negro farmers. Slavery carried the Negro to these lands, and mosquitoes, malaria, typhoid, and floods tended to keep the white people out. Thus in the Arkansas plain Negroes represent 74 per cent of the total population; whereas they constitute but 26 per cent of the population of the state as a whole. The population of two Mississippi counties is more than 90 per cent Negro.

It is an impressive sight during the cotton picking season to see the almost continuous fields of cotton stretching far across the level land. Probably no other equal area in the world provides clothing materials for so many people.[14]

The Inner Piedmont-Tennessee Valley-Western Mississippi Region. This area (section "B," Fig. 125) is the most important cotton-growing section of the South. The grade of cotton produced in this section is fair and the yield good. Most of the farms are small and operated by tenants who use little machinery. The hoe, two-horse plow, ten-foot harrow, and one-row cultivator are the major farm tools. Most of the land is in slopes, and, as a consequence, soil erosion is a serious problem. The relatively high yield of cotton is made possible by a liberal use of fertilizers at considerable cost. Although the yield per acre is fair, the total cotton production per family is small and the income scarcely provides more than the bare necessities of life.

The Old South. The Old South (section "C") was, in early times, the greatest cotton-growing area of the South. However, poor methods of farming and serious soil erosion have robbed this area of much of its soil fertility. Moreover, the warm moist climate is ideally suited to the ravages of the boll weevil. As a result, cotton culture has declined while the acreage given to tobacco, peanuts, sweet clover, pecans, and other crops has increased. The diversification of crops came after much of the soil had been all but ruined. This loss of the soil—the most valuable resource of the region—is a permanent handicap to the economic recovery of the region known as the Old South.

Western Sections of the Cotton Belt. A small but very important cotton-growing region is situated in central Texas and is known as the *black waxy prairie* (section "D," Fig. 125). It is a region of great

[14] Reprinted by permission from Case and Bergsmark, *Modern World Geography*, J. B. Lippincott Co., 1938, pp. 111–112.

fertility, but the light rainfall reduces the cotton yield per acre to approximately one-half that of the Mississippi flood plain. To offset this disadvantage the farms are large and the farmers increase their income from cotton by growing corn, small grains, and other feed crops. The livestock industry is also an important source of income on almost every farm.

The area lying west of the Mississippi and designated as section "F" is as a rule generally infertile and produces a low yield of medium or poor grade of cotton. The minor areas designated as "G" are given largely to fruit, vegetables, and diversified agriculture. Cotton is secondary in the cropping system.

During the last thirty years a most interesting development of cotton culture has taken place on the "staked plains" and on neighboring parts of Texas and Oklahoma. This area was once known as part of the "great American desert." Formerly it was considered that an annual rainfall of 23 inches was necessary for a profitable crop of cotton, but it is now known that 17 inches of rain is sufficient for a profitable crop provided 75 per cent of it falls during the growing season of 185 days.[15]

The staked plains, an area once thought to be too dry for cotton, is one of the most progressive areas of the South. Here the farmers have taken rapid strides forward in methods of agriculture. The tractor is replacing the horse and the mule; the gang plow and the cultivator are taking the place still held in many parts of the South by the two-horse plow, the double-shovel, and the hoe (Fig. 126); and the "sled," a cotton-harvesting machine which does the work formerly done by six or seven men, is relieving the farmer and his family of much of the drudgery which cotton picking still necessitates in other parts of the cotton belt.

Climatic and topographic conditions on the staked plains have facilitated the use of large-scale machinery to a greater extent than in most other parts of the cotton belt. In most sections of the South, the acreage which a farmer plants to cotton is limited to the amount which he and his family can pick. Since this acreage is small there is little need to use large-scale machinery in preparing the soil and in planting and tending the crop. However, on the staked plains and neighboring parts of Texas and Oklahoma the cotton-harvesting machine is oper-

[15] Fortunately, in the cotton belt, autumn is the driest season of the year, practically all the important cotton regions receiving less than 10 inches of rain during the fall months. *Atlas of American Agriculture*, Part V, U. S. Government Printing Office, 1918.

ated successfully and has become a great labor-saving device, though it has not been used with any considerable degree of success in the more humid areas situated farther east. This difference in the use of machinery is largely the result of contrasts in climate during the picking season. Not all the cotton bolls of a given field mature at one time. Some bolls are ready for picking several weeks before others are ripe. Unfortunately, cotton grown in the more humid parts of

FIG. 126. By use of the four-row cultivator two men can tend as much cotton as is normally cultivated by the work of twenty-eight mules and fourteen men. (Courtesy International Harvester Co. of America.)

the cotton belt must be picked soon after it matures or the fiber may be discolored and damaged by rain. No cotton-picking machine has been devised, as yet, which is completely successful in picking the ripe bolls and leaving the remaining ones to mature and to be picked later.[16] On the staked plains, however, all the cotton may be gathered at a single picking. Since the rainfall is exceedingly light and the

[16] Trial experiments in 1946–1947 indicate that a mechanical picker has been devised which can pick as much cotton in 1 hour as can be picked in 25 to 50 hours by hand. The machine is expensive and does not completely solve the problem of mechanization for the cotton-belt farmer. Wherever the mechanical picker is used, hand pickers usually gather the bolls that open early and again those that open late. It is not economical to send the machine through the field to gather a small amount of cotton. The extent of the future use of mechanical pickers in the humid part of the United States is still unknown.

atmosphere relatively dry during the winter—the period when the bolls are ripening—the bolls that mature first are left on the stalks without damage until all are ripe. Under such conditions the "sleds" are operated with success and much of the former drudgery of the cotton farmer is eliminated.

The level topography of the staked plains lends itself to large-scale machinery in preparing the soil for seeding and in planting and culti-

Fig. 127. Cultivating cotton on the staked plains. Note the nature of the topography and the size of the field. (Courtesy International Harvester Co. of America.)

vating the crop. Consequently, within this area each laborer can plant, tend, and pick a much larger acreage than is possible in the eastern part of the cotton belt. The area has therefore become a land of the "bonanza cotton farm" (Fig. 127).

Economic Aspects of Cotton Culture in the South

Cotton occupies the best land and is the chief source of the farmer's income. Since cotton grows on practically all well-drained soils, resists drought, and yields well on light, sandy soils to which fertilizers have been applied, it is better suited to many of the soils of the South than other staple crops. Furthermore, the South has a denser agricultural population and cheaper labor than other parts of the United States. Both these circumstances favor the production of cotton, as it requires a large amount of hand labor—except as previously mentioned within that part of Texas where large-scale machinery is used—and yields high returns per acre. As a result, cotton is produced to the neglect of other crops. On many farms not enough food is grown for home use or to feed the livestock. Every year large quantities of foodstuffs and grain are imported to be distributed not only to the city population but also to the cotton growers on the farms.

In the early 1940's the acreage given to cotton declined in practically all parts of the cotton belt. During the years 1926–1930 an average of 42,212,000 acres was planted in cotton annually. In 1945 only 17,241,000 acres were planted. This decline is associated with (1) the increasing world competition in cotton production and the resulting low price of the fiber; and (2) the encouragement given to cotton growers by the United States Government to reduce the acreage given to cotton.

With the decline in acreage there has been an increase in the yield per acre. During the decade 1921–1930, the average yield of fiber per acre was 126 pounds; during 1931–1940, the yield was 225 pounds; and during 1941–1945, the yield was 240 pounds. This increase in the yield per acre during recent years has been largely a result of (1) a reduction in the acreage planted, making it possible to select more fertile areas for the cultivation of this fiber; (2) a partial control of the boll weevil; (3) an increase in the use of fertilizers; and (4) an improvement in the methods of cultivation.

The reduction of the ravages of the boll weevil has been especially marked. In 1929, approximately one-third of the cotton crop was destroyed by this pest; in later years the loss has been held to less than 10 per cent.

Cotton Laborers Poorly Paid. The cotton farmer is paid less than any other large class of labor in the United States. Cotton is produced by the help of hundreds of thousands of women and children, both Negro and white, who get a mere pittance for their labor. Many a cotton farmer's wife works all day in the field during the planting and chopping season and again during the picking season. These laborers are really competing, indirectly it is true, with the laborers of India, Egypt, and other tropical countries that produce cotton on a large scale. If an efficient, labor-saving cotton-picking machine were to be widely used, it undoubtedly would lift the income of the cotton-belt farmer, but it would also create technical unemployment and would probably result in a shift of cotton-belt farmers to new locations and industries. (See footnote, p. 321.)

Factors Tending to Decentralize the Cotton-Growing Industry. Almost every industrial country in the world is fostering the development of the cotton-textile industry. The unreliability of the cotton crop of America (Fig. 128) together with the increasing demands of the American mills have created a problem of international concern.

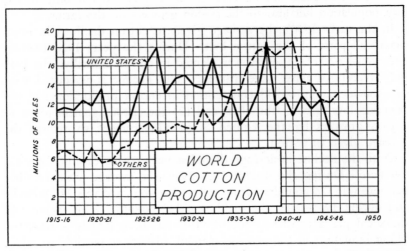

Fɪɢ. 128. Prior to 1934 the United States produced more than one-half of the world's crop of cotton. Since then the United States has produced less than one-half of the world's crop each year except 1938.

Foreign countries must have cotton. They are, therefore, promoting its culture on a wide scale. As a result, experimentation in cotton growing is being carried on in more than a dozen countries, and in some places with surprisingly good results. The acreage suitable for non-American cotton culture is widespread and exceedingly large; the yield per acre in several regions is greater than in America; and cheap labor, cheap land, and cheap animal power favor some of the newly developed countries. These facts should stimulate the American cotton grower to give careful consideration to diversified agriculture.

Cᴏᴛᴛᴏɴ Cᴜʟᴛᴜʀᴇ ɪɴ Oᴛʜᴇʀ Hᴜᴍɪᴅ Sᴜʙᴛʀᴏᴘɪᴄᴀʟ Rᴇɢɪᴏɴs

China. China normally produces approximately 2,000,000 bales of cotton annually. Since 1936, because of the Japanese invasion of

China and subsequent unsettled political conditions, the cotton production of that crowded country has undoubtedly decreased. Even in normal times China's cotton production is not sufficient to supply the local needs of her enormous population, and she is compelled to import from India and America. The most productive area is the lower Yangtze Basin, where the small province of Kiangsu, situated on the coast, grows about one-fourth of the country's crop. This cotton, although better than the average Chinese fiber, is short staple adapted only to weft and short-end work. Experimentations indicate that it will be difficult, if not impossible, to improve the quality to such an extent that it will compare favorably with the American fiber. Only native Chinese cotton is suitable for the lower Yangtze as several factors militate against the introduction of American species.[17] The more important of these difficulties are: (1) The American varieties develop three or four weeks later than the Chinese, and, therefore, winter comes on before the bolls open in the cooler area near the coast. (2) The greater humidity of the area, similar to that of our own coast, stimulates the destruction of both the plants and the bolls by fungus diseases, rendering such as may be picked low in quality and discolored. (3) The fact that the American bolls turn upward renders them more liable to such destruction than the pendent Chinese bolls. (4) Practically all the coastal land is a two-crop area where cotton follows in rotation after a small grain or beans, leaving a season too short for the better varieties of cotton to mature. This practice can scarcely be changed to a one-crop system because of the great pressure for food. Even if the American cotton could be grown successfully it would stand little chance of being as valuable as two crops. Since the Chinese farmer has so small a margin over subsistence he necessarily plants the crops which yield the most income.

A considerable amount of cotton is grown in the southern part of the North China plain, but the season there is too short to produce a good grade of fiber and the rainfall of most of this area is extremely uncertain. In the middle and upper Yangtze Basin the climate seems to be well adapted to cotton culture, but, as in the lower Yangtze Basin, the population pressure is so great that the cotton season is shortened in order to get a food crop from the land before the cotton is planted.

Cotton Culture in Humid Subtropical South America. The Paraná Basin contains an area, suited to cotton growing, which is comparable

17 J. B. Griffin, *China Year Book,* University of Chicago Press, 1926, pp. 695–696.

in size to the cotton belt of the United States. Development has been most rapid in southern Brazil, where, according to the report of the International Cotton Commission (British), the natural conditions are "superior" for cotton. The fundamental factors which favor this region are: (1) a large potential cotton-growing area, (2) favorable climate, and (3) fertile and well-drained soils. Credence is lent to the large estimated acreage by the fact that cotton is being grown on a commercial scale in every state in southern and eastern Brazil. Suitable soil and climate are evidenced by the high yield, particularly in the state of São Paulo, where as much as 890 pounds of lint per acre have been reported and where the average acreage yield is much larger than that of the United States. The fiber compares favorably with the best upland American staple. Why, then, has cotton production lagged in Brazil, especially since land is cheap and plentiful? The answer is found in social and economic conditions. It has been difficult to procure labor acquainted with the needs of cotton culture; modern agricultural machinery is expensive, and its value is not fully understood; the local government has given little assistance to crops other than coffee, the principal source of revenue; and the tariff on exported lint makes it difficult for the planter to compete in the world markets with the producers in those countries that do not tax exports. All these handicaps might have been overcome but for the fact that coffee has proved, on the whole, a more profitable crop than cotton, and has absorbed most of the energies and capital of the planters.

Northern Argentina contains 250,000 square miles of land much of which is excellently suited to cotton growing. Its cultivation is attended with many difficulties, but most of them are associated with frontier conditions that may be overcome. The leading drawbacks to the rapid expansion of the industry are: (1) lack of adequate transportation facilities in the sections cultivated, (2) an inadequate supply of labor, (3) uncombated diseases and the pests of locusts, ants, and caterpillars, (4) a system which compels the laborers to trade with the country stores of the employers, and (5) the dependence of the producer on grasping speculators for the sale of his crop. All these disadvantages can be overcome.

Sericulture

Silk is less extensively produced than cotton and has fewer uses, but it represents an excellent if not the supreme accomplishment in the production of high-grade textile fiber. Although physical conditions are suited to sericulture in all humid subtropical regions, the industry has been developed in only one of them—subtropical Asia—China and Japan. Prior to World War II, more than 90 per cent of the world's output of silk was produced in these two countries and most of the remainder came from southern Europe, primarily from Italy and France.

Sericulture and Labor. The fact that silkworm rearing is essentially dependent upon manual labor has been a vital factor in determining the regions in which sericulture has prospered. All attempts to devise labor-saving appliances adapted for the care of the worms have failed. Consequently, the dominance of the industry in China and Japan is largely a response to cheap, but frequently inefficient, labor. It is an outstanding fact that the silk industry of China and Japan is supported by the masses of women who work long hours for little pay. For each pound of silk that is produced 150 pounds of leaves must be gathered and fed to approximately 2,500 worms. No machinery has been devised that is suited to this task. Later a vast amount of work is required for reeling the silk even when machinery is used. However, much of the silk is still reeled by hand. Fortunately for the industry, the crowded districts of the silk-producing areas of Asia furnish the large supply of labor demanded, and the need for a cash crop in these areas affords the necessary stimulant for the hard and tiresome work necessary to the industry.

Silk Culture in China. Prior to 1900, China ranked first among the countries of the world, both in silk production and in export. Since that date, however, the sericultural development of Japan has increased rapidly, whereas in China it has made little progress. Consequently, for the years 1930 to 1939, Japan supplied 87 to 91 per cent of the world's commercial silk.

Most of the Chinese silk of commerce is produced in a few restricted areas of the Yangtze and Si Kiang river valleys where the silkworms feed upon the leaves of the mulberry tree, native to these areas. However, wild silk, the product of silkworms fed upon oak leaves, is produced in small quantities in both Shantung and Manchuria. It is coarse, in comparison with the white and yellow silk made by the worms fed upon the mulberry leaves, and is made into the tussahs of commerce.

Most of China's white silk is produced in the provinces of Chekiang, Kiangsu, and Kwangtung. The yellow silk comes mainly from Szechwan and Shantung.[18] The most important silk-producing area of the

[18] *China Year Book,* University of Chicago Press, 1938, p. 70.

country is that surrounding Tai Ho Lake. Here, within an area of about 100 square miles, mulberry plantations cover much of the land, and the care of the silkworm is the major occupation of the farmer and his family.

The chief silk-producing center of the Kwangtung Province lies approximately 30 miles west of Canton. Here, within an area of 250 square miles, are operated 180 filatures (mills for reeling the silk from cocoons), each affording employment for 300 to 500 girls. The moist climate of this area together with the long, warm growing season makes it possible to produce from six to eight crops of cocoons each year, whereas in most parts of Japan only three crops are produced. These favorable climatic conditions, together with an abundance of cheap labor, are ideal for the development of sericulture, provided that the disease of the silkworm can be brought under control.

The hot, humid atmosphere which favors the development of the silkworm also favors the spread of disease germs and makes the control of diseases among worms difficult. Until a few years ago the farmers of China gave little attention to the selection of disease-free eggs. Consequently, it was not uncommon for more than one-third of a crop to be destroyed by diseases. Recently some improvement has been made in this respect, but the loss from disease is still great. Unfortunately, many of the unhealthy worms live until they are almost mature, and, consequently, are given the same care and feed as healthy worms. Some idea of the loss in such a case may be judged by the fact that the worms from an ounce of eggs will consume about a ton of mulberry leaves, provided that they all live to maturity. It requires 50 pounds of leaves to produce 1 pound of dried cocoons.

If the diseases of the silkworm can be controlled and the sericulture of China can be put on a scientific basis there is reason to believe that the silk production of the country may be materially increased, for there is an abundance of rugged land in China that is better suited to the growth of the mulberry tree than to the cultivation of food crops, and there is an almost unlimited supply of labor for the promotion of sericulture.

Sericulture in Japan. Before World War II, silk was Japan's most valuable export, and sericulture was second only to rice culture among the industries of the island empire. In 1940, more than 2,000,000 families were engaged in rearing silkworms. Thus in the economy of the country, sericulture plays an important role. For 10,000,000 people (2,000,000 families) silk is practically the only cash crop. The large-scale use of nylon, rayon, and other artificial fibers is adversely affecting the silk industry. Sericulture has been declining for several decades in southern Europe and has made little progress in Japan since 1930.

Silk versus Rayon and Nylon.[19] In recent years the silk industry has suffered from the competition of rayon, nylon, and other synthetic fibers. The achievements in the development of rayon have been remarkable. In 1926, the total world production of rayon and nylon was 60 million pounds; in 1941, the output reached 2,835 million pounds. Since 1941, world production of rayon and nylon has declined but the United States production has continued to increase as indicated by the following table. The importance of rayon and nylon

RAYON AND NYLON PRODUCTION *

Year	United States	World
1941	591,000,000	2,835,000,000
1942	620,000,000	2,680,000,000
1943	656,000,000	2,573,000,000
1944	704,000,000	2,080,000,000
1945	769,000,000	1,530,000,000
1946	875,000,000	1,800,000,000

* *Rayon Organ*, February 1947, p. 19; March 1947, p. 38.

in the textile industry of the United States is further indicated by the following table. Whenever world industry recovers sufficiently from

UNITED STATES AND WORLD CONSUMPTION OF FOUR FIBERS IN 1946

Thousands of pounds

Fiber	United States	World
Cotton	4,844,900	11,870,000
Rayon and nylon	875,400	1,800,000
Wool	748,400	3,710,000
Silk	6,300	

World War II to get back to full production schedules, it seems probable that the world production of synthetic fibers will quickly surpass that of wool.

Rice Culture

Rice is the most valuable crop of the humid subtropics. This distinctive position is the result of the intensive cultivation of rice in one region—southeastern Asia—rather than of its widespread growth in this

[19] In most production figures, nylon is included with rayon.

climatic type. In fact, although extensive tracts of lowland situated in other humid subtropical regions could be given to rice, the quantity now grown is negligible except in small sections of the United States and Brazil. This fact is indicated more forcefully in the table.

APPROXIMATE RICE PRODUCTION IN THE HUMID SUBTROPICAL PART OF EACH CONTINENT

Continent	Production in thousands of pounds
Asia	70,000,000
North America	1,580,000
South America	480,000
Africa	less than 200,000
Australia	less than 500

Rice the Major Crop of Humid Subtropical Asia. Agriculture of southeastern China is inseparably woven around rice production. Rice is given the dominant place wherever land forms are suited to its production, especially during the summer season when weather conditions favor its growth. On many of the small plains of southeastern China (Fig. 129) more than 80 per cent of the land is given to rice during the summer season. Cotton, peanuts, sugar cane, mulberry trees, and a variety of vegetables occupy most of the other cultivated land. Wheat, barley, beans, and rapeseed represent major winter crops.

Most of the steep slopes of the hill-land remains uncultivated. The soil on many slopes is thin and relatively unproductive, and that which remains is difficult to retain when cultivated. Under such conditions, yields are insufficient to pay for the great amount of human effort required to cultivate the land with the crude agricultural equipment possessed by the backward Chinese farmers of this region.

The Yangtze River plain and the Si River delta have ideal environments for water-loving rice. The summer rainfall is abundant and well distributed, the temperatures are high, and the soil is fertile and easily irrigated by a network of canals. Under such conditions rice yields are large.

The Yangtze plain (Fig. 129) produces more food and supports more farmers than any other comparable area in the world with the possible exception of the Nile Valley and the lower Indus Valley. This alluvial plain is divided into innumerable patches of land. It is irrigated by a fine network of canals and is fertilized by the mud of irrigation waters and by night soil. The fields are always in use and three crops a year are common. The crops of the Yangtze plain are

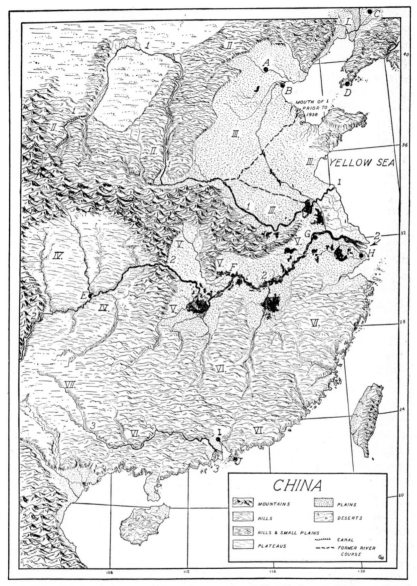

FIG. 129. Most of the land of China is rugged and ill-suited to agriculture. Land
forms: (I) Liao plain or south Manchurian plain, (II) loess uplands, (III) North
China plain, (IV) Szechwan Basin, (V) Yangtze plain, (VI) hills and small plains,
(VII) plateau. Cities: (*A*) Peiping (Peking), (*B*) Tientsin, (*C*) Mukden, (*D*)
Dairen, (*E*) Chungking, (*F*) Hankow, (*G*) Nanking, (*H*) Shanghai, (*I*) Canton,
(*J*) Hong Kong. Rivers: (1) Hwang Ho, (2) Yangtze, (3) Si Kiang.

very similar to those of the small plains of southeast China as previously given. The mulberry tree is important in the deltas of both the Yangtze and Si rivers. These trees are often grown along the canals or lake shores where an abundance of mud for fertilizers can be obtained.

The Szechwan Basin is one of the most scenic and productive areas of China (Fig. 129). This basin was occupied by a lake in former geologic times. After the lake was drained by the headwaters of the Yangtze River, the old lake bed was badly dissected by streams that have cut valleys 1,000 to 1,500 feet deep. Thus the basin is exceptionally rugged except for a few river flood plains, the most notable of which is the Chengtu plain.

The climate of the Szechwan Basin is warm and humid, and the surrounding mountains protect the region from cold winter winds. The soil is fertile and the streams carry an abundance of sediment which fertilizes irrigated fields. The land is therefore exceedingly productive. Some of the hills have been terraced to the top.

These factors permit an exceedingly diversified agricultural development. Consequently, Szechwan is less dependent on rice than are many other sections of southern China. Only about 30 per cent of the cultivated land is given to rice culture. The major crops are rice, winter wheat, barley, beans, cotton, tea, poppies for opium, oranges, sugar cane, the mulberry tree, tobacco, hemp, and a great variety of vegetables.

Japan represents an extreme case of a nation that is land hungry. Stripped of her empire, Japan consists of four large islands together with hundreds of smaller islands clustered around the larger ones. Only 20 per cent of Japan's land can be cultivated and only 15 per cent of the land is classified as level. With less than 30,000 square miles of cultivable land, Japan finds it difficult to produce enough food to supply her 68,000,000 people.

Fortunately, Japan is the rice-producing country *par excellence* and more than one-half of the cultivated land is given to this cereal. Among the food crops rice stands pre-eminent with no other crop even a close second (Fig. 130). A prodigious amount of work must be done to grow the Japanese rice crop. The field for paddy rice must be made almost perfectly level; then low banks of earth must be built around the plot in order to keep in the water; and finally a system of irrigation must be arranged to make good the loss of water by evaporation, leakage, and the continual movement of some of the water to adjoining plots having a lower elevation.

More than one-third of the paddy-field area of the country can be dried off and made suitable for a second crop of barley, wheat, rye, beans, or peas. The farmer has two advantages if, owing to the topography, the land can be readily drained: first, he can grow two or more crops each year; and second, he has the pleasure of tending all but the rice crop dry shod. The one-crop paddy is under water practically all the year, and consequently the laborer usually has wet feet while cultivating the land.

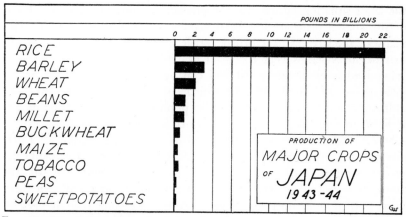

FIG. 130. No other country depends so largely on one major crop as does Japan. (*Statesman's Yearbook*, 1946, p. 1052.)

After the paddy fields are prepared for cultivation, swamp-rice culture still necessitates an abundance of labor under unpleasant conditions. The fields must be plowed, the rice must be sown and later replanted by hand, and all the while the fields must be properly flooded from time to time and carefully cultivated. There still remain the harvesting, threshing, and cleaning of the grain—which is all done without the aid of machinery. Most of this work in addition to being tiresome drudgery is unhealthful. But rice is the crop best suited to support a dense population on hot, wet lands unfit for other cereals. The yield is large, and the rice is a wholesome food, quickly and easily digested—factors which are important in warm, damp areas where other cereals cause indigestion.

Rice Culture in the United States. Rice growing has been a plantation industry in the South since early colonial days, and the need of a forced labor supply in fields so ill-famed for their unhealthful conditions was a major influence in making slavery a recognized institution in the United States. Perhaps no other American crop was produced so completely with slave labor before the Civil War. Since that time the industry has declined on the east coast until today only a few thousand acres are harvested each year. In 1849, more than 200,000,-000 pounds were grown in North Carolina, South Carolina, and Georgia; in 1863, the production was less than 2,000,000 pounds. After the Civil War the industry was revived in these states for a time but soon fell into decay once more.

The present neglected state of rice culture on the east coast reflects the labor situation rather than the physical conditions. Large sections of the coastal plain are low tidal marshes of exceptional fertility, and many of the streams have broad, fertile plains which merge into reedy marshes or swamps near the level of high tide. Much of this low-lying land is exceedingly flat and can be easily irrigated after it has been diked and ditched.[20] In China such land would be carefully cultivated and would support a dense population. But in America it is difficult to find laborers willing to work in steaming rice fields except where modern machinery can be used to lighten the drudgery. Little advance has been made in devising harvesting machinery suitable for coastal swamp lands, and Oriental hand-labor methods are still the rule. It is not likely that rice culture will expand rapidly in these areas until population pressure becomes much greater than at present.

During the last few decades a new method of rice culture has been developed in Louisiana, Texas, and Arkansas which differs as markedly from that of the Orient as the East does from the West. In these states American machinery has been substituted for hand labor, and most of the rice is grown on level prairie lands which are more health-ful than the coastal swamps. Here dikes and ditches are made by steam-driven shovels; the ground is plowed and cultivated by ma-chinery much like that used in the corn belt; and irrigation waters are supplied from reservoirs, wells, and streams by the simple operation of levers, switches, or other mechanical devices. Before harvest time the water is drained from the gently sloping plain so that the ground becomes firm enough to support heavy binders or, in some cases, combines. Thus by use of modern machinery one man may take care of 80 to 160 acres of rice each year with less drudgery than is

[20] For an excellent summary of the physiography of the coastal plain see I. Bowman, *Forest Physiography*, John Wiley & Sons, 1914, pp. 518–542. For a more detailed study of soils, drainage, erosion, and other factors influencing the agriculture of the coastal plain see Nevin M. Fenneman, *Physiography of Eastern United States*, McGraw-Hill Book Co., 1938, pp. 1–120.

required of the Chinese farmer who ekes out an existence from a few small paddy fields, frequently scattered about in patches of less than an acre each (Fig. 131).

It has been estimated that there are 10,000,000 acres of land in the South well suited to rice culture, an acreage 25 per cent larger than is given to the paddy fields in Japan. It seems probable, therefore, that as population pressure increases more land will be given to this valuable cereal. Such development will probably be slow, as under the best

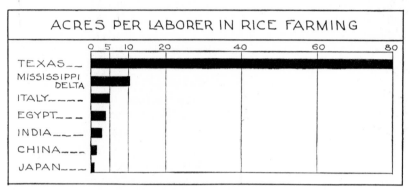

Fɪɢ. 131. The Texas farmer can tend fifty to eighty times as much land in rice as is cultivated by the average Japanese or Chinese farmer, and some farmers can produce sixty times as much rice.

conditions rice growing remains an unhealthful occupation. Even on the prairie, the warm, moist atmosphere and wet soil are well suited to malaria and other subtropical maladies, and the debilitating climate weakens man's constitution, making him more susceptible to these diseases.

Rice Culture in South America. There is much marshy land suited to rice culture in northern Argentina and southern Brazil, but because of the sparse population only a small acreage can be given to a crop which requires so much labor. In Paraguay most of the rice is grown on the flood plains lying between the Paraguay River and the railway. In southern Brazil most of the rice is grown in small patches here and there for local consumption.

Sugar-Cane Production

Although sugar cane may be grown in all parts of the humid sub-tropics, it is of minor importance except in a few favored localities.

The yield is so greatly reduced by short seasons, frosts, droughts, diseases, and insect pests that artificial stimuli, such as tariffs and bounties, are usually necessary to make cane growing profitable. In spite of government aid, less than 3 per cent of the world's commercial crop is grown in humid subtropical regions. The reason for this situation results primarily from the fact that the climate of humid subtropical regions is not well suited to the production of sugar cane. Since it is a plant of tropical origin, its culture in subtropical areas, near the poleward limits of production, is attended with climatic hazards. This warmth-loving crop thrives best in frost-free areas which have a rhythmic rainfall such as that of the wet-and-dry realm of the tropics.

Sugar-Cane Production in Southeastern United States. Sugar cane is grown in all the South Atlantic and Gulf states for the manufacture of syrup and in Louisiana for the production both of syrup and sugar. Since frost occurs in all these states it is necessary to harvest the cane before it matures and while the sugar content is low. Since cool weather hastens the maturing process it is common practice to let the cane stand in late fall until warnings of damaging temperatures are received; then every available man is set to the harvest.[21] Under the most favorable conditions the sugar content is still low at harvest time. Thus, in Louisiana the average yield of sugar per ton of cane is only 60 to 70 per cent of that of Hawaii, Cuba, and Puerto Rico. Moreover, in Louisiana there is always more or less loss as a result of low temperature.

This handicap is partly offset by the fact that immature cane is rich in invert sugar, rendering it peculiarly suitable for the manufacture of syrup and molasses. The receipts from the sale of these two products by the sugar factories of the South, primarily Louisiana, are larger proportionally than in any of the major regions of cane-sugar production.

Frosts and short seasons are not the only climatic handicaps to sugar production in these regions; rainy winters, floods, droughts, and wind storms all add to the planters' difficulties.[22] Cane needs a wet season

---

[21] In Louisiana several hundred thousand dollars' worth of cane may be cut in the 24-hour period following a cold-wave warning; in New South Wales and southern Brazil the crop is frequently cut short by unexpected frosts. China, with her large cane production in areas where frosts are frequent and severe and where weather service is poor, undoubtedly sustains heavy losses each year, although statistical proof is lacking.

[22] These climatic hazards exist in all humid subtropical regions. For example, in the fall, when the cane needs an abundance of sunshine and a light but well-distributed rainfall, the Natal farmer watches the weather with anxiety, for it is the season of worst storms and greatest extremes in rainfall. Between 1890 and

to give it a full growth, and a drier sunny period to insure a large sucrose content. In southern United States the autumn and winter rainfall is heavy, and in most of the other regions it is extremely uncertain. In Louisiana the sugar harvest is increased by any variation from the normal uniformly distributed rainfall tendencies, towards closer approximation to its seasonal character near the tropics. Heavy winter rains not only reduce the sugar content but also favor the development of the principal insect enemy—the corn-borer moth. Data gathered by Louisiana Experiment Stations from many parts of the world show that the yield is closely related to this seasonal rainfall régime, provided that the crop is not injured by storms or pests.

Unfortunately for the sugar-cane planter, tropical cyclones and accompanying floods are most frequent in the autumn when the cane is maturing and is least suited to stand such conditions. In 1927 one such storm along the coast of Queensland caused a loss of 50,000 tons of sugar (500,000 tons of cane). Such a storm frequently twists the cane of Louisiana in every direction and then beats it to the ground, reducing the yield and making the harvest difficult and expensive. When the harvest is completed the Louisiana farmer must put aside almost one-eighth of his crop for planting the following year, whereas his competitors of the tropics harvest crop after crop from one planting.[23] The total effect of these adverse conditions is shown clearly in the fact that, during the years 1925 to 1945 inclusive, the average acreage yield of sugar in Louisiana was only 1,870 pounds while that of Hawaii was 13,140 pounds. The average production per acre in Java is approximately 8,660 pounds, in Cuba 4,910 pounds, and in Puerto Rico 4,540 pounds.

Citrus Fruit Production

Oranges are grown in all humid subtropical regions, but they are an important commercial crop in only one of them—southeastern United

1937 there were seven occasions when the precipitation for the month of March was more than 10 inches (20.17 in 1925, and 19.09 in 1927). On the other hand, there were nine years when the total record was less than 2 inches.

[23] Sugar cane is propagated from either seed cane or roots. If the roots are left in the ground new shoots (ratoons) will spring from them and a crop may be obtained without further planting. The other method of propagating is by laying the canes in furrows and plowing them under. Shoots will then spring up from each joint. The climate of Cuba is so admirably adapted to the growth of cane that it may be ratooned profitably for ten or more years, whereas in Louisiana it is not profitable to ratoon for more than two years. The third year the land is usually plowed and planted to some nitrogenous crop such as peas.

States. Florida is surpassed by two regions, Mediterranean Eurasia and southern California, in the production of oranges. The peninsular position of Florida assures the state milder winter temperatures than are found in any other part of eastern United States. Even with this protection frost sometimes invades the state, and the northern section frequently experiences severe freezes. During the winter of 1894–1895 a severe frost not only destroyed most of the orange crop of Florida but in addition killed many thousand trees. When the industry revived, most of the groves were located farther south, where the northwest winds of winter were tempered by the warm waters of the Gulf. Recently the industry has been pushing northward again, but, since the dangers of the location are better known than in 1894, the planters make provision to protect their groves when necessary by some of the methods of artificial heating which have been devised.

The climate of southern Japan is suitable for oranges, and the empire ranks third among the countries in production. On many of the hill slopes of the southern islands the orange tree is an important feature of the landscape.

Paraguay, southern Brazil, and northern Argentina have great potentialities for orange production, and both wild and cultivated trees appear in great numbers. Paraguay is especially well suited to orange culture, and within the more populous districts along the main rivers and the Central Railway groves are abundant. Although little care is given to the tree the fruit is large, juicy, and of excellent flavor.

Unfortunately Paraguay is a long distance from the important orange markets of the world; transportation facilities are poor and too slow and unreliable to be well suited for the export of a product that is so highly perishable as the orange; and finally the Paraguayan orange meets severe competition by Brazilian and Argentine oranges in the larger urban markets of southern Brazil and Argentina, and especially at Buenos Aires, the major orange market of South America.

Alfalfa, Wheat, Corn, and Flax

Although alfalfa, wheat, corn, and flax are grown in all humid subtropical regions, only the South American region gives a large acreage to each of these crops, and a relatively small acreage to rice, citrus fruits, and tea—crops usually associated with humid subtropical agriculture. This situation is a response in part to the sparse population of the region, and in part to the necessity of growing crops best suited to a relatively light and unreliable rainfall.

Alfalfa. Alfalfa is Argentina's most successful crop. It occupies more than 13,000,000 acres, or about the same as that harvested in the

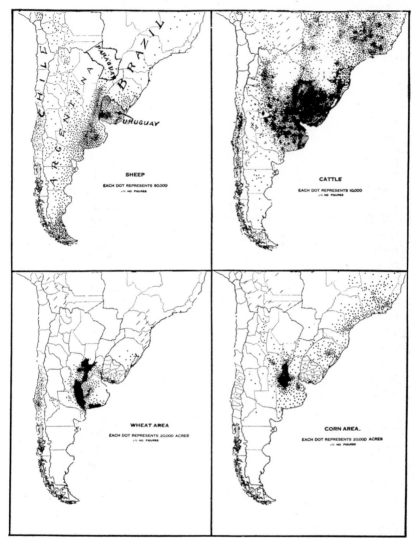

FIG. 132. (Courtesy U. S. Department of Agriculture.)

entire United States in 1945. Alfalfa is well suited to the unreliable[24] rainfall of the pampas because of its ability to send its roots deep into

[24] *Commodity Year Book*, Commodity Research Bureau, New York, 1939, p. 172.

the porous subsoil of this region in search of moisture. It therefore
yields well even during dry years and supports from three to five times
as many cattle per square mile as the native grasses. At the same time
it enriches the soil because of its nitrogen-fixing characteristics.

Cattle that are pastured on alfalfa grow rapidly, becoming exceedingly fat, and their meat is of much better quality than that of cattle
fed on native grasses. Since alfalfa land supports not only more cattle
but also better cattle than are raised on native pasture, the introduction
of this nutritive crop increased the value of some of the Argentina
pampa land eight to ten fold (Fig. 132).

Wheat. Wheat is the major commercial crop of Argentina and is
grown to a lesser extent in Uruguay and southern Brazil. The fertile
soil and level topography of the pampas both favor the extensive cultivation of wheat. But the poor agricultural methods employed in
many sections, the climatic handicaps of drought, excessive rains, or
frost, and the invasion of locusts all tend to induce low yields. The
northern part of the wheat belt is frequently invaded by locusts, which
fly south from the Chaco in great numbers. The females lay eggs
which bring forth countless millions of locusts—the greatest scourge
of the northern part of the wheat belt. Fortunately much of the
wheat is harvested before the plague of locusts reaches its height, so
that the damage done to this crop is less than that to corn, which
matures later. Drought may occur in any part of the wheat belt, and
heavy rain at harvest time sometimes injures the crop, especially along
the tropical border of the belt in Santa Fé.

The Corn Belt of Argentina. Corn is grown in all the humid subtropical regions, but there is only one area of any considerable size
which may be designated as a corn belt, and that area lies within the
lower Paraná Basin, Argentina. Although the Argentine corn belt is
not ideally suited for corn, that cereal is the dominant crop of the
area, occupying more than one-half of the cultivated land.

On the whole, the corn yield is extremely unreliable (Fig. 133).
During bad years the yield may drop to less than 12 bushels per acre,
and in 1943 it was only 6.3 bushels per acre; during good years the
yield exceeds 30 bushels per acre. This extreme fluctuation is largely
a response to the great variation in the amount and seasonal distribution of rainfall. Years of drought are followed by years of superabundance of precipitation. For maximum yield, corn needs an abundance of rain during the earing period, which in Argentina comes in
December and January; but the rainfall of this period fluctuates widely.
During years of drought, locusts are likely to be a serious pest and

may completely destroy not only the corn crop, but all other green
vegetation over a considerable portion of the corn belt, and thereby

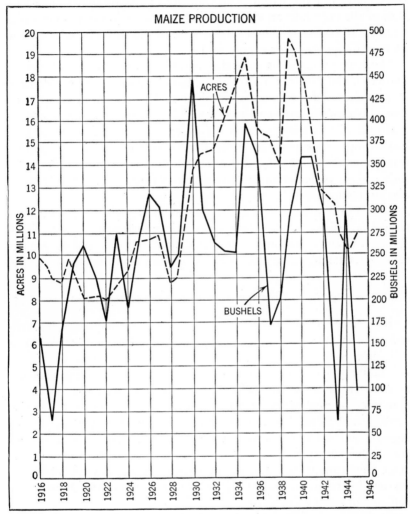

Fig. 133. Corn production in Argentina. The acreage yield of corn in Argentina
is exceedingly unreliable. In 1943, the average acreage yield was only slightly
more than 5 bushels per acre, whereas in 1944 the yield was almost 30 bushels
per acre.

bring distress or ruin to many farmers. Even when a fair crop matures, much of it may spoil in the field as a result of high temperatures,
high humidity, and excessive rainfall.

In spite of these handicaps, Argentina normally ranks second only to the United States in the production of corn, and stands first among the countries of the world as an exporter of this product. The location of the corn belt on either side of the Paraná River permits ocean steamers to penetrate almost to the heart of the area, giving Argentina an enviable position for export trade.

Flax. Argentina now leads the world in the production of flaxseed (linseed), the raw material from which the linseed oil of commerce is manufactured. Flax is well suited to the region in that it is a drought-resisting crop and can stand high temperatures and variable weather. Consequently, the yield is less variable than that of most other crops of the pampas. Since flax makes heavy demands upon the fertility of the soil it is fortunate that the land is given to this crop for only a short period—two or three years—before it is sown to alfalfa, a soil-enriching crop.

Flax is grown largely as a stepping-stone in getting the land sown to alfalfa. Since flax is a cash crop which brings quick and reliable returns, wealthy landowners are able to rent their land to tenants, who, after taking off a few crops of linseed, sow the land in alfalfa.

SOCIAL CONDITIONS AND ENVIRONMENT

The science of social geography is exceedingly complex, as is clearly indicated in the humid subtropics. The geographic bounds for races, religions, customs, manners, recreation, and architectural designs are not limited by rainfall, temperature, relief, and other physical factors to such an extent as are most of the economic activities. Man is a wanderer on the earth. He may move quickly from one physical environment to another, but he takes with him his biological, psychological, and cultural characteristics. These he cannot cast off immediately—perhaps not at all, even though some of them may be distinct handicaps in the new environment. In any society today the culture has been "borrowed" from so many sources that it would be difficult to trace its origin.[25]

The most diversified social conditions are to be found in Natal. The fertile fields and favorable commercial opportunities of this territory have attracted people from more than a score of countries. William D. Boyce writes in *Illustrated Africa* that the east coast is a

[25] Culture may be spread simply by transmitting the symbols of culture without the migration of peoples. An excellent discussion of cultural diffusion is given in A. L. Kroeber, *Anthropology*, pp. 194–215, Harcourt, Brace & Co., 1923.

combination of the quaintness of India, the color of Zululand, the well-ordered administration of British government, and the business ability of English and Scotch merchants and shipping agents. English churches, Jewish synagogues, Mohammedan mosques, and Hindu temples are side by side. Motor cars driven by white chauffeurs and jinrikishas pulled by fantastically garbed Zulus compete for the passenger business. Laborers from a score of countries work in fields, markets, and shops.

In southeastern United States the need for labor able to stand the hot humid atmosphere of the rice fields and cotton plantations resulted in the importation of the Negro and created America's most perplexing color problem, ramifying the political, social, and economic organizations of the South. The political problems culminating in the Civil War are not yet ended; the social problems such as intermarriage, lynching, and racial superiority are ever with us; and even in some economic activities the color line is rigid, making it difficult for the Negro to succeed.[26]

But the racial problem might have been worse. The region was settled at a time when eastern Asia was exceedingly remote, considered in terms of time and cost of transportation. As a result, Chinese, Javanese, and Indian laborers could not be so cheaply and easily secured as they could in Natal at a later date when her plantations were being developed. The African slave trade consequently seemed the best solution for the labor problem of the South.

The same demand for plantation labor that brought Negro slavery into southeastern United States brought it into Brazil. But as in America where it did not flourish in the North, so in Brazil it made little progress in the southern part. From Rio de Janeiro southward, people who are wholly white or nearly white predominate, and in Argentina and Uruguay the institution of slavery was never developed. In these lands the wide range of pastures, the broad expanse of plateau near the tropics, and the ease with which cereal culture could be promoted, all made for an agricultural and pastoral development suited to European peoples. Plantation agriculture has not been especially prosperous except in the coffee district, where the harvest season (winter) has a delightful, pleasant climate well suited to European labor. It is not surprising then that the humid subtropical South America has attracted immigrants from every part of Europe. Almost a million German colonists had gone to southern Brazil prior to the outbreak

[26] See Benjamin Brawley, *A Social History of the American Negro*, The Macmillan Co., 1921, pp. 297–340.

of the World War in 1914; about 80,000 Poles, Austrians, and Russians live in the little state of Pará; and thousands of French, English, Swiss, and Swedes have made southern Brazil their home. Similarly Argentina has attracted many European peoples. Approximately 2,000,000 Italians, 1,150,000 Spaniards, 200,000 French, 70,000 Austrians, 50,000 Germans, 30,000 Swiss, 21,000 Belgians, and 75,000 other Europeans have emigrated to Argentina since 1895. Truly humid subtropical South America is a veritable melting-pot for European races and cultures.

Indian blood is still dominant in some of the interior sections, but the race is no longer pure. Only a minor fraction of the people of Paraguay are pure Indians, but even a smaller fraction are pure whites. It is essentially a *mestizo* race, but the official and literary language is Spanish.

In the other humid subtropical regions no serious racial problems have been created. The populations of Japan and southern China are almost 100 per cent native, while that of southeast Australia is dominantly British. Remoteness of Australia from the great industrial centers of the world and the resultant difficulty of marketing bulky products have retarded the development of plantation agriculture. Consequently there has never been any large demand for cheap labor in that continent. Moreover, the Australians have taken note of the serious consequence of racial problems in other countries and have decided to keep Australia white.

It is seen from the foregoing discussion on social conditions within the humid subtropical regions that the human element is as important as the physical. The exact social situation in any one of these regions is related to the time of settlement, the moral, political, social, and economic standards of the colonizers at the time of settlement, the exact nature of the opportunities for various types of people during the period of migration, and the proximity of the region to various races and types of culture. Physical conditions have been important factors in that they have set the broad limits to what man can do successfully. Man has made his selection, so far as he was free to choose, in response to the opportunities afforded in these regions.

REFERENCES

ALLEN, G. C., *Modern Japan and Its Problems*, George Allen & Unwin, London, 1928.

ARNOLD, JULEAN, *Commercial and Industrial Handbook of China*, U. S. Department of Commerce, 1926.

Atlas of American Agriculture, Part V, Section A, U. S. Government Printing Office, 1918, pp. 1–28.

BENNETT, H. H., *The Soils and Agriculture of the Southern States*, The Macmillan Co., 1921, pp. 53–136.

BRAWLEY, BENJAMIN, *A Social History of the American Negro*, The Macmillan Co., 1921.

BROWN, H. R., and B. M. MACE, "Cost of Transportation and Handling of Argentine Wheat," *Trade Information Bulletin* 439, U. S. Bureau of Foreign and Domestic Commerce, 1926.

CLARKE, JOSEPH I .C., *Japan at First-hand*, Dodd Mead & Co., 1918.

Commodity Year Book, Commodity Research Corporation, New York, 1939.

CUNNINGHAM, R. B., *The Conquest of the River Plate*, Doubleday, 1924.

DAUTROMER, J., *The Japanese Empire and Its Economic Conditions*, T. J. Unwin, London, 1915.

DUVAL, L., "The Production and Handling of Grain in Argentina," *Yearbook of Agriculture*, U. S. Department of Agriculture, 1916, pp. 281–298.

JAMES, PRESTON E., "The Process of Pastoral and Agricultural Settlement on the Humid Pampa," *Journal of Geography*, April 1941, pp. 121–137.

JONES, C. F., "The Agricultural Regions of South America," *Economic Geography*, Vol. 2, 1927, pp. 303–321.

LIPPINCOTT, ISAAC, *Economic Resources and Industries of the World*, D. Appleton & Co., 1929, pp. 379–389.

MAYO, NATHAN, *From Field to Market with Florida Vegetables and Citrus Fruits*, Department of Agriculture, Tallahassee, Florida, 1931.

PARKINS, ALMON E., *The South*, John Wiley & Sons, 1938.

PHOEBUS, M. A., "Economic Development of Argentina since 1921," *Trade Information Series* 156, U. S. Department of Commerce, 1923.

SCOTT, J. W. ROBERTSON, *The Foundations of Japan*, John Murray Co., London, 1922.

SEMPLE, ELLEN CHURCHILL, "Influence of Geographical Conditions upon Japanese Agriculture," *Geographical Journal*, Vol. 40, 1912, pp. 589–603.

SYCKES, D. C., "Cattle Raising in Argentina," *Trade Information Bulletin* 647, U. S. Bureau of Foreign and Domestic Commerce, 1929.

TAYLOR, GRIFFITH, *Australia*, The Clarendon Press, 1928, pp. 147–154.

TAKENOBU, Y., *The Japan Year Book*, Foreign Affairs Association of Japan, Tokyo, 1939.

TOWER, W. S., "The Pampa of Argentina," *Geographical Review*, Vol. 5, 1918, pp. 293–315.

TSURUMI, Y., *Present Day Japan*, Columbia University Press, 1926.

The China Year Book, Simpkin, Marshall Co., London, 1931.

"The Grain Trade of Rosario, Argentina," *Bulletin of the Pan-American Union*, Vol. 57, pp. 254–261.

TREWARTHA, GLENN T., "A Geographic Study in Shizuoka Prefecture, Japan," *Annals of the Association of American Geographers*, Vol. 18, 1928, pp. 127–159.

An Introduction to Weather and Climate, McGraw-Hill Book Co., 1937, pp. 268–281.

U. S. DEPARTMENT OF AGRICULTURE, "The Argentine Corn Crop," *Foreign Crops and Markets*, Vol. 18, 1929, pp. 496–502.

Yearbook of Agriculture, 1921, pp. 327–348.

WOODHEAD, H. G. W., *The China Year Book*, Agents for U.S.A., University of Chicago Press, 1939, annual.

Chapter 10

REGIONS OF MEDITERRANEAN
CLIMATE

LOCATION

Several widely scattered regions of the world have climatic patterns
that are very similar to the one that prevails on much of the border-

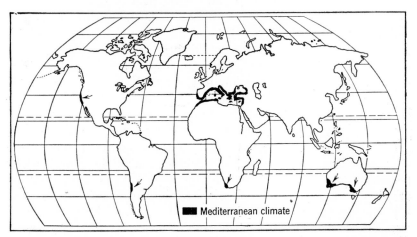

Fɪɢ. 134. The regions of Mediterranean climate occupy only a small percentage
of the earth's surface.

lands of the Mediterranean Sea. The climate that has these patterns
has been almost universally accepted as the Mediterranean climate.
Although this type of climate is most widely developed in the borderlands of the Mediterranean Sea, it also prevails in southern California,
central Chile, southwest Africa, and southern Australia (Fig. 134).

Mediterranean climates are located on the western side of continents
and on the tropical margins of middle latitudes (latitude 30± to 40±).

347

They are intermediate in location between areas of the westerly winds with their rain-bearing cyclonic storms on the one side, and the relatively dry high-pressure areas and trade winds on the other.

THE CLIMATIC PATTERN

Although the climates of all these regions are similar in pattern, each region has a considerable range in precipitation and temperature. This diversity in climatic conditions, together with the diversity in topography, affords opportunity for a variety of human adjustments to the environment and especially to the uses of the land.

General Characteristics. The Mediterranean climate possesses essential unity and individuality in spite of the notable differences from one locality to another. It is distinguished by three main characteristics: (1) most of the rain falls in the winter half-year, and there is drought, more or less complete, in summer; (2) the winters are mild with average temperatures for the coldest months above 40° F., and the summers are hot and dry, with mean temperatures for the hottest month averaging 70° F. to 86° F.; and (3) as previously indicated the skies are sunny, being almost cloudless in summer and having a high percentage of sunshine in winter. There are, however, local differences, and these are due mainly to (1) latitude, that is, location with respect to the westerlies and trade winds; (2) proximity to mountains, deserts, or large bodies of water; (3) topographic conditions—exposure to winds from deserts, mountains, or large bodies of water.

Precipitation. The rainfall of regions having the Mediterranean climate is alternately that of the westerlies and of the tropical high-pressure belt or the trades. During the winter of the northern hemisphere, the southern position of the sun, and consequently of the wind systems, brings southern California and the borderlands of the Mediterranean Sea under the influence of the westerlies; likewise, during the winter of the southern hemisphere, central Chile, southwest Africa, and southern Australia are more or less in the path of the westerlies. Moderate rainfall is the result (Fig. 135).

In summer, when the trades are extended poleward the regions having the Mediterranean climates lie in the high-pressure belt (tropical calms) and the trades. Both are drying winds, and, accordingly, fair weather prevails. The trade winds blow equatorward, become warmer, and, therefore, give up little moisture. The air in the tropical high-pressure belts is being warmed by a downward (settling) movement, and its capacity for moisture is increased. Such air movements

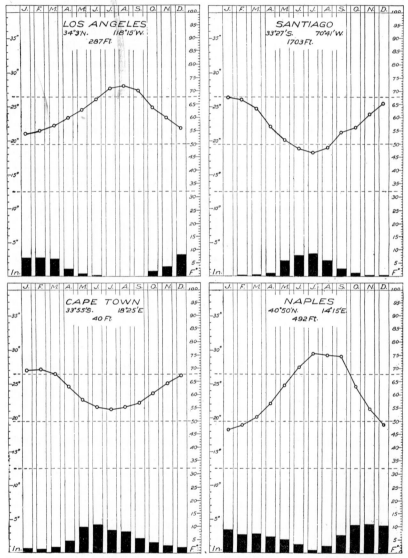

Fig. 135. Rainfall and temperature records for four stations of Mediterranean climate.

result in a rainless summer except on the windward slopes of mountains or where strong convection results in local showers. Convectional storms are not frequent, but at times they are violent.

Since the westerly winds with their cyclonic storms supply most of the moisture to the regions having Mediterranean climates, it is apparent that the poleward areas have a much longer rainy season than

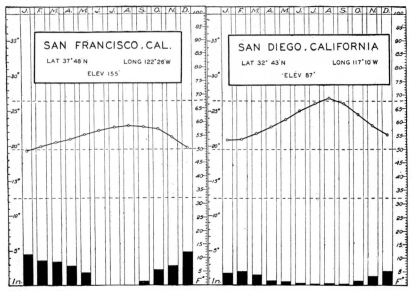

FIG. 136. The westerly winds blow for a longer period of time at San Francisco than at San Diego. The results are clearly shown in both the temperature and the rainfall of these stations.

the equatorward margins. For example, as the westerlies move southward in California they begin blowing at San Francisco with considerable regularity and strength early in November and continue to blow until April. They do not reach San Diego, however, until late November or early December, where they are never strong or persistent, and they become weak after the middle of March. The resultant effect on rainfall is clearly shown in Figs. 135 and 136.

Near the poleward margins of the regions that have Mediterranean climates the season of somewhat reliable rainfall is sufficiently long to permit agriculture without irrigation. Toward the equatorward margins, irrigation becomes more and more necessary until the Mediterranean climates gradually give way to tropical steppe and desert climates, where agricultural development depends almost entirely upon the artificial application of water.

Some of the mountainous areas of these regions have heavy precipitation. The heaviest rainfall of Europe, 183 inches per year, is recorded on the east coast of the Adriatic Sea. This, however, is mountain climate rather than Mediterranean. Precipitation not only increases from equatorward to poleward and from lowland to highland, but where peninsulas or promontories are found in regions of Mediterranean climates the western (windward) sides of such physical features normally receive more rainfall than the eastern (leeward) slopes.

Winter Temperatures. The winters are mild, the coldest month having a mean temperature above 40° F. and, in most of the area, above 50° F. These temperatures are pleasant for light out-of-door exercise, and winter is the principal tourist season.

Near the equatorward margins, especially in areas sheltered from cold continental winds, frosts are rare, and even the lemon tree, sensitive to cold, flourishes. In large parts of the Mediterranean climatic regions frosts seldom occur, and the loss of crops from freezing is consequently small during the normal year. Occasionally, however, freezing temperatures are experienced in a large part of Mediterranean Europe and of southern California. In December 1895, frost caused heavy losses in the orange belt of California; again in 1913 the loss from frost was severe; and in 1921 southern California experienced the worst freeze on record, during which approximately $50,000,000 worth of oranges alone were destroyed.

Summer Temperatures. The summers are hot except where tempered by ocean breezes. Everywhere the temperature increases inland. Wherever the region is open to winds from a tropical desert, the temperature becomes at times exceedingly high.

Effects of Cool Currents. In the Eurasian region, even the sea breezes are often hot, owing to the influence of the Saharan winds which are only slightly modified by the warm waters of the Mediterranean Sea. The other regions of this climatic type are bathed by cool ocean currents from which a sea breeze is always refreshing. Thanks to the presence of the cool Pacific Ocean Current, the summers at Los Angeles average about 11° F. cooler than at Beirut, which lies in the same latitude and is also directly upon the coast. This cool ocean current is a valuable asset to California. The energy of the people is not sapped by the extreme heat, and the ground does not become parched so badly as it otherwise would through rapid evaporation. The cool waters of the Canaries Current, coming from higher latitudes, bathe the coastal region of northwest Africa and give this area a surprisingly uniform temperature curve. In southwest Africa the Benguela Current has the same effect.

Effects of Desert Winds. Many areas where Mediterranean climates prevail are visited by hot winds from deserts which border them on the equatorward or landward sides. In southern Italy these winds are so debilitating and annoying, so trying on the human morale, that leniency frequently is shown to those who commit crimes while such winds blow. In southern California hot winds, called Santa Anas, sometimes blow from the desert to the east, often with great force. They are hot, dry, dusty, lip-cracking, unpleasant visitations. They parch vegetation and blister fruit.

Cold Winds. Cold winds are also experienced in many Mediterranean areas during the winter. All regions that have Mediterranean climates are marginal and are backed by mountainous uplands. Occasionally under the influence of a passing anticyclone the air lies over these uplands until it becomes many degrees colder than the air in the lowlands. It may then flow down into the valleys as a cold, strong wind. Such a wind, the mistral, sometimes rushes down from central Massif (south-central plateau) into the Rhone Valley with destructive force and freezing temperatures, killing vegetation, and causing much suffering of man and beast. A similar wind, the bora, blows at the head of the Adriatic Sea.

Health Conditions in Regions of Mediterranean Climates. Few climates are better suited to general healthful conditions than those of the Mediterranean regions. Yet it was formerly a belief, amounting to almost a conviction, that the warm fall rains, associated with decaying vegetation, produced a "miasmic" atmosphere which caused malaria. This belief was not wholly without foundation. The *Anopheles* mosquitoes—carriers of malaria—breed in stagnant pools, damp lowlands, or water-filled holes situated in warm regions. It is not surprising that this disease, prevalent in all tropical and subtropical climates, should be especially virulent in regions of Mediterranean climates where the rain falls chiefly in winter and the summers are dry. In such a climate, during the hot dry season, stagnant pools usually abound along the water courses and in irrigated districts. These poorly drained areas have been afflicted with malaria at one time or another, and in the lowlands of Italy and Greece its ill effects have been persistent. Unfortunately, the victim of this disease is not immune after the first attack but may have the disease time after time.

If he does not finally succumb to its ravages his health is undermined and he becomes a liability to the community. Long periods of sickness not only break down the physical stamina of the victim but also undermine his moral courage. The results of malaria have been so serious in the past that some medical men have assigned to it a prominent part in the decline of Mediterranean civilizations. Malaria is still the outstanding health problem of Italy. With approximately 2,000,-000 cases a year, the disease is not only a vital factor in the life and health of Italy, but a matter of serious concern to the economic development as well. The situation of the country well within the *Anopheles* belt, the prevalence of breeding places in the many marshes, canals, and sluggish streams choked by vegetation, and the presence of a singularly virulent and hardy type of mosquito make the control of malaria exceedingly difficult. The problem is aggravated by the facts that migratory laborers carry the disease from one region to another and that few of the homes are screened to keep out mosquitoes. All these conditions conspire to create a health problem of first magnitude.[1]

The fight against malaria is a long and difficult one. Its control is more perplexing than that of yellow fever. Yellow fever is spread by the *Stegomyia* mosquito, which breeds most commonly near homes and in clean water, making it an easy prey to traps set by man; the *Anopheles* mosquito may breed far from dwellings and in almost any kind of stagnant water, making its control difficult. Yet drainage rather than climate is the determining factor. When stagnant water is disposed of, malaria disappears.

NATIVE VEGETATION

The climate, with rainfall coming in the winter followed by drought and heat in the summer, is unsuited to most kinds of vegetation. In all the widely separated regions where the Mediterranean climate prevails, the vegetation bears essentially the same stamp and shows a nice adjustment to environment. It is dominated by drought-resisting plants having all or most of the following characteristics: (1) thick, narrow, leathery evergreen leaves, hairy below and shiny above, which are resistant to evaporation; (2) long roots which extend downward many feet in search of water; and (3) low, gnarled, thick-barked trees or shrubs which resist the desiccating winds.

[1] *Ninth Annual Report*, International Health Board, Rockefeller Foundation, 1924, p. 20.

Some of the trees best suited to the production of food are being cultivated with much profit; but as a source of lumber the trees—low, gnarled, and knotty, as most of them are—have little worth.

Numerous forms of bulbous and tuberous plants such as tulips, narcissi, orchids, and gladioli, because of their ability to store up moisture, are able to resist the droughts, but they are of little economic value unless properly watered.

Most of the native grasses are narrow, stiff-leaved varieties, which dry up during the summer and are poorly suited to pasture.

MAN IN THE REGIONS OF MEDITERRANEAN CLIMATE

The several regions of the world that have a Mediterranean climate present marked contrasts in their influence on the evolution of civilization. One of these regions—the borderlands of the Mediterranean Sea—has played a dominant role in the development of Occidental civilization, whereas the others—southern California, central Chile, southwestern Africa, and southern Australia—failed to develop more than the merest rudiments of culture prior to their colonization by Europeans. These contrasts in cultural development were, in part at least, results of differences in opportunity.

Borderlands of the Mediterranean Sea

One cannot help being impressed with the comprehensive sweep of progress made in the Mediterranean Basin within a few centuries. Economic, political, social, and religious developments were rapid, and the brilliance of achievement in philosophy, literature, and art has never been surpassed. Any attempt, however, to account for this development wholly on a geographical basis would be misleading, yet nature provided the materials and the opportunity for this progress and to a certain extent directed the course and marked off the limitations.

Favorable Climate. The progress of the human race has been largely a response to necessity plus opportunity. Climatically, the Mediterranean regions admirably meet both these requirements for the development of man, especially of primitive peoples. The long, dry summer made it necessary that man provide for the future by storing a food supply for this less productive season. This task is made rather simple in that the mild, rainy winter permits the production of crops best suited as food for man, and the abundance of sunshine, both summer and winter, makes it possible to harvest, dry, and preserve these food crops and store them for use throughout the year. Clothing and shelter are also necessary for man's comfort and welfare, but the problem of providing them is simplified by the semi-tropical temperatures.[2]

Protection. Protection is one of the absolute essentials for the development of a people, whether they are a nation or a tribe. They may protect themselves by using some of their energies for defense. In fact, from earliest times, practically all countries have kept armies and in later times many of them have kept navies for this purpose. It is obviously an advantage, however, if protection can be secured with the minimum expenditure of human energy, that is, if it can be secured by geographical barriers. In the early stages of human development it was obviously true that, other conditions being equally favorable, the peoples that had the most complete natural protection advanced from barbarism to civilization most rapidly. Among the best barriers against invasion are broad plateaus, too high and cold to support enough vegetation to feed armies and their beasts of burden; stretches of desert too dry for plants to grow; mountains across which it is difficult to transport armies and their supplies; and large bodies of water. Before any of these barriers could be crossed by armies, a considerable advance in civilization must have been made. Thus in early times the protection they gave must have been almost or quite complete, permitting the peoples so protected to direct their energies towards peaceful pursuits.[3]

The many small valleys of Greece, Italy, Spain, and southern France, hemmed in by highlands, gave opportunities for ease of defense. The narrow valleys and small coastal plains of northwest Africa gave opportunities for the more highly civilized peoples of Mediterranean Europe and Asia to secure and retain a foothold in that region (Fig. 137). Many of the mountains of southern Europe were covered with dense forests which gave added protection against peoples who had attained the pastoral stage of civilization. In writing on this subject, Ellen Churchill Semple says that the dense forests of the mountainous area along the northern rim of the Mediterranean Basin undoubtedly

[2] For the more extensive treatment of the relation of climate to the development of civilization see Ellsworth Huntington, *Civilization and Climate*, Chapter XII, Yale University Press, 1915.

[3] For a fuller discussion of the relation of barriers to the development of civilizations see James Fairgrieve, *Geography and World Power*, University of London Press, 1915.

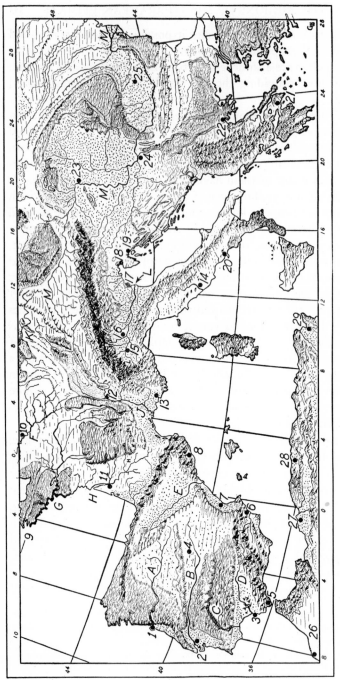

FIG. 137. Part of the area shown above lies outside the Mediterranean realm. Consequently, some of the places indicated on this map are referred to in later chapters. Rivers: (A) Douro, (B) Tagus (Tajo), (C) Guadiana, (D) Guadalquivir, (E) Ebro, (F) Seine, (G) Loire, (H) Garonne, (J) Rhone, (K) Rhine, (L) Po, (M) Danube. Cities: (1) Oporto, (2) Lisbon, (3) Cadiz, (4) Madrid, (5) Gibraltar, (6) Murcia, (7) Valencia, (8) Barcelona, (9) Brest, (10) Paris, (11) Bordeaux, (12) Lyon, (13) Marseille, (14) Roma (Rome), (15) Torino (Turin), (16) Milano (Milan), (17) Venezia (Venice), (18) Trieste, (19) Fiume, (20) Napoli (Naples), (21) Athens, (22) Thessalonikē (Salonika), (23) Budapest, (24) Beograd (Belgrade), (25) Bucuresti (Bucharest), (26) Casablanca, (27) Oran, (28) Algiers, (29) Tunis. (Taken by permission from A. K. Lobeck's physiographic diagrams, The Geographical Press, Columbia University, New York.)

intensified the barrier nature in ancient times and helped to discourage invasion by the pastoral nomads of the Eurasian grasslands.

Since many of the islands and valleys of the Mediterranean border-lands were protected by some or all of the barriers previously mentioned, man was free to give most of his attention to industry, science, and art. Although these barriers were effective against armies they were not so formidable as to prevent the interchange of ideas among the various communities. Thus environmental conditions afforded ease of defense and at the same time permitted the spread of ideas.

Widespread Contacts. Isolation of a people breeds stagnation. This is true not only of small communities such as are found in oases, mountain valleys, and on high plateaus, but of nations such as China and, formerly, India and Japan.[4] Conversely, widespread contacts are conducive to progress. Geographic conditions greatly favored the Mediterranean Basin in this respect. The eastern Mediterranean was the focus of roads from Asia, Europe, and Africa. It was the meeting place of the peoples of three continents and has been subject to repeated migrations and invasions with the associated impact of different cultures. Traders brought glimpses of Oriental life from the Far East, of the barbarian culture from the western and northern part of Europe, and of the desert and nomadic life to the south. Each of these areas, no matter how remote, contributed something to Mediterranean culture. Although the resultant losses and gains would be difficult to evaluate, each new contact contained something novel which awakened man's interest and stimulated his activities.

Plant and Animal Resources. The possession of valuable plants and animals further facilitated man's progress in these regions. Again the borderlands of the Mediterranean Sea were favored. The horse, ass, cow, sheep, goat, and camel—animals well suited to supply meat and dairy products for food and to act as beasts of burden—were all known to these peoples from early times. Wheat, barley, millet, grapes, figs,

---

[4] "The effect of isolation [speaking of India] is ignorance, superstition, and the early crystallization of thought and customs. Ignorance involves the lack of materials for comparison, hence a restriction of the higher reasoning processes, and an unscientific attitude of mind which gives imagination free play. In contrast, the accessibility of Greece and its focal location in the ancient world made it an intellectual clearing-house for the eastern Mediterranean. The general information gathered there afforded materials for wide comparisons. It fed the brilliant reasoning of the Athenian philosopher and the trained imagination which produced the master minds of Greece in art and literature." Ellen Churchill Semple, *Influences of Geographic Environment*, Henry Holt & Co., 1911, p. 19. Reprinted by permission of publisher.

olives, and a variety of other excellent food crops were also native to this region or were imported in prehistoric times.[5]

Thus it is seen that the seasonal nature of the climate made the accumulation of wealth necessary, and at the same time the possession of valuable plants and animals together with the ease of protection made the task relatively easy. Wealth, in turn, permitted of leisure, which is the foundation for the development of the arts and sciences, provided that the people have sufficient energy and the proper stimuli to make the best use of this leisure. Historic accounts indicate that the early Mediterranean peoples possessed this energy. Although the climate is not the most invigorating, it is nevertheless healthful and conducive to active, outdoor life. It is held by some that, during the time when the Mediterranean civilization led the world, the weather in these areas was more changeable than it is now and, accordingly, more invigorating. It is not surprising, then, that the borderland of the Mediterranean Sea, favored by climate, ease of defense and also of communication, and supplied with a preponderance of the most valuable animals and plants for the support of man, should have been among the first to foster a high degree of civilization.

Retarded Development of Civilization in Other Regions of Mediterranean Climates

Although a high stage of civilization was developed on the borderland of the Mediterranean Sea in ancient times, other regions having this type of climate made little advancement prior to their colonization by Europeans. This retarded development may in part be accounted for by the fact that crops which were well suited to man's needs and to the local climatic conditions were unknown in these areas, and that the regions were destitute of animals suited to supply man with meat or dairy products or to act as beasts of burden. Such were the conditions that existed in southwestern California prior to the arrival of a European-made culture and to the importation of European plants and animals.

The present-day economic progress in those sections of California, Chile, South Africa, and Australia where the Mediterranean climates prevail depends more on their farms than on any other material re-

---

[5] Wheat, barley, and millet are proved by remains found beside the lake dwellings of Switzerland to have been cultivated in the late stone age, and the cultivation of cabbage, peas, vetch, parsley, and onions dates from ancient times.

sources. Yet the major sources of income on all these farms are the crops and animals that were originally imported from Europe.

In all these regions the relative importance of agriculture is accentuated because of the lack of any suitable combination of primary minerals needed to promote great industrial development. Gold, sulphur, petroleum, building stone, and other minerals have in the aggregate contributed much wealth to these regions. But the total value is insignificant compared to that of the pastoral and agricultural products, most of which were transplanted from Mediterranean Europe to the other regions that have Mediterranean climates.

European Culture Dominates All Regions of Mediterranean Climates

European culture either has been transplanted to all other regions that have Mediterranean climates or has been superimposed on the culture that already existed there. In the California and Australia regions, the native cultures have been largely or entirely displaced by European; in central Chile and southwest Africa, European culture is dominant in the political, economic, and social structure; whereas in northwest Africa a veneer of European culture has been spread over the native culture.

Central Chile supports approximately 90 per cent of the people of that country. Most of the people live in the Central Valley between Santiago and Valdivia. The people are primarily whites and mestizos who are more white than Indian. The Chilean mestizo is primarily European in customs, manners, and modes of living and has adopted European political, economic, and social institutions.

The major source of income in central Chile is the farm (hacienda). Most of the land is held in large estates and the majority of the people are landless. The standard of living for many whites and most mestizos is exceedingly low. This is especially true of the landless who work on the farms. Many of them were reported, in 1946, to earn as little as thirty-five cents a day.

South Africa has relatively few natives (Hottentots) left in the region of Mediterranean climate. However the "color" problem of this area is complex. The "Cape colored" represents a half-caste stock in which the Hottentot strain is preserved in association with European characteristics. Their customs, manners, and education (in so far as they receive an education) and their mode of living are primarily European. Their economic status is exceedingly low but, perhaps, scarcely lower than that of the "poor whites."

The culture of northwest Africa is closely related to: (1) the ancient Berber civilization; (2) the many invasions of the region from Europe and western Asia and the recent invasion from the United States of America; and (3) the rugged topography and relative isolation of many areas which tends to preserve ancient customs, manners, languages or dialects, and modes of living.

The Mediterranean region of northwest Africa consists of a coastal strip of land that is 100 to 150 miles wide and 1,300 miles long. This coastal belt is usually referred to as the "Tell." The region is rugged and consists of coastal plains (for the most part badly dissected), valleys, hills up to 2,000 feet or more, and high plains that extend slightly above 2,000 feet. To the south of the Mediterranean region lie the Atlas Mountains and the steppelands. (Fig. 137.)

The culture of the region is as complex as the topography. As one travels through northwest Africa today, he encounters a great variety of peoples who speak several languages. Their complexions vary from blonde, except for sun-tan, to a dark, swarthy color of the skin. The natives are mostly descendants of the Berbers who have intermarried with other races—Phoenicians, Romans, Arabs, Spaniards, and French. The Berber blood and racial characteristics are still dominant among the natives. The customs and manners of the masses are more native than European. Even the agriculture is essentially the same as that of southern Europe.

AGRICULTURE

In several respects nature has been somewhat niggardly with her gifts to the farmer of Mediterranean climates. The rainfall is light and poorly distributed for general agriculture, and every Mediterranean climatic region contains large areas of rugged land poorly suited to tillage.

After centuries of experimentation, the farmer, in his attempt to make the most of his environment, has learned to utilize three types of crops: (1) those suited to short, cool seasons of light rainfall, such as grass, wheat, and rye; (2) crops from trees and vines such as the olive, fig, chestnut, and grape, which send their roots deep for moisture and can survive the long droughts,[6] and (3) crops grown by the aid of irrigation. The disadvantage of steep gradient is overcome by terracing, contour plowing, and planting, and by the use of tree and

---

[6] These tree and vine crops may also be irrigated.

vine crops which will produce almost as well on a hillside as on a plain.

In spite of the climatic and topographic disadvantages of regions having the Mediterranean climate, agriculture is the most important industry. About 60 per cent of the laborers in Portugal, Spain, and Italy are engaged in agriculture; in Greece and Algeria 45 per cent and 70 per cent, respectively, are farmers; and even in California, which is so well known for its oil, agriculture is the greatest of all industries. The annual output of the California farms is normally more valuable than that of all the mines, oil wells, gas wells, and quarries combined.[7] Yet in 1946, California ranked third among the states of the Union in the value of its mineral output.

The regions of the Mediterranean climates with their varied climatic, topographic, and soil conditions afford excellent opportunities for the adjustment of crops to the natural environment. This may be illustrated by showing the relationship of crop distribution to environment in California.

Many of the crops of Mediterranean California are widely grown throughout much of the state. Yet, on the whole, there is a definite adjustment of crops to the various climatic, physiographic, and soil patterns of the region. For example, lima beans do well in moist places and are suited to heavy clay soils that hold water tenaciously. Consequently, most of the lima bean crop of California is grown along the coastal lowlands and in the lower Santa Clara Valley—areas of heavy soils and bathed by fog almost nightly during the growing seasons. Most of the lemon crop is grown on frost-free hill slopes of southern California, south of Los Angeles. A large part of the orange crop is grown on lower hill slopes to take advantage of air drainage in a region where frost occurs frequently in the lowlands. Even after care has been taken to select sites of good air drainage, millions of heaters burning low-grade oil are used to heat the air on cold nights. Riverside, Redland, and Orange are important orange-growing centers (Fig. 138). Much of the flat lowlands of California are given to pasture, alfalfa, wheat, and sugar beets because these crops are only slightly injured by frost. Rice is grown chiefly in the easily irrigated flood plain of the San Joaquin River Valley (Fig. 138). The region around Fresno with its bountiful supply of irrigation water and with

[7] Only part of California lies within the Mediterranean type of climate, but this portion of the state contains the major part of the most intensively cultivated land.

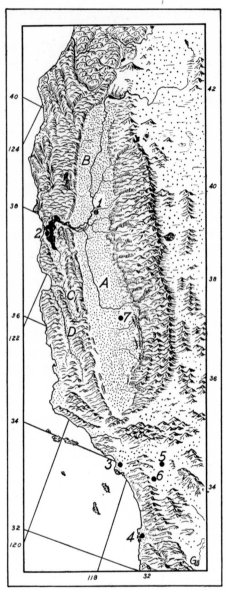

Fɪɢ. 138.   Mediterranean climate of California occurs in the coastal plain, intermountain valleys, the Great Valley, and on thousands of hills.   Places: (A) San
Joaquin River Valley, (B) Sacramento River Valley, (C) Santa Clara River
Valley, (D) Salinas River Valley.   Cities: (1) Sacramento, (2) San Francisco,
(3) Los Angeles, (4) San Diego, (5) Redlands, (6) Riverside, (7) Fresno.

little rain and lots of sunshine is the world's most famous raisin-producing region (Fig. 138).

Cereal

Wheat. Wheat is well suited to the Mediterranean climate and is the most extensively cultivated crop of every Mediterranean climatic region except that of southern California, and even there it was a major crop during the last quarter of the nineteenth century. Thirty-seven per cent of all the cultivated land of Spain is given to wheat, and in Italy, Chile, and those areas of Australia and southern Africa where Mediterranean climates prevail it occupies from one-third to more than three-fourths of the cultivated land.

The double requirement of wheat for a cool, moist formative period and a dry, sunny ripening period are admirably met by the cool, moist winters and the dry, sunny summers. Although wheat culture is widely distributed in the Mediterranean regions, the most important districts are (1) central Chile, (2) southern Australia, (3) southern Africa, (4) northern Italy, and (5) the plains of Old Castile in Spain.

The relative importance of wheat in the various areas is largely dependent upon the stage of development of the area, the local needs for this cereal, and the facilities for marketing the more perishable subtropical fruits, vegetables, and nuts, which may be grown in competition with wheat. Central Chile, being densely populated with a relatively poor people and highly isolated from outside markets, is forced to be largely self-sustaining. Wheat is well suited to meet the needs of such a region. It is an ideal food crop, is well suited to the climate, and can stand the cost and delays necessary to exportation in the event of a surplus. As a result wheat is given nearly seven times the acreage of the closest competing crop (Fig. 139). Wheat is almost or quite as dominant a crop in the lately developed regions of southwestern Africa and southern Australia. In Australia about 60 per cent of the cultivated land is given to wheat and another 10 per cent to wheaten hay.

Wheat does just as well in southern and central California as in Chile. Climatically the two regions are similar and each has relatively large areas of level or rolling topography. The topography of the Valley of California is well suited to the use of large-scale machinery (Fig. 138). Although California produces little wheat at present, this cereal was at one time the most important crop of the state. In 1899 it occupied 22.4 per cent of all improved land in California—

more than twice the acreage of any other crop. Its importance decreased as transportation facilities were improved and as the nation became richer and more populous, demanding expensive subtropical fruits, vegetables, and nuts. As a result the farmers are turning their attention from the lower-valued crops such as wheat, rye, and barley, to lettuce, cauliflower, grapes, oranges, nuts, and other agricultural products which pay a higher return per acre.

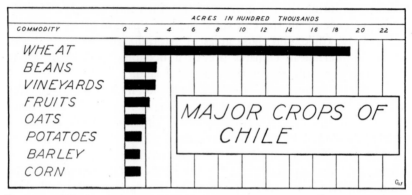

Fig. 139. Chile has little opportunity to market on a large scale such perishable products as lettuce, celery, oranges, and peaches—products for which California is famed—and consequently gives most of her agricultural land to the production of crops needed for home consumption. (Data for 1940–1946.)

Barley. Barley is also well adapted to the Mediterranean climates. Because of the short growing season required to mature this hardy cereal, it is a more certain and better yielding crop than wheat in districts of scanty rainfall. The barley of northern Africa, Asia Minor, and southern California is much in demand in northern Europe for the brewing industry. The dry weather during the ripening period gives the grain a rich color highly desired for malting purposes.

Other Cereals. The successful cultivation of oats and rye requires moist, cool climates, and consequently these crops are little grown in the Mediterranean regions. Corn and rice need much moisture during the warm growing season and are, therefore, poorly suited to regions of almost rainless summer. In regions with a modified type of Mediterranean climate, such as the upper Po Valley, where considerable summer rain falls, rice and corn are important crops, and in central California rice is grown by the aid of irrigation and large-scale machinery.

Pulse, Pasture, and Hay

Peas and beans are valuable crops in most regions of Mediterranean climates. Rich in protein as well as other food elements, they are substitutes for meat, milk, and cheese in many of the poorer districts. Beans grow best in a cool, moist climate, being injured by insects and diseases when the season is warm and moist. During the winter and spring, climatic conditions within these regions seem to be ideal for this crop. California normally grows between 300,000 and 400,000 acres of beans—approximately 40 per cent of the annual dry bean crop of the United States—and southern Europe is the greatest dry bean-producing region of the world.[8]

The Mediterranean climate is naturally poor for the growth of grass because of the heat and the summer drought. The plains afford fair to excellent pasture during the moist, mild winter, but during the almost rainless summer the unirrigated pastures become parched and brown. The mountains, on the other hand, are snow covered in the winter but afford fresh, luscious pasture during the summer. Consequently livestock, easily transported from one place to another, may be pastured on the mountains during the summer and on the plains during the winter. Thus a close bond has been established between highlands and lowlands in many regions of Mediterranean climates, as reflected in the seasonal migrations of herders and their livestock between the highlands of Sierra Morena and the neighboring lowlands, between the Apennines and Roman Campagna, between the Dinaric Alps and the Dalmatian Coast, and between the Pindus Mountains and the plains of Thessaly. In Europe, this practice—called transhumance—plays an important part in the pastoral industry. Each spring thousands of young men take the family herds to the mountains. In some parts of Italy their departure is such an important event that entire villages turn out to deck the young men with floral wreaths or to take some other part in the festal ceremonies.

Since the mountain pastures are not sufficient to supply more than a small part of the needs of the Mediterranean regions, it is necessary that hay be grown in the lowlands to tide the livestock over the dry period, or that part of the irrigated land be given over to summer pasture. Some hay is grown without the aid of irrigation and is har-

[8] Parts of Manchuria are even more completely given to the bean as a commercial crop—soybean.

vested at the beginning of the dry season. Most of it, however, is produced on fields that are artificially watered.

Hay is a low-value crop requiring little labor and yielding only a moderate return per acre. In countries in which a dense population presses upon the means of subsistence, it can scarcely compete with higher-value crops—those which require intensive cultivation and give a large return per acre. Consequently, in the thickly peopled countries of southern Europe hay is less important than in California and southern Australia, where the population pressure is not so great and where labor costs are high. In California, hay occupies a larger acreage than any other crop and occasionally ranks first in value. Most of it consists of alfalfa grown on irrigated land.

The hay crop of Mediterranean Australia, although always large, fluctuates markedly from year to year. Since the hay is mostly wheaten or oaten, the farmer can decide shortly before harvest whether he wishes to cut the crop for feed or for the grain. If the year has been dry so that the pasture is short and the grain yield poor, a large acreage will be cut for hay; if the grain yield is good and the price fair, the farmer lets the grain ripen and cuts but little hay.

Market Gardens

The Mediterranean climates are well suited to market garden crops, especially during the winter season when the prices of such crops are high. California, located in a rich country, now ranks first among all areas of the world in the production of truck crops. The state normally produces one-fifth to one-fourth of the truck crops of this entire nation with more than 140,000,000 actual or potential customers (Figs. 140 and 141). Cincinnati alone normally consumes more than 1,000 carloads of garden and orchard products from California. The major part of the California truck crop is produced in that part of the state where the Mediterranean climate prevails.

Tree Crops

The Olive. The olive is the most characteristic economic crop of the Mediterranean climatic regions, its production being almost unknown in other parts of the world. The tree yields best in the warmer portions of these subtropical regions where the winters are mild and the summers are hot and dry.

The olive tree is well suited to regions of light rainfalls and rugged topography; it is drought resisting, sends its roots deep for moisture, and can grow on exceedingly steep slopes. As a result many European orchards are planted on land too dry for general agriculture and too stony or rugged for irrigation. This distribution is not from

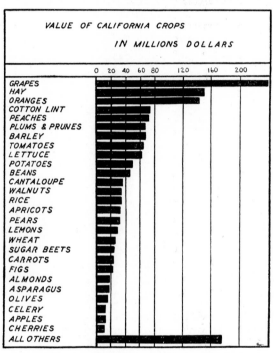

FIG. 140. About one-half of California's agricultural land is given to intensive or semi-intensive agriculture. Most of the agricultural income of the state is derived from intensive agriculture. Which of the above listed crops are grown by intensive agricultural methods?

choice but from necessity, since the tree yields best on irrigated land. In fact, in California or other regions where labor costs are high, olive culture is scarcely profitable unless the orchards are watered.

The olive tree has been successfully introduced into all the regions of Mediterranean climates, into the high plateaus of Mexico, and into the area of Mendoza, a middle-latitude desert, of Argentina. The industry has not developed very rapidly in its new homes, and it still remains many times more important in the borderlands of the Mediterranean Sea than in all other parts of the world combined (Fig.

142). In Spain the per capita production of olive oil exceeds that of butter in the United States, and in several of the Mediterranean countries a larger percentage of the land is given to olive orchards than is sown to wheat in the United States.

The commercial production of olives requires an abundance of labor. The tree needs almost constant care by trained workers; the tillage,

Fig. 141. Southern California has become an important gardening center for the most prosperous nation on earth. Carload lots of iceberg lettuce are shipped from southern California to hundreds of cities located in all parts of the country. (Courtesy Southern Pacific Railway Co.)

grafting, and pruning should be done just when needed; and the harvest period is short and requires hand labor. Finally, the olive tree comes to full bearing only after many years of care, and it cannot be developed without the help of a stable labor supply.

Spain has an abundance of rugged land that is ill suited to most crops but yields profitable returns when given to olives. Consequently, Spain produces more olives than any other country in the world. More than 3.5 per cent of the entire area of the nation is planted with olive trees, and olives and olive oil are the second most valuable export of the country. Most of the olive orchards are planted on rugged, unirrigated land that is situated in the southern and eastern half of the country, with almost two-thirds of the total output coming from the Ebro and Guadalquivir basins (Fig. 137). Forests of olive trees cover extensive areas on the southern slopes and foothills of the Sierra Morena and Sierra Nevada mountains, where they yield a large return on land that is too rugged for ordinary cultivation. Few olives are grown on coastal lowlands or on the alluvial soils of river valleys. Most of these areas are irrigated and given to crops that require more water than is given to the olive tree.

Italy, another rugged country, ranks second only to Spain in the production of olives but stands first in the acreage given to this crop.

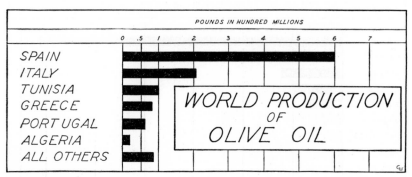

Fig. 142. The borderland of the Mediterranean Sea still produces practically all the olive-oil supply of the world. Data of the chart are for 1946. In 1938, prior to World War II, the production in pounds for each of these countries was as follows: Spain, 800,000,000; Italy, 420,000,000; Tunisia, 150,000,000; Greece, 220,000,000; and Portugal, 148,000,000.

Italy must produce food for a large population. Consequently the land is given to wheat, maize, beans, olives, potatoes, rice, barley, rye, and sugar beets—crops that yield large returns in *calories* per acre (Fig. 143). Hay and pasture, crops not shown in the graph, are important as feed for cattle, goats, and sheep.

Olives are grown largely on rugged, dry land, ill suited to most other crops. More than 8 per cent of the entire country is given to this hardy tree. The extent of cultivation is further emphasized by the fact that in Italy a larger percentage of the total land area is given to olive orchards than is given to both corn and wheat in the United States. The corn and wheat crops of America, however, occupy much of the most productive land of the country, while in Italy much of the land given to olives is rugged, stony, relatively infertile, and poorly watered. Consequently, the acreage yield of olives in Italy is low, frequently less than half that of Spain.

In the southern part of the Italian Peninsula the tree flourishes without shelter, and in the rugged but relatively low areas about Bari, Lecce, and Taranto there are miles of continuous woods of nothing but olive trees, some of them occupying land that is so stony and unpromising that it would be left uncultivated in most parts of the United States. The tree flourishes also in northern Italy, where it is sheltered by the Alps, but it cannot stand the severe climate of the open plains of the Po Valley (Fig. 137).

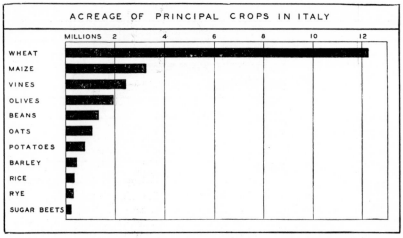

ACREAGE OF PRINCIPAL CROPS IN ITALY

MILLIONS 2   4   6   8   10   12

WHEAT
MAIZE
VINES
OLIVES
BEANS
OATS
POTATOES
BARLEY
RICE
RYE
SUGAR BEETS

FIG. 143. If Europe were all one country, the crops of the continent could be better adjusted to the natural environment. Because of the dangers of wars or of political conditions that may interfere with freedom of exchange of goods, each country desires to be as nearly self-supporting in food products as possible.

In Greece, man is more dependent upon the olive tree than upon any other plant. Bread and olive oil are as universally used in the Grecian diet as bread and butter in the American. The annual production of this little country is from 60 to 80 pounds of preserved olives and about 3 gallons of oil per capita. Much of Greece is so dry that even the olive tree grows very slowly and the yield of fruit is small. Under such conditions the population depending upon the olive orchards cannot be very dense.

Most of the world's olive crop is used for the manufacture of oils, which may properly be given first place among the vegetable oils. In addition to being the prime substitute for butter in several Mediterranean countries, it is of increasing importance to the industrial world, and 300 to 500 million pounds of olive oil enter international

trade annually. The olive oil of inferior quality is used in the manufacture of soaps and chemicals; that of better quality is used in the
manufacture of salad dressing and other foods. The United States
and Argentina are the largest importing countries, taking more than
one-half the exports of the entire Mediterranean borderland. The
United States with its large soap industry, its large Latin population,

Fig. 144. An olive-curing plant near Los Angeles, California. (Courtesy Los
Angeles Chamber of Commerce.)

and millions of well-to-do people who can afford to purchase the most
palatable foods, imported from 65 to 153 million pounds annually between 1929 and 1945. Argentina, supporting many wealthy Latin
peoples accustomed to the use of olive products, imported 24 to 112
million pounds annually during the same period.[9]

Where labor costs are high, only the larger varieties of olives can be
grown with profit. In California, where the cost of picking is $40 to
$60 a ton, it is cheaper to import olive oil from countries where labor
is plentiful than to produce it locally. This limits the cultivation of

[9] The Latin peoples of America are large consumers of olive oil, and the Italian
colonies of New York City constitute one of the best markets for this "Italian
butter."

olives largely to those varieties which grow fruit large enough for curing (Fig. 144).

Citrus Fruits. The orange is of far more value to the commercial world than all other citrus fruits combined. Orange growing is widely distributed throughout the borderlands of the tropics, the

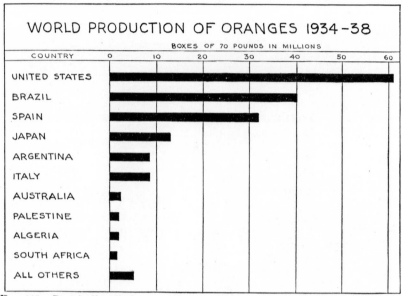

Fɪɢ. 145. Practically all the world's oranges are grown in regions of Mediterranean or humid subtropical climates. World production of oranges was so disrupted by World War II that postwar data by countries is somewhat meaningless. However, since 1938 orange production within the United States has increased rapidly. The average production for four years, 1943–1946, inclusive, exceeded 118,000,000 boxes—almost double the 1934–1938 average.

fruit being abundant in many of the local markets of Paraguay, central Chile, the West Indies, and along the coastal regions of the Caribbean Sea; but the bulk of the world's commercial crop is grown in southern California and southern Europe and in the humid subtropical regions of the United States and of Brazil (Fig. 145). The Sunkist orange of California is advertised in every American market and in many other parts of the world, and the oranges of southern Europe, primarily of southern Spain and of Palestine, are as widely known. These three regions dominate the world's commercial orange market in spite of their distinct handicaps in producing this golden fruit (Fig. 146).

Orange culture in California and southern Europe requires irrigated land valued at hundreds or even thousands of dollars an acre, but in Florida, the West Indies, and other humid tropical and subtropical regions there still remains an abundance of cheap, fertile, and well-watered land. The abundance of moisture, however, is not an unmitigated blessing, for the warm, humid atmosphere is conducive to the growth of fungus diseases which at times greatly injure the trees or fruit. Thus, in spite of the plentiful supply of cheap and fertile

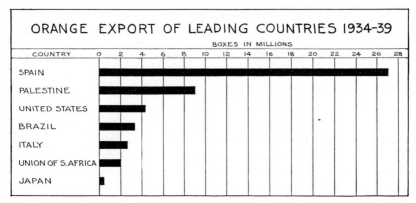

ORANGE EXPORT OF LEADING COUNTRIES 1934-39

Fig. 146. Palestine data are for 1939 only. Spain, located close to the greatest foreign markets of Europe, is normally the leading exporter of oranges. Palestine's production and export of oranges were increasing rapidly before World War II.

land and the abundance of moisture, only two subtropical areas, Florida and southern Brazil, are competing in a large way for the commercial trade in oranges; and even in these areas the development of the industry has been a hazardous undertaking because of frost and diseases.

The orange industry of California has had no such serious setback as that caused by the "Florida freezes," when the low temperatures not only have destroyed the fruit over a large area but also occasionally killed many thousand trees. The industry of California, on the contrary, has had a steady growth, experiencing only moderate losses of fruit except during the year 1922 when approximately one-half of the orange crop was destroyed by freezing temperatures. The nature and extent of this loss have been admirably described by Floyd D. Young.

The delivery value of the citrus fruit crop of California during 1921 was fully $100,000,000. A larger crop than this, and of better quality, was on the trees January 19, 1922, the date when the "freeze" began. Three days later, fully 50 per cent of the crop had been damaged so severely by low temperatures that it was a total loss, and a considerable portion of the remainder had been frozen to a degree that prevented its being included in the fancy grades. The law of supply and demand, through increased prices obtained for the fruit saved, operated to decrease the amount of the monetary loss to the industry as a whole; the delivered value of the 1922 crop was $95,993,485.58. However, the return for the crop was so unevenly distributed among the growers, that the results were serious. Literally hundreds of orchards [owners] received not one cent in returns, while others, who were located in districts where the damage was not so severe, or who saved their fruit through the use of orchard heaters, profited enormously.

But the frozen fruit was paid for by the consumer in higher prices, by the railroads in reduced railroad receipts, and by the people who make their living in the harvesting and picking of the crop. Some picking houses did not open their doors during the season.

Think of it, a loss to the country at large of more than fifty million dollars! Small wonder that the fruit growers are giving more serious consideration to the frost menace than ever before.[10]

Fortunately the orange belt is well supplied with weather stations, and the Weather Bureau has given valuable aid in forecasting freezing temperatures. The cold spells are always of short duration, and usually the streams of cold air are very shallow—often only a few meters in depth. The problem is one of keeping this shallow layer of air warmed for a few hours. Large open fires are of little use, for most of the heat goes into higher levels where it is of no value. It has been found, however, that by scattering many coal or oil heaters about in an orchard the temperature of the air may be materially increased and the danger from frost greatly reduced.

As a rule the freezes of the orange belt of California are not so severe but that they can be controlled by artificial methods of heating. Even when not thus regulated they seldom are severe enough to kill the trees, and thus the damage is not of such a permanent character as that caused by the Florida freeze.

The crop of southern Spain is even more reliable than that of California. The commercial predominance of the industry of Spain is not wholly due to superior physical conditions for orange growing but, in part, to scientific methods of culture, favorable location for marketing the perishable fruit, well-developed marketing systems, and the cooperation of those engaged in the industry.

Ninety per cent of the Spanish orange crop is grown on the narrow coastal belt of eastern Spain (Fig. 137). This area may be divided into

[10] Quoted by permission of Floyd D. Young in the *Bulletin of the American Meteorological Society*, Vol. 4, No. 2, pp. 17–18.

the Valencia district and the Murcia district. The coastal plain on which Valencia is situated contains only about 2,000 square miles of land (20 miles wide by 100 miles long), but it produces approximately 80 per cent of the nation's oranges. This low, narrow, coastal belt is fertile and easily irrigated, and the winter cold is tempered by breezes from the warm Mediterranean Sea. Moreover, it is well situated for the export of oranges by water to northwest Europe. The orange crop is to this coastal district what corn is to the American corn belt. When the orange crop is poor or prices low, times are hard for the farmer; when the orange crop is good and prices are high, prosperity results.

The hill-land of the Murcia district ranks second to the Valencia Plain in orange production, but the output is usually less than 10 per cent of the total national crop. Seville and Malaga are the only other Spanish provinces that produce any appreciable quantity of oranges, and most of them are of a sour variety. Eighty per cent of the oranges grown in Seville are sour, and the greater portion are shipped to England for use in the manufacture of marmalade.

The orange production of coastal Palestine was rapidly increasing before World War II, and many thousand young trees were being planted each year. In 1927–1928 the orange exports of Palestine scarcely exceeded 2,000,000 boxes; a decade later the exports approximated 10,000,000 boxes. Before World War II, Palestine ranked second among the countries of the world in the export of this wholesome fruit, and the acreage given to orange orchards was increasing rapidly.

Oranges grown in the southern hemisphere come into the market during the summer of the northern hemisphere and consequently sell in Europe at the high prices of an off-season product. Brazil and the Union of South Africa constitute the most important source of summer oranges for Europe, but imports from Australia and South Rhodesia are also of increasing importance. The acreage suited to orange production in South Africa and humid subtropical South America is large; these regions without doubt will become of increasing importance in the orange markets of the world.

The lemon, less hardy than the orange, is at its best in the more temperate portions of the Mediterranean climatic regions (Fig. 147). The commercial production is confined almost entirely to southern Italy, Sicily, and the coastal counties of California south of latitude 35° N. Southern Italy and Sicily, primarily Sicily, tempered by air drainage from the slopes of many hills and low mountains (Fig. 137),

FIG. 147. Picking lemons on the largest lemon ranch of the world, located near Santa Paula, California. (Courtesy Chamber of Commerce, Los Angeles, California.)

FIG. 148. Sunshine is one of the most widely advertised benefits of southern regions. Drying apricots in the sunshine, San Fernando Valley, California. (Courtesy Chamber of Commerce, Los Angeles, California.)

and warmed by the waters of the Mediterranean Sea, constitute the foremost lemon-producing district of the world, and the light green of the lemon tree is one of the most prominent aspects of the agricultural landscape. California supplies most of the American demand for lemons and is a close second to southern Italy and Sicily in production.

Temperate-Zone Fruits. The Mediterranean regions are well suited to the production of temperate-zone fruits, and California ranks first among the states of the Union in the production of peaches, plums, and apricots (Fig. 148).

Nut Crops. The major portion of the commercial nut crops of the world comes from regions of the rainy low-latitude and Mediterranean climates. The value of tropical nuts is well known in the industrial world, but the great importance of nut crops in dry subtropical regions is scarcely appreciated. The value of the nuts exported from all regions having Mediterranean climates compares favorably with that of the widely famed olive-oil export. Walnuts and almonds, the most valuable commercial nut crops, thrive in soils too dry for fruits. In regions where the subsoil retains moisture, these nut trees can stand the summer droughts even though the soil becomes exceedingly dry. On portions of the hot, shimmering plains of southeastern Italy the almond tree yields abundant crops year after year without irrigation, and the normal value of the exports of almonds from Italy exceeds that of wine, olive oil, oranges, or lemons. Even in Spain, the greatest olive-oil-exporting country in the world, the value of the olive-oil export is less than three times that of almonds.

Other Tree Crops. The chestnut grows widely throughout the highlands of the Mediterranean Basin. In southern Europe the beech and numerous varieties of deciduous oaks have long been valuable plants for food and are particularly indispensable to rural hog raising. Fig trees produce best in the hotter portions of the regions where the Mediterranean climates prevail or within the borders of the deserts. The cork oak is of exceptional interest as a plant of economic value. It will grow on steep, rocky, barren slopes. Although the tree is best known for its cork, it also yields nuts and wood. More than one-half of the swine of Portugal are fed on the nuts of the cork oak, and the wood of the tree is very useful since it grows in a land where timber is scarce.

Vine Culture

The physical conditions necessary for vine culture are a well-marked warm season, no excess of rain, and land that is dry or well drained. Successful grape culture requires not only suitable climate and drainage, but also an abundance of labor. The land must be carefully tilled; irrigation is often demanded; the vines need to be pruned and trellises must be set; and spraying is necessary several times each year. Finally, successful harvesting and caring for the crop require many laborers during the gathering season.

Raisins. Raisin, currant, table, and wine grapes may all be grown in close proximity, but this practice is not common, as each variety has its own peculiar climatic needs. The production of raisins is confined almost wholly to regions having the Mediterranean type of climate, the best climatic conditions being an abundance of sunlight, low humidity, and high temperatures during the ripening and drying periods. Soil moisture is needed, but this should be supplied by irrigation. Many regions have the requisite climate for maturing the grapes and curing the raisins, but commercial production is confined principally to (1) the San Joaquin Valley of California, (2) southern Spain, (3) Greece, and (4) Asia Minor (primarily Smyrna). This localization is partially caused by ease of irrigation, as well as suitable climate.

The greatest raisin-producing region in the world is situated within the San Joaquin Valley near Fresno, California (Figs. 138 and 149). During the present century the California raisin crop has increased very rapidly, being 378,000,000 pounds for the five-year period 1942–1946—more than two-thirds of the world's supply. This phenomenal growth has been favored by exceptionally good physical environmental conditions. The warm, dry summer gives the grapes a full sugar content, and the hot, sunny, and almost rainless fall provides ideal conditions for curing the raisins (Fig. 149). The land is relatively easy to irrigate, and there is an abundance of water just when needed. The rapid growth of the raisin industry of California cannot be wholly accounted for by the excellent physical environment; the human element has also played an important role. The California growers have spent vast sums of money in advertising and marketing their product, and Fresno raisins are known around the world.

Wine Grapes. Italy ranks first among the countries of the world in the percentage of land given to grapes. Her widespread, rugged, limestone areas, cheap labor supply, and light rainfall with an abundance of sunshine have been so stimulating to vine culture that the acreage given to grapes is surpassed only by that for wheat and maize, and more than one-ninth of the cultivated land is given to vineyards. The significance of this figure is indicated by the fact that in the

United States the two leading crops—corn and wheat—occupy only a slightly larger percentage of the cultivated land. Most of the Italian grape crop is used for making wine, the normal annual production of which exceeds a billion gallons—more than 20 gallons per capita.

French wine is even more widely known than Italian. Usually the grape crop is the most valuable agricultural product of France. More than 1,500,000 people are engaged in raising grapes or in making and

FIG. 149. The sun is the power plant which supplies directly the heat necessary for curing raisins in Fresno County, California. (Courtesy Sun-Maid Raisin Growers Association.)

marketing wine. Wine production is the most characteristic industry of the nation, and the French consumption of this beverage is approximately 200 gallons per family annually. Although grape culture is widely distributed in France, the principal areas of production are the Languedoc and Garonne Valley areas. Normally one-third of the national supply of wine is produced in Languedoc (Fig. 150).

The vineyards of France yield about three times as many grapes per acre as those of Italy. This contrast in production is probably accounted for by the fact that the vineyards of France are situated on richer soil, are more heavily fertilized, and are more scientifically tended than those of Italy.

The French wine production averages about 1,600,000,000 gallons annually during normal times, but the output varies greatly. In good years the production approximates 2,000,000,000 gallons, whereas during bad years it drops to but slightly more than 1,000,000,000 gallons. The demand for French wine, either for local use or for export, is so large that millions of gallons of Italian and Spanish wines are imported annually to supplement local production. The French also import millions of pounds of currants from Greece for the manufacture of high-grade wine suitable for export. Spain and Portugal are important grape-growing countries; in Spain the per capita production of wine is even greater than that of Italy. Sherry, of Spain, and port,

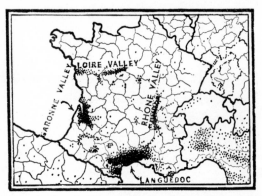

Fig. 150. Grape production in France. Each dot represents 10,000 tons. (Courtesy U. S. Department of Agriculture.)

of Portugal, must be given prominent places among the best brands of wine on the market. Their fame is almost world wide.

Other countries that have Mediterranean climates are not so widely known for their wines. Nevertheless, Australia, central Chile, and southern California are important producers of wine grapes. In Chile, occupied by wine-using Latin Americans, the acreage given to the wine grape exceeds that of any other crop except wheat and beans, and the production of wine is about 15 gallons per capita; in contrast, in Victoria, Australia, occupied by thrifty English settlers, the wine production is less than 2 gallons per capita (Fig. 151).

Southern California continues to be an important grower of grapes suitable for the production of dry wines, sweet wine, or grape juice. Grapes for dry wine are grown most profitably in the coast countries from Mendocino to San Diego, where the cool, moist atmosphere favors acidity of the fruit. Sweet-wine grapes are grown in the great interior valleys from Shasta to Kern, and also in parts of San Gabriel Valley, where the abundant sunshine gives the fruit a high sugar content and where the soil is fertile, yielding large crops.

Table Grapes. Table grapes are widely grown throughout the regions having Mediterranean climates, but their commercial production is limited principally to two areas, the valley of California and southeastern Spain. Most of the California product—3,000,000 to 4,000,000 tons—is consumed in the United States, but Spain produces large quantities for export. Most of the table grapes of Spain are

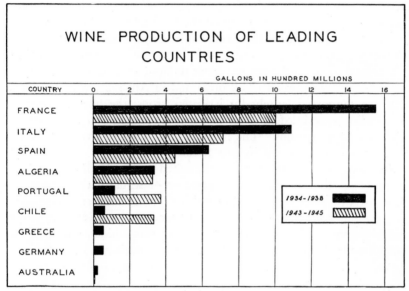

Fɪɢ. 151. Wine production decreased materially in the war-torn countries of Europe during and after World War II, while production expanded rapidly in Portugal and in the New World.

grown on the irrigated coastal plain near Almeria, but they are commonly sold as Málaga grapes because Málaga exporters developed the trade. These grapes are normally exported in barrels containing 44 to 46 pounds of grapes, packed in 4 to 6 pounds of cork dust obtained from the cork forests of Spain or Portugal.

Currants. About nine-tenths of the world supply of currants come from Greece, where they have been produced from a small seedless grape for hundreds of years. From 200,000,000 to 300,000,000 pounds are exported each year, together with olive oil, representing the principal agricultural exports of this small nation. Currant grapes have been successfully introduced into other regions of Mediterranean climate, but only Australia, with an export of 27,000,000 pounds, has developed the industry on a commercial scale.

ANIMAL HUSBANDRY

The animals of the Mediterranean climatic regions, like the crops, tend to be drought resisting. In place of the horse we find the ass and the mule, both noted for their ability to withstand great heat and to survive coarse and scanty fare. Southern Italy and particularly Sicily, where it is both dry and rough, have several times as many mules as horses, but in the plains of the Po Valley the horses outnumber the mules. Spain has three times as many asses and mules as horses. Moreover, the horses are most numerous in Galicia where the rainfall is heaviest; mules and asses are most numerous on the dry Mediterranean coast. In southern California and in Australia, where the animals are supported largely by irrigated crops, the horse is still the principal beast of burden. This fact may be related also to the greater wealth of these regions. The horse is more comely than the ass and has a firmer grasp on the human affections.

The sheep and goats are also well suited to the Mediterranean climates, being able to live on a scanty fare of scrubby vegetation. In some parts of Spain, Italy, and especially Greece they are more common milk animals than the cow. In Greece the goat is the principal source not only of milk, but also of meat, skins, hides, and hair. In Australia, South Africa, and California the cow is almost exclusively the dairy animal, and even in Chile with its Latin population the goat is seldom kept for milk. This preference for the cow, especially in the drier and unirrigated districts, is largely a matter of prejudice and custom rather than of economic adjustment.[11] However, in the alfalfa-growing districts the dairy cow is a more profitable animal than the goat.

REFERENCES

Adams, H. C., "A Longitudinal Journey through Chile," *National Geographic Magazine*, Vol. 42, 1922, pp. 219–237.

Ballert, A. G., and M. C. George, "Notes on the Climate of the Coastal Fringe of North Africa," *Journal of Geography*, March 1944, pp. 97–107.

Bennett, M. K., "Climate and Agriculture in California," *Economic Geography*, Clark University Press, April 1939, pp. 153–164.

Blache, P. Vidal de la, *Principles of Human Geography*, Henry Holt & Co., 1926, pp. 129–160.

[11] A few herds of fine Angora goats are being kept in southern California for dairy purposes. The milk is sold largely to hospitals, to children's homes, and to the few citizens who have learned the value of goat's milk and are willing to pay a price somewhat higher than that of cow's milk.

BRYCE, JAMES, *South America*, The Macmillan Co., 1920, Chapter IV.

COLBY, C. C., "The California Raisin Industry," *Annals of the Association of American Geographers*, Vol. 14, pp. 49–108.

ELSELEN, ELIZABETH, "The Central Valley Project: 1947," *Economic Geography*, January 1947, pp. 22–31.

FAIRGRIEVE, JAMES, *Geography and World Power*, University of London Press, 1915.

FOSTER, ALICE, "The Malaga Raisin District," *Journal of Geography*, Vol. XXXII, January 1938, pp. 1–14.

Greece, a Handbook, Geographical Section, British Naval Intelligence Division, London, 1920.

KENDREW, W. G., *Climate*, The Clarendon Press, 1937.

LIPPINCOTT, ISAAC, *Economic Resources of the World*, D. Appleton & Co., 1929, pp. 306–313.

MEIGS, PEVERIL, "Current Trends in California Orchards and Vineyards," *Economic Geography*, July 1941, p. 275ff.

"Water Planning in the Great Central Valley, California," *Geographical Review*, 1939, pp. 252–273.

Ninth Annual Report, International Health Board, Rockefeller Foundation, 1924, pp. 46–65.

PRICE, WILLARD, "Unknown Japan," *National Geographic Magazine*, August 1942, pp. 224–252.

SEMPLE, ELLEN CHURCHILL, "Climate and Geographic Influences on Ancient Mediterranean Forests and the Lumber Trade," *Annals of the Association of American Geographers*, Vol. 9, pp. 13–37.

"The Influence of Geographic Conditions upon Ancient Mediterranean Stock-raising," *Annals of the Association of American Geographers*, Vol. 12, pp. 3–38.

"Irrigation and Reclamation in the Ancient Mediterranean Regions," *Annals of the Association of American Geographers*, Vol. 19, pp. 111–144.

The Geography of the Mediterranean Region, Henry Holt & Co., 1931.

SMITH, J. RUSSELL, *Tree Crops*, Harcourt, Brace & Co., 1929, pp. 126–180.

North America, Harcourt, Brace & Co., 1925, pp. 539–564, 572–597.

"The Oak Tree and Man's Environment," *Geographic Review*, Vol. I, 1916, pp. 3–19.

TAYLOR, GRIFFITH, *Australia*, The Clarendon Press, Chapter XVII.

VISHER, S. S., "Regional Geography of Iberia," *Journal of Geography*, Vol. 21, pp. 325–338.

WARD, R. DeC., *Climates of the United States*, Ginn & Co., 1925. (See Index.)

WHITTLESEY, DERWENT, *The Earth and the State*, Henry Holt & Co., 1939, pp. 235–278.

WICKER, CYRUS FRENCH, "Eastward from Gibraltar," *National Geographic Magazine*, January 1943, pp. 115–142.

Chapter 11

REGIONS OF MARINE CLIMATE

The marine realm which is confined to islands and the western (windward) margins of continents in higher middle latitudes constitutes a very small fraction of the earth's surface (Fig. 152). Not only

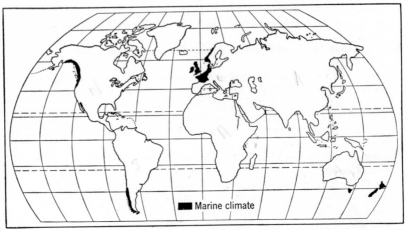

Fig. 152. The region of marine climate in Europe has played a dominant role in world affairs during the last few centuries.

is the realm relatively small, but all except the southern part of the European region suffers from major physical handicaps. Rugged mountains, large patches of unproductive rocky wasteland, forested slopes difficult of access, wet and foggy climate, and relatively small areas of land suited for cultivation constitute some of the most difficult problems with which the people of this realm must contend. The southern part of the marine region of Europe represents the most notable exception to the unfavorable conditions listed above.

In spite of these handicaps man has made great progress in marine regions. Many notable achievements have been accomplished in those

384

areas where the rugged forces of nature seem most forbidding. While nature has made the path of progress in many marine areas difficult, it has also supplied the antidote to human stagnation, for, although the moist climate is not the most pleasant in the world, it is, as we shall see later, invigorating. In all marine regions of the world, man is mentally alert and physically active—human traits that make for the development of masterful peoples who can overcome major obstacles.

A brief study of a few of the accomplishments of peoples who live in marine regions affords conclusive arguments that the people have been and are capable. One of the outstanding facts of world history during the last 400 years has been the spread of western European culture and leadership to all parts of the world. In this development marine regions have had a preponderant share. The British have brought two-fifths of the earth's surface under their control and have been leaders in industry, commerce, and the control of the sea. Some of the territory formerly under British control has already been given complete independence, and other areas have been promised independence. However, the influences of centuries of British control will be felt for an indefinite period. The British are not only losing much of their empire, they are also losing their dominant position in industry and trade and in the control of the sea. Yet Great Britain still remains one of the world's great powers.

Other countries of marine Europe have also helped to spread western European culture to remote parts of the world and have contributed leaders in many fields. Netherlands and France have each brought under their control vast and widespread empire, and it is a well-known fact to students of history that the Norwegians have been capable people from the time of the early Norsemen to the present. The accomplishments of the Danes are scarcely less notable.

The major cultures of all other regions of marine climate have been imported from Europe during the last few centuries, primarily since 1700. Yet all these regions are making rapid progress in agriculture, industry, commerce, literature, science, and art.

The regions that possess the marine type of climate are: (1) western North America from San Francisco to latitude 60° N; (2) western Chile south of Valdivia; (3) western Europe from latitude 45° N to 65° N; (4) Tasmania, New Zealand, and the southern tip of Australia. These regions have moderate to heavy rainfall throughout the year, much cloudy weather and fog, and milder temperatures than those of any other regions except the rainy tropics.

CLIMATE

Temperatures. The regions are situated on the leeward side of the oceans and receive the tempering influence of these bodies of water, hence the name "marine type." The summers are cool and the winters mild. Throughout much of northwest Europe homes are heated by open fires, and in all marine regions woolen clothing may be worn with comfort the year round. The moderating influence of the ocean is indicated by the small average annual range in temperature; in Fort William, Scotland, it is only 18.4° F. as compared with 65° F. in Tomsk, Siberia, situated on the same parallel. On some of the coastal islands the range is still smaller, being less than 15° F. at both Thorshaven, Faeroe Islands, and Valencia, British Isles. Even in high latitudes, as at Sitka, Alaska, latitude 57°, and Bergen, Norway, latitude 60°, the average annual range is less than 25° F. compared with 118.6° F. at Verkhoyansk, and 112.1° F. at Yakutsk, Siberia.

The contrast in temperatures between east and west coast cities may be seen by comparing Sitka, Alaska, with Nain, Labrador, and Biarritz, France, with Vladivostok as shown in the accompanying table.

COMPARATIVE TEMPERATURES OF THE EAST AND WEST COASTS OF CONTINENTS

		Mean temperature	
Station	Latitude	January	July
Sitka, Alaska	57° 3'	30.2° F.	54.1° F.
Nain, Labrador	56° 33'	7.2° F.	48.5° F.
Biarritz, France	42° 28'	45.8° F.	61.2° F.
Vladivostok, Siberia	43° 5'	4.8° F.	69.4° F.

This contrast is further illustrated by the fact that the January temperature at Fort William, Scotland, is higher than that of Shanghai, China, situated 1,600 miles closer to the equator.

The length of the growing season is as noteworthy as the mildness of the temperatures. The summers are always long, but cool. Everywhere one looks one finds the agriculture and native vegetation bearing the stamp of these climatic characteristics. Green pastures, oats and rye, root crops, and magnificent forests dominate the cultural and natural landscape. Cattle, horses, and sheep browse in the fields during a large part of the year. The Scilly Islands, England, latitude 49° 58', are frost-free the year round. Northead, Washington, has a frost-free season of 316 days, whereas that of Pensacola, Florida, is only 285 days; Seattle, Washington, enjoys a growing season of 246 days, whereas in Atlanta, Georgia, it is only 225 days. In the poleward half of the

marine coastal areas the snowfall is relatively heavy; in the equatorward half the snowfall is light and seldom remains long on the ground.
Spring opens about the first of March (in the northern hemisphere),
and autumn holds over until late in November.

This mild climate is primarily a result of oceanic influence. Warm
ocean currents, which flow to the west of these regions, are also a
factor in warming the winds and supplying them with moisture. The
Gulf Stream, together with the North Atlantic Drift, seems to be
the most effective of these currents, as is seen by the fact that northwest Europe receives more warmth than any other area situated in the
same latitude as indicated by the accompanying table.[1]

COMPARATIVE TEMPERATURES OF THE COLDEST MONTH IN THE SEVERAL MARINE REGIONS

Station	Latitude	Mean temperature for coldest month
Group 1		
Sitka, Alaska	57° 3'	30.2° F.
Aberdeen, Scotland	57° 10'	38.3° F.
Khristiansund, Norway	63°	34.7° F.
Group 2		
Massett, Queen Charlotte Islands, Canada	53° 58'	35.3° F.
Punta Arenas, Chile	53° 10'	36.8° F.
Dublin, Ireland	53° 20'	41.7° F.
Group 3		
Victoria, Canada	48° 27'	38.9° F.
Scilly Islands, England	49° 58'	45.8° F.
Group 4		
Evangelist Island, Chile	51° 30'	37.4° F.
Valencia, British Isles	51° 56'	44.7° F.

Precipitation and Humidity. Cloud, fog, mist, drizzle, and rain—
these are characteristics for which the marine regions are as well known

[1] There is much dispute concerning the influence of the Gulf Stream. James
Croll says: "The amount of equatorial heat carried into the temperate and polar
regions by this stream alone is equal to one-fourth the heat received from the
sun by the North Atlantic from the Tropic of Cancer to the Arctic Circle."
(*Climate and Cosmology*, D. Appleton & Co., p. 146.) Willis Luther Moore, on
the other hand, believes that the influence of the Gulf Stream has been exag-
gerated but recognizes the importance of the general oceanic circulation as an
important factor in climate. (*The New Air World*, Little, Brown & Co., 1922.)
Unless the Gulf Stream and North Atlantic Drift are more effective than the
warm currents off the coast of North America and South America, it is difficult
to explain why stations situated on the northwest coast of Europe are from 5°
to 8° warmer than those situated in the same latitude on the west coast of the
other continent.

as for their long, cool summers and mild winters. Gloomy weather is the rule in winter, and even during most of the summer light mists usually obscure the view of distant objects. The rainfall is moderate to heavy and is well distributed throughout the year. The heaviest precipitation occurs in those areas where the westerly winds, heavily laden with moisture, blow against a mountainous coast. Perhaps the best example is that of the rain-drenched land of southern Chile. "It is a vast morass—where the rocks are not too steep to hold any soil— dripping, oozing, showering, with no roads possible but corduroy, where there are people enough present to maintain a corduroy. For 900 miles the woods are so wet that it is impossible to set a fire for clearing without constant relighting, even when all the people of the countryside turn out to attempt it. In the southernmost islands the attempt would be quite hopeless."[2] This same disagreeable climate exists along the wetter parts of the coasts of North America and Europe. Dr. Fairgrieve once said, "The first essential in touring west Scotland is a raincoat." The American soldiers who landed in northwest France—anticipating "sunny France"—found to their discomfort gloomy skies, rain, and mud. Much of the rain comes in the form of gentle drizzles which last for days together, especially during the winter when the moisture-laden winds from the ocean are chilled as they pass over the colder land. Throughout the year, umbrellas, raincoats, rubber shoes, and woolen clothing are indispensable to comfort in all parts of the marine regions.

Fogs, prevalent along all the coasts, are a great menace to shipping. At times the beams from the most powerful searchlight will penetrate the fog but a few yards. It is difficult for ships to enter or leave harbor under such conditions, and they occasionally crash together on the open ocean. In London, farther inland, fogs are commonplace. As the milky billows roll over the city all becomes darkness and confusion. Lights must be turned on in midday; traffic is slowed up— almost stopped; and congestion of the worst kind results. In the business districts millions of dollars are lost in sales. In many coastal cities these fogs mean the loss of time and money; on the ocean they mean the loss of lives and property.

The marine regions rarely experience violent outbursts of weather. The wind is variable and sometimes strong. Thunder squalls are almost unknown in marine regions, and torrential rains accompanied by severe lightning and thunder storms seldom occur.

[2] Reprinted from Mark Jefferson, *The Rainfall of Chile*, American Geographical Society, Research Series No. 7, p. 1.

NATIVE VEGETATION

The natural vegetation of the marine regions consists of heavy forests which, in places, are almost impenetrable because of the rich profusion of undergrowth. In the wetter sections of these coasts the forests are fairly dripping with moisture, and the water-loving mosses, liverworts, and ferns are developed to an extraordinary degree. They form dense carpets on the forest floor, cover stumps and fallen logs with soft living cushions, and wrap even the trunks and branches of the trees in a thick drapery of shade-loving epiphytes.[3] The remarkable luxuriance of this forest growth is a response to (1) the abundant precipitation which is well distributed throughout the year; (2) the vegetative season which is cool but of long duration; (3) the relatively fertile soils of glaciated areas; and (4) the resistance of the largest forest species to diseases and fungus growth.

It would be a mistake, however, to infer that, since all the marine regions are, or have been, forested, the native vegetation is therefore similar throughout. In fact, these forests differ strikingly from one coast to another both in composition and in value; broad-leaved evergreen trees constitute the principal stand in some, while conifers are dominant in others; likewise, the timber of some is unrivaled in value but it is of modest worth in others.

The Pacific Coast Forest of North America. The forests of northern California, Oregon, Washington, British Columbia, and Alaska are extremely luxuriant. In the more favored locations trees more than 200 feet in height stand within a few yards of each other (Fig. 153). The Douglas fir, spruce, red cedar, redwood, and hemlock constitute the most valuable timber of this forest area. The Douglas fir is the most abundant species about Puget Sound and the most important timber tree of the Pacific Coast. It ordinarily attains a height of 175 to 200 feet, and a diameter of 3 to 6 feet. Many trees grow to a height of 250 feet and have a diameter of 6 to 9 feet. This great size of the Douglas fir is a response to the mild climate, the fertile glacial soil, the hardy nature of the tree, and its resistance to diseases and insect pests.[4] In places, these magnificent trees form almost a solid

[3] An epiphyte is a plant that grows upon other plants but is not parisitic, deriving the moisture for its development from the air; an air plant.

[4] The Douglas fir does not suffer from insect pests or fungus diseases to the same extent as hemlock and cedar. *Forests of British Columbia,* Commissioner of Conservation, Ottawa, Canada, 1918, p. 193.

stand and make a picture which delights the eye of any lover of the forest.

Fig. 153.   A heavy stand of red fir with a luxuriant undergrowth of hemlock, ferns, and other shade-loving plants.   (Courtesy U. S. Forest Service, photo by A. Gaskell.)

Along the coast of southern Alaska and most of British Columbia spruce and red cedar are the dominant species.   In places the red cedar has been largely depleted, as its wood is especially prized for the large dugout canoes and for wood carvings which the Indians have made for centuries.[5]

The outer coast ranges from the Oregon boundary to Santa Cruz are characterized by the redwood formation which constitutes about 85 per cent of the stand. The forests of this region vie with those of the Douglas fir for majesty of development and yield of lumber per acre and are also easily reproduced and grow very rapidly. So far as is known, the redwood exceeds all other trees in height, an authentic measurement being 342 feet. Many of the trees are 10 feet in diameter and a few are much larger. The redwood reaches its greatest development in the Eel River Valley of northern California, where in places huge trees 300 feet in height grow so close together that on account of the dense shade there is little undergrowth except ferns and a few low green shrubs. Here, perhaps, is the heaviest stand of timber to be found any place on earth.

The main body of redwood is confined to the western slopes of the coastal mountains north of San Francisco. The range is controlled by the summer coastal fogs. Only where these are common does the redwood flourish, apparently requiring the fog blanket against the hot sun of summer.

North of latitude 43° the lower slopes of the Cascade Mountains are clad with lighter woodlands of composition similar to that of the coastal forest. South of 43° commence the famed high forests of the Sierra Nevadas—the home of the big or mammoth sequoias.[6]

South Chilean Forests. In density of growth and magnificence of development the coastal forest of southern Chile is somewhat similar to that of the Pacific Coast north of San Francisco, but in composition it is strikingly different and in value decidedly inferior. Whereas the North American forest is composed almost exclusively of conifers —redwood, spruce, fir, hemlock, and cedar—these play a very sub-ordinate role in the Chilean forest, where the prevailing trees are broad-leaved evergreens which are not found in the northern forest.[7] The broad-leaved forest occupies the whole coast of southern Chile to the extreme tip of the country. With the decreasing temperatures to

[5] Douglass Houghton Campbell, *Outline of Plant Geography*, The Macmillan Co., 1926, p. 128.

[6] Andreas Franz Schimper, *Plant Geography*, The Clarendon Press, 1903, pp. 566–569.

[7] Douglass Houghton Campbell, *Outline of Plant Geography*, The Macmillan Co., 1926, p. 365.

the southward, there is a marked falling off in the number of species, and the trees become more stunted; but the vegetation is still, for the most part, evergreen, for although the wind is boisterous and the climate raw, it is not very cold. Ascending the mountains to the east, the broad-leaved forest is replaced by one in which coniferous trees are more abundant. One of the most important commercially is the alerce, which is highly esteemed for its timber.

The physical aspect of this forest is magnificent, but the trees are sadly disappointing for timber. The coihue trees, large evergreen beeches which constitute 30 to 38 per cent of the forest stand, are especially stately and impressive, but inquiry concerning their value reveals the fact that they are "the pest of Chile." "They are simply giant weeds and only too abundant. Too heavy and weak for lumber, too wet to burn; they simply keep out the sun and make a quagmire of the ground, cumbering the earth with their useless presence." [8]

New Zealand. New Zealand has a flora unmistakably related to that of southern Chile; indeed so intimate is the relationship that it seems extremely likely that some sort of land connection must have existed at one time between these countries now so widely separated. Not only are there many genera in common, but some fifty species are cited as belonging to both regions.[9]

In both New Zealand and southern Chile the forests are extremely luxuriant, containing stately trees with a ground floor of countless ferns, mosses, lichens, climbers, creepers, and shrubs so dense that they are almost impenetrable. The tree fern, not found in North America, is especially beautiful and abundant in New Zealand. It grows to heights of 50 feet and is probably unsurpassed in beauty by any tree fern.

The forests are usually of a mixed character, some one or two species being predominant. The red pine, remu, is the principal lowland species of South Island. It reaches a diameter of 4 feet or more but makes only fair lumber. On the lower slopes of the mountains, beech trees of excellent quality are abundant.[10]

In northwestern Europe the native vegetation has been practically destroyed, but secondary forests of mixed hardwoods and softwoods

[8] Reprinted from Mark Jefferson, *Recent Colonization in Chile*, American Geographical Society, Research Series No. 6, p. 13.

[9] Douglass Houghton Campbell, *Outline of Plant Geography*, The Macmillan Co., 1926, p. 369.

[10] M. E. Hardy, *The Geography of Plants*, The Clarendon Press, 1920, p. 193.

cover extensive areas in Norway and Sweden, forming the basis for the development of scientific forestry and wood-product industries.

LAND FORMS OF MARINE REGIONS

No climatic realm shows greater similarity of land forms from one region to another than the marine. Rugged mountains, cold and snow capped throughout most of their extent, stand as mighty barriers to the east of a considerable part of each of these coastal belts, casting their morning shadows across the lowland into the ocean beyond.

On these uplands the exceedingly heavy snowfall of winter is greater than can be melted by the cool breezes of summer. As a result, glaciers creep down the western slopes of these mountains, near the poleward margins, almost or quite to the shoreline. On the western slopes of the Andes of southern Chile and the coast ranges of Alaska are situated the most extensive glaciers to be found on these two continents; and from the southern Alps paralleling the western coast of South Island, New Zealand, glaciers descend almost to the base of the mountains. For hundreds of miles in Norway, Scotland, Chile, United States, British Columbia, Alaska, and New Zealand these mountains are formidable barriers against the migrations of plants, animals, and man. Even the winds are compelled to drop most of their load of moisture on the windward slopes of these uplands. Here and there these mountains are subdued, and in parts of Europe they almost or wholly disappear.

Descriptions of the coasts of Norway, British Columbia, Alaska, and southern Chile would read much alike. All are deeply indented, fiorded, and fringed with islands; they possess innumerable harbors which are sheltered from the westerly winds; they have an abundance of timber for the building of ships; and all have a paucity of agricultural lands. Thousands of mountain spurs rise directly out of the ocean, and in many places the ceaseless waves beat against bold cliffs hundreds of feet high. Many of the outlying mountains are entirely surrounded by water, forming picturesque islands. Unnumbered fiorded valleys are so narrow and the walls so steep that they contain no agricultural land, and in places there is scarcely enough room for the little fishing villages. These coasts are hard lands, suited only to a hardy people (Fig. 154).

From such lands the Norwegians made their forays to the British Isles and the continent of Europe, and in their attempts to find an environment less harsh they discovered Iceland, Greenland, and America. For hundreds of years Norway has been a land of emigration. Her sons and daughters are still migrating to America and other foreign lands in search for a more hospitable environment. The Indians who dwelt on the narrow coasts of Alaska, British Columbia, and Tierra del Fuego were probably no less daring and bold in their

Fig. 154.   Gold mines at Juneau, Alaska, together with a landscape typical of thousands of miles of the coast of marine United States, Canada, and Alaska.

hungry, restless wanderings, but they had developed only an inferior civilization and possessed meager equipment for navigation.

Fortunately, on the equatorward margins of all the marine regions the coastal lowlands broaden out or the mountain uplands disappear or are more subdued, affording increased opportunity for agricultural development. Western Europe is most favored in this respect, but all the other regions have more or less agricultural land.

LUMBERING AND WOODWORKING INDUSTRIES

The forest is one of the major resources of every marine region, and lumbering and woodworking rank high among the chief industries. In fact, one of these regions, marine North America, is the most productive lumbering and woodworking area in the world today. In

1944, the total lumber production of California, Oregon, and Washington exceeded 13 billion board feet, most of which was produced relatively close to the coast. The output of these three states exceeded that of all the southern states combined (Fig. 155). In the other marine regions lumbering is one of the major industries, but the total

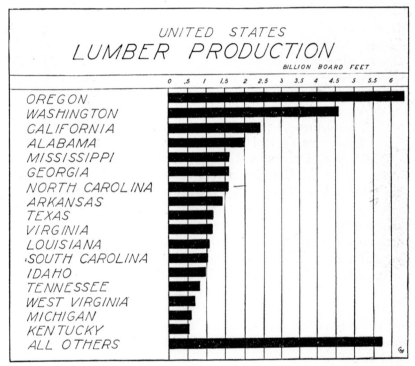

UNITED STATES

LUMBER PRODUCTION

BILLION BOARD FEET

Fig. 155. Marine United States produces more lumber than any other region in the world. Approximately 40 per cent of the lumber of the United States is normally produced in Oregon, Washington, and California. (*Statistical Abstract of the United States*, U. S. Department of Commerce, 1946, p. 710.)

value of the product is small compared with that of the same climatic type in North America. In marine Europe most of the primeval forest has long since been cut, and the better land is being utilized for agricultural purposes. Several factors combine to discourage lumbering in both Chile and New Zealand. These lands are remote from the great lumbering markets of the world; they contain much timber of inferior quality; and they yield, for the most part, a small amount of good lumber per unit area. Yet in both places lumbering is of increasing importance, especially since uses are being found for the lumber of certain trees formerly considered worthless.

The Pacific Forest of North America

The forest represents the greatest natural wealth of the Pacific Coast north of San Francisco, and lumbering is the dominant industry. In 1937, 53 per cent of the wage earners of Washington were dependent upon the lumber industry, and more than 46 per cent of the value of all products manufactured in the state were made from the native forests.[11]

The Pacific forest zone contains the greatest timber reserves of North America and has lately become the foremost lumber producer. In 1945, more than 64 per cent of the remaining saw timber of the United States was situated in northwestern United States, primarily in Washington, Oregon, and northern California.[12] Approximately 70 per cent of the Canadian reserve of saw timber is to be found in British Columbia. The extreme concentration of this reserve of saw timber stands within 200 miles of the Pacific Coast, between San Francisco and Alaska. Nowhere in existence can be found another contiguous forest area of approximately 200,000 square miles that has such a large timber reserve, and quite certainly the area contains the most productive stands of high-grade timber on record.

Five million board feet of lumber have been cut from 10 acres of the Douglas fir zone, and a production of 100,000 to 200,000 board feet per acre is not uncommon. It is estimated that over the entire areas the average stand of original forest per acre was sufficient to build two five-room bungalows. These magnificent forests of redwood, Douglas fir, and red cedar are veritable "gifts of the gods." [13]

The Douglas fir, the most abundant species about Puget Sound, constitutes the most valuable timber of the marine region of North America. Mature fir trees usually contain 2,000 to 6,000 board feet of lumber, and many contain more than 10,000 board feet each.

[11] *Census of Manufacture for the State of Washington*, U. S. Department of Commerce, 1939.

[12] These data were obtained by taking the stand of saw timber as estimated in 1938 and subtracting the estimated cut since that time. No account was taken of new growth or of loss by fire and diseases.

[13] An excellent description of the forests and forest industries of British Columbia is given in *The Canadian Year Book*, Dominion Bureau of Statistics, 1947, pp. 384–418.

The Douglas fir, being intolerant of shade, sheds its lower branches, leaving one-half to two-thirds of the bole clear, and a large percentage of the wood is free from knots. The lumber is remarkably strong and light. It can be dried rapidly with little danger of cracking, warping, or twisting in the process. Such qualities make the Douglas fir well suited for the production of lumber for construction purposes and of veneer used in the making of plywood. One species of Douglas fir is spoken of by the lumbermen as a peeler. The trees grow to be 4 to 6 feet in diameter, and this species is the principal one used in the manufacture of plywood. The name "peeler" comes from the fact that, when the logs of this specie are pressed against long sharp knives and then rotated, long thin strips of veneer can be peeled off very easily.

The Sitka spruce and yellow cedar are the most valuable forest species of southern Alaska, and the red cedar is widely scattered from southern Oregon to south-central Alaska. The spruce is light, strong, and straight. It is highly valued in the manufacture of spars, such as masts or booms for boats. A tall straight Sitka spruce is probably the most valuable, per cubic foot, of all commercial trees of the west coast. The red cedar supports the world's greatest wood-shingle industry. Oregon, Washington, and California produce more than 90 per cent of American-made wood shingles, and British Columbia produces 85 per cent of the Canadian supply. Prior to 1926, between 11 and 18 million squares [14] of shingles were manufactured along the Pacific Coast each year. Fortunately the output is now decreasing because of the keen competition of composition shingles. Since 1929 the output has never reached 5,000,000 squares a year and in 1944 the production dropped below 3,000,000 squares.

GROWTH OF THE LUMBER INDUSTRY

The first commercial sawmills were built in Oregon in 1844 and near Puget Sound in 1845. Since the region was remote from the great lumber markets of the world, the first demand for lumber was for local construction and for shipment to California and Hawaii. It was not until 1884 that the first railroad from the East reached Seattle, opening up a new market for lumber. The opening of the Panama Canal in 1914 gave low freight rates for lumber to our east coast and to Europe. Since then the lumber production of Wash-

[14] A square of shingles is enough to cover 100 square feet.

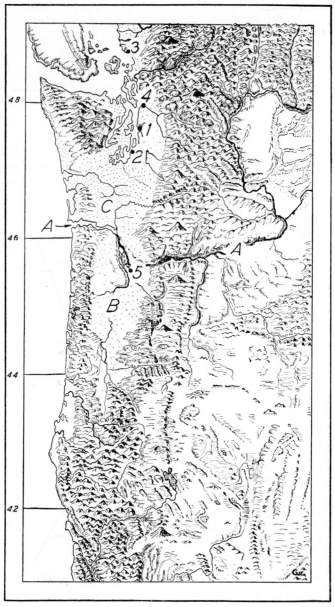

Fig. 156. (A) Columbia River, (B) Willamette Valley, (C) Puget Sound low-land. Cities: (1) Seattle, (2) Tacoma, (3) Bellingham, (4) Everett, (5) Portland.

ington and Oregon has increased rapidly. Portland, Seattle, Tacoma, Bellingham, and Everett are all important lumber-export centers (Fig. 156).

Outlook for the Lumber Industry

Throughout this entire coastal belt from central California to latitude 60°, most of the land is ill suited to agriculture and should be kept permanently in forest. Natural reforestation takes place readily, and the long, moist, cool growing season encourages rapid growth. In the Douglas fir zone it has been estimated that an average of 32,000 to 44,400 board feet per acre can be grown in 60 to 80 years, depending upon the quality of the soil. Insects do little damage except in the yellow pine forests; fungus diseases have been serious for the most part only in overmature timber. These are the conditions which make for profitable scientific forestry, and recent studies in forest finance show that the practice of forestry is not only sound but attractive financially.[15] Forestry, therefore, will probably remain one of the major industries of the region, provided that measures are taken to conserve the timber stand.

The Lumbering Industry of Chile

More than 30,000,000 acres of southern Chile are covered with forest, but only about one-tenth of this is classed as "lumber forest." During the decade prior to 1938 the average annual cut was approximately 400,000,000 board feet, less than 3 per cent of the output of marine North America. Attempts to exploit the forest resources of Chile have for the most part been disappointing. Inferior timber, rugged topography, poor logging methods, low yield of good lumber per acre, and remoteness from good markets are among the factors most difficult to overcome.

The Chilean forests are too thinly sprinkled with useful trees. There are several species of the coihue tree, one of which makes fair lumber, but the most common species are not considered valuable since the wood is extremely perishable when exposed to the weather and checks badly when used inside.[16] In the more accessible places the stand of

[15] Hanzlik, "Financial Aspect of Reforestation by Private Owners in the Douglas Fir Region," *University of Washington Forest Club Quarterly*, Vol. 1, No. 2, June 1922.

[16] Zon and Sparhawk, *Forest Resources of the World*, McGraw-Hill Book Co., 1923, Vol. II, pp. 742–744.

good saw timber averages only 5,000 to 15,000 board feet per acre. (Compare this with the acreage production of marine North America, p. 396.)

Small areas of pine forest are to be found far up in the Cordillera, but the difficulty of transporting the lumber to market makes the cost prohibitive. These pine trees are more valued for their seed cones, which provide the Indians with an important article of food and which even reach the Santiago market.

The alerce, another conifer, makes good lumber but unfortunately it is scarce. For more than a hundred years the Indians have carried out alerce boards from the almost impenetrable interior. In Darwin's day they were the only money product of Valdivia. Today the merchantable timber of this valuable tree is almost gone.

This backward state of lumbering in Chile is not primarily due to lassitude or ignorance, for progressive and intelligent lumbermen are active there. The fact is simply that the Chilean forests are of very moderate value. Puerto Montt, situated in the forest country of Chile, can never develop a great lumber industry similar to that of Seattle, Bellingham, Olympia, Tacoma, and Everett, all surrounded by forests that are unrivaled.

Forest Industries of New Zealand

As regards the number of men employed and the amount of money expended in wages, timbering in New Zealand is probably first among the industries, although the value of the product is not so great as that of agriculture. The average annual cut of saw timber is about 500,-000,000 board feet, primarily kauri and white pine. At the present rate of cutting these two most important commercial trees will soon be almost destroyed, but other forest species will probably maintain the industry at present levels for a generation or more.

The bulk of the export lumber of New Zealand goes to Australia, the largest amount being taken by the neighboring states of Victoria and New South Wales. But exploitation has been rapid, and New Zealand already imports about half as much lumber as she exports, the bulk of it coming from western United States and Canada. Some forest products, such as laths and shingles, come entirely from America

Since the depletion of the New Zealand forests seems imminent the government has passed some of the most progressive forestry laws enacted by any country. Modern conservation measures have been put into operation, plans have been made to reforest 700,000 acres of cut-over land, and the exportation of lumber has been restricted.[17]

Forest Industries of Marine Europe

British Isles. Three hundred years ago the British Isles were densely wooded, but under the pressure of an enormous growth in population the forest products have been needed for industrial purposes and the land for agriculture and pasture. Today, less than 4 per cent of the area is wooded, and even this small acreage contains inferior stands of timber. The United Kingdom has the least forest area per capita of any country in Europe, the amount being only 0.067 acre. Consequently, the local lumber production is only 5 or 6 per cent of the amount consumed. In addition, the United Kingdom imports annually almost a million tons of wood pulp and pulpwood.

Forests of Norway. The long extent of the country from north to south, the varying height above sea level, and the diversified soil conditions combine to produce such a variety of conditions for growth that the forest vegetation is highly heterogeneous. The pine tree grows as far north as 70° latitude and forms the most northern forest in existence. North of latitude 60° the trees are small and of little commercial value. In general, the forest improves in quality southward until in the deep moraine soils of southeastern Norway it is of greatest commercial value.

The total stand of timber is estimated at 120 to 140 billion board feet or about two-fifths that of Oregon. Recently the value of all productive forests in Norway was estimated at $250,000,000, or 10 to 12 per cent of the total wealth of the country.

The commonest kinds of trees are (1) the fir, which, according to estimate, constitutes 50 per cent of the forest stand, and (2) the pine, which makes up another 30 per cent of the forest. The lowland beech, oak, and aspen occupy considerable land in the south, but they are of little commercial value.

The western coast of Norway was never forested because of the strong sea winds, and the convenient access of the western valleys to the coast and the deep sheltered fiords caused the depletion of the forests which formerly occupied the sheltered valleys of the west.

[17] For an excellent discussion of the forest situation in New Zealand, see Zon and Sparhawk, *Forest Resources of the World*, McGraw-Hill Book Co., 1923, Vol. II, pp. 943–947.

In the southern part of Norway the forests are a more conspicuous part of the landscape than the farms. Except around Trondheim and Oslo fiords, most of the Norwegian farms have an isolated position in the forest, or are situated in clusters at the bottom of the valleys and in lowlands.

In the southern part of Norway, lumbering is still a major industry with a commercial production of about 50,000,000 cubic feet of wood each year.

Logging Methods of Marine Regions

Each marine region has developed its own method of logging, depending on such factors as the size of logs, the amount of snow, the nature and number of streams, the seasonal nature of the industry, the size of the sawmills, and the scale of lumbering operations. In some regions the methods are modern and progressive; in others, ancient and backward. Since 1920, the logging industry of our own western coast has undergone marked changes. In the early days logging was conducted in a simple manner and with little machinery. In those districts having plenty of winter snow, the logs were hauled on great sleds over icy roads to the banks of the nearest stream to be floated to the mills after the ice had broken up in the spring. In the southern section of the forest and along the coast, where the snow fall is light, river driving has never proved satisfactory, although it was practiced extensively in the early days. The logs were pulled to the streams by oxen and horses; it was clear from the start that these beasts of burden were poorly suited for the transportation of the larger logs, and as a result the donkey engine was gradually introduced in the nineties. It has since been developed into a powerful and efficient machine which by means of cables can drag and hoist the heaviest logs quickly and easily (Fig. 157).

Living conditions in our western logging camps have also undergone marked improvements. Formerly, the men lived in bunk houses of very rough construction, 30 to 50 men sleeping in one room. Everything was of the roughest frontier type, and sanitary conditions were very unsatisfactory. Today the logging camps are constructed in accordance with the latest improved methods of housing and sanitation. In some of them club rooms with phonographs, radios, newspapers, books, and magazines have also been established.

The logging industry has also changed from a seasonal industry to one conducted the year round. The camps are more permanent than formerly since the logs are brought in from increasing distances.

Permanency permits more home life, and as a result an increasing percentage of the laborers are men with families.   In fact, married men are preferred to single ones, as they are usually more reliable and have a greater interest in the permanency of the work.

This great improvement of the logging in western United States and Canada was made possible because of the large yield of high-grade

Fig. 157.   The donkey engine now handles with ease logs of vast size which formerly had to be split before they could be transported.   (Courtesy Southern Pacific Railway Co.)

lumber per acre and the vast amount of capital invested in the industry.   Improvement was, moreover, necessary in order to handle the large logs, some of which weighed many tons.[18]

Logging in Norway.   Owing to the close network of rivers in the forested areas of Norway, most of the logs are floated to the mills.   In the larger forest areas which are remote from permanent settlements,

[18] For a more complete discussion of logging methods in Washington and Oregon see Lewis and Miller, *The Economic Resources of the Pacific Northwest*, Lowman and Hanford Co., Seattle, 1923, pp. 202–205.

the only dwellings are log shanties built for the laborers. Most of the felling and transportation take place in the winter when farm laborers have time to work in forests and when the deep snows facilitate the transportation of the logs to the streams.

The timber cutters, as a rule, have their own little farms where they work during the summer. Each farmer contracts to clear a certain acreage of land during the winter. In this way the sharp contrast between workers and employers does not arise in forestry as in other industries, and strikes are therefore rare in the former industry.

In both Europe and America the larger mills are located beside ponds where the logs are placed to await sawing. This facilitates the handling of the logs since they are more easily moved in water than on land.

Logging in Chile and New Zealand. Practically all logging operations in Chile and New Zealand are undertaken by the farmers for the primary purpose of clearing the land in order to devote it to agriculture or stock raising. As a result, well-planned extraction methods are lacking. To this lack of planning may be attributed the large percentage of losses in cutting operations.

The use of waterways as a means of conveying logs to mills is not common in Chile as most of the producers have their own sawmills located close to the base of felling operations. A narrow, two-wheeled cart drawn by two or four oxen is the most common method of conveying the logs to the mills, which are rarely more than a mile away. The small mills are moved from place to place as felling progresses. Log ponds are never used in Chile. On the whole, the logs are smaller and more easily handled than in North America, and the mills remain in any given location for so short a time that it is scarcely worth while to make special provisions for ponds.

AGRICULTURE OF MARINE REGIONS

Grass, small grains, root crops, and vegetables are the dominant agricultural crops, which together with cattle, horses, sheep, and poultry constitute, with minor exceptions, the principal source of the farmers' income. Fruits are of considerable importance in small areas; hog raising, associated with dairying, is even more widespread, and on some of the poorer pasture lands goats outnumber the sheep. The growing season is too cool and moist for the successful cultivation of maize, and, although in certain districts wheat yields abundantly, the moist, cloudy, ripening season often prevents the grain from fully maturing, or makes it difficult to preserve the crop.

Fortunately, most of the land having a topography suited to farming and pasture lies in the equatorward half of the marine regions where the winters are least severe and the growing season is longest.

Agriculture in the Equatorward Half of the Marine Regions

The major portion of the agricultural development of marine regions has taken place in the equatorward sections, but in western Europe a live interest is shown in agriculture as far north as the Arctic Circle.

Ireland an Area of Extreme Marine Climate. "The Emerald Isle" is a notable example of the influence of a marine climate little modified by the continental land masses lying to the leeward. Moreover, the poor drainage of the glaciated soils together with the heavy rainfall and slow rate of evaporation result in much of the land being too wet for cultivation but suited to pasture. Green colors dominate the agricultural landscape throughout most of the year. Pastures, fields of grain, and the broad succulent leaves of root crops may be seen everywhere. More than 75 per cent of the cultivated land is given to hay and oats, and most of the remainder is in root crops and barley.

The cropping system is admirably suited to animal husbandry—the most important industry of the land. The number of cattle for each 1,000 acres of arable land exceeds that of any other country except the Netherlands and Denmark, both of which have a climate similar to that of Ireland. That the commercial products of Ireland are almost entirely dependent upon agriculture is clearly reflected in the exports of the country.

In 1938, cattle represented more than one-third of the total value of the exports. Butter, bacon and ham, horses, and poultry products were the only other commodities having an average annual export value of more than $5,000,000 each. Out of the first twenty exports of Ireland, fish was the only one that was not a direct product of the agricultural and pastoral industries.

In south Ireland the mild, moist marine climate is at its best. The cropping and growing season is long, and the land is rugged enough to have fair drainage. This is the chief dairy and poultry region of Ireland. The somewhat sheltered areas of southeastern Ireland with their fair to good drainage constitute the principal cereal and sugar-beet region of the island. A large part of the flat interior of the island is given to pasture and livestock breeding (Fig. 158).

The most valuable export of Ireland is beef cattle, shipped to the markets of the great industrial centers of England. Many of these cattle are fattened in England before they are sent to the slaughter

Fig. 158. Map of the British Isles showing the chief highland and lowland areas. The dotted areas are highlands above an elevation of 1000 feet. Note the location of low hills in southeastern England, known as the North and South Downs. Study the location of leading cities. (Altitude according to J. Paul Goode.)

pens of packing plants. In this respect the animal industry of Ireland differs materially from that of the Netherlands, Denmark, and northwest France. where meat production is primarily a by-product of dairying.

Great Britain. Before the Industrial Revolution most of the people of Britain were supported by the agricultural and pastoral industries. Today less than 5.6 per cent of the working population of the United Kingdom—England, Scotland, Wales, and Northern Ireland—are engaged in agriculture, whereas approximately 60 per cent are now normally employed in manufacture and trade. This change has taken place in little more than a century. During this time millions of acres of crop land were given over to pasture or waste, while industrial and commercial cities were growing rapidly.

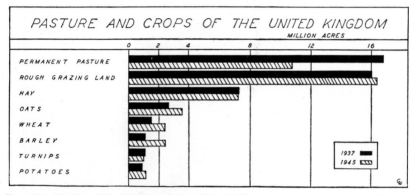

Fig. 159. During World War II the United Kingdom put forth great effort to increase her production of food crops. Approximately 5,000,000 acres of permanent pasture were given to food and feed crops.

Soon after this shift in the population from the country to the city began, Britain was no longer able to feed her industrial population. She therefore quickly adopted a free-trade policy which favored the importation of food from foreign lands, especially from the extensive agricultural regions of the western hemisphere and from Australia. England's trade policy, although no longer one of free trade, still favors the importation of food products.

World War II, with its strain on the shipping facilities of the world, brought on a food shortage in the United Kingdom which caused the British to put forth great effort to increase their home food supply. The area given to permanent pasture was reduced approximately 5,000,000 acres, whereas the area given to major food crops was increased several million acres (Fig. 159).

Most of the United Kingdom is still given to pasture and hay, only a small acreage being devoted to cultivated crops (Fig. 159). This supremacy of pasture and hay is closely related to four factors: (1) a large part of the island consists of rugged uplands poorly suited to agriculture (Fig. 158); (2) the marine type of climate is ideal for the growth of a variety of grasses; (3) industry and commerce have absorbed a large part of the laborers; and (4) many food products can be imported more cheaply than they can be grown. Nevertheless, a

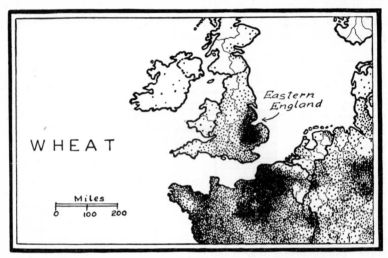

Fig. 160. Distribution of wheat in the British Isles and on adjacent areas located on the continental mainland of Europe. Notice the importance of wheat in eastern England and the small amount produced in the western areas of the British Isles. Each dot represents 100,000 bushels of wheat. (U. S. Department of Agriculture, with modifications.)

considerable part of the lowlands is given to those crops that are adapted to marine regions.

The oats crop is second only to hay in acreage. It is a cool-season crop and thrives in Scotland, Wales, and western and northern England. Oats are used as food for people and also as feed for horses. This cereal fills a very important role in the diet of the Scotch highlanders and of other people who live in the cooler and moister sections of the United Kingdom.

Wheat is grown in practically all sections of the British Isles, but the lowlands of eastern England are the chief area of cultivation (Fig. 160). There the rainfall is relatively light (25 inches more of less) and the amount of sunshine exceeds that of any other part of the British Isles.

Wheat is only one of the crops grown in the eastern lowlands of England. Oats, barley, rye, turnips, potatoes, and a great variety of other vegetables, fruits, and berries are cultivated.

THE LIVESTOCK INDUSTRY. A study of Figs. 158 and 161 leads one to conclude that the livestock industries of Great Britain are very important. This conclusion is well founded. The total value of live-

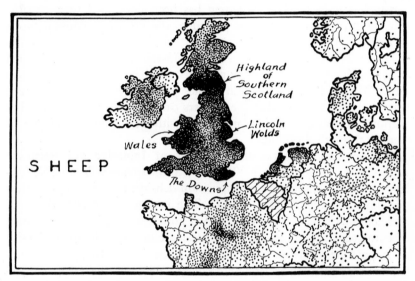

FIG. 161. Distribution of sheep. Note the areas of greatest density of sheep in the British Isles. Each dot represents 10,000 sheep. (U. S. Department of Agriculture, with modifications.)

stock products is approximately three times that of all crops. Natural and human factors have combined to favor the animal industries. Chief among the factors are a mild and moist climate, a rugged topography, a great city population that needs meat and dairy products, and ease of importing agricultural commodities.

Special emphasis is given to the raising of sheep and cattle. In 1938, the United Kingdom had approximately 25,000,000 sheep, 8,000,000 cattle, 4,000,000 hogs, and 1,000,000 horses. Sheep are raised in all parts of the British Isles, but the highlands or rugged areas support the greatest number of sheep per square mile.

Northern France. In marine France, as in the United Kingdom, the livestock industries and the growing of wheat, hay, pasture, vegetables, and fruits represent the major agricultural industries. The cash income from the sale of animal products makes up approximately 75 per cent of the income of the average farmer of northwest France. Wheat is the most important crop in the better agricultural sections (Fig. 160). Apples and small fruit are abundantly grown in the more rugged areas, and the region is nationally famed for the making of cider. Along the more accessible coastal districts, and on some of the Channel Islands, market gardening has been developed to a remarkable extent. Vegetables are exported to the crowded industrial areas of England and Belgium.

Marine France is not *sunny France*. Instead it is a region of much rain, drizzle, fog, and high humidity. Mud is more common than dust. Many of the houses and stables join each other or are placed very close together so that the farmers can go from one to the other without exposure to the weather and without the inconvenience of wading through the mud.

Belgium and Netherlands—Countries of Intensive and Scientific Agriculture. Belgium, with 706 people to the square mile, and Netherlands, with 628, rank high in population density, even among the most populous countries of the world. The nature of the agriculture of these countries reflects their density of population, their advanced state of commerce and trade, and their marine climate. The great density of population of these countries has made it necessary for the inhabitants to farm their land intensively. Most of the farms contain from 2 to 12 acres, and the agriculture, except for the pasture and hay, is largely of the garden type.

Both these countries export large quantities of such agricultural products as butter, cheese, poultry, and eggs. They import large quantities of foods that can be grown more cheaply and easily elsewhere.

The following facts indicate the close relationship between the agriculture of these countries and the marine type of climate. Forty-five per cent of the cultivated land of Belgium is in pasture and hay; 33 per cent in cereals, chiefly oats, rye, and wheat; and 15 per cent in root crops. In the Netherlands 55 per cent of the cultivated land is in pasture and hay; 20 per cent is in cereals; and 11 per cent in root crops.

The livestock industry has also reached a high point of development in Belgium and the Netherlands. The Netherlands ranks first among all countries in the world in the number of cattle per square mile and in the average milk production per cow.

Agricultural Development Slow in Northwestern United States. In western Oregon and Washington the agricultural development has lagged behind the lumbering and commercial activities. This delay is a response in part to the difficulty of clearing the land for the plow, and in part to the better opportunities afforded by other industries. Many of the stumps are large and resistant to decay, making the task of clearing the land expensive. On much of the best land the cost of stumping is approximately $125 per acre. Much of the gutted forest land, therefore, is lying idle or is being slowly reconquered by the forest. Unfortunately, frequent forest fires destroy much of the second-growth timber and injure the soil.

The best agricultural areas of marine United States are the Willamette and Puget Sound valleys and scattered areas west of the coastal ranges (Fig. 156). These lowlands are well suited to the dairy industry and support many fine herds of dairy cattle. These moist areas are also well suited to the production of wheat, hops, plums, apples, and a great variety of vegetables, small fruits, and berries. Every large city supports its nearby market gardens, and plums, small fruits, berries, wheat, and dairy products are produced in sufficient quantities for export. The Willamette Valley ranks first among the regions of the United States in the canning of berries and small fruits.

AGRICULTURE VERSUS OTHER INDUSTRIES OF MARINE UNITED STATES. The industrial and commercial opportunities of northwestern United States surpass those of the agricultural industries. The urban population is increasing much more rapidly than the rural. Puget Sound contains many good harbors and the city population bordering this body of water already approximates 1,000,000 people. The population of Seattle has increased from 90,426 in 1900 to 305,394 in 1940, while Tacoma's population increased from 37,714 to 109,408 during the same period. Puget Sound cities and Portland, Oregon, are ideally located for freight and passenger traffic of much of the North American continent to meet that of the North Pacific area (Fig. 156). Manufacturing industries are also developing rapidly in both the Puget Sound area and in the lower Columbia River Valley. Hydroelectric power is cheap and abundant; the neighboring forests are the finest in the world and supply raw materials for wood-working plants; scores of other raw materials may be obtained merely by stopping them in transit as they pass through these cities to world markets; and finally, the present and potential markets of the North Pacific regions are large.

AGRICULTURE AND CITY DEVELOPMENT IN MARINE UNITED STATES. The agricultural land of marine United States may in the remote future support a dense population. The region is especially well suited to the growth of a great variety of foods—cereals, potatoes, and other root crops, most deciduous fruits, many kinds of berries, and a great variety of vegetables. The climate is almost ideal for the dairy industry. The growth of industrial and commercial cities will stimulate the agricultural industries.

Agriculture in the Poleward Margins of the Marine Regions

Northwest Europe is the only marine region in which agriculture has been developed to any considerable extent in the higher latitudes. Along the west coast of North America no agriculture worth mentioning has been undertaken north of latitude 50°, and, except for a little pasture in the sheltered valleys of the extreme southern part of Chile, the agricultural frontier of that country scarcely reaches the forty-first parallel. In Europe the farmer has established himself much farther poleward. Denmark, lying north of latitude 55°, is famed for her agricultural products; the Scottish lowlands situated in the same latitude are well known for their pastures, root crops, and small grains; in Norway, agriculture is one of the three major industries, and excellent wheat crops are grown about Trondheim Fiord, latitude 64°, the most poleward position where this grain will mature regularly. Nevertheless, it may be noted that with increasing latitude the farmer is more and more dependent upon pasture, hay, oats, and root crops.

Agriculture in Denmark. Denmark is an agricultural nation, more than 50 per cent of the population living on farms and many of the manufacturing industries being closely related to the agricultural development. The country has no water power, and the forests are insignificant; it lacks minerals and has few natural advantages for the production of other raw materials except those derived from the soil. Even the soil is thin and sandy and the winters are long, but by scientific use of the land and by cooperative methods of selling the Danes have prospered and have become famed for their dairy, poultry, and meat products.

Pasture and hay are the major crops, and most of the remaining cultivated land is utilized for small grains and potatoes. The climate is well adapted to oats, barley, and rye, but the summers are too cool and moist to produce the best grade of wheat. The cool climate and sandy soil are well suited to potatoes, the foremost food crop of the land, with an average annual production of about one-third ton per capita.

Small grains, green fodder, root crops, and pasture occupy more than three-fourths of the arable land. The root crops are grown primarily for cattle feed, 92 per cent being grown for fodder, 4 per cent (mostly potatoes) for food, and 5 per cent (sugar beets) for the manufacture of sugar. The fodder roots are beets, swedes, turnips, and carrots. Even the grain is grown largely for cattle feed, although the little wheat that is harvested and part of the rye are used in the making of bread. It is estimated that 50 per cent of the local food crop is grain, 40 per cent root fodder, and 10 per cent hay. Only a little land is given to pasture, a wasteful method of utilizing the better arable land. Most of the cattle are fed, at least in part, even during the grazing season.

Denmark was one of the first European countries to adjust herself to meet changing conditions in world agriculture brought about by the opening up of the extensive wheat lands of the Americas. When overseas competition in the production of grain began to make itself felt in western Europe about 1880, Danish farmers began to concentrate on animal husbandry and to take full advantage of the cheap foreign grain, whereas in certain other countries this same grain was regarded as foreign competition calling for the introduction of duties to exclude it from local markets.

The Danes are pre-eminent in dairying and stock-raising, and although Denmark is only one-third as large as New York State it exports more butter and eggs than any other country in the world. By improving the breeds of cattle and methods of feeding them, the annual yield of milk per cow has been increased from 3,306 pounds in 1881 to 6,600 pounds in 1937; during the same period the average production of butterfat was increased from 106 to 242 pounds.

Closely associated with the dairy industry is the raising of swine. Cooperative creameries have large amounts of skimmed milk as a by-product. Some of this is made into cheese, but by far the greater part is hauled home by the farmers and fed to pigs. Hogs fed on milk, barley, and rye make the excellent bacon for which the Denmark bacon factories are well known in England.

Agriculture in Norway. The arable soil of Norway is situated in comparatively narrow strips, gathered in deep narrow valleys which branch into the mountain tableland and around fiords and lakes. Most of the farms are small and irregular in shape owing to the rugged relief of the land (Fig. 162). The small fields are not adapted to heavy and expensive machinery such as is used by the American farmer. Hand labor is the rule, and the land is intensively cultivated.

The principal crops are the same as those of Denmark—pasture, hay, rye, barley, wheat, and potatoes. Owing to marine influences,

Fig. 162. Use of land in Norway. Crop land in Norway is limited to the valleys and the lower slopes. The land is poorly suited to the use of large-scale machinery. Most of Norway is rugged highlands unsuited for crops. (Courtesy National Travel Association of Norway.)

most of these crops are grown successfully north of the Arctic Circle, and some of them extend to 69° N (Fig. 163). It is not expected, however, that in a country extending through 900 miles of latitude these crops would do equally well in all parts. The country has about 10 acres of arable land for every inhabitant, but about two-thirds of this acreage is in pasture and hay, and most of the remainder is in small grains and potatoes (Fig. 164). The importance of pasture and hay is further indicated by the size of the livestock industry: the country supports more than 1,000,000 cattle, 1,500,000 sheep, and 250,000 goats, the goats being most numerous in the far north where pasture is poor.

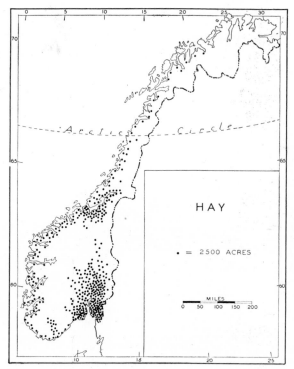

FIG. 163. Map showing distribution of hay in Norway.

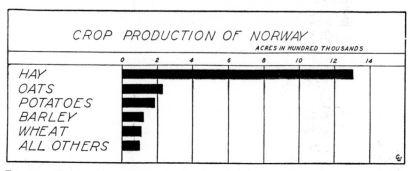

FIG. 164. Contrast the acreage given to hay in Norway, where the feeding season is long, with that of Ireland, where cattle graze throughout the year. Several million acres are pastured in Norway but much of it is poor forest land and is not shown in the graph. (*Statesman's Yearbook*, 1946, p. 1131.)

SALMON FISHERIES OF NORTHWEST NORTH AMERICA

The early history of Oregon, Washington, British Columbia, and Alaska is inseparably associated with the fur trade and fisheries of this region. It was in the wake of the trapper and fur trader that the

Fig. 165. Hauling in the seines on the Columbia River. It is an easy matter to catch salmon as they go up the river to spawn. Unless the salmon is protected by law, extinction is the inevitable result. (Courtesy Portland Chamber of Commerce. Arthur M. Prentiss, photographer.)

English and American pioneers advanced across the continent to the Pacific; and it was the search for valuable seal skins which attracted ships from all parts of the world to this coast. This search for fur led to the exploration of the entire region at little expense to the nations involved. It is doubtful, however, that this trade could have attained its far-famed importance without the aid of the fisheries, which have long since become vastly more important than the fur industry.

There is no place where conditions are more ideal for the development of fisheries than the Pacific Coast north of California; at the same time there is no place where the industry can be more easily destroyed by a continued overcatch. This is especially true of the salmon and sealing industries. Although the waters of this coast contain salmon, halibut, cod, herring, shrimp, clams, whales, and other marine and river products, it is the salmon that give the fisheries their chief commercial product and the world practically all its canned salmon. The story of the salmon is an account of the ruthless destruction of one of our greatest natural food assets. The habits of the salmon make it an easy prey of the fishermen (Fig. 165).

The Annual Salmon Run. Every spring and summer the rivers from northern California to the Bering Sea are the scenes of one of the world's most spectacular fishing industries. Early in the spring millions of salmon, driven by the urge to spawn, start their journey to the headwaters of the Columbia River and other long streams. The early start is made necessary by the long journey which must be completed before winter sets in. The salmon that move to spawning grounds less remote from the ocean begin their journey later in the season. Finally, those that spawn in the shorter streams of the mainland or of Vancouver Island may not enter the streams until late in the fall. Thus the salmon runs last for a period of approximately six months, and the fishing season is correspondingly long.

Before winter sets in, each salmon has reached the lake or quiet stream of its birth. There it scoops out a shallow nest where it deposits its eggs and covers them with a layer of coarse sand or gravel.

The eggs hatch in about two months, and the fish emerge from the gravel into the quiet fresh water. Here they remain from three months to three years, depending upon the species. They then make their trip to the ocean where they remain in salt water for periods ranging from two to six years. Where they go no man knows.

When life is about spent, the adult salmon returns again to the spot where life began and there spawns and dies. This peculiarity has two inevitable results: First, the fish are easily caught in nets as they return to their birthplace to spawn; and secondly, since each stream is visited only by the fish hatched in it, that stream ceases to be a salmon run if all the ascending fish are caught and propagation prevented. No other salmon will visit it until it is restocked artificially.

Decline of West Coast Salmon Runs. Salmon canning began in central California in 1864. The runs were large, and in the early eighties more than 200,000 cases were packed annually on the Sacramento River alone. Thereafter, the runs declined steadily and finally disappeared.

Salmon canning along the small coastal rivers of California, Oregon, and Washington reached a peak in 1911, after which it declined to approximately one-tenth its maximum development. In a similar manner there was serious depletion or destruction of the salmon industry in other west coast streams prior to 1924.

Fig. 166.   Canned salmon ready for the market. From 200,000,000 to 500,000,000 pounds are canned on the west coast of North America each year. (Courtesy Portland Chamber of Commerce, Arthur M. Prentiss, photographer.)

One of the most serious declines of the salmon industry occurred on the Columbia River. Overfishing, the diversion of irrigation waters and also of fish onto dry land, and the building of dams have all played a part in injuring the fishing industry of the largest of all salmon streams (Fig. 166).

A study of the salmon industry in other parts of western North America reveals the same story of destruction. In practically every stream flowing into the Pacific Ocean from San Francisco to the Arctic Ocean, the salmon industry rose for a time and then declined. Thus, by 1920, the North American salmon industry was threatened with serious depletion.

Conservation of Salmon Industry.   By 1920, American statesmen began to recognize the urgent need for conservation of the salmon industry.   Finally, in 1924, after three years of controversy, Congress passed a bill placing the management of Alaskan fisheries under the control of the Secretary of Commerce.   The most important feature of this bill provided that at least 50 per cent of the salmon entering a stream must be permitted to escape the fishermen's nets and reach the spawning grounds.   In 1937, a treaty was ratified by Canada and the United States which has helped to preserve the salmon industry of the Fraser River.

In recent years, the dams built on the Columbia River and its tributaries have created serious problems for the salmon industry.   Fish ladders have been built around these dams to permit passage of the salmon to the spawning grounds.   Fish are also caught below the 350-foot Grand Coulee Dam and hauled in tank cars to the stream above the dam.   On the whole the gains made in conserving the salmon industry have exceeded the losses.   As a result of conservation measures established within the United States and Alaska, the salmon runs have been increasing in many streams, and an increased catch has been permitted.   In 1936, the canned salmon output of the United States reached an all-time high of almost 9,000,000 cases of 48 pounds each.   Since then catches have been somewhat smaller.

The salmon is still the most valuable of the North American fish. In 1946 the salmon catch exceeded 447,000,000 pounds, and the canned salmon was valued at $211,000,000.

REFERENCES

ANDREWS, J. H., and R. W. COWLIN, "Forest Resources of Douglas Fir Regions," *Miscellaneous Publication No.* 389, U. S. Department of Agriculture, 1940.

BRENNAN, B. M., *Possible Methods of Preserving Columbia River Salmon and Steelhead at Grand Coulee Dam*, Department of Fisheries, State of Washington, 1938.

Census of Manufacture for the State of Washington, U. S. Department of Commerce, released March 6, 1939.

Forests of British Columbia, Commissioner of Conservation, Ottawa, Canada, 1918.

FREEMAN, OTIS W., and HOWARD H. MARTIN, *The Pacific Northwest*, John Wiley & Sons, 1942.

GREGORY, HOMER E., "Salmon Industry of the Pacific Coast," *Economic Geography*, 1940, p. 409ff.

HARDY, M. E., *The Geography of Plants*, The Clarendon Press, 1920.   (See Index.)

HOWELL, J. P., *An Agricultural Atlas of England and Wales,* Ministry of Agriculture and Fisheries, London, 1925.

HUNTINGTON, ELLSWORTH, *Civilization and Climate,* Yale University Press, 1915. (See Index.)

Season of Birth, John Wiley & Sons, 1938.

JEFFERSON, MARK, *Recent Colonization in Chile,* Oxford University Press, 1921.

JONES, C. F., "The Agricultural Regions of South America," *Economic Geography,* Vol. 4, pp. 165–180.

KÜCHLER, A. W., "The Broadleaf Deciduous Forests of the Pacific Northwest," *Annals of the Association of American Geographers,* June 1946, pp. 122–147. This article also treats of the forests of all marine west coast climates—southern Chile, New Zealand, and northwest Europe.

LEWIS and MILLER, *Our Pacific Northwest,* Lowman & Hanford, 1925.

MORGAN, F. W., "Rotterdam and Waterway Approaches to the Rhine," *Economic Geography,* January 1948, pp. 1–18.

OXHOLM, ALEX H., "Forest Resources, Lumber Industry, and Lumber Export Trade of Norway," *Special Agent Series No.* 211, U. S. Department of Commerce, 1922.

O'MALLEY (U. S. Commissioner of Fisheries), "The Fisheries of Alaska," *Scientific Monthly,* July 1926, pp. 37–39.

Red Cedar Shingle Industry, Report U. S. Tariff Commission, 1927.

REES, HENRY, "A Growth Map for the Manchester Region," *Economic Geography,* April 1947, pp. 136–142.

"Leeds and the Yorkshire Woolen Industry," *Economic Geography,* January 1948, pp. 28–34.

STAMP, L. DUDLEY, "Land Utilization in Britain," *Geographic Review,* October 1943, pp. 523–545.

Statistiske Centralbyraa, Statistisk for Kongeriket Norge, Oslo, 1925.

TANSLEY, A. G., *The British Isles and Their Vegetation,* Cambridge University Press, 1939.

VALLAUX, CAMILLI, "The Maritime and Rural Life of Norway," *Geographic Review,* Vol. 14, 1924, pp. 505–518.

WARD, HENRY B., "Icthyology—Salmon Psychology," *Journal of the Washington Academy of Sciences,* Vol. 29, No. 1, January 1939, pp. 1–14.

ZON and SPARHAWK, *Forest Resources of the World,* Vols. I and II, McGraw-Hill Book Co., 1923. (See Index.)

Chapter 12

THE HUMID CONTINENTAL CLIMATE
WITH LONG SUMMERS

Extending northward from subtropical and semi-arid regions to the northern coniferous forests of North America and Eurasia, the humid continental types of climate are confined to the northern hemisphere. These regions comprise some of the most extensive areas of good agricultural land to be found anywhere, and here also manufacturing, mining, and commercial activities have reached their maximum development. The black prairies of the United States with their richness manifested in luxuriant stands and abundant yields of corn and various other crops, the black soils of the wheat belt of the U.S.S.R. covered by thousands of square miles of waving grain, some of the most important spring-wheat regions of the world, the largest dairy section of our own country—these are among the important agricultural regions of this climatic realm.

The humid continental climate may be subdivided into three types: (1) humid continental with long summers, (2) humid continental with short summers (Chapter 13) and (3) the modified humid continental (Chapter 14). All three types are found in North America and Asia, but only the first two occur in Europe.

LOCATION

In North America this climatic type extends southward to the boundary of the cotton belt and stretches in an east-west direction from the Atlantic on the east to the Great Plains on the west. It is bounded on the north by the humid continental climate with short summers and the modified humid continental climate. In Europe it embraces the Po Valley, the middle and lower parts of the Danube Basin—especially the fertile plains of Hungary, northern Yugoslavia,

421

and Rumania—and stretches eastward into southern Soviet Russia (Figs. 71 and 167). In eastern Asia it is confined to the Hwang Ho Valley and to southern Manchuria (Fig. 129).

CLIMATE

A major characteristic of this type of climate is variability, not only from season to season but also from day to day. This daily variability

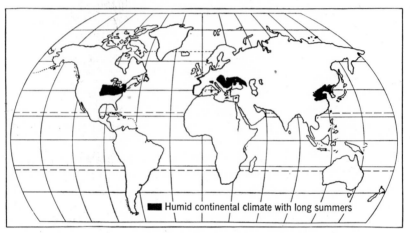

Humid continental climate with long summers

FIG. 167.   The humid continental climate with long summers exists only in the large land masses of the northern hemisphere.

is greater in the corn belts of the United States and Europe than in the monsoon region of Asia. In the first two areas, days of bright sunny weather may be followed by days of cloudy and muggy weather; days of heat may be followed by days of relatively cool weather.

Another major characteristic of this type of climate is the summer maximum of precipitation. The heaviest precipitation comes during the season of greatest heat and of maximum plant growth. In this respect the humid continental climate with long summers contrasts strikingly with regions of Mediterranean climates. The summer maximum is most pronounced in the humid continental climate of Asia where the rain comes with the summer monsoons. Thus in Peiping (Peking), China, about 94 per cent of the precipitation occurs during the summer half-year (Fig. 168). On the other hand, in the humid continental climate at Indianapolis, Indiana, only 53 per cent of the precipitation comes during that period.

In the humid continental climate with long summers, the summer temperatures are usually high and may indeed be higher than those of the rainy low latitudes. But in general the sensible temperatures are lower than those of the latter areas because of lower relative humidity.

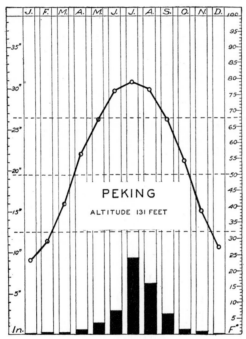

Fig. 168. Climatic graph of Peiping (Peking), China.

On the other hand, the winters are severe. For days and even weeks at a time the temperatures may go as low as those of the frigid north. Thus regions with this climatic type have a moderately high seasonal and monthly range in temperature, which—owing to the influence of the monsoon—is most pronounced in the corn-belt climate of Asia. In Peiping, China (39° 55′ N), the average temperature range from the coldest to the warmest month is 55.3° F., whereas in Indianapolis, Indiana (41° 39′ N), it is 45.7° F., and in Budapest, Hungary (47° 30′ N), it is 39.7° F. The greatest temperature range at Peiping as compared with that at Budapest is the more striking when it is considered that Peiping is more than 500 miles nearer the equator.

The average frost-free season of this type of climate is from five to six months, which is too short for the production of rice or cotton, but it is long enough for the growth of corn, sorghums, grasses, and small grains. The length of the frost-free period varies with latitude and altitude. A marked variation is sometimes found within a relatively small area of land. Thus in the Ohio Valley, the frost-free period of some bottom lands is only 173 days, whereas steep slopes adjacent to such lands have more than 190 days.

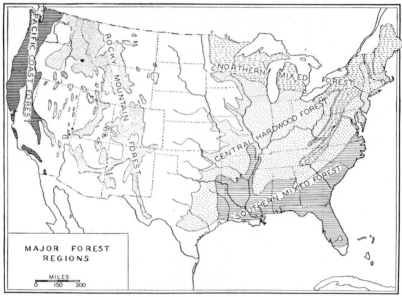

Fig. 169. The main forest regions of the United States. The corn-belt climatic region had a cover of hardwood forest in the East and prairies in the West.

NATIVE VEGETATION

The native vegetation of this type of climate consists chiefly of hardwood forests containing such trees as the oak, hickory, and maple, but in the drier sections these give way to open grasslands, as, for example, in the western part of the North American corn belt. Here the first permanent settlers utilized the forest rather than the more easily cultivated grasslands, since they believed that land lacking forests was infertile.

In North America, the central forest originally covered about 280,-000,000 acres of land and contained a stand of timber that was estimated at approximately 1,400 billion board feet (Fig. 169). But this large timber reserve has been exploited to such an extent that only 14,000,000 acres of saw timber remain. Large amounts of valuable wood were wasted in the process of clearing the land. Even at the present time, timber cut exceeds timber growth by a considerable margin.

In the hardwood forest of Rumania, however, the annual forest growth exceeds the cut. These forests have an annual yield capacity of about 380,000,000 cubic feet, whereas only 282,000,000 cubic feet are required for domestic use. This would leave a considerable amount for export if the forests were utilized to their full capacity. Even under the present backward conditions of forestry Rumania normally exports timber. Some of it is sent by rail to Germany, Switzerland, France, and the Netherlands; but a much larger amount of the better grade of timber is shipped *via* Galatz or Odessa to the timber-denuded Mediterranean countries and to the Orient.

Forests at one time covered a part of this climatic region of Asia, but most of these forests have been cut long since in order that the land may be cultivated to feed the teeming millions. Thus in the densely populated areas of North China the land has been depleted of its forests, and a large part of the remaining timber is found in areas that are difficult of access. In Hopeh, one of the provinces of North China, only 4 per cent of the land is in forests.

SOILS

In those humid continental areas where grass is the chief type of native vegetation, the dark-colored prairie soils predominate. The upper or A horizon of the prairie soil is dark brown to nearly black in color. Beneath it lies a well-oxidized subsoil or B horizon. These are among the best soils in the United States, especially for the production of corn and oats. They differ from the chernozem group of soils in having a slightly lighter color in the upper horizon. They also differ in the absence of a zone of lime accumulation. They are relatively more fertile than the yellow and red-colored soils of the cotton belt mainly because of development in regions of lesser precipitation and in areas of native grasses, and because of the longer period during which these soils are frozen. Hence relatively less leaching takes place.

In the more humid parts of these climatic regions the brownerths and the gray-brownerths predominate. These are somewhat less durable than the prairie soils. There are, however, some highly productive types of soil among these groups, especially where the parent material has been derived from limestone.

In the Hwang Ho Valley, soils made from wind-blown material called loess are widely distributed. The location of this region has favored loess deposition. The outward-blowing winds, especially during the winter half-year, and the relatively dry conditions of the continental interior to the west of the Hwang Ho Valley are favorable to the transportation of soil from arid and semi-arid Mongolia. Winds from the east are moist; hence they hold the soil particles and thereby check the movement of these soils back to their original source.

Loess is intermediate in texture between clay and sand and generally weathers into a fertile agricultural soil. However, it does not make a good soil for rice production because of its porosity. Another marked characteristic of the loess is its yellow color, and the vast quantity of this soil washed into the Hwang Ho gives the river its color (Hwang Ho is Chinese for Yellow River). In the hills of the western part of the Hwang Ho Valley earth dwellings have been excavated in the loess—an environmental advantage in a region generally lacking in timber.

AGRICULTURE

The cultural landscape varies materially from one region of the humid continental climate with short summers to another. The North American corn belt with its large farm buildings, rectangular fields, and large modern machinery contrasts strikingly with the small irregular fields, the small agricultural buildings, and the general paucity of modern machinery found in Rumania, Hungary, and southern U.S.S.R. Even more pronounced are the contrasts between these regions and the humid continental region of Asia, where the cultural landscape reflects a preponderance of spade and hoe cultivation, in contrast to the use of large-scale machinery in the American corn belt.

Although the physical environment of these several climatic regions permits the production of the same types of crops (corn, hay, wheat, beans, oats, barley, sorghums, and millet are common to all), the relative importance of each crop varies from region to region. Corn and wheat are the chief cereals of the North American region where the humid continental climate with long summers prevails. However tobacco, hay, vegetables, and fruit crops are important. In fact this type of climate is well suited to diversified agriculture. Corn, wheat, and rice are important in the Po Valley, while around Milan (Milano) the mulberry thrives and sericulture represents an old industry. The Danubian Plain of Hungary and Yugoslavia has been called the wheat, wine, and fruit region; the lower Danube Valley is a corn and wheat region (Fig. 137).[1] In North China and in southern Manchuria the grain sorghum (kaoliang), soybeans, and wheat are more important than corn (Fig. 129).

The North American Region

In North America two major agricultural regions occupy the greater part of this climatic region (Figs. 167 and 170).[2] The southernmost of these is the corn and winter-wheat belt, sometimes called the "middle country," a transition zone between southern and northern agriculture. North of this region lies the corn belt, an agricultural region which produces more feed for livestock and more meat for man than any other area of equal size in the world.

In both these regions corn is the chief crop, but the secondary crops differ. In the corn and winter-wheat belt, corn occupies approximately one-third of the crop land, whereas in the corn belt more than two-fifths of the cultivated land is given to this crop. In the corn belt, moreover, approximately 60 per cent of the land is cultivated, whereas only 32 per cent of the corn and winter-wheat belt is devoted to crops. This smaller percentage of cultivated land in the southern region is due mainly to the large areas of rugged topography, such as the Ozark highlands of Missouri and the Appalachian highlands of Kentucky, Tennessee, North Carolina, and Virginia. In these rugged areas a large part of the land is in forest. In fact, 40 per cent of the total area of the corn and winter-wheat belt is devoted to forests, whereas only 8 per cent of the corn belt is forest covered.

In addition to corn, both regions produce wheat, hay, and oats. Special crops such as fruit, tobacco, and vegetables, however, are relatively more important as special enterprises in the corn and winter-wheat belt. In fact, about 70 per cent of the tobacco produced in the United States is grown in this region.[3] The chief centers of produc-

[1] George Kiss: "T.V.A. on the Danube," *Geographical Review*, April 1947, p. 298.

[2] The boundaries of belts in regions drawn by different scientists for different purposes seldom coincide throughout their extent.

[3] Rewritten by permission from "Agricultural Regions of North America," by O. E. Baker, *Economic Geography*, Vol. 3, p. 320.

tion are found in western Kentucky and adjacent counties in Tennessee, in the Bluegrass area of Kentucky, and in the Piedmont of North Carolina and Virginia (Fig. 171).

The Corn Belt. This agricultural region comprises the most productive part of this humid continental type of climate in North Amer-

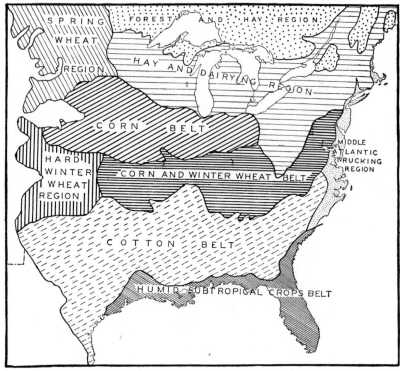

FIG. 170. Agricultural regions in eastern United States. (After O. E. Baker, with modifications by Daniel R. Bergsmark, from O. E. Baker, "Agricultural Regions of North America," *Economic Geography*, Vol. 3, 1927, p. 310.)

ica, and it is indeed the largest continuous body of well-drained, fertile, level crop land on that continent. It stretches westward from central Ohio through the important corn- and hog-producing states of Indiana, Illinois, Iowa, and northern Missouri and into southeastern South Dakota and eastern Nebraska (Fig. 170). Its southern boundary marks a transition to the more rugged lands of the corn and winter-wheat region; along its northern and eastern borders hay and dairy products become relatively more important than corn and hogs. To

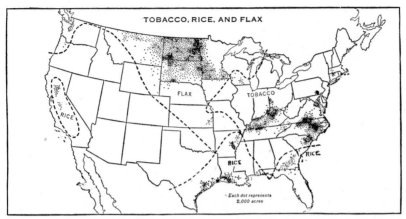

Fig. 171. Note the intermediate location of America's leading tobacco-producing areas. They are located mainly in the humid continental climate with long summers (the corn-belt type), whereas rice is a product of semi-tropical areas and flax is grown mainly in the humid continental climate with short summers (the spring-wheat belt type of climate). (U. S. Department of Agriculture.)

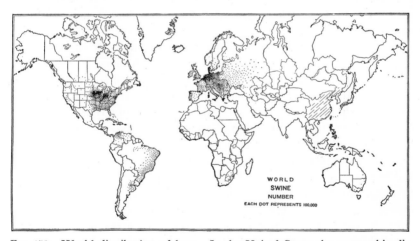

Fig. 172. World distribution of hogs. In the United States the geographic distribution of hogs corresponds closely with that of corn, but in Europe it coincides more nearly with the distribution of potatoes and dairy cows. Thus in Denmark bacon is one of the major exports. (U. S. Department of Agriculture.)

the west the boundary is climatic. There precipitation becomes too small for profitable corn production, and wheat displaces corn in the cropping system.

LIVESTOCK, THE MOST IMPORTANT SOURCE OF AGRICULTURAL WEALTH. Corn-belt farming is two-story farming. The lower story consists of crops; the upper, of livestock and their products. The principal source of farm income is from the second group, especially from the sale of hogs, poultry and eggs, beef cattle, and dairy products. In fact, three-fourths of the income of the corn-belt farmer is derived from livestock products and only one-fourth from the sale of crops. Hogs constitute the most important single source of livestock income, followed in order by poultry and eggs, beef cattle, and dairy products (Fig. 172).

The distribution of various kinds of livestock is closely related to the variations in crop production, climate, and population. Thus, in general, hogs are numerous where corn is most abundant and cheapest. Dairy cattle are densest in the northern and eastern parts of this region, chiefly because of proximity to large urban populations, cooler climatic conditions, and the relatively great importance of hay and pasture. Beef cattle are found chiefly in the prairie portions of the corn belt, in areas where grasses rather than forests constitute the native vegetation.

CROPPING SYSTEMS. The typical cropping system of the corn belt is built around corn, small grain, and clover with timothy. Successful farmers want all the land in corn that they can care for and still have a good cropping system from the standpoint of efficient use of labor and of the productivity of the land. They devote from one-fourth to one-half of the cultivated land to corn, the average for the corn belt being two-fifths.

A widely practiced, simple rotation consists of corn, small grain, and clover. In this rotation, corn is followed by oats, winter wheat, or other small grain that has been seeded to clover. The crop of clover is cut for hay the third year, and the sod is turned under for corn the next year, repeating the rotation. In areas where dairying is relatively important, especially in the northern and eastern parts of the corn belt, the demand for additional hay or pasture often makes it desirable to lengthen the rotation. Under such conditions timothy is generally seeded with the clover, and the succession of crops on a given field becomes: corn, one year; small grain, one year; and clover with timothy, two years. But many farmers living in the corn belt want more than one-fourth or one-third of their crop land in corn, which they get either by having two years of corn in succession in the rotation or by utilizing a field outside of the regular rotation.

In the northern part of the corn belt, oats constitute the most important small grain crop in the rotation; winter wheat is relatively more important than oats in the southern part of the region. The hay crop consists chiefly of clover and timothy in the greater part of the corn belt, and alfalfa is concentrated chiefly in the western area. Because of the greater expense of establishing alfalfa and on account of its

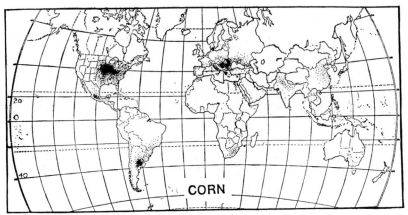

Fig. 173. World corn acreage. Each dot represents 100,000 acres.

perennial nature, rotations that include this crop are usually five or more years in length, the alfalfa being grown approximately three years in succession.

THE CORN CROP. The corn belt constitutes the most important corn-producing region in the world (Fig. 173). Iowa, Illinois, and Nebraska normally produce almost two-fifths of the corn that is grown in the United States. It is the possibility of converting enormous quantities of corn into meat, together with the suitability of climate and soil, that account for the large acreage of corn in this region. Since corn is a cheap, bulky commodity, it cannot stand high transportation costs, and it is therefore utilized mainly on the farms of this region as feed for livestock.

The climatic environment of this region favors production of corn. Here the long growing season of 150 to 180 days permits the production of the large, late-maturing varieties. The beginning of the growing season for corn starts when the average day temperatures reach approximately 55° F. During the growing season, corn requires high temperatures both day and night. Practically no corn is grown where the mean summer temperature is less than 66° F., or where the average night temperature during the three summer months (June, July, August) falls below 55° F.

Amount of rainfall during the growing season is another factor of major importance in corn production, the yield per acre in any locality being influenced both by the amount and by the seasonal distribution of the rain.   It has been found by studying yields of corn and the

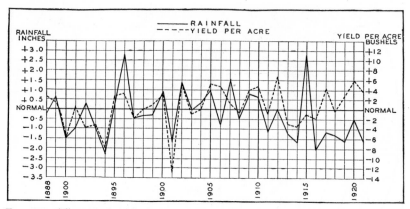

FIG. 174.   The relationship between July rainfall and the yield of corn.   The records of precipitation and yields cover the states of Indiana, Illinois, Iowa, and Missouri from 1888 to 1921.   (U. S. Department of Agriculture.)

distribution of rainfall for many years that within the corn belt there is a close relationship between rainfall in July and yield of corn.   In general, when the rainfall was above normal for that month corn yields were above normal; when the rainfall was below normal the corn yield was also below normal (Fig. 174).

There are also disturbing factors that the corn-belt farmer encounters.   Thus certain types of animal and plant life are frequently important factors in reducing yields of corn.   Of the animal life injurious to corn, the gopher, grasshopper, chinch bug, the corn-ear worm, white grubs, and billbugs cause greatest loss.   In many sections the corn-ear worm causes a loss of at least 7 per cent of the grain on the ears attacked, and chinch bugs cause injury to the corn, especially during seasons of comparative drought.   Recently the European corn borer has increased the problems of the corn-belt farmer.   First appearing in the general region of Lake Erie, the corn borer has spread southwestward and is causing great losses on the farms of the corn belt. Stringent measures are being taken to prevent the corn borer from spreading into uninfested areas.

SMALL GRAINS. The corn belt holds a prominent place not only in the production of corn, but also in the production of oats, winter wheat, and hay. Corn is grown on approximately two-fifths of the cultivated land in this region, and most of the remaining crop land is almost equally divided among oats, wheat, and hay. In normal years this region produces half of the oats grown in the United States, which

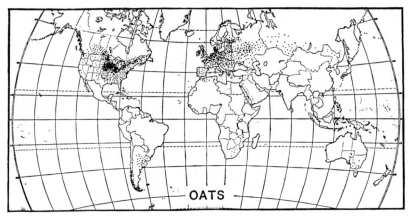

FIG. 175. World oats acreage. Each dot represents 100,000 acres. (Map plotted on Van der Grinten projection.)

in fact is the major oat-producing country in the world (Fig. 175). Oats constitute the leading small grain crop in the northern part of the corn belt, and winter wheat in the southern part. "The line separating winter wheat from oats follows in a general way that of 53° F. average winter temperature. This division is doubtless owing also in part to the fact that in the southern corn belt the corn can be gotten off the ground in time to seed wheat in the fall, whereas farther north, where this cannot be done, it is necessary to use a spring sown crop."

OTHER CROPS. Clover and timothy together constitute the most widely grown hay crop in the corn belt, especially in the humid eastern part of the region, where proximity to some of America's largest cities has favored the development of the dairying industry.

Alfalfa can be grown practically throughout the corn belt, although it is not well adapted to the acid soils of the humid part of this region. The principal difficulty in growing alfalfa is that the first cutting must be made just at the time of the first cultivation of the corn crop, and the second cutting comes just at the time of wheat and oat harvest. These labor conflicts constitute a major reason why alfalfa is not a more important hay crop in the corn belt.

The production of soybeans is becoming increasingly more important in the corn belt. In the southern half of the region the farmers have long felt the need of some spring crop to occupy the place between corn and wheat in the rotation. It is not satisfactory to sow wheat after corn unless the corn is cut and shocked, and it is not practicable to utilize the corn fodder from such a large acreage as is grown here. Oats have hitherto been much used for this place in the rotation, but in this part of the corn belt oats are an uncertain crop, and the yield averages low. Thus soybeans appear to be the ideal crop to substitute for oats in a system of rotation following corn and preceding wheat. Beans leave the land in excellent condition for wheat without plowing unless it is weedy, and even this difficulty can be overcome by planting the beans in rows and cultivating them a few times. Moreover, since the crop is a legume, it adds considerable nitrogen to the soil for the wheat crop that follows. Soybeans after corn and preceding wheat also assist in controlling scab, which is due to a fungus affecting both corn and wheat.

Farther north where oats are a logical small grain crop, soybeans are often planted with the corn. This practice is particularly advantageous on farms where corn is "hogged off." The soybean crop may also be fed as hay, being a splendid substitute for alfalfa. When ground the beans may serve as a concentrated feed for hogs and cattle.

The European and Asiatic Regions

The European belt of humid continental climate with long summers extends from the Po Valley of northern Italy eastward almost to the Caspian Sea (Fig. 137). Hungary and Rumania constitute the most important corn-producing area of Europe. The agriculture of these countries is somewhat similar to that of the corn belt of North America in that corn and wheat are the most important crops. These European countries receive less precipitation than the central or best part of the American region, being similar climatically to the drier western part of our corn belt.

In Rumania more than three-fourths of the people are engaged in agriculture, chiefly in the production of corn and wheat. Forty-five per cent of the land is under cultivation, and corn is the most widely cultivated crop. No other country in Europe and only two countries in the world, the United States and Argentina, produce more corn than Rumania. Wheat, barley, rye, and forage crops rank next to corn in acreage. The wheat is grown largely for export, since the staple food of the peasants is corn.[4] In a normal year, however, the corn and wheat production of Rumania is only as large as that of Kansas.

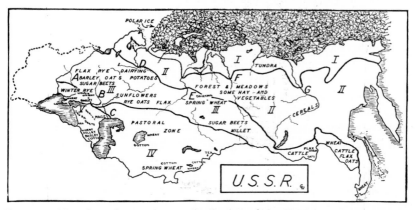

Fig. 176. Climatic regions and crop distribution of the U.S.S.R. The boundaries of the climatic regions and the distribution of the crops as indicated here are intended to give a very general picture. Regions: (I) tundra, (II) northern coniferous forest, (III) humid continental with short summers, (IV) humid continental with long summers, (V) arid and semi-arid region of middle latitude. Mountainous areas are not indicated. Rivers: (A) Dnieper, (B) Don, (C) Volga, (D) Dvina, (E) Ob, (F) Yenisei, (G) Lena.

Hungary, a country of 35,800 square miles, is smaller than Ohio. Most of its land constitutes an extensive plain, once the floor of an inland sea. This lowland, which also includes part of northern Yugoslavia, is the most productive agricultural area of Europe and is given primarily to wheat, corn, grapes, fruit, and tobacco. Much of the wheat is ground into flour at Budapest which is sometimes called the "Minneapolis of Europe."

The U.S.S.R. In the U.S.S.R. most of the area that has the humid continental climate with long summers lies on the drier margin of this climatic belt. Consequently, crops more drought-resisting than corn, such as wheat, barley, and sunflowers, occupy much of the cultivated land. Also, in the area that lies between the Black and

[4] Olaf Jonasson, "Agricultural Regions of Europe," *Economic Geography,* Vol. 1, January 1926, p. 322.

Caspian seas, the sugar beet is an important crop. The U.S.S.R. has only a small area of cultivable land that possesses sufficiently mild climate for many types of deciduous fruits and grapes. These crops are accordingly grown in areas where the climate is only moderately well suited to them. The most important apple-growing region of the U.S.S.R. is situated in the "Russian corn belt" mostly north and west of the Black Sea. Most of the Russian grape crop is grown on the drier margin of the humid continental climate with long summers or within neighboring parts of the semi-arid region that borders it on the south (Fig. 176).

North China and South Manchuria. North China and southern Manchuria, like their climatic counterparts in North America and Europe, are important agricultural areas, more than three-fourths of their inhabitants being directly dependent upon agriculture. These areas, however, produce relatively little Indian corn; but wheat, millets, beans, and grain sorghums, especially kaoliang, are widely cultivated. Climatically, these Asiatic areas are similar to the western drier part of the American corn belt.

In the North China plain (Yellow Plain) much of the soil is made from loess and does not encourage rice production (Fig. 129). Here the climate is too dry (24 inches at Peiping) and cool, and irrigation ditches are easily choked by the fine-textured loess soil. The loess uplands situated farther inland are even drier and have shorter frost-free seasons than the North China plain. These two regions, however, produce much of China's wheat, grain sorghums, and millets. In some districts more than three-fourths of the cultivated land is given to these three crops. Thus the winter-wheat acreage alone constitutes as much as 70 per cent of the cultivated land in parts of southern Shansi. In the drier northern parts of this province, millet is relatively more important than wheat. In those areas it makes up about 60 per cent of the cultivated crops; kaoliang 15 per cent; and oats, beans, peas, potatoes, and spring wheat the other 25 per cent.

The grain sorghum, kaoliang, is well suited to the environmental conditions of North China, where large areas are frequently visited not only by droughts but also by floods. It suffers much less than corn during seasons of drought, and it is able to withstand considerable flood water, whereas corn is quickly injured or ruined by standing water. Thus kaoliang takes the place of corn as a major large grain crop in the agricultural economy of North China.

FAMINES. In North China precipitation decreases in amount and becomes more erratic in occurrence with distance inland, and famines of varying magnitude have occurred repeatedly, according to the history of this area. Not only erratic climatic conditions but also other factors have caused famines in North China. Among the major factors are (1) the high ratio of population to the average productivity of the land, which permits little or no surplus for famine years; (2) the lack of good transportation facilities, which prevents an affected region from being supplied from remote districts; (3) widespread floods; (4) frequent and prolonged droughts; and (5) brigandage and incessant warfare between local military factions.

South Manchuria. Like North China, south Manchuria produces millets, sorghums, and wheat. But the crop which gives the region its distinctive characteristic is the soybean. Today Manchuria is "the soybean empire of the world," normally producing more than 100 million bushels a year. When the soybeans of China are added to those of Manchuria the total amount constitutes approximately 80 per cent of the world's production.[5]

REFERENCES

BAKER, O. E., "Agricultural Regions of North America—The Corn Belt," *Economic Geography*, Vol. 3, 1927, pp. 447–465.

CHANG, CHI-YUN, "Climate and Man in China," *Annals of the Association of American Geographers*, March 1946, pp. 44–74.

KISS, GEORGE, "T.V.A. on the Danube," *Geographical Review*, April 1947, pp. 274–396.

MILLER, G. J., and A. E. PARKINS, *Geography of North America*, John Wiley & Sons, 1934, pp. 229–238.

ROUCEK, J. S., "Economic Geography of Rumania," *Economic Geography*, Vol. 7, 1931, pp. 390–399.

SMITH, J. RUSSELL, *North America*, Harcourt, Brace & Co., Chapter XV.

STEWART, J. R., "Manchuria, The Land and Its Economy," *Economic Geography*, Vol. 8, 1932, pp. 134–160.

[5] Chang, Chi-Yun, "Climate and Man in China," *Annals of the Association of American Geographers*, March 1946, pp. 44–74.

Chapter 13

THE HUMID CONTINENTAL CLIMATE

WITH SHORT SUMMERS

LOCATION

This type of climate is situated to the poleward of the regions having the humid continental climate with long summers. In North

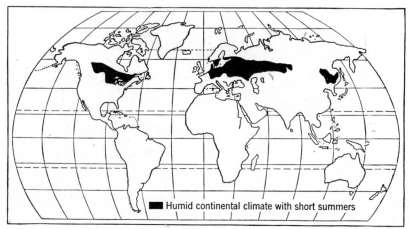

Humid continental climate with short summers

Fig. 177. The regions that have this type of climate occupy the poleward margins of the great agricultural areas of the northern hemisphere.

America it spans the gap between the humid continental climate with long summers and the northern coniferous forest, and it includes both the spring-wheat belt and the northern hay and dairy region (Fig. 177). In Europe it stretches in a long east-west belt and includes the most important grain-producing areas of that continent. In eastern Asia it practically coincides with northern and central Manchuria (Fig. 177).

438

CLIMATE

This climate, like that of the humid continental type of climate with long summers, is characterized by irregularity of weather conditions and by a summer maximum of precipitation. It differs from the latter type of climate in having lower average annual temperatures, lighter precipitation, and a shorter growing season.

The growing season of the humid continental climate with short summers lasts from four to five months. It is, therefore, too short for the production of late-maturing varieties of corn and in general for the production of corn for its grain content. But large quantities of corn are grown for silage. The growing season is also generally too short for the planting of wheat after corn harvest, and the winters are too severe for this crop. Spring wheat and other spring-sown grains are therefore relatively more important than they are in regions situated farther south. Winter precipitation is chiefly in the form of snow. This has been an advantage in forested areas where the lumbering industry has developed.

NATIVE VEGETATION

The native vegetation is directly related to precipitation, varying from grasses in the drier areas to mixed coniferous and deciduous forests in areas with more abundant precipitation. Thus in this climatic belt of North America the forests give way on the west to grasslands. In Europe the native grasses are found southeast of the forested areas, and in Manchuria forests give way on the west to the grasslands that extend far into the semi-arid districts of Mongolia. In all these areas forests occupy the parts with most abundant precipitation, that is, areas characterized by a wetter phase of this type of climate.

FOREST EXPLOITATION

The environment of the northern parts of this climatic realm is well suited to timber exploitation. The fall of snow is heavy, and it covers the ground for a relatively long time owing to the protracted period of winter cold. In the upper lake states of North America, where forest exploitation has been most marked, snow frequently comes in November and lasts until March, thereby affording a surface for the "skidding" of logs through the woods to favorable "landings" and for hauling the forest products to various logging centers. More-over, the winter cold of these northern areas is sufficient to freeze the swamps and soggy lowlands, so that man may go into them and obtain cedar for posts, tamarack for logs and pulpwood, black ash for barrel staves, and spruce for pulp and paper.

In North America, timber exploitation has gone on with tremendous speed, and indeed some areas have been completely denuded of their

Fig. 178.   Burned-over area in Michigan.   There is not only a loss of timber, but frequently topsoil is also almost completely ruined.

forests. At best it has been a process of timber mining, with little thought of the conservation of such a valuable resource (Fig. 178). A comparison of the original and present-day reserves tells a sad story. The original northern forest of the United States covered about 150,-000,000 acres of land and contained about 1,000 billion board feet of timber, of which less than 15,000,000 acres of saw timber remain.

Although this region is no longer the leading producer of lumber, the sawmill industry having passed to the South and the West, it still is an important source of pulpwood.   Many of the small, second-growth hemlocks, spruces, and fir trees are better suited for pulpwood than for lumber.   Many pulp and paper mills are now located in this area, especially in northern Michigan, Wisconsin, and Minnesota.

The forests of the former Poland, eastern Germany, and the south central Soviet Union [1] constitute the counterpart of the forests of

[1] South of the northern coniferous forest.

northeastern United States. The mixed coniferous and deciduous character of these European forests is reflected in the preponderance of such trees as pine, spruce, larch, fir, oak, basswood, and beech. The annual timber cut in sections of the U.S.S.R., in contrast to that of the United States, is much less than the annual growth. This is due mainly to the fact that many of the more extensive forests of the U.S.S.R. are found in undeveloped regions that are remote from means of transportation.

From the standpoint of present-day exploitation, the forests of the humid continental regions of Asia are among the most important of that continent. Large forests of virgin timber are found in Manchuria, including stands of fir, aspen, elm, oak, birch, pine, spruce, poplar, and larch. These attest the mixed character of the forests found in this humid continental type of climate. The development of highway and railroad transportation within Manchuria will bring a further development of lumbering activities, since most of these forests are accessible and the lumber will find a large market in the densely populated areas of the Far East. As a result of the development of the match industry in Japan, large quantities of poplar have been exported from Manchuria to be used as match-stick material.

AGRICULTURE

Agriculture is the dominant activity and the chief source of wealth of this climatic realm. No climatic region is more important in the production of small grain. The most important spring-wheat region of the United States, the chief grain-producing areas of Canada, and the most extensive grain fields of the U.S.S.R. are found in this type of climate.

Spring-Sown Hard Wheat. More than three-fourths of the spring wheat of the world is produced within this climate (Fig. 179). Three of the major regions—central and northern Manchuria, southeastern European U.S.S.R. and adjacent southwestern Siberia, and the region in north central North America that extends through western Minnesota and the Dakotas through Manitoba and Saskatchewan—grow spring-sown hard wheat almost exclusively. In general, these regions extend from areas where corn and winter wheat may be grown, or where the isotherm of summer is 70° F., northward to areas where the average temperatures of the summer months are approximately 58° F.

RELATION TO CLIMATE. In these regions the winters are long and cold, and the land receives so little snow that fall-sown seed would be poorly protected; hence wheat is sown in spring (usually March and April) rather than during the fall of the year. The planting proceeds from south to north with the advance of the season. In the United States this activity usually begins in the Dakotas when the normal daily temperature rises to 37° F. On the other hand, a crop like corn is not planted until the temperature reaches approximately 55° F. Indeed, wheat may be sown at a lower temperature than any other major spring crop.

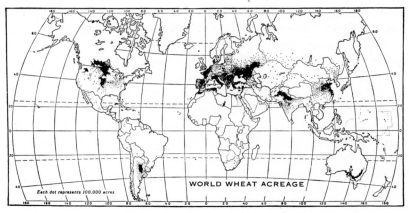

Fig. 179. Major wheat-producing areas of the commercial world, according to the Bureau of Agricultural Economics, U. S. Department of Agriculture. Each dot represents 100,000 acres.

The quality and chemical composition of wheat depend largely on the climate of the region in which this crop is grown. Wheat produced in the more humid areas has a tendency to be soft and starchy, whereas that grown in less humid climates is hard and dark in color. But in the major spring-sown hard-wheat regions precipitation is usually light and is associated with an abundance of sunny weather during harvest; hence the wheat is relatively low in moisture and high in gluten content. Before the time of modern milling, hard wheat brought a lower price in the world market than soft wheat, because of the difficulty of milling. Prior to 1870 the ancient process of grinding wheat between the upper and nether millstone was in use, which turned into middlings [2] much of the precious gluten of the hard wheat. In 1872 an emigrant French miller named Legroux devised an ap-

[2] The middlings are coarse particles of grain sifted from the fine particles of flour during the process of manufacture. Middlings are used as feed for livestock.

paratus for purifying middlings. Later, Hungarians invented a process of milling hard wheat which disposed of the ancient millstones—a process in which the wheat is carried between rolls of smooth and corrugated surface until the desired fineness is obtained.

LAND SURFACE AND WHEAT PRODUCTION. Soil and topographic conditions facilitate wheat production in these humid continental regions. The soils are largely dark-colored, easily worked loams and silt loams. A large part of the North American region contains fertile lacustrine soils of the glacial Lake Agassiz plain of the Red River Valley, whereas the fertile chernozem soils of Russia cover the spring-wheat area of that country. In addition, the level to gently undulating topography of these regions favors the use of large agricultural machinery, which is necessary in regions occupied by only sparse to moderately abundant populations. In fact, the local labor is insufficient to meet the demand during the harvest season, and there is an influx of laborers from other areas—in the North American region, from the winter-wheat areas to the south and the northern dairying region to the east. In the U.S.S.R., however, large machinery is less prevalent, partly because the population is relatively more abundant and partly owing to the poverty of the people. In the area of Manchuria, also, less large machinery is used than in the spring-wheat belt of North America.

INJURIOUS ANIMAL AND PLANT LIFE. Closely related to wheat yields is the presence or absence of injurious insects and fungus diseases in the wheat regions. Severe losses of wheat are caused each year by insects. Most important of these are the Hessian fly, chinch bug, joint worm, grasshopper, and green bug. Wheat is also subject to many fungus diseases, of which stem rust, leaf rust, stripe rust, bunt or stinking smut, loose smut, and scab are the most important. In severe epidemics the losses caused by stem rust alone sometimes amount to more than those caused by all the other diseases combined. This disease has ravaged the spring-wheat region of North America several times with great losses to wheat yields. In 1916, this rust destroyed approximately 180,000,000 bushels of hard red spring wheat in the United States and about 100,000,000 bushels in the prairie provinces of Canada. The common barberry carries one stage of this rust. Thus the U. S. Department of Agriculture and many north central states are now cooperating in a campaign to eradicate this plant.

THE SPRING-WHEAT BELT OF NORTH AMERICA. Normally the winter-wheat crop of North America, which varies from less than 600,000,000 bushels to more than a billion bushels, is somewhat larger than the spring-wheat production. The spring-wheat crop of this continent is grown primarily in Minnesota, North Dakota, South Dakota, Montana, Manitoba, Saskatchewan, and Alberta. This spring-wheat belt is probably more completely given to commercial farming than any other equally large region in the world. Here large-scale mechanized farming is at its best. On some of the most highly mechanized farms less than an hour of human effort is required to take care of each acre of wheat. Six hundred forty acres of land may be plowed, prepared for seeding, sown to wheat, and later harvested, threshed, and marketed, all with less than 640 man-hours of work. Under such conditions wheat may be profitably grown on land that will yield less than 5 bushels per acre provided the price of wheat is reasonably good.

Although wheat is the major crop of the spring-wheat region, several supplementary crops are grown. Oats, barley, and rye are grown throughout most of the region, while corn, especially for ensilage, is grown in the southern border. Flax is a cash crop, and potatoes are grown both for local use and for sale.

Because of the mechanization of agriculture, relatively few laborers can care for many acres of crops. The rural population is therefore sparse. Urban development has been retarded by the lack of large markets for manufactured goods, and also by the high cost of a good grade of coal and of many other raw materials.

SPRING-WHEAT BELT OF EURASIA. The largest spring-wheat region in the world is that of Eurasia, mostly in the U.S.S.R., the largest wheat-producing country in the world. The U.S.S.R. is unfortunately situated in high latitudes and possesses relatively few climatic types suited to agriculture.[3] This paucity narrowly limits the variety of crops that can be grown under optimum conditions. Therefore, in order to grow as great a variety of crops at home as possible, the U.S.S.R. is growing various crops in climatic belts that are poorly suited to them. Thus many kinds of crops are grown in her spring-wheat belt. Wheat, rye, barley, oats, flax, sunflowers, millet, sugar beets, potatoes, dairy products, vegetables, and even deciduous fruits are cultivated. Some of these crops are poorly suited to the humid continental climate with short summers.

Before World War II, the U.S.S.R. possessed many million acres of land located on the drier margin of the spring-wheat belt, especially east of the Ural Mountains, that had never been plowed. Much

---

[3] Turn to Fig. 71 and note the number of climatic zones suited to agriculture in the U.S.S.R. compared to the number in the United States.

of this land could be expected to yield normally less than 10 bushels of wheat to the acre. Such land cannot be profitably given to wheat except by use of efficient machinery. As soon as the U.S.S.R. becomes efficient in the use of large-scale machinery, her wheat acreage may be expanded materially. A large part of the spring-wheat region that lies east of the Ural Mountains has never been cultivated as indicated by a comparison of Figs. 176 and 179.

DIVERSIFIED AGRICULTURE DESIRABLE IN THE SPRING-WHEAT BELT. Over large parts of the several spring-wheat regions, wheat has been grown year after year on the same land. Growing wheat continuously results in depleted fertility and poor physical conditions of the soil, increased weed growth and accumulation of destructive plant diseases in the soil, lowered yields, and poor quality of grain. In the spring-wheat regions of European U.S.S.R. and central Manchuria, crop rotations are common. On the other hand, in the spring-wheat sections of northern Manchuria, Siberia, and the United States, crop rotations have been little practiced. In the more densely peopled southeastern part of the spring-wheat region of the United States, crop rotation and the raising of livestock are taking their place in the agricultural economy of the area. Local conditions determine the rotation and the crops chosen for it. A good crop rotation for areas with a sufficiently humid climate should include a legume and a cultivated crop. Cultivation keeps weeds in check and has a beneficial effect upon the soil, and it is a common practice not to plow the land after a cultivated crop, thus reducing the cost of sowing wheat. The legumes add nitrogen as well as humus to the soil; but, where the climate is too dry, difficulty is experienced in growing legumes and in rotting them in the soil in preparation for other crops.

The future of spring-wheat production looks promising. Expansion of wheat acreage may take place in all three of those major areas, especially in Siberia, in which one will find a large potential reserve of land well suited to wheat. Production can and will be increased whenever improved mechanization of agriculture and the price of wheat make such increases profitable.

Rye. Rye is one of the most adaptable of small grain crops, which accounts for its popularity in many parts of the earth, chiefly in the northern hemisphere. The world production of rye, however, is not so great as that of wheat, averaging about 1.8 billion bushels per annum in recent years, whereas wheat averages about 4 billion bushels.

DISTRIBUTION OF THE RYE CROP. A world map of rye output shows that Europe is the leading producer. There it is grown in two major areas—the sandy plains of Prussia, and north of the wheat belt of the U.S.S.R. Before World War I, the U.S.S.R. produced more than one-half of the world crop of rye,[4] and she still holds the leading place as a world producer.[5] Germany normally grows 250 to 300 million bushels annually. A part of the rye area of Germany is in the marine climatic region of northwest Europe, whereas the eastern part is located in the humid continental climate with short summers. The rye region of European Russia also is located in the humid continental climatic region.

In the United States, on the other hand, rye is comparatively unimportant, forming in recent years less than 1 per cent of the total value of the twenty principal crops. The people of the United States have a decided preference for bread made from wheat flour. This, no doubt, is due in part to the greater palatability of wheat bread, at least according to our standards, and in part to the fact that wheat flour can be worked up more easily and produces more attractive bread, cake, and pastry. As the preference of the American people is not in favor of rye food products, their production of rye is limited, being only about 5 or 6 per cent that of wheat.

RYE PRODUCTION AS RELATED TO SOIL AND LAND SURFACE. Although rye has been called "the grain of poverty" because it will grow on soil too poor for the successful production of wheat, corn, or barley, it thrives best on fertile soils. The rye soil of European U.S.S.R. is in part the fertile chernozem found in the wheat belt, and in part forest soil. Moreover, in two of the principal centers of production of North America—southeastern Michigan and North Dakota—it competes successfully with other crops for the occupancy of the best soils.

Most agricultural experts agree that, of non-legume crops for sandy soils, rye is probably the best.[6] It grows as well on acid as on non-acid soil and is much better adapted to sand than wheat, oats, or barley. The rye acreage of western Michigan, Wisconsin, and Minnesota is densest in areas of sandy and sandy loam soils.

The chief rye-producing regions of the world are extensive plains areas. Hence topography favors the use of large machinery in the production of this crop. In Europe, however, large machines are not so common as in the United States.

---

[4] *Yearbook of Agriculture*, U. S. Department of Agriculture, 1922, p. 501.

[5] *Foreign Crops and Markets*, No. 13, 1928, p. 402.

[6] A. R. Whitson and H. W. Ullsperger, "Sandy Soils and How to Farm Them," *Bulletin* 299, Agricultural Experiment Station, Madison, Wisconsin.

In the United States rye is commonly grown in the rotation after a cultivated crop. It is frequently seeded at the time of the last cultivation of corn or at the time of potato harvest; in other cases the corn field is disked after harvesting and rye is planted. These methods give fairly good results, but it is advisable to prepare the land as for other crops to secure a large yield. Moreover, disking or rolling fall-sown rye in the spring has materially increased the yield in rye-producing districts of the United States.

INFLUENCE OF INSECTS AND DISEASES ON RYE CROP. Rye is comparatively free from damage by insects. It is, however, subject to occasional infestation by the Hessian fly and joint worm, and to the inroads of grasshoppers and plant lice.

The only disease that causes serious damage is ergot. The black bodies which are sometimes found in the grain, or that come out in the head where the kernels should be, are ergot bodies. When planted with the grain, these bodies grow and cause further infection. Ergot must be carefully watched in milling or the flour will be of poor quality. If much ergot is present, the flour will be poisonous.

FUTURE OF RYE PRODUCTION. Although there are vast tracts of land into which rye production may be extended, this crop will not realize any material increase in acreage. In the United States, expansion of rye production has been most rapid in the spring-wheat belt. The risk of growing rye is generally somewhat less than it is with wheat. Rust and hot weather do not affect it so unfavorably, and the Hessian fly and other insect pests are not so likely to cause damage. Thus in recent years rye has become an important competitor of spring wheat, and a spring-wheat state (North Dakota) is the leading rye producer of the United States.

With plentiful supplies of wheat, the consumption of rye products is not likely to be largely increased in this country. Our own present domestic use of rye is rather narrowly limited. Rye grain is not especially desirable as a feed for livestock, although some of it is fed. The increase in rye production in the United States since 1912 has been due in great part to the enlarged foreign demand of rye-consuming Europe. Moreover, the production of rye would probably decrease very materially in some sections of the United States were it not for the value of the straw. In eastern New York, New Jersey, and Pennsylvania the straw is often as valuable as the grain. Rye straw, being longer and tougher than wheat or oat straw, is in demand as bedding for horses, and is also used in packing fruit trees, pottery, and many other products.

As a feed for stock, rye is not on equal terms with such grains as oats, barley, wheat, and corn. When fed alone or in large amounts, rye is likely to cause digestive disturbances. As a feed for swine, rye meal ranks a little below cornmeal. Cows that eat large amounts of rye produce a hard, comparatively dry butter. Care must be exercised in feeding rye to horses, as colic is likely to result. These factors in part explain why rye will probably not realize any material expansion in the near future. From an agricultural standpoint it is unfor-

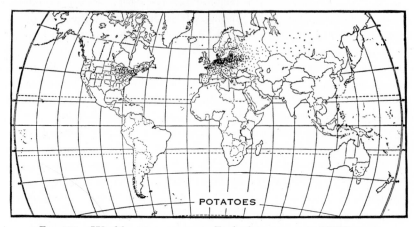

FIG. 180. World potato acreage. Each dot represents 25,000 acres.

tunate that local demands for rye are not larger. There is much land on which it can be grown to advantage, in fact to better advantage than wheat.

The Potato Crop. Although the potato is indigenous to the New World, it has, like corn, spread far from its original home, and at present this crop is widely distributed (Fig. 180). But a world map showing the potato acreage indicates that the largest potato-producing areas are concentrated mainly in a few major regions and almost entirely in the northern hemisphere. Of all these regions, that of Europe is most important. This area extends in the form of a large east-west trending belt from Prussia into the U.S.S.R. The western part of this region has a marine climate, but the larger part lies in the belt of the humid continental climate with short summers. The region of greatest potato production practically coincides with the area of maximum oats, rye, and flax production.

RELATION OF POTATO PRODUCTION TO CLIMATE. It is in part because of their relatively low summer temperatures that the world's major potato-producing regions practically coincide with the northern and central parts of the humid continental types of climate. The potato crop yields best where the temperature of summer does not average much more than 65° F., but the growing season must be more than 100 days in length.

RELATION TO SOIL AND LAND SURFACE. The potato thrives best on a deep, cool, fertile sandy loam. Such soil encourages maximum expansion of tubers and the development of potatoes that are high in quality. In general, this crop yields best on soils well supplied with potash. Thus frequently even peat bogs, when drained and supplied with potash, have produced large yields. A sandy soil, on the other hand, is often deficient in mineral plant foods, and consequently the yields are low, but the quality of the tuber is generally high.

Potatoes are grown on land with all grades of relief, from low peat-bog areas to mountain slopes and valleys. In the United States the crop is grown chiefly on gently undulating to rolling lands, such as are common in the northeastern part of this country. But the production has recently been extended into the level spring-wheat lands of the Red River Valley of the North, especially the outer beaches formed at the time of prehistoric Lake Agassiz. Gentle relief is greatly desired in our country where modern machinery is used. In Europe the largest potato acreage is also on gently undulating topography, but here modern machinery is used to a very small extent in potato cultivation, where planting, spraying, and digging are chiefly hand operations.

INFLUENCE OF INSECTS AND DISEASES ON PRODUCTION. The potato farmer has many worries, chief among them being the insect pests and fungus diseases which infect the potato plants. The most destructive of the fungus diseases is blight, the ravages of which are checked by means of spraying with the fungicide, Bordeaux mixture. Chief among the destructive insect pests are the potato beetle, the potato flea beetle, and certain plant lice. The first two are leaf-eating and the last are sucking insects. Quite frequently the potato grower makes a practice of combining with Bordeaux mixture the arsenical poison used in destroying the potato beetle, thereby providing a check for the ravages of the beetle as well as the injurious effects of early and late blights.

THE FUTURE. The outlook for the future world's potato crop is bright, and an increase may take place in various regions. But when an increase comes there is often a flooded market and prices fall, much the same as in the trucking industry. A glutted market is one of the dreads of the commercial potato grower. Nevertheless, production will always be on a large scale, especially in lands in which the environmental factors are favorable, because of the high food value of potatoes per unit area of land.

Other Crops. In addition to its conspicuous place in the production of wheat, rye, and potatoes, the spring-wheat climatic region is also an important source of oats, flax, hay, and barley. Oats are widely grown and are utilized mainly as a feed for livestock. Flax is grown chiefly in the area of the spring-wheat producing region in North America and in the European area of the U.S.S.R., the latter region being the world's most important source of flax fiber (about 60 per cent of the world's total). In Russia the area of maximum production of flax practically coincides with the oats region, north of which barley becomes relatively more important in the cropping system.[7]

The cool summers and extensive area of glaciation of these climatic regions suggest the widespread cultivation of hay. In the United States the area of maximum hay production practically coincides with the spring-wheat-belt type of climate and the New England region, and therefore extends in a long east-west belt from the spring-wheat area through the lake states to the Atlantic. In Europe it extends eastward from the marine region. In both these major regions of the world a widespread production of hay has been a dominant factor in the development of the dairying industry.

The Dairying Industry. The dairy belt of the United States, in the northeastern part of the country, is practically coextensive with the area of maximum production of hay. This belt therefore falls into two types of the humid continental climate—the more moist eastern part of the humid continental type with short summers and the modified humid continental type. Here the industry has developed mainly in response to (1) a climate that is well suited to hay crops and pasture, and (2) the largest concentration of urban centers in America, and therefore large markets for dairy products.

DAIRYING IN WISCONSIN. Wisconsin is the ranking dairy state of the United States. At one time the state's spring-wheat crop was more valuable than her dairy products. However, with the development of large areas of fertile lands farther west, the Wisconsin farmers adjusted their farm practices to a more intensive type of agriculture.

[7] See Olaf Jonasson, "Agricultural Regions of Europe," *Economic Geography*, Vol. 2, 1926, pp. 324, 325.

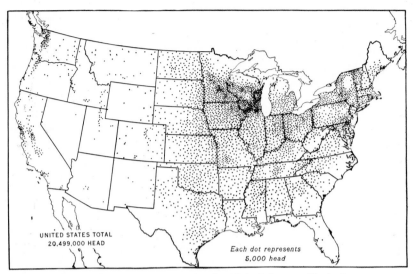

FIG. 181. Distribution of dairy cows in the United States. Each dot represents 5,000 head. (U. S. Bureau of Agricultural Economics, U. S. Department of Agriculture.)

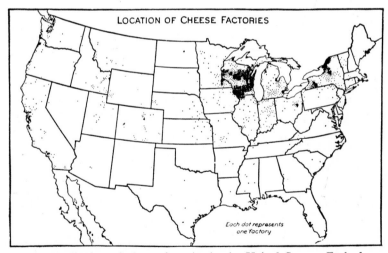

FIG. 182. Distribution of cheese factories in the United States. Each dot represents one factory. Note the concentration of factories in Wisconsin, also the grouping in the northern and southwestern highland sections of New York State.

Wisconsin has more dairy cattle (2,577,000 in 1945) than any other state. It produces more than three-fourths of the nation's total of foreign types of cheese (brick, Swiss, and Limburger) and approximately two-thirds of the American cheese manufactured in this country (Figs. 181 and 182). Moreover, it is the source of 9 per cent of our butter. Such concentration of dairying within a single state reflects a combination of favorable environmental conditions. It attests (1) the abundance of suitable crops and pasture; (2) relatively cool climatic conditions during summer; (3) an abundance of good water; (4) proximity to large urban centers and therefore ready markets, especially Chicago; and (5) the presence of an agricultural population with long experience in the dairying industry.

In Wisconsin the average summer isotherm of 70° approximately bounds on the south the cheese regions of the state, and the cheese factories located between the isotherm of 69° and 70° are not numerous. The areas of commercial cheese production are further bounded on the south with approximate accuracy by the line of 150 days in the average growing season, except along the Michigan shore, where, although the growing season is long, the climate is cool. North of these climatic lines corn is not the dominant crop, since it sometimes fails to mature before frost; but instead, grass is more extensively grown, from two-thirds to four-fifths of the improved land in northern Wisconsin and the southern highlands being in meadow or pasture. The pasture encourages summer dairying and cheese production.

On the other hand, the southeastern part of the state specializes in the production of fresh milk. Here Milwaukee, Chicago (northern Illinois) and intervening cities demand large quantities of fresh milk, which is quickly transported on the many improved roads found in this section.

REFERENCES

Baker, O. E., "Agricultural Regions of North America—the Hay and Dairying Belt," *Economic Geography*, Vol. 4, 1928, pp. 44–73.

Federal Writers' Project, *Kansas*, Viking Press, 1939.

Hartshorne, Richard, "A New Map of the Dairy Areas of the United States," *Economic Geography*, Vol. 11, 1935, pp. 347–355.

Landes, K. K., and O. R. Bingham, *Resourceful Kansas*, University of Kansas, 1940.

Miller, G. J., and A. E. Parkins, *Geography of North America*, John Wiley & Sons, 1934, pp. 213–229, 238–246.

Smith, J. Russell, *North America*, Harcourt, Brace & Co., 1925, Chapter XVII.

TREWARTHA, GLENN T., "The Dairy Industry of Wisconsin as a Geographic Adjustment," *Bulletin of the Geographical Society of Philadelphia*, Vol. 23, 1925, pp. 93–119.

WAINES, W. J., *Prairie Population Possibilities: A Study Prepared for the Royal Commission on Dominion-Provincial Relations*, Ottawa, 1939.

WOHL, PAUL, "Transportation in the Development of Soviet Policy," *Foreign Affairs*, April 1946, pp. 466–483.

Chapter 14

REGIONS OF MODIFIED HUMID

CONTINENTAL CLIMATE

Modified humid continental climatic areas are confined to only two regions in the world. One of these regions embraces the New England states and the maritime provinces of Canada; the other comprises the coastal parts of northeastern Korea, the neighboring southeastern coastal area of Siberia, the Japanese island of Hokkaido, and the northern part of the island of Honshu (Fig. 183). One is North American, the other is Asiatic. Both are east-coast regions in higher middle latitudes, and both are located to the east of the interior continental types of climate. Since they are situated to the leeward of large land masses, they receive the continental influences of the land together with the moderating influence of the sea. They are, therefore, commonly called modified humid continental regions.

THE CLIMATE

Precipitation and Humidity. By reason of their seaward location, the modified humid continental climatic regions receive precipitation that is more abundant and more uniformly distributed than that of the interior continental regions, such as the spring-wheat belt and the corn belt. In New England precipitation varies from 45 inches a year in the southern coastal districts to 30 inches in the north. Boston, Massachusetts, has an average annual precipitation of little more than 40 inches a year, with a difference of only 1 inch of rainfall between the wettest and the driest months. On the other hand, southeastern Siberia, northeastern Korea, and the east-coast regions of Hokkaido and northern Honshu all have a marked summer maximum of precipitation, the winters being comparatively drier (Fig. 184). These Asiatic areas receive their greatest precipitation when the summer

454

monsoons bring moist warm air from the adjacent oceanic areas. The chief exception to this general rule is to be found in western Hokkaido and Honshu.[1] These west-coast areas of the Japanese Islands have a

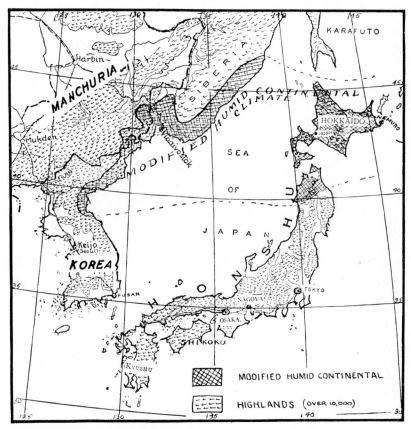

Fig. 183. Map showing Japan proper, Karafuto, Korea, a part of Manchuria, and southeastern Siberia. The heavily shaded areas show the extent of the New England type of climate in Asia.

fall and winter maximum of precipitation, since they occupy a leeward position relative to the summer monsoons and a windward location in regard to the monsoons of winter. During winter, cold air from the continent of Asia blows over the Japan Sea, undercutting the warmer stratum that surrounds the islands and forcing it to rise along the

[1] Only the northern part of Honshu has the New England type of climate. The rest of Honshu is humid subtropical.

slope of land. Thus, gloomy weather with snowfall prevails on the side facing the Japan Sea. Precipitation either in the form of rain or snow is experienced almost every day during the winter season on the west coast of Hokkaido and northern Honshu.[2]

Abundant snowfall is one of the major characteristics of the New England climatic regions. In the western coastal districts of Hokkaido and northern Honshu, snow covers the ground and a thick veil of

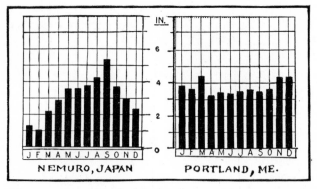

Fig. 184. The mean monthly precipitation in two cities that have the modified humid continental climate. Nemuro, Japan, is located on the eastern coast of Hokkaido. Although there is no month without rain at Nemuro, the rainfall is nevertheless greater during the summer half-year than it is during the remainder of the year.

clouds overcasts the sky during winter. In some districts the houses have prolonged eaves, the ground under them being the only thoroughfare for the people, since snow often covers the streets to a considerable depth. The roofs of houses are designed to shed the load. Transportation is seriously handicapped. Similarly in New England and maritime Canada, winter snowfall necessitates the expenditure of considerable energy and often involves great expense in keeping the highways open to traffic. Ice and sleet are commonly associated with the New England "northeasters," causing damage to trees, shrubs, and telephone poles and wires.

In both the Asiatic and North American regions the winter storminess is due mainly to the greater intensity of cyclonic storms. Both regions are affected by cyclones (low-pressure areas) and anticyclones (high-pressure areas). Cyclonic storms are well known and have long

[2] D. R. Bergsmark, *The Economic Geography of Asia*, Prentice-Hall, 1935, pp. 381–383.

been studied in North America. They have been less thoroughly studied in Asia. Yet in both regions they are an important factor in causing changes in the weather from day to day. In the Asiatic region, however, these storms are smaller and on the whole less intense. During winter the cyclonic storms of the Asiatic region appear to come from the Yangtze Kiang Basin of China and move northeastward. Some of them cross the Japan Sea, and others follow the eastern coast of the Japanese Islands.[3] Their tracks tend to unite in Hokkaido, just as the cyclonic storms of North America tend to converge upon New England and the neighboring St. Lawrence Valley. In both regions the cyclonic storms are dominant in winter.

Fogs are often experienced. Maritime Canada and New England receive the cooling influence of the Labrador Current which flows from arctic regions along the eastern coasts of Greenland and Labrador and thence to New England. Winds blowing from the east bring cool weather, which is often piercing and unpleasant during winter. Winds that blow from the south and the southeast bring warm moist air, which is cooled as it reaches the Labrador Current. This cooling of the moist air causes fog. Similarly, in the Asiatic region the cool Okhotsk Current flows from arctic areas southward along the coast of northeastern Asia. The current divides in the northern islands of Japan. The western branch thus formed flows toward the continental mainland of Asia, whereas the eastern branch follows a course southward along the eastern coast of Hokkaido. When the warm, moist air of the summer monsoons is drawn northward over this cool ocean current, condensation takes place and fogs are created, especially in the east-coast region of Hokkaido.

Temperature. The temperatures of the modified humid continental climatic regions reflect the influences of the humid continental climates of the interior and the moderating effects of the adjacent waters. The average annual temperatures are approximately the same as those of the continental interiors in the same latitudes, yet the range of temperatures from season to season is less. There is little difference in the temperatures of winter, when cyclonic control is dominant in both the continental interiors and in these east-coast regions. In eastern Asia the vigorous outblowing winter monsoons reinforce the westerlies and cause a considerable drop in temperature. At that time of year the cyclonic storms are also most active. During summer, on the other

[3] Glenn T. Trewartha, *A Reconnaissance Geography of Japan,* University of Wisconsin Studies, 1934, pp. 16–20.

hand, there is a milder and more intermittent indraft of air. It is also a season of weakened cyclonic storms. In North America the summer is characterized by rapidly rising temperatures in the continental interior. Yet the modifying influence of the Atlantic does not extend far inland because the prevailing wind is from the interior. Thus, the summers of humid continental regions are decidedly less hot and the winters are somewhat less cold than continental interior places in the same latitudes. On the other hand, the range in temperature from season to season is greater than that of west-coast climates in similar latitudes.

FIG. 185. Apple orchards in the Annapolis Valley of Nova Scotia. Fruit production is an important activity in many parts of the modified humid continental climate.

The frost-free period is from 150 to 180 days in length, or approximately as long as that of the corn-belt type of climate. But the cooling influence of the waters in part reduces the beneficial effect of a long frost-free season, though this cooling influence attracts tourists during the summer and is capitalized by some of the local inhabitants. Thus spring is usually long and protracted in the New England climatic region; the adjacent waters warm slowly and therefore the cold of winter is extended for a longer period in this coastal section. Fruit growers have taken advantage of this phenomenon, since the cold weather of spring inhibits the blossoming of the trees, and thereby tides them over the period of frost danger (Fig. 185).

During the fall of the year, on the other hand, when the land is cooling rapidly, winds from the ocean check the frost hazard and bring warmth to the coastal dweller. This climatic advantage is turned into account by growing late crops in some sections, such as tomatoes in the eastern part of Long Island.

SOIL RESOURCES AND THEIR USES

Soils of New England and Maritime Canada. The podzol is the dominant soil of the northern and northwestern parts of New England and the greater part of the adjacent provinces of Canada. The cool, moist climate and the mixed coniferous deciduous forests of these areas have favored the development of podzol, a soil that also extends into other northern forest regions, such as the northern coniferous forests of Canada and Eurasia (see pp. 95 and 100). In the undisturbed forested areas of New England and maritime Canada the A horizon or topsoil of the podzol contains a thin layer of organic matter above a gray leached layer. The B horizon or subsoil is generally more compact than the overlying A horizon. It contains much fine-textured material, iron oxide, alumina, and sometimes organic matter which has been removed from the gray A horizon and deposited in the dark-brown B horizon.[4] Together the A and B horizons—which constitute the soil or solum—have a total thickness of less than 3 feet. Much of the podzol land of New England and maritime Canada has remained in forest because the soil is either too stony or too sandy for profitable crop production. The finer-textured soils such as the sandy loams are planted to grains, hay, tubers, and other crops in support of the dairying industry. The best potato lands of New England are the Caribou podzols of Aroostook County, Maine.

In the southern and southeastern parts of New England, the brown and gray-brown podzols are the most widespread of the mature soils. Where they have remained undisturbed, as in forested districts, they have an organic mat on the surface, with a thin leached horizon below it. The leached horizon varies in thickness from about an inch in the poorer brown podzols to 8 or 10 inches in the gray-brown soils of the region. These soils also vary greatly in utilization. Stony and sandy areas of brown podzol remain largely in forest; many of the sandy loam areas are used for pasture, hay, and general farm crops; and the stone-free areas of fine-textured brown podzols of stream terraces are often devoted to truck gardens, especially near the large cities. All these podzolic soils (the brown and the gray-brown) are responsive to liming and to the application of organic matter and fertilizers.

[4] In general, podzols have developed eluvial A horizons (surface layers of removal) and illuvial B horizons (lower layer of accumulation).

Soils of the Asiatic Region. In the humid continental region of Asia the gray-brown and brown podzols predominate in the southern part, the typically gray podzols being found chiefly in the northern areas, such as the northern peninsula of Hokkaido. Over large areas the soils of Hokkaido have been derived from volcanic ash.[5] In some areas—mainly in the southern and eastern margins—the volcanic detritus is so young that soils have not had sufficient time in which to reach maturity in such parent material. In still other parts peaty soils are found. These include the unused moor peats and the lowland peats. The lowland peat soils are used chiefly for rice production.[6]

NATURAL VEGETATION AND FORESTRY

The New England Forests. These are much like the forests of the adjacent regions of the continental interior. In general, they may be divided into two major classes: (1) those of northern New England, where extensive areas of forest land still remain, and (2) those of the agricultural zone, in which the forested areas are narrowly limited. In the northern uplands the trees consist mainly of spruce, fir, pine, and northern hardwoods. Pine often occurs on the sandy soils; spruce and fir appear at higher elevations. High-grade pine and the larger spruce were cut in the early days. Then followed repeated cuttings, many areas having been logged several times. Recent lumbering for pulpwood has further reduced the timber stands, especially the softwoods. Hardwood or deciduous trees now occupy the land in many of the areas in which the original stands consisted mainly of softwood trees. On many of the upper mountain slopes and ridges, where fir and spruce constituted the chief trees, cutting has greatly depleted the timber reserves. In some places only a spindling stand of timber remains.

Fires have caused considerable damage by destroying the seed trees, the seedlings, and the seeds. Repeated fires may thus change the very composition of the forest. Hardwoods have, in fact, taken the place of the conifers in many of the burned-over areas. Hardwoods have the ability to reproduce through sprouting. They are, therefore, more resistant than the softwoods to complete devastation by fire. Yet a fire may be so severe that even the sprouting capacity of the stumps has been destroyed.

[5] D. H. Davis, "Agricultural Occupation of Hokkaido," *Economic Geography,* Vol. 10, 1934, p. 351.
[6] *Ibid.*

In the forests and woodlands of the agricultural zone there is much evidence of sprout growth rather than seedling growth; hence hardwoods predominate. Most of the old timber has been removed, and only in some places have old trees been carefully protected. Most

Fig. 186. A pulpwood landing in New Hampshire. Logging is a major winter occupation in many parts of the modified humid continental climate. (Courtesy U. S. Forest Service.)

of the forested areas consist chiefly of trees less than fifty years of age. In general the forests of this agricultural zone occupy the poorer soils, and they are owned by the farmers. Since these areas are accessible to the densely populated centers of New England, they have long provided raw material for local industries and for the farms. Overexploitation has characterized the forest industry in this part of New England. Only a small part of the original stand of timber remains. In some places the depletion of the forest has caused abandonment of farming, especially in the less fertile sections, where the small irregular patches of land could not support a farm family without some supplementary resource.

A large part of the New England timber is too small to be utilized for lumber, yet it is suitable for pulp (Figs. 186 and 187). This region, indeed, is one of the leaders in pulpwood and paper manufacturing in the United States. Similar development has taken place in the maritime provinces of Canada.

Fig. 187. Floating spruce pulpwood bolts in New England. (Courtesy U. S. Forest Service.)

In some parts of New England and in New Brunswick, one of the maritime provinces of Canada, an important early spring activity in the forested districts consists of gathering maple sap for the manufacture of syrup and sugar. The sap is obtained chiefly from the sugar maple, one of the finest of maple trees.

Forests and Forestry in Hokkaido. In the modified humid continental type of climate in Asia, the mixed coniferous and deciduous forests have been exploited on a large scale for only a relatively short time. Thus utilization of the timber resources of Hokkaido, the northern island of Japan, did not become important until the 1890's or 1900's. "Since that time, however, cutting has been rapid, and though there remain considerable areas of forest untouched by the woodman's axe, the not distant future will probably see a rapid decline in logging and lumbering. As usual in a new country logging methods are wasteful, taking only the best and leaving slashed and cut-over forests to disastrous fires, reminding one of early logging in Wisconsin and Michigan. The chief woods cut for lumber are oak and pine. The larger sawmills are near the mouths of the principal rivers, for most of the logs are driven down the streams, although now use is also being made of railroad transportation." [7] In the southern part of the island large quantities of spruce are converted into pulp in some of the largest mills of their kind in the Far East. [8]

AGRICULTURE

The Agriculture of New England. Agriculture is a major extractive industry in these climatic regions. It is characterized by an abundance of land devoted to hay, pasture, tubers, and small grains. Corn and wheat, the chief staples of interior humid continental climates, occupy a comparatively less important place in the cropping system. Coolness rather than length of growing season makes corn production less profitable (especially in the northern parts of these regions) than in the continental interiors. Moreover, this climatic region contains large areas of rough upland and poorly drained lowlands. Such areas are commonly poorly suited to grain production, but they can be utilized for pasture and hay. In general the environment favors the production of crops that may be used as feed for livestock, and the livestock industry is well developed, especially in the American region.

THE DAIRYING INDUSTRY. In this glaciated region with its small and irregular fields and its cool summer climate the dairying industry is the chief source of wealth. A large and rapidly increasing city population in this region provides a market for an enormous quantity of fresh milk. The cows required to produce this milk consume most of the hay which occupies the greater part of the crop land of this region. Cheese and butter manufacture, at least during the season of the summer surplus of milk, is a desirable adjunct to the market milk business and even a necessary one in some districts.

On the majority of the dairy farms of New England various other activities are associated with dairying. In most areas forest industries

---

[7] Reprinted by permission from "Hokkaido, the Northland of Japan," by W. D. Jones, *Geographical Review*, Vol. 11, p. 21.

[8] *Op. cit.*, p. 22.

of one kind or another occupy a part of the farmers' time (Fig. 188). For example, the family wood supply is usually furnished by the farm. Northern and central Vermont contains a large dairying-forest products area in which maple syrup and sugar are produced during one season of the year. On many of the New England hills, dairy farmers devote a part of their time to producing fruit crops, notably apples. Moreover, the farms of the interior experience higher summer tem-

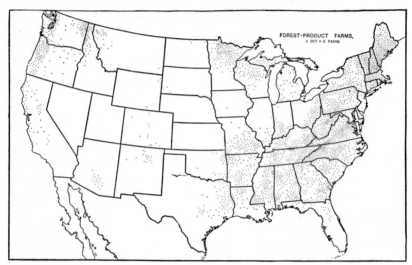

FIG. 188.   Over large areas in New England forest industries of one kind or another occupy a part of the farmer's time.   (U. S. Department of Agriculture.)

peratures and a drier harvest season. Large areas, especially in the northern part of New England, have summers that are too cool for the profitable production of corn for grain. Yet corn is grown for fodder and silage. Much of it is cut before it is ripe. Yet these climatic regions produce some high-grade corn. Thus, the production of sweet corn for the canning factories has become an important supplementary activity on many of the dairy farms of central and eastern Maine. As compared with wheat, crops such as oats, rye, potatoes, and hay are better suited to the natural environment of New England, especially the northern areas.

CROPS.   Hay is the most widely grown crop in New England. The bulkiness of hay, with the relatively high cost of transporting it, favor its production locally, especially since the development of the dairying industry.

Oats, barley, rye, and field peas are also grown as feed for dairy cows. These crops are produced, sometimes for grain, but more often for hay or for green fodder. A mixture of oats and peas is sometimes sown. Occasionally oats, barley, and peas are sown together for grain, but the total acreage of all these crops is small.

Wheat and corn are little grown on New England farms. Like Wisconsin, this region formerly produced a considerable quantity of

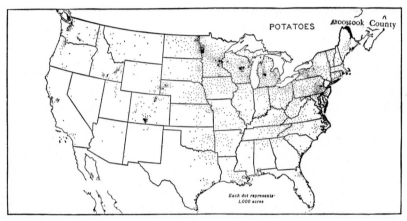

Fig. 189. Distribution of the potato acreage in the United States. Note the concentration in Aroostook, Maine. (Bureau of Agricultural Economics, U. S. Department of Agriculture.)

wheat. The reduction of acreage is probably due to the need of good land for the growing trucking industry and competition with wheat-producing lands farther west.

It was largely competition with the West that drove New England from the production of small grains. Western farmers, with their large fields and level lands, had a distinct advantage in the utilization of labor-saving machinery, and therefore in the production of grain at low cost.

FRUITS AND VEGETABLES. Although these crops occupy but little land in the New England region, they are an important source of farm income. Here both climate and nearby markets contribute to the development of the fruit and trucking industry. The large population to be fed renders truck farming and fruit growing logical agricultural adjustments. The advantage of production near market, especially for truck crops, enables New England producers to compete favorably with more distant regions. In fruit production the competition has a wider range, particularly in respect to apples.

In the production of potatoes one district, Aroostook County, Maine, is especially famous. The cool, moist, cloudy weather and the fertile, sandy loam soils of this county represent approximately the optimum climatic and soil conditions for potato production (Fig. 189). The average potato yield per acre for Maine during the ten years 1936–1946 was 281 bushels, whereas that for the entire United States was only 124 bushels. Unfortunately for the Aroostook County farmer, potato prices vary greatly from year to year and the seasonal income of the commercial potato grower is exceedingly unreliable.

The Connecticut Valley is as famous for tobacco as Aroostook County is for potatoes. In 1945, Connecticut and Massachusetts produced 22,000 acres of tobacco, much of it being grown under a cheesecloth covering. The cheesecloth is expensive and must be replaced every few years. Consequently only high-grade tobacco can be profitably grown under such conditions.

Although the Connecticut Valley is widely known for its tobacco crop, other crops—chiefly market garden crops—taken together occupy a larger acreage.

TREE-CROP AGRICULTURE. Large areas of New England are handicapped by rough land and poor soil and cannot compete with other regions of the United States in growing exportable crops. Yet there is room for considerable expansion in the production of tree crops. Some crop-yielding trees, such as the sugar maple and the apple, have already been mentioned. Still others, such as walnuts, hickories, chestnuts, and honey locusts, offer possibilities of more complete use of New England land, especially areas that are too rough for the plow.

Agriculture in Maritime Canada. In Nova Scotia, Prince Edward Island, and New Brunswick a mixed crop and animal type of farming predominates. The cool, moist, New England climate favors the production of grasses, tubers, and cool-season cereal crops. In some places the soil moisture supply is too great for cereals, and tubers, although it is satisfactory for the growth of hay. High tides in the Bay of Fundy cause rivers in the adjacent lowlands of New Brunswick and Nova Scotia to overflow their banks. Much of this land has been reclaimed by diking. Without diking such land is suitable for the production of hay; diking makes possible the production of still other crops.

Like New England, maritime Canada has most of its farm land in pasture, oats, hay, and root crops. The livestock industry is well developed, especially dairying. Moreover, like New England, this Canadian region has certain agricultural specialties. Thus the chief money crop of Prince Edward Island is potatoes. In addition, the island is noted for its output of silver foxes. The chief type of specialized farming in Nova Scotia is the production of apples. These are grown mainly in the Annapolis Valley, which is sometimes called the "Garden of Nova Scotia." As in many parts of southeastern Canada first settled by the French, the Annapolis Valley contains long narrow farms, which have meadow land in the bottom, orchard land midway on the slopes, and pasture and woodland at still higher elevations.

Agriculture in Hokkaido. The agriculture in the modified humid continental climate of North America and Asia possesses certain points of similarity. Such similarity is in part reflected in the agriculture of Hokkaido, the northern island of Japan. This island differs from the rest of Japan not only in climate, but also in major economic adjustments. "The climate of the main island [of Japan], excluding the northern portion, is similar to that of the Carolinas, in the eastern part of the United States Cotton Belt, whereas the climate of Hokkaido is much like that of New England." [9] Climatic similarity is in large measure matched by a similarity in types of crops grown, with the exception of rice, a crop that is often grown in Japan, even where physical conditions are unfavorable and where the production of this grain does not appear to justify the amount of labor that is required.[10] The widespread cultivation of rice reflects the requirements of the Japanese diet. Thus rice has become the most important cereal crop in Hokkaido, especially on the peat and peaty soils of the alluvial plains. The development of a 90-day variety of rice has made it possible to grow the crop even in the northern and northeastern districts. On the basis of purely physical conditions, such production could also take place in New England if the American people were very heavy consumers of rice. Nevertheless, rice is comparatively less important in Hokkaido than farther south in humid subtropical Japan. On the uplands of this northern island, oats rank first in importance among the cereal crops and in acreage nearly match the rice crop of the lowlands. Hokkaido reflects the modified humid continental climate also in its large acreage of land devoted to potatoes, a crop that is grown in all parts of the island. It is used as food for man as well

[9] W. D. Jones, "Hokkaido, the Northland of Japan," *Geographical Review*, Vol. 11, pp. 21–22.

[10] D. H. Davis, "Agricultural Occupation of Hokkaido," *Economic Geography*, Vol. 10, 1934, p. 358.

as feed for livestock. Hokkaido also has a better-developed livestock industry than the southern islands of Japan. Moreover, the greater part of Japan's apple crop is produced in Hokkaido.

RECREATIONAL AREAS IN NEW ENGLAND

New England has become one of the chief vacation lands of America. Atlantic coastal areas and the mountains afford respite from the heat of summer. Thus, along the Atlantic shoreline and the margins of the lakes in the White and Green mountains many summer resorts may be found. In the northern highlands, higher latitude combines with high altitude to make the region cool during the summer. Over the whole upland area, from Connecticut to central Maine, one will find important recreational lands, visited by thousands of people who seek rest and pleasure during the summer. The numerous lakes and streams of the forested uplands afford sites for camping, boating, fishing, and swimming. Also, during winter the frozen lakes and snow-covered highlands attract people who are interested in winter sports. In addition, New England contains many historic sites and old homes that are visited by many people each year. More than 20,000,000 people live within a day's journey of this region.

REFERENCES

BERGSMARK, D. R., *The Economic Geography of Asia*, Prentice-Hall, 1935, pp. 381–383.

DAVIS, D. H., "Agricultural Occupation of Hokkaido," *Economic Geography*, Vol. 10, 1934, pp. 348–367.

JONES, W. D., "Hokkaido, the Northland of Japan," *Geographical Review*, Vol. 11, pp. 26–30.

"New England's Prospect: 1933," American Geographical Society, *Special Publication No. 16*.

TREWARTHA, GLENN T., *A Reconnaissance Geography of Japan*, University of Wisconsin Studies, 1934, pp. 82–109.

Chapter 15

ARID AND SEMI-ARID REGIONS OF

MIDDLE LATITUDES

SEMI-ARID REGIONS

The sparsely populated semi-arid regions of middle lattitudes are bounded in part by areas of aridity and in part by humid lands. Although they are found on all the continents, these regions reach their largest size in the northern hemisphere. In North America a long belt of semi-arid land lies east of the Rocky Mountains and stretches northward into Canada and southward into Mexico. In Argentina a similar region extends from the Pampa and Gran Chaco westward to the Andes and southward almost to the extreme southern tip of South America. Even more extensive are the semi-arid parts of Eurasia, which flank the vast interior desert of that land mass. In the middle latitudes of Africa and Australia semi-arid regions cover relatively smaller areas, but here also their position between humid lands on the one hand and desert on the other places them on the margin of crop production and on the frontier of agricultural development (Figs. 71 and 190).

The typical semi-arid region is a sparsely populated area, where, owing to the scant and uncertain precipitation and to the extensive grasslands, stock-raising is the dominant activity and the chief source of wealth for the greater part of the population. Where crops (chiefly wheat) are grown they usually occupy the more humid parts of this realm. Thus in the Great Plains of North America there is a gradual increase in the value and amount of agricultural crops with distance eastward or toward the regions which have a humid climate (humid subtropical in the South and humid continental in the North). From an agricultural standpoint, the dividing line between the humid East and the semi-arid West practically coincides with the belt in which

469

the income from the grazing industry approximately equals that obtained from crops.

Semi-Arid Lands, the Frontiers of Agricultural Development. One of the distinctive features of all semi-arid regions of middle latitudes is their frontier character. In all these regions settlement is still in progress, and systems of agriculture adapted to varying geographical conditions found in these areas are not yet fully established. More-

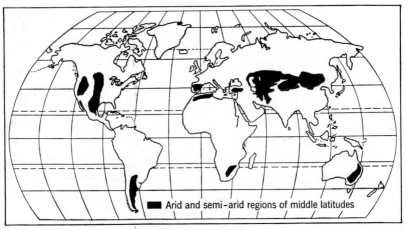

Arid and semi-arid regions of middle latitudes

Fig. 190. The semi-arid regions of the world represent marginal agricultural land where small fluctuations in seasonal rainfall may result in major changes in crop yields per acre.

over, much difficulty has been experienced in making a permanently favorable and satisfactory adjustment to the semi-arid environment, since most of the settlers have come from more humid lands in which rainfall is more abundant and crop production less precarious.

Even as late as the middle of the nineteenth century, geography books, magazines, and newspapers described the semi-arid region of the United States as a vast desert "incapable, probably forever, of fixed settlements." As late as 1858, an article in a leading magazine described the Missouri River as the eastern boundary of a "vast desert nearly one thousand miles in breadth, which it was proposed to traverse, if at all, with caravans of camels." [1] Today, however, the value of livestock and crops produced in this region is calculated in

[1] From an address made by F. D. Farrell before the American Association for the Advancement of Science.

hundreds of millions of dollars. But in this region, as in other semi-arid lands, the element of uncertainty is ever present—years of plenty are followed by years of dearth, frequently causing great losses to the farmers.

Similarly, in other semi-arid lands the frontier character is marked. In Australia vast stretches of such land were called "desert" until the end of the nineteenth century—land which at present produces moderate crops of wheat and provides grazing for large herds of sheep.[2]

From the beginning of the eighteenth century cattle drovers and farmers have been moving into the middle-latitude semi-arid region of South Africa, but much land still remains unoccupied. Typical of a large part of this region is the Great Karroo, which was visited first by Dutch cattle drovers, who pastured their cattle in the region after the summer rains. These cattlemen appear to have migrated from the Cape region of winter rain (Mediterranean climate), moving their goods and families from place to place in great covered wagons drawn by several yokes of oxen.[3]

Patagonia is the middle-latitude semi-arid region of South America. A large part of this region was held by aboriginal Indians until they were driven out by the campaign of 1879–1883. This campaign was intended to open the land to colonization. "Gradually settlement took place. In the northwest, the tiny irrigated spots of Neuquen attracted a first stream of settlers. Here the cattle trade with Chile proved so lucrative that for many years the economic interests of the territory leaned more to Chile than to Argentina. Along the Atlantic coast other groups found means for establishing settlements, while from the Magellanes territory of Chile came sheepherders to seek the pastures of Santa Cruz."[4] But this region remains a sparsely populated (less than 1 person per square mile) agricultural frontier of Argentina.

At present the semi-arid region of Asia is being settled in large part by people from the overpopulated lands of North China. In these vast semi-arid stretches of Mongolia the Chinese farmer is finding ample room for the grazing of livestock and the production of crops. Here still exists an agricultural frontier of China as manifest by settlements

[2] Griffith Taylor, "Agricultural Regions of Australia," *Economic Geography*, Vol. 6, No. 3, July 1930, p. 228.

[3] L. H. Halvorsen, "The Great Karroo of South Africa," *Journal of Geography*, Vol. 29, 1930, p. 290.

[4] Reprinted by permission from *South America*, by C. F. Jones, Henry Holt & Co., 1930, p. 360.

of large numbers of Chinese. Even dairying is becoming an important pursuit of the inhabitants of the eastern part of this area.[5]

Climate

In semi-arid lands the climate is generally unfavorable for maximum crop production, and in many parts of the realm even the grazing industry suffers. Scant and uncertain rainfall, extreme temperature fluctuations, destructive hailstorms, and strong desiccating winds are among the factors which cause the greatest losses of both livestock and crops.

Uncertain Rainfall. As generally used, the term "semi-arid" refers to areas receiving on the average from 10 to 20 inches of precipitation annually. But in determining the degree of aridity or humidity, evaporation must also be considered. Thus in southern Texas where the temperatures are high, the atmosphere dry, and evaporation rapid, much more than 20 inches of precipitation may be required to make a humid country; but 20 inches in the Red River region of North Dakota makes a distinctly humid climate. Climatological studies indicate that 20 inches of rainfall in the northern part of the Great Plains is equivalent to 30 inches of rainfall in the southern part, with its high surface evaporation. Moreover, the seasonal distribution and variations in amount from year to year operate more favorably in the northern than in the southern part of this region. Consequently, although the rainfall is less in the North, conditions there are climatically more favorable for crop growth than elsewhere in the region.

Where evaporation is slow a rainfall of 15 to 20 inches, if properly distributed, is sufficient for the production of middle-latitude crops; it is also sufficient for extensive development of the native grasses suitable for the grazing industry. But the precipitation usually fluctuates widely from year to year, the fluctuation being most pronounced in the drier parts of the realm. Where the average amount of precipitation borders on the minimum required for crop production, the variation from year to year is of major importance. The effect of drought is most serious in those regions where the average annual rainfall is sufficient for crop production, since settlers have established farms on which the crops flourish in years of good or average rain, but the crops may fail completely in dry years. Thus a station located on the Darling River in the wheat belt of semi-arid Australia once

[5] P. Wilm, "The Agricultural Methods of Chinese Colonists in Mongolia," *Chinese Economic Journal*, Vol. 1, No. 12, December 1927, pp. 1023 and 1025.

recorded no appreciable rainfall for thirty months, whereas the records of other years disclose a moderately abundant rainfall.[6] Bloemfontein, situated in semi-arid South Africa, has received as little as 15 inches and as much as 34.5 inches of rain a year.[7] When the rainfall is only 15 inches even the native grasses suffer in this region of rapid evaporation, but rainfall of more than 25 inches usually means luxuriant crops, and therefore a special attraction to settlers.

In the semi-arid Great Plains of North America there is a well-recognized tendency for precipitation records to show several successive years of comparatively generous rainfall, followed, in turn, by several years of deficient rainfall, and this renders farming by ordinary methods precarious in most of the drier western part of this region. Abundant crops in years of ample moisture encourage the western expansion of the cultivated area, but the records disclose the fact that these are only temporary conditions and are likely to be followed by years of drought when the rainfall is insufficient to mature crops.[8]

In the semi-arid region of inner Asia the precipitation occurs in a short period during the summer half-year. In some parts of this region, especially eastern Mongolia, the rainfall is concentrated in the months of July and August. Here some years are characterized by absolute dryness until the end of June, followed by excessive rains, creating unfavorable conditions for agricultural pursuits. Some years are almost rainless, but at times violent storms are experienced, as manifested by the deep channels, now dry, which the torrents have excavated.[9]

The precipitation of middle-latitude semi-arid lands is not only concentrated chiefly in the summer half-year, but it is sometimes violent and destructive. Thunderstorms occur frequently, and hailstorms do much damage to the agricultural crops. Moreover, lightning sometimes kills stock and sets fire to patches of grass. These are some of the adverse weather phenomena characteristic of drier regions, where insolation, radiation, and convection are very pronounced.

Seasonal Distribution of Precipitation. It is the rainfall of the crop-growing season with which the agricultural people are mostly con-

[6] W. G. Kendrew, *The Climates of the Continents*, Oxford University Press, Oxford, 1922, p. 362.

[7] *Op. cit.*, p. 75.

[8] J. B. Kincer, "The Climate of the Great Plains as a Factor in Their Utilization," *Annals of the Association of American Geographers*, Vol. 13, 1923, p. 72.

[9] P. Wilm, "The Agricultural Methods of Chinese Colonists in Mongolia," *Chinese Economic Journal*, Vol. 1, No. 12, December 1927, p. 1025.

cerned. Fortunately most semi-arid lands receive the greater part of their precipitation during the summer half-year (Fig. 191). In semi-arid Asia more than 80 per cent of the precipitation occurs during the summer months, and the Great Plains of the United States get approximately 80 per cent of their moisture supply during the six warmer

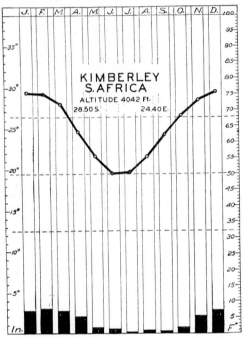

FIG. 191. Mean monthly rainfall and temperature at Kimberley, South Africa. Noteworthy is the pronounced summer maximum of precipitation.

months of the year.[10] It is during these months that the air holds most moisture and the warm land accentuates the inflow of air from the cooler oceans. On the other hand, during the winter cool air accumulates over the land and checks the inflow of moist air. Such winter conditions are most pronounced over Asia, where a dense blanket of cold air settles and gives that continent the highest atmospheric pressure in the world. As a result of the settling air and outflowing air currents there can be little or no precipitation during the cold season.

[10] J. B. Kincer, "The Climate of the Great Plains as a Factor in Their Utilization," *Annals of the Association of American Geographers*, Vol. 13, 1923, p. 70.

Temperature Variations. Temperature conditions vary greatly from one semi-arid region to another, and even within a single region. In general, regions that lie at a considerable distance from large bodies of water have the greatest extremes in temperature. Thus along similar latitudes, the interior (inland continental) semi-arid Great Plains of North America have a greater diurnal and seasonal range in tempera-

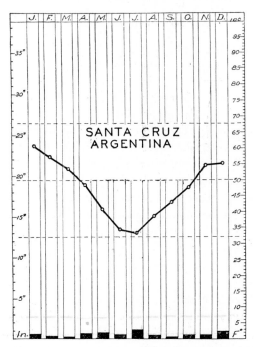

Fig. 192. Mean monthly rainfall and temperature at Santa Cruz, Argentina.

ture than the semi-arid coastal lands of Patagonia. In the former region the temperatures of winter frequently fall as low as 40° below zero, whereas the winter temperatures of semi-arid Patagonia, lying near the sea, are remarkably mild for the latitude (Fig. 192). The less rigorous winter of this area is a distinct advantage to the livestock industry.

Where semi-arid lands are located near mountains the temperature is sometimes modified by winds that blow down the leeward slopes. Along the foothills of the Rockies "the cold is often markedly modified by the familiar chinook winds and the western border of the region in winter is usually warmer, despite its greater elevation, than the section farther east." [11]   The chinook wind is known to have caused a rise in temperature of approximately 50° within half an hour.   It quickly melts the blanket of snow during winter, exposes the native grasses, and thereby provides pasturage for livestock.   Similar winds occur in Patagonia along the eastern base of the Andes Mountains where the westerlies, after crossing the mountains, develop foehn characteristics.

Native Vegetation and Soils

Native Vegetation.   The rainfall of semi-arid lands is generally deficient for the growth of forests, and trees are seldom found in solid stands except along streams or in lowlands where a sufficient moisture supply results from surface or underground flow.

Grasses, which constitute the dominant type of vegetation, vary in size and thickness of stand with the amount of rainfall and the soil and subsoil moisture available for their growth.   In general, tall grasses are found in solid stands only in those parts of semi-arid regions which receive the greatest amount of precipitation, as illustrated by the distribution of the vegetation in the Great Plains (Fig. 193).   Here from east to west the composition of plant cover shows a gradual change accompanied by a decrease in moisture supply.   In the eastern part of this region are found tall prairie grasses such as needle grass, bluestem, and sand grass.   Farther west these give way to wire grass and still farther west to the more widely scattered grama and buffalo grass.[12]   Likewise the native vegetation of other semi-arid regions shows a transition from solid stands of tall grass in the areas of greater rainfall and available soil moisture to short, widely scattered grasses in the drier parts of the realm.

Soils.   Closely related to the vegetation and climate of semi-arid regions are the soils.   (See pp. 95 and 102.)   These belong in general to the lime-accumulating soil division—soils in which lime carbonates accumulate somewhere in the profile, usually in the lower part of the B horizon.   Such lime carbonates owe their presence in the soil profile to the relatively small precipitation, and in the drier parts of semi-arid land the zone of lime carbonate accumulation lies relatively close to the surface.   This is well illustrated in the Great Plains of the

---

[11] *Op. cit.*, p. 74.

[12] For an excellent study of the vegetation of the Great Plains see H. L. Shantz, "The Natural Vegetation of the Great Plains Region," *Annals of the Association of American Geographers,* Vol. 13, pp. 81–107.

United States, in the eastern part of which the carbonate zone lies approximately 2 to 5 feet below the surface as compared with 12 to 15 inches in the drier western part.[13]

Corresponding to the variation in depth of the lime carbonate zone is a change of soil color. As a rule, the dark color predominates in

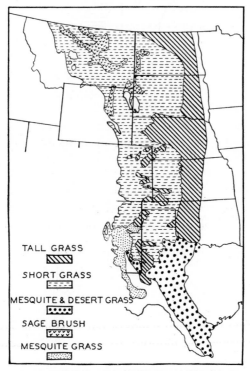

TALL GRASS

SHORT GRASS

MESQUITE & DESERT GRASS

SAGE BRUSH

MESQUITE GRASS

Fig. 193. Native vegetation of the Great Plains. (H. L. Shantz, "The Natural Vegetation of the Great Plains Region," *Annals of the Association of American Geographers*, Vol. 13, 1923, p. 83.)

the more humid parts of the realm—in areas of tall grasses and greatest depth of the carbonate zone. Indeed, in such areas the soil is often black, reflecting an abundant supply of humus. But the color becomes lighter in the drier parts of semi-arid regions, where much of the soil is light brown. In the Great Plains of the United States the black soils are farthest east and give way to very dark brown, dark

[13] C. F. Marbut, "Soils of the Great Plains," *Annals of the Association of American Geographers*, Vol. 13, 1923, pp. 41–66.

brown, and brown soils with distance progressively westward (Fig. 194). Favored by the accumulation of lime, well supplied with humus, and essentially unleached of mineral plant foods, these soils are considered fertile for agricultural purposes, and usually yield large crop

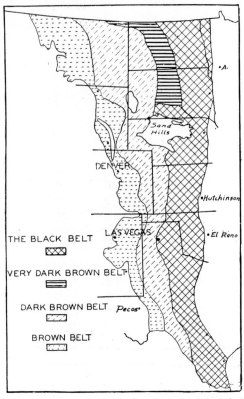

Fig. 194. Soils of the Great Plains. (C. F. Marbut, "Soils of the Great Plains," *Annals of the Association of American Geographers,* Vol. 13, 1923, p. 44.)

returns when they are supplied with a sufficient amount of moisture.

The chernozems of Russia further attest the fertility of semi-arid soils. These correspond to the black earth belt of the Great Plains and are among the most fertile soils of Eurasia. They lie in a major east-west belt and extend from the humid continental parts of European Russia eastward into Asia. South of this belt lie the chestnut-colored soils. Agriculturally, they are less desirable than the soils of the black belt, which contain more humus as well as a thicker top horizon.

According to Griffith Taylor the semi-arid southeastern part of Australia contains soils that are dark in color and similar in some respects to the black soils of Russia. However, "they are poor in nitrogen and humus as compared with Russian black soils, but in phosphoric acid are among the best in the world. They are uniformly deep." [14]

Native Animal Life

The wide distribution of native grasses in semi-arid regions favored the development of a great variety of herbivorous animals. Here the ungulates reached a high stage of development both in numbers and in kinds, especially in the semi-arid lands of Asia and Africa. In Asia the antelope, the gazelle, the horse, and the bactrian or two-humped camel are among the most important of these animals. No less than three kinds of horselike animals are found in the Asiatic steppe—the tarpan or wild horse (*Equus caballus*), Prejevalski's horse (*E. prejevalskii*), and the kiang or wild ass (*E. hemionus*).[15] Even more characteristic of the ungulates of the Asiatic steppe is the saiga antelope, an animal whose yellowish coat becomes white during the winter. The bactrian or two-humped camel is especially well fitted physically to withstand the harsh conditions of the drier parts of semi-arid lands. It feeds upon bitter, hard-fibered plants of the steppe and will drink saline and even brackish water. Moreover, within its two humps fat is stored when the steppe vegetation is most luxuriant, and the animal is therefore capable of withstanding periods of semi-starvation.

In contrast to those of Asia and Africa, other middle-latitude semi-arid lands contain a smaller variety of ungulates. In South America, within the human period, but before the immigration of the white, large ungulates were almost absent. No horse, no relative of cattle or sheep or antelope cropped the herbage of the Great Plains, but their place in nature was taken by enormous numbers of rodents, which reached a size not attained elsewhere. Again, in Australia no ungulate occurred, and the natural pasture was utilized by marsupials or pouched animals, of which the most important grass-eating form is the kangaroo.[16] Within the human period only a few species of

[14] Reprinted by permission from "Agricultural Regions of Australia," by Griffith Taylor, *Economic Geography*, Vol. 6, No. 3, 1930, p. 214.

[15] M. I. Newbigin, *Animal Geography*, The Clarendon Press, Oxford, 1913, p. 59.

[16] *Op. cit.*, p. 56.

ungulates inhabited the steppe lands of North America. Of these animals, the bison constituted the most widespread and important type roaming in countless numbers over the Great Plains of this continent. While the bison were being exterminated by the early settler during the last quarter of the nineteenth century, cattle and sheep were introduced in large numbers. In close pursuit of the bison was the wolf, a carnivorous animal found in large numbers also in semi-arid Eurasia. The wolf has been more difficult to exterminate than the buffalo was, and at present it and its cousin the coyote do considerable damage each year by killing the ranchers' livestock.

Some of the other animals, chiefly prairie dogs, wild dogs, and rabbits, are a distinct menace to agriculture in semi-arid regions. According to Griffith Taylor, rabbits were carried to Australia during the last quarter of the eighteenth century. These animals spread rapidly and became destructive to pastures and crops. In New South Wales the menace was well developed by 1883, and in the subsequent five years nearly £1,000,000 [17] was spent to counteract them. Since about ten rabbits eat as much as a sheep, the damage done by the rodents can be estimated. "Upon three stations in New South Wales (aggregating one million acres) the carrying capacity between 1880 and 1890 was reduced by 120,000 sheep. But, with poisoning, trapping, digging-out, and closer fencing, the rabbit menace is gradually becoming controlled in the chief pastoral districts of Australia." [18]

In the United States, control operations against injurious rodents are conducted by the Bureau of Biological Survey of the Department of Agriculture. In the semi-arid parts of this country, jack rabbits, gophers, and prairie dogs are widely distributed. These animals are particularly destructive to alfalfa, range grasses, and fruit trees. They also destroy cotton plants in semi-arid Texas, and throughout the region they ruin large quantities of stacked hay during the winter.

Utilization of the Land

Owing to the uncertain rainfall, the extensive native grasses, the cheap land, and the scarcity of labor, middle-latitude semi-arid regions are devoted chiefly to grazing. These regions contain some of the most important grazing lands of the world, and in most parts of these

[17] Approximately $4,860,000.
[18] Reprinted by permission from "Agricultural Regions of Australia," by Griffith Taylor, *Economic Geography*, Vol. 6, No. 3, 1930, p. 218.

areas livestock and their by-products constitute the chief source of wealth.

Sheep Most Widely Distributed. Of all the animals raised in the semi-arid regions sheep are most widespread (Fig. 195). Native to the dry plateaus of Eurasia, grazed for centuries on dry, hard-fiber grasses, these animals are a suitable type of livestock for semi-arid regions. Possessing a cleft lip, they are able to nip the short grasses close to the ground and thus survive periods of drought much better than most other types of livestock. Covered by heavy fleeces, they withstand the extremely cold winters characteristic of the poleward parts of these regions. Moreover, these animals furnish cheese, leather, wool, meat, and in some areas even milk—commodities that are essential to the comfort and well-being of the shepherd and his family.

Sheep are becoming increasingly important in numbers and value within these regions. In Argentina the increase of population and more intensive agricultural development have caused a gradual migration of sheep herders from the humid subtropical Pampa into semi-arid Patagonia. In Australia sheep were first raised along the humid southeastern coastal lands. Later with the development of a larger population calling for foodstuffs, sheep were forced out of the coastal region to make room for crops, beef production, and dairying. They were driven to the westward, beyond the mountains of southeastern Australia. Now the most important zone of sheep production on that continent extends from the mountains on the east to the desert on the west and embraces the middle latitude semi-arid region of that continent.

Cattle. Although cattle are found in all semi-arid regions, they are less numerous and less widely distributed than sheep. They are also found in relatively smaller numbers than in humid lands of middle latitudes and, as a rule, occupy those parts of semi-arid regions where rainfall is most abundant and the native grasses have the most luxuriant growth. Cattle, in contrast to sheep, are less able to thrive on short, hard-fibered grasses. Originating somewhere south of the Himalayas in a humid, warm climate, cattle adjusted themselves to a native vegetation that is more abundant and softer in fiber than the grasses of semi-arid and arid lands. Thus in Australia cattle are confined much more closely than sheep to the moist coastal parts of the continent.

Similarly in the Great Plains of the United States cattle are relatively more important in the eastern part, whereas sheep raising becomes increasingly more important with distance westward. "Most of the sheep are located in the arid districts along the Milk, Missouri, and

Yellowstone rivers in Montana, along the Little Missouri brakes and other rough lands in northwestern South Dakota, on the poorer semi-arid lands of northeastern Wyoming, in the North and South Platte Valleys of southeastern Wyoming and northeastern Colorado." [19]

Cattle constitute more than 60 per cent of the total animal unit in the Great Plains region, and 53 per cent of the value of all livestock (Fig. 196). Beef cattle are more important than dairy cattle in all

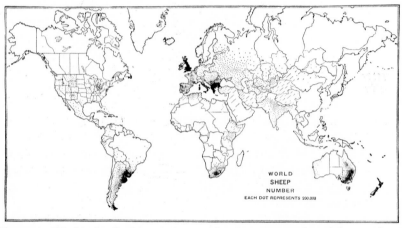

Fig. 195. World distribution of sheep. The importance of sparsely populated regions of the southern hemisphere is noteworthy. Here, distance from market and cheap land favor the sheep industry. The United States and Russia, although they contain large numbers of sheep, are relatively unimportant in number per square mile. (U. S. Department of Agriculture.)

parts of the region, except in the eastern, spring-wheat section of the black-earth belt, "where the two classes of cattle are about of equal importance." [20]

Crop Production in Semi-Arid Regions. Although the grazing industry is most widespread and constitutes the chief source of wealth in most semi-arid lands, the production of crops is increasing in importance. However, the percentage of cultivated land differs strikingly from one semi-arid region to another, and even within a single region. Thus the semi-arid regions of North America, European

[19] Reprinted by permission from "The Agriculture of the Great Plains Region," by O. E. Baker, *Annals of the Association of American Geographers*, Vol. 13, 1923, p. 150.

[20] *Op. cit.*, p. 148.

Russia, and southeastern Australia are relatively more important in crop production than the other semi-arid regions of the world. In all these regions the best and most extensively cultivated lands are found where rainfall is most abundant.

WHEAT, THE CHIEF CULTIVATED CROP. More semi-arid land is given to wheat than to any other crop. Especially significant in the produc-

FIG. 196. Cattle ranching in the semi-arid region of western Canada.

tion of wheat are the Great Plains of North America, southeastern Washington, semi-arid Russia, and Australia. The semi-arid Great Plains of the United States contain more than half the acreage of spring wheat of this country,[21] and in the western part of semi-arid Russia more than one-half of all the cropped land is in spring wheat.[22] In Australia, cultivation of wheat was first confined to the moist coastal area with its annual rainfall of 30 to 40 inches, but here wheat culture was not a success. The discovery that the drier districts inland were more suitable for wheat growing altered the position very much, and

[21] *Op. cit.*, p. 133.
[22] N. M. Tulaikov, "Agriculture in the Dry Region of the U.S.S.R.," *Economic Geography*, Vol. 6, No. 1, 1930, p. 66.

the bulk of the wheat is now grown in districts with a rainfall of 25 inches or less.[23]

REGIONAL STUDIES OF SEMI-ARID LANDS

The Great Plains of North America

Shut off from the moisture-bearing westerly winds by high mountain ranges to the west, located at a considerable distance from the Atlantic Ocean and Gulf of Mexico to the east and southeast, the Great Plains of North America constitute a semi-arid region covering more than 400,000 square miles of land. On the east this region gives way to humid continental and subtropical areas, on the west to highlands and deserts. The eastern boundary of this region coincides roughly with the meridian of 100°.

Wide variations in climatic conditions occur in the Great Plains. It is a region peculiarly subject to high winds, driving storms, and sudden changes in temperature. The light is intense and the relative humidity is usually low. In a large part of this region hail is of frequent occurrence and does much damage to crops.

Problems of the Early Settlers. The Great Plains region was settled chiefly by people who came from the northeastern part of the United States. These in turn had come mainly from northwestern Europe and had brought their agricultural traditions with them—a condition usually associated with great human migrations.

The story of the first three or four decades of settlement in the Great Plains region is a story of heroic struggle with a strange and difficult environment. The early settlers first tried to establish the kind of agriculture to which they had been accustomed in the humid northeastern states. Occasionally they succeeded, especially during times of unusually favorable climatic conditions, when rainfall was above normal and when grasshoppers, the great crop pest of that time, were not dangerously numerous. During such favorable periods, corn, soft wheat, and various other crops that the settlers brought with them yielded abundantly. But, in general as long as the settlers depended upon their traditional farming methods and crop plants they failed. The early failures made themselves felt not only in the new

[23] Griffith Taylor, "Agricultural Regions of Australia," *Economic Geography,* Vol. 6, No. 3, 1930, p. 224.

country but also "back East," as thousands of eastern people who held western mortgages soon learned.[24]

The Agricultural Regions of the Great Plains. According to O. E. Baker, the Great Plains of North America may be divided into four belts, in each of which there is a general uniformity in human adjustments as a result of uniformity in the environment, chiefly the climate, soil, and native vegetation. These are (1) the humid black-earth crop-farming belt; (2) the semi-arid farming-grazing belt, in which grazing is less important than crop production; (3) the grazing-forage belt; and (4) the series of disconnected arid, sandy, or rough areas, which when unirrigated are suitable only for grazing and the growth of drought-resistant forage crops on favorable sites. Only the second and third of these regions may be considered as typically semi-arid, since the black-earth belt is similar in several respects to the humid lands farther east, and the disconnected arid, sandy, or rough areas have much in common with the arid regions still farther west.

THE BLACK-EARTH BELT. "Largest in area and most important agriculturally is the sub-humid, black-earth, crop-farming belt. This is the first transition zone between the humid East and the arid West. It is one of the most productive agricultural areas in North America. The normally high fertility of the unleached soil just about balances the defect of frequently deficient rainfall." [25] The use of the land for crops is limited by topography rather than by climate. Thus the black-earth belt is a transition zone between the humid continental and subtropical regions to the east and the semi-arid west rather than a typical unit of the latter area.

THE FARMING-GRAZING BELT. Adjoining the black-earth belt on the west, the farming-grazing belt covers approximately 126,000 square miles, an area larger than the British Isles. "In this belt crop production, though uncertain, is more important than live-stock production, except in dry years, when the live-stock must provide most of the livelihood. One or two sections of land (640–1,280 acres) are needed normally to yield a comfortable living. The average size of farms in the belt is only 683 acres, but much land not in farms is used for

[24] Adapted from an address made by F. D. Farrell before the American Association for the Advancement of Science.

[25] Reprinted by permission from "The Agriculture of the Great Plains Region," by O. E. Baker, *Annals of the Association of American Geographers*, Vol. 13, p. 120.

grazing and if this were included the average size of farms would be about 900 acres." [26]

THE GRAZING-FORAGE CROP BELT. The third belt is the still drier semi-arid grazing-forage belt. The soils are typically brown to dark brown and the vegetation is largely grama grass. Here "crop production is precarious and the frequency of failure is sufficient to reduce the average acre-yield to about three-fourths of those in the farming-grazing belt and to three-fifths those in the sub-humid black-earth belt. Crop production, however, can probably be carried on with profit in favorable sites, particularly if extensive methods of cultivation are used and per acre cost is kept low." [27]

The more extensive agricultural practices in this belt are reflected in the necessity for larger land holdings. Two to four sections of land are usually needed to make a family-size farm. However, the average farm in this belt is slightly smaller (1,225 acres) than two sections. But relatively few of the farms in this belt are large enough to support a family in accordance with the American standards of living.

THE ARID, SANDY, AND "BADLANDS" GRAZING AREAS. Covered in large part by soils that are brown to ashy gray in color and vegetation that consists chiefly of short wire grass and grama grass, the arid sand and badland grazing areas reflect in the various factors of their environment the influence of a climate in which the rainfall is small and uncertain. Here the zone of lime carbonate accumulation lies near the surface, and in some of the more arid parts even the surface soil will effervesce upon application of acid. In these drier areas crop production is normally impossible, except by irrigation.

The drier lands in these arid areas are better suited usually to sheep than to cattle, and 5,000 to 10,000 acres are often required to support a family of average size. "On the 'benches' and in the less arid portions about 250 acres in the northern plains and 50 acres in the southern plains will carry one cow or steer in a system of year-long grazing, and the number of acres required per farm may be only 2,500 to 5,000. The aggregate area of these arid and badlands grazing areas is about 70,000,000 acres. Most of the irrigated land in the Great Plains region is found in these arid areas." [28]

Pastoral Activity in the Great Plains. The Great Plains possess a natural environment well suited for the grazing of livestock. The native buffalo was replaced by cattle, which today are the chief type

---

[26] *Op. cit.*, p. 122.   [28] *Op. cit.*, p. 123.
[27] *Op. cit.*, pp. 122 and 123.

of livestock of the Plains. The original cattle of this region, the Texas longhorns, were brought by the Spanish from Mexico. From Texas, cattle were driven northward, and the cattle-grazing industry spread in that direction, especially during the last quarter of the nineteenth century. Today cattle raising remains the dominant activity in the semi-arid portions of the Plains. "The Black-Earth belt, except the Corn Belt portion, has become and will continue to be for some years primarily a cash crop country, and probably the value of the wheat and other cash crops in the Farming-Grazing belt will equal the value of the annual production of live-stock products for several years. But in the Grazing-Forage crop belt and in the non-irrigated portions of the arid areas live-stock production will undoubtedly remain the principal industry." [29]

Better grades of livestock are rapidly replacing the Texas longhorn, and a carload of longhorns now causes comment in various cattle-shipping centers, such as Kansas City. Now Hereford and short-horn cattle are the most common breeds in this region. Especially important are the Hereford cattle; they grow more quickly than the shorthorns under relatively harsh climatic conditions and in areas where the vegetation is relatively coarse.

On the whole, the Great Plains region is one of year-long grazing; but from the Panhandle of Texas northward heavy snows cover some of the ranges for limited periods, which interrupt winter grazing and necessitate feeding to prevent or reduce losses. It is also customary among many of the northern producers to supply feed in connection with winter grazing, especially when the range is short through over-stocking and insufficient fall rains. The southern portion of the region is more nearly a year-long grazing zone, owing to the lack of snow-fall. However, feed is often supplied during periods of range shortage, both in summer and winter, especially during the long droughts that are more or less periodic. It is the policy of stockmen throughout the region to utilize native pastures, as far as possible, during the entire year and thus avoid the expense of supplying hay or cottonseed cake, the principal supplementary feeds. In certain sections of the southern portion drought-resistant crops such as sweet sorghums and Johnson grass are used extensively as roughage, and the grain from kafir, milo, and feterita is becoming more common for fattening.

Crop Production in the Great Plains. Although many different crops are grown in this region, wheat is the most important and most

[29] *Op. cit.,* p. 145.

widely cultivated. Durum wheat, which gives a better average yield than other spring wheats and a much better yield in dry seasons, has become a common crop from Kansas north (Fig. 197). Turkey Red winter wheat has advanced into the dry country and is widely cultivated in the central part of the Great Plains. In the southern part of this region, cotton, sorghum, kafir, and milo are relatively more important.

FIG. 197. Large-scale wheat harvesting in a semi-arid section of Kansas. (Courtesy Chamber of Commerce, Salina, Kansas.)

As a forage and grazing crop alfalfa is increasing in importance. The early settler of the Great Plains needed something to take the place that clover occupied in the agricultural system with which he was familiar. Indigenous to the Mediterranean region, alfalfa is the oldest plant to be cultivated mainly for forage, and it has been grown for centuries in Asia and in southwestern Europe. High in feed value and in ability to withstand extremes of heat, cold, and drought, alfalfa is one of the fundamental factors in the livestock industry of the Great Plains.

FALLOW.   Many cultural methods have been tried in the Great Plains. A widely practiced method is called "summer fallow." Settlers in some sections fallow their land to destroy weeds and to hold soil moisture. Land to be summer-fallowed should be plowed in the spring or early summer, worked down immediately after plowing, and kept free from weeds during the rest of the season. This usually requires at least two diskings and several harrowings. In addition to the great labor required, it involves the loss of the land for a year.

Fallow land produces no crop the year that it is fallowed, while if planted to corn from 2 to 4 tons of corn fodder to the acre may be grown. In the northern and central parts of the Great Plains disked corn stubble has been found an excellent substitute for fallow as a preparation for grain. The corn crop requires only a little more labor than the fallow, and the small grains yield almost as well after corn as after fallow. Potatoes and other cultivated crops also are good substitutes for fallow in preparing the ground for small grain. Where winter wheat is grown extensively, some fallowing may be advisable. One year of fallow and two or three years of cropping usually will be more profitable than alternate cropping and fallowing. In general, however, the increased production of livestock is recommended, with the growing of considerable corn and the use of disked corn stubble instead of fallow for small grain.[30]

FUTURE OF AGRICULTURE ON THE GREAT PLAINS. After a careful, analytical study of the relation between crop yields and precipitation in the Great Plains area, E. C. Chilcott states that the Great Plains area has been and should continue to be chiefly devoted to stock raising. All agencies interested in the agricultural, social, and economic development of this vast region of more than 450,000 square miles should unite in bringing about conditions that will make possible the fullest development of its natural resources for stock production. Crop production should be aimed to supplement livestock production rather than compete with it.

For the homeseeker with small capital and without practical agricultural experience the chances of success on the Great Plains are remote. But where practical experience and adequate capital combine, and when real economic demand for increased agricultural production develops, the Great Plains of America are destined to become one of the world's greatest food-producing regions.[31]

[30] F. R. Babcock, "Grains for Western North and South Dakota," *Farmer's Bulletin* 878, U. S. Department of Agriculture, 1929, pp. 7 and 8.

[31] E. C. Chilcott, "The Relation between Crop Yields and Precipitation in the Great Plains Area," *Miscellaneous Circular* 81, U. S. Department of Agriculture, 1927, p. 94.

The Dust Storms. Prior to 1930 the high prices of wheat and other farm crops together with a few wet years brought about the greatest expansion of agriculture that had ever been experienced in our semi-arid lands. Grazing or pasture lands were turned under to supply the demand for wheat. Rich in plant foods and generously supplied with rains for several seasons, these new soils of the Great Plains added greatly to the wheat supply. But an oversupply of wheat brought lower prices in the world markets, and the wet years were followed by some of the driest years on record in the Great Plains. The cultivation of previous years had loosened the soil, leaving it in an excellent condition to be blown away. Dust storms followed with an appalling loss of surface soil. These storms have also been an impediment to transportation and business, and a great danger to life itself (Fig. 198).

During 1933 and 1934 local dust storms became increasingly more common on the Great Plains. On May 11, 1934, occurred the worst dust storm that our nation had ever experienced. This "black blizzard" covered nearly 1,000,000 square miles (about one-third of our total area), and, according to soil-erosion specialists, it swept about 300,000,000 tons of fertile top soil off the great wheat-producing plains. Other dust storms followed, but fortunately these were of lesser intensity.

Together these storms have caused the removal of billions of tons of fertile top soil in the Great Plains. In some places nearly all the top soil (soil to the depth of plowing) has been carried away by the wind; in other areas it has been deposited in piles around buildings, fences, and other objects in the landscape. Millions of acres of seed have been uncovered, and other millions of acres of farm land have been covered with enough dust to destroy the crops. Whenever precipitation is associated with one of these storms, muddy raindrops cover out-of-door objects with an unsightly film of dust. The dust-storm problem has, therefore, become one of nationwide concern.

If the soil-blowing hazard is to be overcome, the land must be used in such a manner that wind erosion will be effectively stopped. One of the best practices is to stop the extensive cultivation of the soil by returning large areas to pasture. Much of the sodland that was plowed during the period of rapid expansion of wheat cultivation in the Great Plains should have been left for grazing. Much of it was rough land, which in the long run proves to be more suitable for pasture grasses than for crops. In the central part of the Great Plains economical and practical methods have already been devised in many areas for the resodding of buffalo grass. Suitable tillage methods should be adopted

Fig. 198. Dust storm approaching (top view). Such "black blizzards" are largely the result of over-expansion of agricultural and pastoral industries of the Great Plains. Behind the storms will be left dust-covered homes (bottom view). (Courtesy Soil Conservation Service, U. S. Department of Agriculture.)

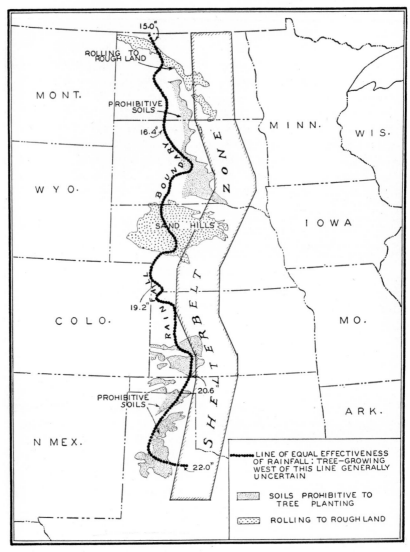

Fig. 199. The great shelterbelt zone which extends through North Dakota, South Dakota, Nebraska, Kansas, Oklahoma, and into Texas. In this zone shelterbelt strips have already been planted. Note the environmental factors that have been considered in determining the western boundary of the zone. (After U. S. Forest Service.)

on all areas that are to remain as crop lands. For example, tillage machinery should be used which will develop a cloddy, roughened surface and which will aid in incorporating stubble and other plant residue in the surface soil. Soil blows when it has become dry, loose, and finely pulverized, and when there is not enough decayed vegetative matter to hold it together. Hence a rough and cloddy surface soil well charged with organic matter is most desirable. In addition, trees may act as a windbreak, and at the same time the roots help to hold the soil. In 1934 the U. S. Congress appropriated a large sum of money for the relief of the people of the drought-stricken Great Plains. As part of the program, shelterbelts were to be planted on about a million acres of farm land within a 100-mile-wide zone extending from Canada to the Texas Panhandle (Fig. 199).

ARGENTINE PATAGONIA

Argentine Patagonia contains the middle-latitude semi-arid region of South America. Located to the east of the Andes, shut off from the moisture-bearing westerly winds, the Patagonian region occupies a position similar to that of the Great Plains of the United States. Like the Great Plains, it also trends north-south and slopes toward sea level with progressive distance eastward from the mountains. Both regions are sparsely populated. But there are points of contrast as well as similarity. Thus Patagonia is covered in part by flows of lava, which are quite fresh; the Great Plains consist almost entirely of sedimentary rock formations. In Patagonia the native vegetation varies from forest and mixed forest and grassland in the foothills of the Andes to sparse grasses farther east, whereas the more luxuriant vegetation is found in the eastern part of the Great Plains. Moreover, the cultivation of crops is much less extensively developed in the Patagonian region.

Sheep, the Chief Source of Wealth. Almost 10,000,000 sheep find pasturage on the sparsely populated lands of Patagonia, and this is about one-fourth the total number of sheep in Argentina. Sheep raising is the outstanding and dominant occupation, and the sheep herder is the lord of the land. Here the cultural landscape in some places reflects large ranches covering hundreds of thousands of acres, and ranch houses that are so widely separated that families may not see their neighbors for days or even weeks at a time. Thus the population is extremely sparse, being approximately 1 person for every 2½ square miles.

A large part of this vast region can support only 1 sheep to every 8 or 10 acres, which is about one-tenth of the carrying capacity of the eastern pampa, and this necessitates a wide ranging of the animals.

> In some sections, transhumance is well developed; the sheep of the plateau move from the winter pastures, when the water supply gives out, to the lower slopes of the Cordillera for the summer ranging; transhumance is practiced only by intrusos, who go from public lands of the tableland to unowned land of the Cordillera. Government concessions to permanent ranchers, who do not desire the migrating flocks, and who put obstacles in the way of the intrusos, are reducing transhumance; gradually both winter and summer range[s] are being controlled by permanent ranchers. Sheep grazed on these arid pastures yield only a medium quality of fair-grade wool, which becomes foul with dust and burrs. The location of a permanent supply of fresh water is the chief concern of the herders, and in some sections sheets of water have been tapped by wells, but none exist on the crystalline areas in the central portion or on the red sandstone districts farther west. On the western margin, wells are sunk in the valleys along the track of an underground stream. Along the eastern coast, south of the Rio Negro, deep borings give every ranch its sheet-iron tank and a tall windmill.[32]

SEMI-ARID SOUTH AFRICA

Located to the leeward of the Drakensberg and other folded mountains in South Africa and flanked on the west and northwest by areas of aridity, this semi-arid region occupies an elevated part of that continent. It is a land characterized by relatively few people, whose chief source of wealth consists of flocks of sheep and goats, of ostrich farms, and of cattle. Here the livestock feed upon scanty pastures, which remind one of the Great Plains and Argentine Patagonia.

The Natural Environment. The major part of this highland region receives most of its precipitation during the summer months of November, December, January, and February, and it is practically rainless during the remaining months of the year. Snow seldom falls and soon disappears when it has fallen, chiefly owing to the dryness during the cold season. As in other semi-arid regions the summer as well as winter precipitation is irregular in occurrence.

The more luxuriant vegetation and the greater amount of rainfall occur along the mountainous eastern part of this region, where the rainfall ranges from 20 to 30 inches a year. Precipitation decreases with distance westward until desert conditions are encountered along the entire western boundary. Here the small precipitation is insuffi-

[32] Reprinted by permission from *South America*, by C. Jones, Henry Holt & Co., 1930, pp. 366 and 367.

cient for any but the shorter grasses, the bunch grass of the desert. As in other semi-arid regions, the vegetation consists almost entirely of grasses and shrubs. There are no forests, and few trees are found except thorny acacias on the open plains and willows along watercourses. Since the precipitation within this region decreases from east to west, the native vegetation also decreases in luxuriance in the same direction.

The Small Stock Industry. As in Argentine Patagonia, the production of small stock is the most widely distributed activity and the chief source of wealth for the greater part of the population. Small stock production represents the most efficient use of this semi-arid region. Thus wool, mohair, and skins are major exports.

Most of South Africa's 40,000,000 sheep are found in this semi-arid region. Here the merino is the chief breed, being a fine-wool sheep which originated in the highlands and drylands of the interior Meseta of Spain. This breed shows well the conditions of its native habitat in its sensitiveness to excessive moisture and is confined almost entirely to the relatively dry parts of the earth. These sheep have been taken from Spain to Argentina, to semi-arid United States, Australia, and South Africa.

Goats, like sheep, are at home in dry lands and in rugged areas—regions where forage is scant and fibrous. But the goat is even hardier than the sheep in its ability to subsist on scant forage and in regions of tough topography. It has the added advantage of being a relatively large milk producer. In this region, however, the goat is raised largely for its mohair. The Angora goat, introduced from Asia Minor, finds in South Africa conditions very favorable to its development. The expansion of this industry has made goats more numerous than any other animal except sheep, and South Africa has become one of the world's chief mohair-producing regions, with the major production within this semi-arid unit.

THE SMALL STOCK INDUSTRY OF THE GREAT KARROO. The Great Karroo, a part of semi-arid South Africa, may be taken as typical of the larger area. From the standpoint of regional geography, the Great Karroo is a province which covers about 36,000 square miles and is inhabited by some 30,000 people.

The earliest systematic European invasion of the Karroo was by Dutch cattle drovers, who pastured their cattle in the region after the summer rains. These cattlemen appear to have migrated from the Cape region of winter rain to the interior region of summer rain from season to season, moving their goods and families from place to place in great covered wagons drawn by several yoke of oxen.

Apparently as a result of the occupation of the free grazing lands of the winter rain region by settlers of more or less sedentary habit, the roving Dutch came to spend more and more of the year in the Karroo. Since the forage is of the nature of browse, wool and mohair are somewhat easier to market than cattle where markets are distant in an arid region, the winters dry and relatively cool with very little forage, the drovers turned to sheep and goats. . . . Cattle are practically absent except in the somewhat better watered east.[33]

Small Amount of Cultivated Land. One of the marked features of the agriculture of this region is the small amount of land under cultivation. Thus in the Great Karroo less than 1 per cent of the land is in agricultural crops. This land is used chiefly for the production of forage plants, which are important in an area frequently visited by drought. Of the crops grown for forage and grazing, alfalfa is rapidly increasing in importance. It has high feeding value, and its long roots enable it to withstand periods of drought. Of other cultivated crops, wheat is most important—a characteristic fact of semi-arid regions in middle latitudes.

SEMI-ARID AUSTRALIA—A PASTURE AND PASTURE-CROP REGION

This region is similar to semi-arid South Africa in several major respects. Like that region it is flanked by humid highlands on the east and extends to desert on the west. It also is bounded by Mediterranean and humid subtropical lands on the south and low-latitude steppe on the north. Like the African region, it is important in sheep raising. But there are also contrasts between these two regions. Thus the Australian area is relatively more important in the production of wheat, and the raising of goats is of little significance.

Importance of Sheep. Near the close of the eighteenth century merino sheep were introduced into the humid subtropical coastal zone of Australia, where the first settlements were located. Here, however, the humid climatic conditions were not the best for the merinos, a breed of sheep accustomed to dry highland regions. As the population increased in this coastal region more foodstuffs were required and the sheep were forced out, giving room for more intensive agriculture,

[33] Reprinted by permission from "The Great Karroo of South Africa," by L. H. Halverson, *Journal of Geography*, Vol. 29, No. 7, October 1930, pp. 290 and 291.

the production of crops, dairying, and beef raising. The sheep industry moved gradually across the mountains of southeastern Australia, into the semi-arid region. At present this area raises more sheep
than any other region on that continent (Fig. 200).

This area, like most other semi-arid regions, suffers severely from
periods of extreme drought, the flocks of sheep being greatly reduced
by starvation. Thus Griffith Taylor writes about a great drought
which culminated in 1902 and resulted in a decrease of the total num-

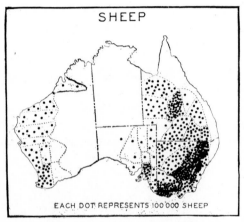

Fig. 200. The distribution of sheep in Australia. Noteworthy is the concentration of sheep in the semi-arid region of that continent. (After Griffith Taylor.)

ber of sheep from 95,000,000 to 55,000,000. But as more railways are
built, it will be possible to move the sheep to coastal regions where
feed is usually available. Thus the tremendous losses of the past are
not likely to recur.[34]

During the early days of the Australian sheep industry there was
only one major objective in commercial sheep raising—the production
of wool for the British market. In those days transportation was poor,
the local population small, and mutton almost worthless. With the
progress of settlement the open range began to be fenced for cultivation, chiefly of wheat. At the same time, progress was being made in
the construction of refrigerator ships, and in 1880 frozen meat was
first successfully carried to London. Cultivation of the land has increased its capacity to support sheep, and the foreign demand for

[34] Griffith Taylor, "Agricultural Regions of Australia," *Economic Geography*,
Vol. 6, No. 3, 1930, p. 236.

mutton has led to the introduction of English breeds and the production of cross-bred lambs.[35]

Wheat Production. During normal years Australia produces more than 100,000,000 bushels of wheat, a large part of which is grown between the desert and mountains of semi-arid Australia (Fig. 201). In this region, sheep grazing and wheat growing are the two major uses

Fig. 201.   Harvesting wheat in a semi-arid section of Australia.   The harvesting machines shown in this picture make a 10-foot cut of grain.   They indicate the introduction of large, labor-saving machines into this area.

to which the land is put.   Here the inner margin of the wheat belt is determined by aridity or the 10-inch isohyet, the outer limit by increasing humidity and more rugged topography (Fig. 202).   In this wheat-producing section, farms are large in size and usually cover more than 300 acres.   But not all this land is in crops.   Indeed, in much of the region only one-third of the area is under wheat at a time; and the dry farming methods of fallowing and careful tilth become increasingly important as the arid interior is approached.[36]

[35] V. C. Finch and O. E. Baker, *Geography of the World's Agriculture*, U. S. Government Printing Office, p. 135.

[36] Griffith Taylor, "Agricultural Regions of Australia," *Economic Geography*, Vol. 6, No. 3, 1930, p. 227.

SEMI-ARID EURASIA

Flanking the interior middle-latitude deserts of Eurasia, the semi-arid regions of that continent are among the most extensive in the world. One great east-west belt extends from the southeastern part of European Russia eastward to the Hwang Ho Basin of China, and covers an area of more than 2,000,000 square miles. Another large stretch of semi-arid land embraces much of Persia and Afghanistan.

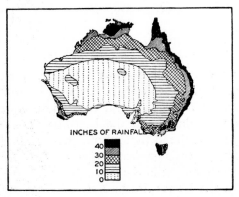

INCHES OF RAINFALL

40
30
20
10
0

FIG. 202.   Mean annual rainfall of Australia.   (After Kendrew.)

In general, these regions are covered by grasses and relatively fertile soils, and they receive a precipitation of 10 to 16 inches a year, most of which falls during the summer half-year. But very little accurate information is available for the greater part of these areas, the better-known sections being located in European Russia and in eastern Mongolia.

Features of the Natural Environment. In general, these regions contain soils that are relatively fertile. These have developed in a region in which the precipitation is small; hence they are not leached to the extent of soils of humid lands, and they are usually well supplied with humus, having developed under a cover of native grasses. Characteristic of the more fertile soils of these areas are the chernozems, soils similar in several major respects to the black earths of the Great Plains of North America.

As a rule, fluctuations in crop yields result not from the lack of plant foods in the soil, but instead from the quantity and distribution of the rainfall and from the availability of moisture in the soil. Thus in semi-arid Russia the precipitation varies from 10 to 16 inches per annum. The principal climatic disadvantages consist not only in the small quantity of precipitation during the year but even more in the irregular and uncertain distribution during the period of plant growth. For instance, the rain often falls after wheat and rye have completed their growth, and thus it is useless. In the semi-arid district of the Volga River Valley in Russia, the year 1909 had the lowest precipitation in a decade, but the crop yields were almost the highest in the history of the province. The explanation lies in the time when the precipitation occurred. Since this is a region in which spring wheat is the most widely cultivated crop, rainfall during spring and early summer is essential.[37]

Similar climatic disadvantages are found in semi-arid Mongolia, where the normal precipitation is sufficient. But it is frequently concentrated in six weeks of the summer half-year. Sometimes there is absolute dryness until the end of June, which creates extremely unfavorable conditions for agricultural enterprises, especially the production of spring grain. Even the later-maturing grain sorghums, millets, and corn are injured by such rainfall distribution, since these crops are retarded in their growth and are often unable to ripen before the time of early frost in the fall.

Agriculture in the Lower Volga Area. This area is typical of a large part of semi-arid Russia. This Volga region has experienced large losses of crops, and at times the government of Russia has been forced to take special measures of relief to save the population from starvation. Such conditions occurred in 1891, 1901, 1906, and again in 1911.

One of the chief reasons for crop failures in this region has been the irregular precipitation. As has been noted, early spring grains, particularly wheat, are the least resistant to spring droughts. In this region, spring wheat covers 55 per cent of the land. However, an increasing acreage is being devoted to sunflowers and corn—intertilled crops that mature later. Since the drought is commonly broken by rains in June and July, sunflowers and corn utilize these summer rains for their rapid development and continued growth. Corn can even utilize the August rain, which as a rule can be depended upon (Fig. 176).

Agriculture in Semi-Arid Mongolia. From the standpoint of crop production in this region, the factors of the environment can by no

[37] N. M. Tulaikov, "Agriculture in the Dry Region of the U.S.S.R." *Economic Geography*, Vol. 6, 1930, p. 61.

means be called ideal. The soil is of good quality, being a fine-struc-
tured loam. After bearing the steppe vegetation through centuries
it is abundantly supplied with humus and plant foods, which have not
been leached away in this semi-arid environment. But the climate,
with its marked extremes, often causes unsatisfactory yields. The
winter—a season almost without rainfall and having an average temperature below zero—is too long and too severe for the production
of any kind of winter crop. Vegetative growth starts very late in
Mongolia, and frequently the farmers cannot begin sowing before
June, since the first spring rains come late—a condition that is found
also in semi-arid Russia. Vegetation then springs up quickly during
the hot days of summer. But there are years in which the summer
is not long enough for the major crops of the region, barley, spring
wheat, millet, buckwheat, rape, and potatoes, to ripen completely.

ARID REGIONS OF MIDDLE LATITUDES

Location, Mountain Barriers, and Climate. The arid regions of
middle latitudes reach their greatest extent in the northern hemisphere,
where, in contrast to the hemisphere south of the equator, a large part
of the land lies in the temperate zone. In this northern half of the
world the major regions of aridity are found in western North America and in inner Asia. The North American region stretches northwestward from the intermountain plateau of northern Mexico, reaching considerable dimensions in the Great Basin of the United States.
This arid region of North America is flanked on its western side by
mountains that run transversely to the rain-bearing westerly winds.
These winds ascend the mountains and expend much of their moisture
on their windward slopes. Moreover, by reason of the compression
and warming of the air attendant upon its descent on the leeward side,
the basins and plateaus located immediately east of these mountains
remain arid. Only on windward slopes of ranges located within this
region is precipitation sufficient for the production of crops without
the aid of irrigation.

In inner Asia, valleys, basins, and highlands interlock. The drier
interior of the continent is flanked by highland barriers. The Tarim
Basin (eastern Turkestan), for example, with an average elevation of
approximately 3,500 feet above sea level, is surrounded on three sides
by very lofty mountains. On all sides it lacks available sources of
moisture supply. Thus air coming from the north moves from colder
to warmer regions and its moisture-holding capacity is increased.

Winds moving into this region from the east, south, and west descend the slopes of highlands and therefore are additionally capable of retaining and absorbing moisture.

To the north the Tarim Basin passes almost imperceptibly into the plateau of Mongolia, with its rainless district of the Gobi Desert. To the south the basin is flanked by the Kunlun Mountains. Westward and northwestward, it is separated from Russian Turkestan by the Tien Shan Mountains. These three regions—Turkestan, the Tarim Basin, and the Gobi Desert—comprise the important middle-latitude arid lands of Asia.

In South America a north-south-trending belt of middle-latitude desert is located east of the Andes Mountains, occupying a latitudinal position similar to that of Mediterranean Chile on the opposite side of the Andes. The westerly winds which give Mediterranean Chile a winter rainfall expend their moisture on the western slopes of the Andes, and upon descending the leeward side their moisture-holding capacity is increased.

Native Vegetation and Grazing. The greater part of these arid lands of middle latitudes is used for grazing, and animal husbandry is in general a pioneer enterprise of these lands. Where irrigation is lacking, the indigenous vegetation, composed mainly of xerophytic types, is more productive and also more profitably maintained than the ordinary field crops. Animals, easily transported from place to place, can be moved to favorable situations when the pasturage in a locality becomes inadequate. In addition, large areas of arid land are either too rugged or too high in salt content to make irrigation agriculture a profitable enterprise.

Of the various arid regions of middle latitudes, the lands of inner Asia are distinctive as pastoral areas. Here the thin, straggling herbage of summer supports nomadic peoples with their flocks and herds. In these areas pastoral activities may be traced back to ancient beginnings. In fact, goats and sheep, animals which now are widely distributed, are believed to have originated somewhere in the dry highlands of Asia.

Irrigation. As in the low-latitude desert, so in these arid regions of middle latitudes, irrigation makes cropping possible where quite commonly only the hardy desert shrubs could exist (Fig. 203). Although they may be handicapped in some respects, irrigated districts possess a marked advantage over many humid lands in that the water may be applied to the land just when it is most needed. Where temperatures are suitable, irrigation agriculture may be carried on continuously, thereby avoiding periods of enforced idleness common in lands that must depend upon erratic rainfall. In addition, many of the soils of these arid lands are relatively fertile. Since leaching is at a minimum, the mineral plant foods and lime have been preserved. Only the solvent influence of water is required to render these constituents

FIG. 203. Sage brush desert before irrigation, Klamath Project, Oregon-California.
(Courtesy U. S. Bureau of Reclamation.)

effective and thereby bring the desert land into line with other agriculturally productive regions. The record per acre yields of potatoes, sugar beets, and alfalfa in various irrigated districts of our West attest this twofold advantage: soils relatively rich in mineral plant foods, and proper watering of the crops.

IRRIGATION IN ARID WESTERN UNITED STATES. In western United States there are approximately 23,000,000 acres of land under irrigation, an acreage which is second only to the total irrigated area of India. This irrigated land of the United States lies west of the 100th meridian and is distributed mainly with reference to streams and catchment basins (Fig. 204). Here the rugged, mountainous surface of the land favors the storage of water, and the westerly winds expend their moisture on the highland slopes thereby supplying the streams and catchment basins with water.

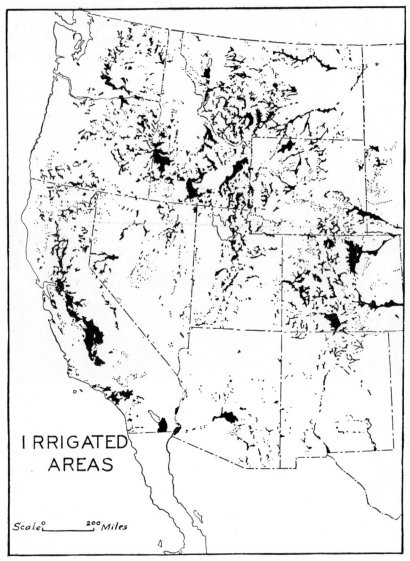

Fig. 204. The irrigated areas of western United States.

The irrigated lands of our arid West are devoted to a number of crops, some of which have been discussed in connection with the Mediterranean and low-latitude desert regions. Among the major irrigated crops of the middle-latitude desert areas of the West, alfalfa, wild hay, barley, wheat, corn, cotton, sugar beets, oats, potatoes, and fruit occupy prominent places.

Alfalfa is well suited to these lands. This lime-loving plant gets a good start on the little-leached soils and is capable of thriving even in a somewhat alkaline or salty soil. Alfalfa (Arabic: *al-facfacah*,

FIG. 205. Cutting irrigated alfalfa in the arid region of western United States. (Courtesy U. S. Bureau of Reclamation.)

good food) is also widely used as a feed for livestock in this part of the country, where large areas of land, because of rugged relief or difficulty of irrigation, are devoted to grazing. In these regions, alfalfa is an important winter feed. Moreover, because of the great amount of sunlight natural to these arid lands, the harvest may be gathered several times a year, and the yield is heavy (Fig. 205).

In contrast to alfalfa, which is produced mainly for local consumption, sugar beets and potatoes are widely grown as cash crops. In the Great Basin, the piedmont areas of Colorado, the Snake River Valley, and in the arid irrigated valleys of Idaho, sugar-beet production is one of the major activities of the agriculturists. Potatoes are also produced in large quantities in these areas, especially in the valleys of

Idaho, the Idaho potato being a well-known trade name in the eastern markets of the country (Fig. 206).

Apple production is a specialized enterprise in many of the irrigated districts of the West, reaching a marked development in various arid valleys of Washington. Here the Yakima and Wenatchee valleys, with their deep deposits of glacial materials and easy access to waters

Fig. 206.   Irrigated potatoes, King Hill Project, Idaho.   (Courtesy U. S. Bureau of Reclamation.)

for irrigation, have made rapid development in the production of this commodity. Other important commercial apple districts of the arid West are found in southwestern Idaho, northern Utah, and western Colorado (Figs. 207 and 208).

Major problems in irrigated districts.   Irrigation in the West, however, is not without risks. In some areas the irrigation causes an excess of moisture and waterlogged soils, and other areas suffer from an excess of alkalies. In some districts where the desert soil is porous the water sinks easily downward until it is brought up against buried layers of impervious rock. In the course of time this may lead to an accumulation of such a large quantity of water that the lower lands become waterlogged. This condition is quite common in the Great

Basin of the United States, where the basin character facilitates the movement of water to the lower parts of intermontane areas. One remedy for this superabundance of water consists of digging wells and open ditches, the waters of which provide extra supplies for irrigation.

Alkali refers to the presence of soluble salts in the soil in sufficient

FIG. 207. Irrigating an apple orchard in Colorado. (Courtesy U. S. Bureau of Reclamation.)

concentration to injure plants. It may, indeed, include salts which in small concentration are beneficial to plant growth as, for example, nitrate of soda. Experience has demonstrated that the alkali evil may be greatly aggravated by irrigation, and very often alkali salts appear in the surface soil in harmful quantities only after the land becomes irrigated. Much saline matter, such as sodium nitrate, may be dissolved in the underground water, and it may rise to the surface by the process known as capillarity, where, under the influence of the sunshine and dry air, evaporation takes place, the dissolved salts remaining on the surface as a solid precipitate.

Not all arid regions are affected by alkali, but arid conditions in general favor the accumulation of alkaline salts; in humid regions, the abundant rainfall, together with natural drainage, prevents this harmful accumulation of soluble salts. This observation of the general lack of injurious alkali in humid lands suggests a method that is effective in removing this substance in some arid regions. When the ground water of a field to be cultivated is found to contain an excess

Fig. 208. Showing the packing room of the American Fruit Growers of Yakima, Washington. (Courtesy *Better Fruit Magazine*.)

of alkali, this injurious substance may be removed by inundating the field with good (fresh) water. After the ground is sufficiently soaked, drainage is effected by the digging of suitable ditches, thereby washing out the alkali.[38]

Pasture versus Agriculture of Arid Asia. East of the Caspian Sea is situated a large area that is normally too dry for crop production without irrigation. Nevertheless these dry lands support large numbers of cattle, horses, sheep and camels. A large expanse of this dry steppe is required to feed a herd of cattle or flock of sheep. Conse-

[38] E. H. Carrier, *The Thirsty Earth*, Christophers, London, 1928, p. 157.

quently nomadic herdsmen are compelled to wander over large areas. Many deep wells are required to water the livestock since the region has few permanent streams.

The southern part of this zone is desert (Figs. 71 and 176) and is visited by hot, dry winds during the summer season. The soil is fertile and yields large crops when properly irrigated. Cotton is the major crop. The quality of the cotton is good and the yield per acre is large. Russia is now the second largest cotton-producing country in the world with an estimated output of 2,700,000 tons (10,800,000 bales of 500 pounds each in 1938).[39]

The Tarim Basin, located in the interior of Asia, is similar in various ways to the Great Basin of the United States. It is an arid region with an interior drainage system in which irrigation agriculture is one of the major activities of the inhabitants. Here the people have done their best with the water that is available, and along the edge of the basin at the foot of the Tien Shan Mountains there is a considerable number of oases, both large and small. These lie athwart an ancient caravan route like beads upon a thread. The permanency of these oases is due to the water supply obtained from the adjacent highlands, and to the configuration of the ground, which is of such a nature as to be advantageous for irrigation purposes. Among the oasis towns located in this area are Yarkand and Kashgar, cities that long have functioned as trade centers in this inner heart of Asia. The cultural landscape of these towns reflects low, flat-topped houses surrounded by gardens and fields of rice, wheat, maize, mulberry, cotton, and fruits. These gardens contain fertile unleached soils, which have developed in silt carried by winds and by irrigation streams in flood season.

The Arid West of Argentina. Although more than half the land of Argentina receives too little rainfall for the cultivation of crops without irrigation, only a relatively small area is irrigated. Much of this irrigated land is located in the arid west of Argentina, at the base of the Andean slope, where the soil contains relatively large amounts of coarse sand and gravel. In this arid region, water is obtained from the Andean streams, which flow out upon alluvial fans, supplying water to the irrigation ditches and canals. Here storage reservoirs of large capacity are not used. This part of Argentina has two specialties—the vine and the sugar cane. Here the provinces of San Juan and Mendoza

[39] James S. Gregory and D. W. Shave, *The U.S.S.R.—A Geographical Survey*, John Wiley & Sons, 1946, p. 190. *The Statesman's Yearbook*, 1946, p. 1223, gives a production of 10,760,000 bales of 500 pounds each.

together produce 95 per cent of the native wine. Vineyards are cultivated halfway up the sides of the alluvial fans found in these areas, the
gravel of the summits being too coarse and the bases too wet. Because
of the dry atmosphere of these irrigated areas the harvest may continue for as much as two months without any injury to the grapes.
In addition, the quality of the grapes, with their somewhat high
amount of sugar and low amount of acid, prevents fermentation taking
place without exterior aid.

Tucuman, the smallest province in Argentina, normally produces
more than three-fourths of the cane sugar consumed in that country.
But here production fluctuates widely from year to year mainly because of frost and extremes of drought. In fact, during years of
record production more than 900,000,000 pounds of cane sugar are
produced, whereas during poor years the yield has been less than
200,000,000 pounds.

REFERENCES

BABCOCK, F. R., "Grains for Western North and South Dakota," *Farmers' Bulletin*
    878, U. S. Department of Agriculture, 1929.
BAKER, O. E., "The Agriculture of the Great Plains Region," *Annals of the
    Association of American Geographers*, Vol. 13, 1923, pp. 109–167.
    "The Grazing and Irrigated Crops Region," *Economic Geography*, Vol. 7, 1931,
    pp. 325–364.
    "The Columbia Plateau Wheat Region," *Economic Geography*, Vol. 9, 1933,
    pp. 167–197.
CHAMBERS, WM., *A Geography of Texas*, Steck Co., Austin, Texas, 1946.
CHILCOTT, E. C., "The Relation between Crop Yields and Precipitation in the
    Great Plains Area," *Miscellaneous Circular* 81, U. S. Department of Agri-
    culture, 1927.
COLE, J. S., and O. R. MATHEWS, "Use of Water by Spring Wheat on the Great
    Plains," U. S. Department of Agriculture *Bulletin*, 1004, 1923.
GOODALL, GEORGE, *Soviet Russia in Maps*, George Philip and Son, London, 1944.
GREGORY, JAMES S., and D. W. SHAVE, *The U.S.S.R.—A Geographical Survey*,
    John Wiley & Sons, 1946.
HALVERSON, L. H., "The Great Karroo of South Africa," *Journal of Geography*,
    Vol. 29, 1930, pp. 290–291.
HOFFMEISTER, HAROLD A., "Alkali Problem of Western United States," *Economic
    Geography*, January 1947, pp. 1–10.
JONES, C. F., *South America*, Henry Holt & Co., 1930, pp. 366–367.
KINCER, J. B., "The Climate of the Great Plains as a Factor in Their Utilization,"
    Annals of the Association of American Geographers, Vol. 13, 1923, pp. 67–80.
LEPPAN, H. D., *The Agricultural Development of Arid and Semi-Arid Regions*,
    Central News Agency, Limited, South Africa, 1928.
MANNS, E. N., and JOSEPH STOECKELER, "How Are the Great Plains Shelterbelts,"
    Journal of Forestry, April 1946.

MARBUT, C. F., "Soils of the Great Plains," *Annals of the Association of American Geographers*, Vol. 13, 1923, pp. 41–66.

NEWBIGIN, M. I., *Animal Geography*, The Clarendon Press, Oxford, 1913, pp. 52–71.

PEATTIE, RODERICK, *Struggle on the Veld*, The Vanguard Press, 1947.

ROTERUS, VICTOR, "Spring and Winter Wheat on the Columbia Plateau," *Economic Geography*, Vol. 10, 1934, pp. 368–373.

SHANTZ, H. L., "The Natural Vegetation of the Great Plains Region," *Annals of the Association of American Geographers*, Vol. 13, pp. 81–107.

TAYLOR, GRIFFITH, "Agricultural Regions of Australia," *Economic Geography*, Vol. 6, 1930, pp. 213–242.

TIMOSHENKO, V. P., and C. F. MARBUT, "The Expansion of the Wheat Area in Arid Russia," *Geographical Review*, Vol. 23, 1933, pp. 477–483.

TULAIKOV, N. M., "Agriculture in the Dry Region of the U.S.S.R.," *Economic Geography*, Vol. 6, 1930, pp. 54–80.

VIVIAN, C. H., "Colorado–Big Thompson Project Progresses," *Compressed Air Magazine*, December 1946, pp. 314–320.

WILM, P., "The Agricultural Methods of Chinese Colonists in Mongolia," *Chinese Economic Journal*, Vol. 1, December 1927, pp. 1023–1043.

Chapter 16

THE NORTHERN CONIFEROUS

FOREST

Written by

HOWARD H. MARTIN

Head of the Department of Geography
University of Washington

Located northward beyond the waving grain fields and busy harvest-ing outfits of the spring-wheat belt is the first of the high-latitude

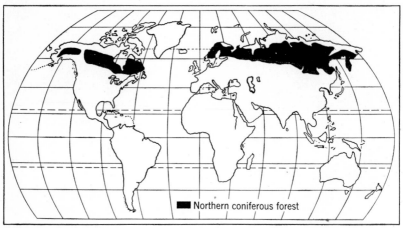

Northern coniferous forest

FIG. 209. The northern forests of both North America and Eurasia are largely undeveloped.

regions—the coniferous forest. This great subarctic belt is confined to the northern hemisphere and in America includes the forested in-teriors of Alaska and of Canada almost as far south as the St. Lawrence

512

River. In Eurasia this high-latitude region embraces those parts of central Sweden and Finland, and north central Russia and Siberia, where the forest is dominant (Fig. 209). Thousands upon thousands of square miles of this region are as yet practically unexplored and unmapped (Fig. 210). Bleak, frozen, and snow-covered during the long, cold winter, much of it a dripping muskeg swamp during the

Fig. 210. The natural landscape of a northern coniferous forest area located in Ontario, Canada. (Courtesy Department of the Interior, Canada.)

short, hot summer, this region has offered scant encouragement to the agricultural settler. A few valuable raw materials such as furs and precious metals have come out of it. But not until the era of twentieth-century man with his need for huge quantities of cheap timber, paper, basic minerals, and water power has there been any systematic attempt to develop all its natural resources.

CLIMATE

The climate of the northern forest is interior continental of the subarctic type with an extreme seasonal range. Seven months of winter and three months of summer are connected by a month of spring and an equal period of autumn. Winter is the dominant season, and throughout most of the region it comes early and stays late. In September, the temperature drops rapidly and severe frosts begin. On the poleward margins of the region they may occur even earlier than September, as at Dawson on the Yukon and along the Amur River of Siberia where a killing frost is usually expected before the last week in August. Snowfall begins in September, and before the end of November the forest is covered with the first layer of its annual blanket of snow. Month after month the steady, intense cold is broken only by snowstorms and by occasional waves of still colder weather. This is the region of the lowest temperatures ever recorded, −93.6° F. at Verkhoyansk, Siberia. A drop of 40° within a period of 24 hours is not uncommon.

The coming of spring is long delayed. Although the snow often begins to disappear in April, and growth of vegetation commences in May, the last drifts in the deepest woods are sometimes not entirely melted until midsummer. As late as June in northern Russia banks of snow may be seen on the wooded northern slopes. In spite of the unmelted snow, the seasonal transition period is short and spring rapidly merges into summer. On a northern river the break-up of the ice is the traditional beginning of spring. After the ice has gone out with a crash and a roar, a few weeks finds the region in the midst of a short but intense summer. Midsummer temperatures of 80° F. are common, and even 90° F. and over have often been recorded as far north as James Bay.

The range of temperature between winter and summer is one of the most significant features of northern climates. The record minimum in Siberia has already been mentioned; the town of Dawson has registered temperatures of −68° F. and of 95° F. Although in the southern margins and even in the central part of this region such extremes are not experienced, the average temperature spread is far greater than in temperate regions.

The extreme range in temperature is matched by the seasonal change in length of day and night. During the winter the nights are long and the hours of daylight correspondingly short. On the winter survey for the Hudson Bay Railroad the engineers would be at work long before daylight only to find the sun setting rapidly by three in the afternoon. But during the brief summer, daylight lasts from eighteen to twenty hours or even longer, for in July the sun rises at three o'clock in the morning and does not set before nine at night.

With the sun pouring down its rays for so many continuous hours each day, the land warms up to a remarkable degree. Summer days are often as hot as those of the continental spring-wheat or corn belts. The short nights are cool, however, and the northern half of the region is never free from the menace of frost; there may be a sharp drop in temperature nearly any night during midsummer. Frosts in June have often occurred around James Bay.

Precipitation is so slight, 7 to 15 inches annually, that except for the low rate of evaporation most of the region would be semi-desert. In fact, so little of the moisture is lost that tree growth and the production of certain of the hardier crops are possible. Nearly half the total annual precipitation comes in the form of rain during the three summer months of June, July, and August; the winter snowfall is sometimes so scanty that it is difficult to measure. The extremely dry, granular snow is quite unlike the thick blanket of wet, flaky snow common to middle-latitude climates. The amount of both summer rainfall and winter snow diminishes from south to north.

SURFACE CHARACTERISTICS AND SOILS

A large part of the surface of the northern forest regions consists of hard crystalline rocks, which constitute the remains of more extensive highlands on which erosion has taken place through geologic time. Materials removed from these highlands at present make up extensive sedimentary formations in adjacent areas. This hard-rock surface is found in the Canadian Shield (Laurentian Upland) and the Fenno-Scandian Shield of northwestern Eurasia. Such hard rocks weather at a relatively slow rate, especially in these regions in which chemical weathering is narrowly limited because of low temperatures.

The land surface of these regions is not only hard but it also reflects the effects of glaciation. The best soil was scraped off by the southward-moving continental glaciers, which have carved out many glacial lake basins. Northern Canada, Sweden, and Finland contain thousands of lakes and also swampy and marshy surfaces, sometimes known as muskeg. It is estimated that Finland contains more than 50,000 lakes of various sizes, its inland waters covering 12 per cent of the total area. Many of these lakes and swamps are the result of glaciation, Finland having been covered several times by the great ice sheets which spread out over Europe from the Scandinavian Peninsula as a center. The melting ice left its mark on the surface of the country, which today, in addition to the lakes, is thickly strewn with moraines, boulders, and gravel deposits. Much of Finland's area is unsuitable for cultivation and will probably never be put into crops.

The northern forest is considerably dissected by rivers, most of which flow northward because of the general slope of the land in that direction. The mouths of these rivers are, of course, therefore farther north than the middle and upper parts. Thus, while the southern, upper courses of the rivers and streams are melting, the lower parts remain ice bound, thereby creating undesirable drainage conditions. In fact, hundreds of thousands of acres of land, especially in northern Eurasia, become extensive, inaccessible swamps during a part of the year.

Over large areas the soils are the true coniferous forest, podzolized types (see pp. 95 and 100). They are mostly clays and light loams of relatively youthful profile, but amply fertile for the growth of forests and for the production of crops that can thrive under the harsh climatic conditions of high latitudes. The best soils are found mainly in relatively soft, sedimentary formations that flank the hard-rock shields and in basins created during glacial times. Glaciers receding northward sometimes blocked northward-flowing rivers to such an extent that lakes of considerable dimensions were formed. In these lake basins, sediments were deposited which in some areas have weathered into fertile soils.

Over considerable areas, soils are non-existent. As has been stated, the hard rocks weather slowly under the low temperatures of these areas, and in the past glaciers have removed much of the best soil. Moreover, where drainage is poor physical conditions do not favor the development of soils. It is partly because of the extensive areas of rock waste, swamp, and general paucity of soils that such small percentages of cultivated land are found in regions located within the northern coniferous forest.

Natural Vegetation. Upon the ancient hard-rock surface of the northland, blades of grass and small plants have grown in the sediment of crevices and have decayed to form the basis for still more plants. Shrubs and trees have fed upon the remains of those that have gone before. In places this deposit has taken the form of muskeg, a conglomeration of mushy roots and decayed vegetation which covers thousands of square miles of the region. In places the rocks are within a few feet of the surface; in others the muskeg is scores of feet deep. Except where the bare rock is exposed, or where muskeg, swamps, or lakes exist, there are usually thick coniferous forests, growing down to the rocks and spreading their roots like tremendous fans throughout the soil of former vegetation growths.

The best forest areas follow the general direction of the isotherms. As a result of variations in temperature and precipitation these areas shade into prairies or mixed hardwood and softwood forests on the south and into the tundra on the north. The trees nearest the tundra margin have been stunted to such an extent that the forests can never be of much economic value for their wood. Trees 50 years old may be only a few inches in diameter and less than 10 feet high.

Even throughout the better forest areas there are innumerable swamps, glacial lakes, and rivers. During the hot summer the stagnant muskeg swamp is an excellent breeding place for insects; clouds of mosquitoes and vicious swarms of black flies are a common annoyance to all who try to penetrate the swamp areas during the warmest months.

THE FUR TRADE

Trapping and the Fur Trade. As a material for clothing the skins of animals probably go farther back into antiquity than any other fabric. Primitive man was a meat eater, and when he slew a wild beast he obtained at one stroke both food and a covering of a thicker and warmer skin to protect his own. To modern mankind, clad in a variety of fiber textiles and insulated from cold by a number of ingenious devices, furs are not the necessity they were to the cave man of central Europe. But because of their beauty and superior heat-conserving properties, they are in as great demand as ever and are one of the most prized commodities man—and particularly woman— buys. Furs have consequently become a luxury garment in many lands, where they are worn more for their beauty, style, and costliness than because they are needed for warmth.

Fur-bearing animals are found nearly everywhere, not only in the cold zone and in temperate lands, but even in the tropics.[1] Cheaper furs tend to come from the warmer lands; those of the finest quality

[1] Monkey fur from the tropics and white fox from the northern ice cap are now auctioned at the same fur sale. From Louisiana with its subtropic climate there were sold in one year 7,000,000 pelts worth over $6,000,000, most of them muskrat, an animal exceedingly prolific and abundant in marshes. Pelts from Argentina, Paraguay, and Uruguay are collected at Buenos Aires for shipment, and furs from mountainous Asia are marketed through Bombay. Many of the best tropical pelts, however, are taken in high altitudes where the coolness of the north is partially duplicated.

and the highest value come from regions of severe winters, usually
the northern forest and, to a lesser extent, the tundra. The fact that
fine-quality fur is dependent upon cold climate is usually well understood. Not so well recognized is the relation between quality of fur
and the amount of forest cover. A trade commissioner of the Hudson's Bay Company states that the finest furs are obtained in the most
densely wooded districts, and the depth of coloring and luster of pelt
increase in direct proportion to degree of forestation, because of
shelter, shade, and better food.[2] Whatever else it may lack, the northern forest is ideally suited to the production of fine-quality furs.
Although many high-grade skins are taken in the tundra region, its
open coast and bare winter plains are poorly equipped by nature to
shelter and feed large numbers of animals.

Hunting and trapping was probably the first commercial industry
in the northern forested areas of both hemispheres. Long before the
discovery of America, the fur business was ages old in the forests of
northern Europe. In that period when the trade of the medieval
world centered in the Mediterranean Basin, furs from the Baltic were
part of every return cargo from Hanseatic ports. Siberian furs made
their way slowly through the devious paths of the interior until they
reached Moscow and Leipzig. Furs from north of the Amur were
bartered in Peking. In an age when houses were poorly constructed
and even baronial castles in southern Europe were bitter cold during
the winter, the importance of this trade to mankind cannot be over-
estimated.

Soon after the early navigators carried back to Europe the report
that there was a new fur-bearing land in the North American continent, fairly teeming with animals, there was a rush of exploiters across
the Atlantic. The eastward-flowing rivers offered access to a virgin
interior, but not one tapped such a rich field as the broad St. Lawrence.
The Indians, with their accumulated stores of beaver and otter skins,
were at once the object of much commercial zeal. Explorer, trapper,
and trader bought pelts for a mere pittance, and soon thousands of
bales of these skins began to flow back to the waiting markets of
Europe. Old stocks were purchased and the Indian was urged to
secure new supplies. Even fishermen from France and Spain, interested primarily in codfish of the Newfoundland banks, found time to
ascend the Saguenay and barter trinkets for pelts. Such was the value

[2] H. A. Innis, *The Fur Trade of Canada*, University of Toronto Library, 1927.
An excellent and authoritative discussion of the fur industry.

of the business that it was not permitted for long to go unorganized, and powerful companies were formed. A desperate struggle for commercial supremacy affected the North American continent from one end to the other. In this battle of the fur giants, the Hudson's Bay Company gradually won out and finally came to hold sway over the greater portion of forested Canada. Montreal, with its strategic location as a collecting as well as a shipping point, became the foremost fur center in the New World, and has retained this prominent position.

The earliest fur routes blazed by trapper and trader have long since become Canada's principal commercial routes, traversed by railroads and lined with permanent settlements. Trading posts have grown into modern cities. But new fur trails like outstretched groping fingers have penetrated even deeper into the unsettled back country, and new fur stations have been established to meet the pressing needs of the business. Around Hudson Bay, on most of the larger interior lakes, down the Athabaska, Slave, and Mackenzie rivers, the Hudson's Bay Company has located its posts. Even in the frozen tundra region and along the Arctic Ocean there is a chain of fur posts from the delta of the Mackenzie River to the coast of Victoria Land, a distance of more than a thousand miles. The log store of the Hudson's Bay Company is ever the last outpost of civilization in the Far North.

The trapping business of Canada is carried on mainly by Indians and half-breeds, with here and there a sprinkling of adventurous and hardy white men. Every fall before the rivers freeze over, thousands of trappers leave the posts with a store of supplies—flour, bacon, dried fruit, steel traps, blankets, guns, and ammunition—usually purchased on credit, and in quantities sufficient to last until the following spring. Winter is the trapper's work season. When land and water are frozen solid all the disadvantages and annoyances of swamp, muskeg, mosquitoes, and black flies disappear. This is also the time of year when pelts are "prime." The trapper makes a permanent camp on some northern lake or river from which he sets and runs his line of traps and hunts with rifle during the long northern winter. In the late spring after the break-up of the river ice he returns to the trading post with his winter's catch. The factory buys the furs, deducting the value of the supplies advanced, and for the trapper there ensues a summer of unemployment seldom broken until he sets out for his next winter's work.

The annual value of all pelts purchased from the trappers and fur farmers of Canada during the decade 1935–1944 ranged from $13,000,-

000 in 1938 to $33,000,000 in 1944. Approximately 95 per cent of these pelts were taken in the northern forest. Most of the remainder came from the Rocky Mountain area. More than 25 per cent of the pelts came from fur farms. Montreal is the leading Canadian market for furs, but auction sales are also held in Winnipeg, Edmonton, Toronto, Regina and Vancouver.[3]

The Fur Business in Eurasia. Fur hunting is one of the most profitable industries carried on by the scattered population through the area of northern forested Soviet Union. This area is one of the world's important sources of furs. Although there is no single organization corresponding to the Hudson's Bay Company with its chain of posts, the trading methods are quite similar to those of North America, but for the fact that the trappers often form bands of as many as 48 men to operate in a given area. Trapping goes on steadily throughout the winter until large stores of pelts are accumulated, and with the coming of early summer the trappers bring their stock to one of the Siberian rivers or to the railroad where skins are sold or bartered for goods and provisions. Traveling fur merchants formerly carried on large-scale buying operations over a wide territory, dealing not only in the more valuable furs such as mink, sable, and ermine, but in the cheaper ones as well. It is not uncommon for a single trader to buy as many as a million squirrel skins in a season. After World War I, furs became a government monopoly in Soviet Russia, and now they reach the market through official channels.

Riga, once an important outlet for the north Eurasian fur crop, is no longer Russian territory, and Moscow is the recognized primary market. Leipzig was for many years before World War I the best-known European fur market and the center of a large dressing and dyeing business. But when the war cut off the supply of Russian pelts, Leipzig lost its supremacy and has been unable to regain it. In normal times Peiping is also a buyer of Siberian furs.

Over-Exploitation of Native Fur-Bearing Animals in the Northern Forest. The rapidly mounting price of pelts after World War I caused a wave of intense and ruthless trapping which threatened the complete extinction of the more valuable furred animals. The increasing demand for furs resulted in the rapid depletion of the musk-rat, fox, raccoon, and skunk. Canada became alarmed at the rapid destruction of one of her most valuable industries—fur production—and passed a number of regulatory measures designed to preserve the

[3] *Canadian Year Book*, Ottawa, Canada, 1947, pp. 419–424.

native fur-bearing animals in those regions well suited to them but otherwise of little present economic value. Owing to the ignorance of many of the trappers and to the ease of evading the law, these regulations have been only partially successful as conservation measures.

Fur Farming. It has long been the practice in Canada for the trappers to keep alive, when possible, foxes caught in warm weather, until winter when the fur is prime. This method of caring for foxes resulted in the development of the modern industry of fur farming—

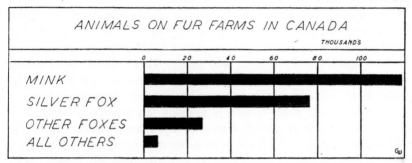

Fig. 211. Minks and silver foxes are the major fur-bearing animals raised on the fur farms of Canada. (Data for 1946.)

the raising of fur-bearing animals in captivity. The beauty of the fur of silver foxes, and the consequent high prices realized from the sale of their pelts, caused attention to be directed to the breeding of these animals in captivity. This development took place during the early years of the present century.

For the first several years of its development, the fur-farming industry expanded so rapidly in Canada and abroad that the chief source of income of ranches was the sale of live animals for breeding purposes. Animals were so valuable that the production of pelts was a minor feature of fur farming. Thus, in 1925, a pair of high-grade silver foxes was worth $45,000 on the ranches of Canada, and the total value of live silver foxes sold was $2,755,000, while the value of the pelts sold was but $736,000. As the number of foxes on fur farms increased, ranchers had to readjust their economy to declining values of both animals and pelts. By 1944, good silver foxes could be purchased for $200 a pair. The total value of all silver foxes sold in 1944 was only $328,000, but the value of silver fox pelts was $4,241,000.

The development of the mink industry is now progressing rapidly since this animal thrives in captivity when well cared for. Attempts are being made to raise other kinds of fur-bearing animals on farms, especially the raccoon, skunk, and chinchilla, but the results have not been encouraging (Fig. 211).

Although fur farming is being carried on in many places throughout Canada and the United States, the northern forest affords the best environment for this industry. The superior coloring and softness of the pelts secured through trapping in this region are apparently equaled by those produced on the ranches.

Fur farming has now passed through the experimental stage and has become recognized as a permanent branch of animal industry, in which certain animals are bred and raised for their pelts just as others are now raised for meat, hides, and wool. This industry more nearly fits northern-forest conditions than does the production of grain or beef. Poor soil and rough topography are not obstacles to the fur farmer—the long, cold winter is actually an advantage, since the quality of the pelt is greatly improved by a season of steady severe cold. The raising of fur bearers in captivity may even be the beginning of new strains of domesticated animals, although it will probably be some time before they can be turned loose around the barnlot like pigs and sheep.

FORESTS AND FOREST INDUSTRIES

The northern coniferous forest has become one of the most important commercial sources of timber for the entire world. Modern man with his constantly growing demand for wood has been rapidly consuming most of the timber in the temperate zone. In the United States all the better stands of softwoods in New England and the lake states have been depleted; softwoods from the southern pine belt and the Puget Sound region are now furnishing the bulk of the timber needed in the United States. But already the United States is beginning to import large quantities of wood from forested Canada. In Europe all the best agricultural land has been deforested and settled, and consequently at present most of the timber comes from the sandy, mountainous, or cold lands. The Scandinavian Peninsula, Finland, and the Soviet Union have become the main timber sellers of Europe. This trade was badly disrupted by World War II in Europe.

Canada. This great forest includes the northern softwood belt and the subarctic forest belt (Fig. 212), and it covers more than one-half of the land area of Canada. It extends from the Atlantic Ocean to Alaska and is hundreds of miles wide. Not all this area is covered with forests. Some of the highlands, especially those near Alaska, are too cold for forest growth and are designated as tundra. These highlands are irregular and scattered. Consequently the exact boundaries between the forests and the tundras are unknown in such a wild region. No attempt has been made, therefore, to indicate the

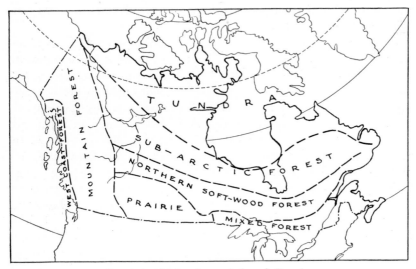

Fig. 212.   Major forest belts of Canada.

location of the several tundra regions that lie within the bounds of the northern forest.[4]

THE NATURE OF THE FOREST. The principal trees of the Canadian northern forest are white and black spruce, balsam fir, poplars, white birch, and jack pine.

Not all the northern forest region is covered with usable timber. Probably one-half of it consists of lakes, swamps, muskegs, or barren rocks. Even much of the timber is of poor quality. No sharp line of demarcation can be drawn between the real commercial timber areas and the woodland of the scrub variety, which, though inferior as saw timber, can often be used for mine props, pulpwood, and fuel.

[4] A map, general in character, showing the tundra areas within the northern forest is given in the *Canadian Year Book*, Ottawa, Canada, 1938, between pp. 282 and 283, and also in the 1947 edition between pp. 384 and 385.

The first superficial explorations of Canada were followed by timber estimates far too large, since the timber explorers oftentimes followed the river courses and estimated the interstream areas as a solid timber stand, when many of them were largely covered with open lake or rock country or even scrub timber. The timber-bearing region of the Canadian northern forest may be divided, in a general way, into three commercial areas as follows: (1) the southern or more accessible parts of the northern softwood forest (Fig. 212); (2) the northern or less accessible parts of the northern softwood forest; and (3) the subarctic forest.

COMMERCIAL DEVELOPMENT. The wood products of the more accessible northern softwood area are already being used in large quantities. In general the best commercial forests of Canada lie in that part of the region where the rivers flow southward to the St. Lawrence. This area has thick stands, and the trees are bigger and better than in areas farther to the north. Also the rivers are an aid in getting the timber out. The southward-flowing rivers, such as the Ottawa, are jammed with logs and pulpwood southbound to the sawmills and pulp mills. During the decade 1935–1944, the pulpwood demands on the forest have averaged about 8,000,000 cords annually with the trend of production upward. The production in 1944 surpassed 8,800,000 cords.

All pulpwood cut on Crown lands must be manufactured into pulp in Canadian pulp mills unless special permit is obtained from the government for the export of the wood. The pulpwood which is exported is therefore cut from private lands. Since the forests of private ownership are being rapidly depleted, it is to be expected that an increasing percentage of Canada's pulpwood will be manufactured into pulp in Canadian mills. National industry is thereby fostered.

During 1944, Canadian mills turned out 5,271,000 tons of wood valued at approximately $105,000,000. In other words, the value of the product was more than doubled through the process of manufacture. This fact indicates why Canada has passed the law prohibiting the export of pulpwood obtained from Crown land.

At the present rate of production Canada's pulpwood supply would last only a few decades except for reforestation. Even with the aid of the excellent reforestation methods now being introduced, the pulpwood industry is compelled to push farther and farther north. The northern part of the northern softwood forest belt (Fig. 209) is relatively inaccessible. The wood is of relatively little value except as fuel, mine props, or homebuilding materials. Since few people live in this area the demand for these products is exceedingly small. The subarctic forest will probably never be of commercial value except for minor local uses. The severity of the climate limits the size of the timber and also its value. Much of the timber is (1) too small to make lumber, (2) poor in quality, (3) badly burned over, and (4) hard to get out.

Fig. 213. Floating logs to the pulp mills.

Canada's new concept of timber—a crop to be grown rather than a mine to be exhausted—is particularly applicable to much of Canada's timber area. Most of Canada's timber land is not adapted to agriculture and should be permanently given to softwoods. Unfortunately, many of these forests have suffered great destruction from fire. Then, too, the rate of growth is slow.

Canada as a source of pulpwood has been vividly portrayed as follows: "Along the railroad tracks, beside filmy, rutty roads, stretching into the swampy bush, everywhere, it seems there displays itself the steady stream of pulpwood, piled beside the cut-up mills in veritable mountains, or rolling forth white and shiny from the rossing mills which have removed the bark and made the wood ready for grinding; pulpwood piled in the streets of little towns, jamming the rivers, crossed and locked and piled like jackstraws flung from the hand of a giant into the back swirl of a rapids, rolling down the skidways, loafing at the banks of every sluggish stream—such is pulpwood, traveling onward to the mills which have sprung up like magic in the North Country" (Fig. 213).

Eurasia. The coniferous forest belt of Eurasia extends from Scandinavia eastward across Finland and northern Russia to the Urals and onward across Siberia to the Pacific. A comparatively large portion of the region should be kept permanently in forest since the summers are too short for much agricultural development.

Forest Industries of Russia. The forest resources of Russia have been estimated at 1,527,300,000 acres, of which 370,000,000 acres lie in Soviet Europe. The finest of these forest areas are situated north of latitude 60° N in areas drained by the Onega, Dvina, Mezen, and Pechora rivers. These rivers are relatively ice free for 160 to 180 days each year, during which time millions of logs are floated or shipped from the interior to Archangel, Mezen, Onega, Pustozersk, and other ports or shipping points along the northern coast of Russia (Fig. 176).

Normally, forest products represent the second largest export of the Soviet Union, being surpassed only by wheat. Most of these forest products go to countries of northwest Europe. Prior to World War II the shipments from Archangel alone exceeded 8 billion board feet in a single year, and some of the shipments have been billed to areas as remote as Cape Town, South Africa.

Formerly lumber exports from the northern parts of Russia were confined to the summer months. Now icebreakers keep several ports open for eight or ten months a year, and Archangel is kept open all year except during a few weeks in the spring when the ice goes out of the Dvina River.

The lumbermen live in log houses, burn wood as fuel, and help support themselves by growing cabbage, lettuce, beets, strawberries, and other quick-maturing food crops. A few cattle, fed on locally grown hay, are kept for their dairy products.

Many sawmills are operated in the southern margin of the forest to supply local needs and to produce lumber for the vast section of grassland to the south. However, most parts of these grasslands possess meager transportation facilities and lumber products are expensive. Consequently, the poor agricultural peasant and even the urban population must get along with a minimum of lumber products.

The Soviet Union has made little progress in the woodpulp and paper industries. Her potentialities for the manufacture of these products are tremendous. If or when Europe becomes a prosperous continent again, the paper industry of Russia may be expected to increase rapidly.

Sweden. About 53 per cent of the area of Sweden is covered with forests, pine, spruce, and fir being the predominant species. Nearly all the northern part is forest-clad or barren, little land being suitable for agriculture. Most of the land not suited to agriculture is in forest growth of some sort. Sweden is wisely leaving this northern area in the crop for which it is best suited.

It has been said that the future of Sweden lies in the proper utilization of its forests. No other country except perhaps Finland relies so heavily on the products of the forest for national welfare. Wood products form 40 to 50 per cent of the annual Swedish export, and Sweden is the leading wood-exporting country in the world unless recently surpassed by the Soviet Union.[5] The export value of these products increased from about $25,000,000 in 1903 to $200,000,000 in 1937. World War II practically stopped Sweden's exportation of wood products. In the future, Russia will be a strong competitor for the wood products market of northwest Europe.

As in northern United States and Canada, Sweden's lumbering operations are carried on largely in the wintertime when snow is on the ground. Then in the spring, when the streams are flooded, the logs are floated down from the mountain with the spring freshet. Heavy snows in the mountains produce spring freshets which carry the log drives, and a single river sometimes floats down to the mills from 8,000,000 to 14,000,000 logs each year. Sawmills are located at falls in the rivers, sometimes at the coast. Steamers loading with lumber are a familiar sight in summer along the Swedish coast.

Not all the Swedish timber is suitable for lumber; because of the severity of the climate in northern Sweden, trees grow slowly and many are stunted and inferior. The smaller growth is suitable for pulpwood, however, and Sweden has become one of the foremost makers and exporters of both woodpulp and paper.

Sweden is one of the few countries in the world which is growing trees faster than it is cutting them. This is quite the reverse of the American method. The Swedes decided that they must put their

[5] Sweden lies partly in the continental type of climate, where agriculture is the dominant industry, and partly in the northern forest, where woodworking is the most important industry.

leading industry on a permanent basis and guard against timber depletion. Timber is a valuable asset; it must be safeguarded as an annual
source of wealth, not cut recklessly and the thin soil allowed to
become waste land.

The government forest policy, as worked out some years ago, calls
for a limitation of cutting to the amount grown every year. No more
timber can be cut annually than replaces itself, either by natural means
or by scientific reforestation methods. As fast as the forests are cleared
of marketable timber the areas are replanted, so that Sweden will be
assured of a permanent wood industry. Part of the reforestation is
being carried out by private owners, part by the government. Many
of the Swedish forests are municipally owned.

In a typical forest about 100 miles north of Stockholm a timber crop
has been harvested regularly for several centuries. Today this forest
contains more millions of feet of lumber than it did a century ago.
In it is found every stage of growth from the tiny seedling to the
full-grown lumber tree awaiting the sawmill.

Finland. Trees are by far the most valuable national resource in
Finland. Their importance is forcibly indicated by the fact that, before the war with the Soviet Union, woodworking industries employed nearly one-third of all industrial workers, and their products
constitute approximately one-half of all exports. The greater part of
the country lies in a belt of coniferous forests, with pine, spruce, and
fir predominating. In the far north the timber becomes smaller and
less valuable, grading off into the subarctic birch trees; in the extreme
south there is a narrow belt of hardwoods.

About 60 per cent of the entire country is forested (62,429,000
acres), or there are 17 acres of forest for every person in Finland.
The government owns approximately one-third of the forested area;
the remaining two-thirds is privately owned (35 and 65 per cent).
In southern Finland there are large private forests of great importance.

Pine was originally the most valuable of the conifers, but it is being
gradually superseded by spruce, which now has first rank; furthermore, there is a growing demand for spruce pulpwood which has led
to an increased acreage of this forest species. Of the hardwoods, birch
is most widely distributed. Black alder and white alder are also found.
Aspen is used in some sections for match and pulp making, although
Finland has been unable to compete with Sweden in the manufacture
of matches. Efforts are being made to discourage the cutting of small
trees required for round timber and props. Many of the privately
owned forests have decreased in value owing to excessive cutting and

wasteful clearing of land for agricultural use. The state-owned forests, in contrast, are well managed. The government, through legislation, subsidies, and forest bureaus, is doing much to educate the Finnish farmer in forestry. All matters pertaining to the forest policy are controlled by the Board of Forestry under the Ministry of Agriculture. Pulp and paper mills have bought large tracts of land in order to control and insure their own supply of raw materials. To the north, two-thirds of the entire cut is saw timber.

The export of timber is encouraged by the ease of water navigation. The gulfs of Bothnia and Finland provide access to the Baltic and North seas and permit timber vessels from all over the world to load with ease in Finnish ports. Government icebreakers keep the ports of southern Finland open the year round so that there is little interruption of the timber trade during the winter. The state railways penetrate not only the better agricultural regions of the south but also the more lonely forested areas of central and northern Finland.

POWER AND MANUFACTURING

Hydroelectric Development. A large part of the northern forest region of Canada is designated as the Laurentian Shield, an ancient land mass with its surface dotted with innumerable glacial lakes. This low plateau provides a natural catchment and storage basin for the eastern Canadian rivers, most of which tumble off its sloping margin in a series of rapids and waterfalls. The combined potential water power of Ontario and Quebec is estimated at about 14,000,000 horsepower minimum flow and 19,000,000 horsepower available 50 per cent of the time. Thousands of interior lakes in central Sweden and other thousands in Finland feed the swift rivers and provide these countries with an abundance of power. Already the hydroelectric power development of these two countries exceeds 2,000,000 horsepower. The construction of hydroelectric plants in these northern countries is a fairly recent development. The installed hydroelectric power of Ontario and Quebec increased from 823,581 horsepower in 1910 to 8,521,862 horsepower in 1946. There remains unharnessed in these two provinces almost one-half the hydroelectric power that could be produced during the time of minimum flow (Fig. 214).

Users of Power. The demand for developed horsepower comes from both local and outside sources. In addition to industries located at or within a short radius of the waterfall, cities and industries in

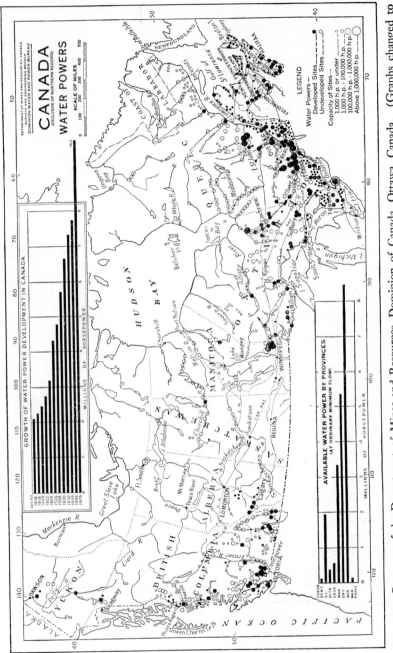

Fig. 214. Courtesy of the Department of Mines and Resources, Dominion of Canada, Ottawa, Canada. (Graphs changed to bring data up to January 1, 1946.)

regions farther south are securing cheap northern power by means of long-distance transmission lines.

The gradual perfecting of means of long-distance transmission has made it possible for the hydroelectric power of the Canadian Upland to be used on the farm and in the factory along the St. Lawrence Valley, and the steel towers of the high-power lines are now a familiar sight in the North. Power from the falls of the Grand Discharge, near the outlet of Lac St. Jean, is carried by a high line a distance of 140 miles to Quebec. This is but one of a number of lines supplying current to Montreal, Quebec, and Ottawa. To a region lacking fuel —both Ontario and Quebec are practically without coal—this new supply of "white coal" is of inestimable value.

An interesting development based on hydroelectric power has taken place in the rather isolated Saguenay River Valley of Quebec. This river valley collects enough water to produce 2,000,000 horsepower the year round and 2,050,000 horsepower has already been developed. This cheap power has attracted to Arvida one of the world's largest aluminum industries. The aluminum plant of this region has a capacity for the production of 80,000 tons of aluminum annually.[6]

Similarly water power is one of the most valuable resources of Finland and Sweden. Finland is a rocky, ice-scoured, lake-strewn plateau which lies almost entirely within the coniferous forest belt. The many lakes, estimated at more than 35,000, serve as reservoirs which regulate the flow from many rivers. Since the country has no coal, water supplies most of the power for its industrial plants. Although the forest industries use approximately two-thirds of the power generated, power is also distributed to other industries and to the farms.

In Sweden, hydroelectric power is utilized on a large scale in the mines and forests, on the farms, and in the electrification of railways. Sweden leads the world in the use of electricity on the farm. At present, electric current is distributed to almost one-third of the farm homes, where it serves not only for light but also as a source of power.

Pulp and Paper Manufacture. The industry which has so far been the largest consumer of power in the northern forest, and which probably owes its rapid growth to hydroelectric development, is pulp and paper manufacture. Ever since tree trunks became the leading raw material for paper there has been a gradual northward movement of the industry, until now mills are widely scattered over the more ac-

[6] W. M. Goodwin, "Low Cost Power on the Saguenay," *Compressed Air Magazine*, December 1946, pp. 326–329.

cessible timber lands along the southern margin of the region. Large tracts of pulpwood are necessary to the life of the industry; cheap power to run the mills is equally vital, since about 100 horsepower is required to make a ton of paper a day. Short bolts of spruce, poplar, or other woods with the bark removed are fed into a grinder and emerge as a fibrous mass which can be dried, pressed into pulp, and

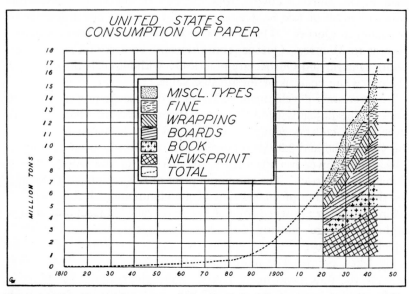

FIG. 215. The demand for paper within the United States seems almost insatiable. Our per capita consumption in the last twenty years has practically doubled, and our total consumption has more than doubled.

then made into the huge rolls of print paper which feed the news presses in every city.

The best location for a mill is on a river which can float the pulpwood to the mill and at the same time furnish water power for the machinery. Continuous operation, usually 24 hours a day, enables the manufacturers whose mills are located directly on a waterfall to get the maximum return on the value of their investment. Ontario and Quebec are the largest producers of woodpulp and of paper in the world.

Canadian newsprint finds its largest market in the United States, where the 50- or 100-page Sunday supplement is popular. Since 1875, the United States has been the world's greatest paper market and during much of this time has used more paper than all other countries combined. Our consumption in 1926 was estimated by the American Paper and Pulp Association at approximately 10,000,000 tons. Twenty years later, 1946, our consumption had reached the amazing total of 16,871,000 tons. Moreover, our increasing demands for newsprint and other paper products seems to be insatiable. In 1859, we used only 8 pounds per capita; since then our annual consumption has increased with such rapidity that in 1946 it exceeded 240 pounds per capita (Fig. 215).

This rapid growth of the American paper consumption made it inevitable that we should have to buy an increasing amount of wood, woodpulp, and paper from our neighbor to the north. In 1890, Canada's pulp and paper exports were valued at $120; in 1944 her exports of these two products were valued at $285,000,000. Today, pulp- and paper-making industries represent Canada's greatest manufacturing enterprises.

In 1937, Canada supplied approximately 40 per cent of the newsprint of the entire world. The importance of her newsprint industry is indicated by the fact that she exported almost two and one-half times as much newsprint paper as her five closest competitors combined (see the accompanying table). In 1946, Canada produced a larger percentage of the world's newsprint and paper than in 1937,

EXPORTS OF NEWSPRINT PAPER FROM PRINCIPAL PAPER-PRODUCING COUNTRIES

Country	1913 Short tons	1937 Short tons
Canada	256,661	3,455,240
Finland	77,213	421,503
Newfoundland	49,755	298,406
Sweden	67,938	222,851
Germany	75,761	217,951
Norway	108,507	195,472

but exact data for 1946 are not available. The large available supplies of wood, pulpwood, and water power, the chief factors on which the future expansion of the industry depends, are shown in the accompanying table.

PULPWOOD AND WATER POWER RESOURCES

Province	Estimated pulpwood resources (million cords)	Available water power at ordinary minimum flow
Quebec	290	8,459,000
Ontario	191	5,330,000
Prairie provinces	185	4,214,000

The manufacture of paper is an older industry in Scandinavia than in Canada. Originally a handicraft, paper making has now become a carefully organized factory industry employing skilled labor. The Scandinavian mills, equipped with modern and expensive machinery, are turning out not only woodpulp and newsprint, but also wallpaper and writing, bond, envelope, and parchment papers in grades ranging from the coarsest to the finest. Most of this paper goes into the export trade. Instead of selling low-priced raw materials Sweden and Finland have been using water power and skilled labor to turn forests into higher-priced wood products.

During the last few decades the exports of lumber from Sweden have scarcely held their own while the exports of products manufactured from wood have increased rapidly. In 1900, the exports of Swedish forest products were valued at $25,000,000; in 1937, they exceeded $853,000,000. World War II resulted in a major decline in the wood-working industries of Sweden. Recovery of her exports is slow, primarily because Europe is too poor to buy her products in large quantities. Thus in 1944 Sweden's exports of wood products was approximately $81,000,000 or less than one-tenth of her 1937 exports.

Raw Material Goes to the Power. Industrial development in the northern forest is a direct outgrowth of abundant water power plus the abundance of raw materials. But certain types of industry can afford to locate at the source of power, even though raw materials must be imported from remote lands. This fact is indicated by the erection of a 400,000-horsepower aluminum plant far up the Saguenay River in the Province of Quebec, remote from supplies of bauxite. Cheap power is the keynote of the aluminum industry; nearly all this modern industrial metal is being manufactured where large amounts of hydroelectric current are available. Early in 1940 Great Britain, needing large quantities of this metal for the manufacture of war supplies, announced her intention of expanding the aluminum industry in Canada. Plans are now under way to make Canada one of the foremost aluminum-producing countries in the world.

British Guiana has one of the best and cheapest supplies of bauxite— the raw material from which aluminum is made. Ocean freighters carry cargoes of bauxite nearly all the way from the Guiana mines to the waterfall on the Saguenay. This combination of the low costs of ore, water power, and ocean transportation made it profitable to erect an expensive hydroelectric station in the wilderness, build several acres of factories, construct an entire town, and import trained workers to man the plant.

Manufacturing, a Natural Adjustment. The possibilities of using cheap hydroelectric power as the basis for a widespread industrial development are most easily illustrated by Sweden, where forests, iron ore, and water power are the most valuable resources. For many centuries the existence of high-grade iron ore was unknown; the forests were used only for local fuel and building purposes; the power went to waste. Lumbering was the first forest industry to make use of water power, and surplus timber in the form of rough lumber was exported to foreign markets. Pulp and paper mills represent a later stage in the utilization of timber. Today Sweden is turning out thousands of skillfully manufactured timber products—practically all of them made in factories run by water power. Her output includes lumber, woodpulp, various kinds of paper, matches, furniture, and artificial silk. Rich iron ore is smelted by electricity, a process too expensive to be practical in countries lacking cheap and abundant water power, and the electric arc is also used to produce high-grade tool steel. The making of fertilizers and ammunition is a recent development of the electrochemical industries. In 1947, 40 to 50 per cent of the Swedish farms were using electricity. However, in the United States, over 65 per cent of the farms are linked to power lines. Sweden has also enough power to electrify, eventually, all the railroads and is now exporting current to Denmark by means of a marine cable, for Denmark has neither coal nor waterfalls. Sweden's use of one resource in order to unlock others is the most advanced stage of resource utilization.

Although Canada lacks an abundance of easily mined, high-grade iron ore which means so much to Sweden, it has a number of other mineral developments within the Laurentian area, many of which are present or potential users of electric current. Power lines have been extended to the asbestos mining region, and to some of the copper and gold camps. Canadian electrochemical works are also buying current. The manufacture of rayon offers excellent possibilities in a region where unlimited cellulose from scrub timber is available; and cheap power affords opportunity for nitrogen fixation, an industry which resembles aluminum manufacture in its dependence upon cheap power.

Most of these industries require expensive machinery but no large supply of cheap labor—a natural adjustment in such a sparsely populated region. The resultant expense of starting a power plant and factory unit, however, necessitates such an outlay of capital that the large-scale corporate project is the general rule.

MINERAL RESOURCES

In respect to mineral development the northland is making a far more impressive showing than many of the more densely populated temperate-zone regions. The search for precious and semi-precious metals has ever been an industry adapted to regions of scant population. Even when mining advances from the stage of the individual prospector to that of the mining company, the number of additional workers is not commensurate with the increase in output of metal since machinery does such a large part of the work.

The northern-forest region has been producing not only large stores of precious metals, but some of the industrial minerals as well. Coal in general is lacking; when present in quantity, as in parts of Alberta and Saskatchewan, it is poor in quality. Northern Scandinavia has iron. One of the earliest industries in Finland was the small-scale manufacture of a good grade of malleable iron from lake and bog ores. Sweden has the best deposits of high-grade ore in Europe, some of it grading more than 60 per cent pure iron; about two-thirds of it is north of the Arctic Circle.

The mineral wealth of northern Canada includes valuable deposits of gold, silver, copper, nickel, zinc, cobalt, and asbestos. Much of the Laurentian Upland is a rich mineral-bearing area, but, because it is so bleakly frozen in winter and a sea of almost impassable muskeg swamps and forests difficult to traverse in summer, 90 per cent of it is still unprospected. Most of the known metal deposits have been discovered by chance rather than by methods of scientific prospecting. In fact, within a large part of the Canadian forest, scientific prospecting is difficult because of (1) the nature of the rock—faulted, folded, recrystallized; (2) large areas are covered with glacial till, lakes, swamps, and muskeg; and (3) many parts of the forest are difficult to penetrate. Within other parts of the forest, large areas of barren rock have been scoured clean by the glacier, exposing dikes, faults, and other geological structures which aid the prospector and geologist in their search for metals. Nearly every year sees new mineral discoveries in the Far North followed by a rush of prospectors and mining men to the new field. Among the more important mineral discoveries which have been made in the past, the gold rush to the Yukon in 1897–1898 is the best known and most spectacular. The

Sudbury district supplies more than 90 per cent of the world's nickel and is an important copper-producing center. The rich Cobalt silver district of northern Ontario was discovered in 1903 and yielded from 10,000 to 12,000 ounces of silver to the ton; Cobalt (330 miles north of Toronto) is still one of the leading silver camps of the world, and Canada owes its position as the third largest silver producer largely to the Cobalt district.

Gold was discovered in the Porcupine Lake district in 1909, and this small area of about 6 square miles has become the richest gold camp in North America; Porcupine is situated about 450 miles north of Toronto. A score of smaller camps are located at different places throughout the region, and new ones are being discovered from time to time. In 1924–1925 rich copper deposits were found at Rouyn, almost due east of Porcupine, and a new copper-mining city is being constructed in the wilderness. Ontario and Quebec produced more than 327,000 short tons of copper in 1940, or approximately 11 per cent of the total world output. Since 1940 the Canadian output of copper has declined (171,000 tons in 1945), owing in part at least to a labor shortage brought on by World War II.

Recently uranium ores have been discovered in northern Canada. However uranium metal was so little known up to 1940 that its physical properties, such as the smelting point, were not known with precision. Prior to the end of 1941 only a few grams of usable uranium were available. The difficult technical problems of large-scale output were solved in 1942 but data of production are not published.

The forest belt of Eurasia is known to contain many valuable minerals, some of which are being exploited.

AGRICULTURE

Although the advancing pioneers have pushed northward into the forest, cleared land, built cabins, and started crop raising, this region is adapted to the cultivation of few crops. Agriculture is limited by climate, the growing season being even shorter than that of the spring-wheat belt, and the long winter is so cold that there is poor chance for root growth. In general the region lacks fertility, but scattered here and there are pockets of deeper, more fertile soil which are suitable for cultivation.

The growing season is short—from two to four months at most—but the long days partly make up for the shortness of the season. Plants measure their summer not by the calendar but by the number

of hours of sunlight; at Fort Yukon, Alaska, with its 20 hours of daylight, there would be approximately as much growing time as in two
average days in the humid tropics. Certain plants, such as cabbages,
grow to even greater size in the subarctic than in the temperate zone
or in the tropics owing, perhaps, to their maintaining a constant and
fairly even rate of growth during the almost continuous midsummer
daylight. Other hardy and quick-growing vegetables and fruits, such
as potatoes, turnips, beets, radishes, lettuce, cauliflower, and strawberries, have time to ripen. Rye and oats are often raised, and sometimes wheat and barley. Excellent crops of hay for pasturage can
also be grown.

One of the best examples of a favorable soil pocket within this rock
and muskeg country is the Great Clay Belt of the Abitibi District on
the Ontario-Quebec boundary, some 450 miles north of Toronto.
This district, with its 10,000,000 acres of good clay soil, is being
rapidly developed through grain growing, livestock raising, and dairying. The sturdy French-Canadians who colonized it engaged in a
type of general farming carefully adapted to the climatic conditions.
In some twenty years' time their efforts have changed an unsettled
wilderness into a thriving settlement with small communities, schools,
churches, and more than 25,000 inhabitants.

Three railroads have been built into the Great Clay Belt, providing
the farmers with a means of marketing their surplus. Interior Alaska
has a scattered agricultural development of this same type although
on a much smaller scale. A number of farmers along the Tanana River
are growing excellent crops of potatoes, and sometimes even wheat,
though that is not always a dependable crop.

Sweden and Finland have paid more attention to agriculture than
Canada has. These Scandinavian countries with their few natural
resources and a greater need for agricultural crops than is experienced
in the western hemisphere have pushed the agricultural boundary far
north. On the best land they are raising hardy cereals such as oats
and rye, and root crops, including sugar beets. Glaciation scraped
this region clean of its best soil, leaving much of the land unsuitable
for crop growing but suitable for pasturage. Consequently, this rock-
covered country with its cold winters and cool summers has found
it profitable to imitate the cooperative dairying of Denmark. The
long, cold winters necessitate the construction of large barns for livestock and for storing quantities of feed; if the home supply is insufficient, feedstuffs must be imported. The Finnish farms are usually

near tidewater, and importation is both easier and cheaper than in northern interior Canada, where a long railroad haul is necessary.

Except in fertile areas such as the Great Clay Belt, northern agriculture has not been perfected to the point where it is a profitable full-time occupation. The farmer of the northland may and often does supplement his scanty agricultural income by some other means. Thus a storekeeper or farmer in Scandinavia turns fisherman at the time of the herring run. In Canada the settler may become woodsman during the winter—pulpwood properly peeled and stacked beside the railroad or river is worth $6 to $8 a cord.[7] Other farmers spend the winter trapping for furs and often obtain a higher return from their winter catch than from their summer tillage. Still others may even migrate to Montreal, Toronto, or Detroit, in search of factory work during the long winter.

Although agriculture occupies a prominent position throughout most of the world, in these high-altitude regions it is distinctly a side line. Farming is important only on the southern edge, but there is a possibility that the development of additional cold-resistant and shorter-maturing crops may push the line farther north. Until all the potential farming lands of the temperate zone are fully settled it seems unlikely that subarctic agriculture will be greatly extended. This region will probably continue to import most of its food, exporting those other commodities in the production of which it has a greater comparative advantage.

THE FOREST AS A SUMMER PLAYGROUND

The vacation, originally regarded simply as a respite from one's regular occupation, has gradually come to mean "going some place"— a trip away from home for the purpose of change and recreation. This vacation idea—two weeks, a month, for many people a full summer—has taken firm possession of many peoples who have a surplus above their actual subsistence needs. The annual holiday is now a fixed habit, not merely with thousands but with millions of people; this is particularly true in the United States, which ranks first in average standards of living and consequently where many people can afford to travel.

[7] During the years 1925 to 1946 pulpwood frequently sold at American paper plants for more than $15 a cord.

During midsummer the vacation rush often assumes the aspects of a seasonal migration. People from Wisconsin regularly go to California, and Californians visit Wisconsin. West Virginians acquire a sunburn at the seashore while the residents of Atlantic City are spending the summer in the Canadian Rockies. European vacationists take trips to their own recreation areas, or cross national boundaries to visit the Alps, the Black Forest of Germany, the lake district of Scotland, or the Norwegian fiords. To those areas which have superior attractions for summer visitors, the vacation influx has its distinct commercial phase. When properly developed and advertised, a strip of sandy beach in New Jersey or a beautiful range of mountains in Switzerland may become a financial asset.

A forest wilderness, not too inaccessible, may also be capitalized. The great north woods of Canada, one of the last frontiers of untouched wild life, appeals to the primitive strain in man's nature. The desire to shoot wild game and to fish in untouched waters, the lure of possible adventure in an unknown region, is but slightly hidden beneath the surface in many a business man who sits at a city desk eleven months out of every year. The urbanite finds keen pleasure in turning his back on civilization and becoming for a short period a fisherman, a woodsman, or an explorer. For the seasoned camper the open trail with canoe, tent, and guide leads to thousands of square miles of tangled bush country with clear glacial lakes and rushing streams rich in trout, bass, and maskinonge. Other nature lovers prefer to "rough it" vicariously during the daytime but return at night to the comforts of hotels and summer camps which already fringe the more accessible lakes and rivers. Indians and French-Canadians engaged in hunting and trapping during the winter often supplement their incomes by acting as guides or boatmen during the summer vacation season. Tourist patronage helps swell the revenues of the railroads and of the fur posts which act as outfitting stations for hunting and fishing expeditions.

Scandinavia is also having a recreational development on a smaller scale; the inland lake districts of both Sweden and Finland are becoming increasingly popular for steamer tours during the summer except as interrupted by war. But Scandinavia is distant, an eight-day ocean voyage from the United States, whereas Canada, with a border untroubled by bothersome customs and passport regulations, may be reached in a short time from New York, Philadelphia, or Chicago. Consequently, Scandinavia is unable to attract any large proportion of the American vacation travel business. Europe has less money to spend on recreation; some countries, such as Russia, have almost none. A few Russian officials may pass their annual vacations hunting in the northern forests of Russia and Siberia, but this part of the world is still undeveloped as a popular playground.

A REGION OF ISOLATION

Within the northern forest, climate, surface, and vegetation have offered the maximum difficulties for human settlement. The migration waves which have gradually spread a layer of land-using peoples over most of the temperate zone have been slow in affecting this north frontier, and it is still a region of comparative isolation. Forested Canada is almost an empty land; the population is sparse and oftentimes of the migratory type; and urban centers are few. Because of its greater pressure of population, Sweden probably has the largest proportion of settled area in the coniferous forest. Otherwise northern Eurasia is as thinly populated as Canada.

In Canada individual trappers and fur traders carry on their work over thousands of square miles of bush country, where the meeting of a fellow man during the course of the winter is an event. Mining claims are few and far apart; even where towns have sprung up in the richest mineral-bearing areas so far discovered, they are small and isolated. Power and pulp developments use expensive machinery and few workers; the villages growing up around them are tiny islands in a sea of bush country. Railroads are manned by a handful of men, scattered thinly along the right of way. Towns and their conveniences —schools, churches, and general community life—are so widely spaced that such advantages enter the luxury class.[8]

WINTER THE WORK SEASON

In one particular the natural economy of the northern forest is a direct reversal of temperate-zone practice. Winter is not only climatically dominant in this northland, but economically and socially dominant as well. In the temperate zone, summer is the crop time

[8] Schools on wheels, cars provided by the Canadian National and the Canadian Pacific railways and fitted up with all the conveniences of the modern schoolroom, are now being tried out in this region. These railway cars stop a few days on a siding or beside a water tank, give out books and assign lessons to a handful of pupils; then they move on to new locations and return in four to six weeks to hear lessons and check up on results.

and the best work period; winter with its snow and ice is the time of lesser activity. In the northern forest snow is the friend of man and winter tends to be the work time. The native Indian inhabitants of interior Alaska and Canada have long regarded summer as that unpleasantly warm season during which black flies and mosquitoes are troublesome pests, trapping becomes impossible, and life is generally made more difficult. When the snow begins to fly and the muskeg freezes solid, most of these annoyances vanish. As the weather becomes crisp, the people feel more energetic, they begin the business of hunting, they get out their sleds and visit their friends and relatives. These natives consider the summer a nuisance.

Even the newer white residents find that winter is the friend of man. Furs are prime, and trapping can proceed. Frozen ground and thick ice on the lakes and rivers offer firm footing for travel. Timber is cut and hauled easily on sleds. Much of the railway mileage in the northern forest is built during the winter when the ground is frozen, supplies can be hauled and track laid. Winter snow provides the spring freshets which carry logs and pulpwood south to the mills. Even that new giant of the north, water power, also relies on the winter snows for part of its strength.

A REGION OF EXPLOITATION

Despite the fact that portions of the northern forest constitute what is probably the last agricultural frontier for the land-hungry colonist, the keynote of this region is not cultivation but extraction and exploitation. Most of the present inhabitants are engaged in taking what nature has provided, using it once, and then passing on to new fields. Furs, minerals, and timber are resources which tempt the exploiter rather than the homemaker, a fact which helps to explain the scant population.

Since it is not a region where trees can be cut, the stumps pulled, and the land cleared for farming, careful cutting of timber lands to preserve the stand of young trees is a vital necessity if there is to be a second or third crop at all soon.

Water power is almost the one resource which at present is being utilized along lines of development rather than exploitation. Conservation—not in the sense of locking up resources, but of using them carefully and eliminating waste—should be applied to the northern forest before the richest of its treasures have been stripped away.

REFERENCES

ADAMS, JOHN Q., "Settlement of the Northeastern Canadian Arctic," *Geographical Review*, January 1941, pp. 112–126.

CAMERON, D. ROY, "Canada's Forests," *Canadian Geographical Journal*, Ottawa, Canada, May 1939, pp. 248–268.

Canadian Year Book, Dominion Bureau of Statistics, Ottawa, 1947, annual.

GIBSON, R. A., "National Forest Program," *Canadian Geographical Journal*, Ottawa, Canada, August 1939, pp. 119–135.

HOLLIDAY, W. E. D., "Forest Regions of Canada," *Canadian Geographical Journal*, Ottawa, Canada, October 1939, pp. 229–244.

JOHNSTON, F. J., "Canada's Water Power Wealth," *Canadian Geographical Journal*, September 1937, pp. 115–150.

STEPHENSON, J. NEWELL, "Canada's Pulp and Paper Industry," *Canadian Geographical Journal*, Ottawa, Canada, November 1939, pp. 269–288.

Chapter 17

THE POLAR REGIONS

TUNDRAS, POLAR ICE CAPS, AND HIGH-LATITUDE SEAS

Prior to World War II the arctic and antarctic regions were considered relatively unimportant economically, commercially, and strategically. Although these areas were not entirely neglected, no intense international struggle took place in order to gain possession of the land in these high latitudes. The readily accessible resources, especially valuable animals, had been exploited for their furs, oils, meat, and ivory. The rich uranium deposits of northern Canada were not yet in demand, and other minerals had been exploited on only a small scale. The potential commercial and strategic significance of these areas had been given relatively little serious consideration. The great powers of the world had never striven to gain commercial or strategic superiority by the establishment of bases in these waste or near-waste areas. Thus, until recently, the polar regions attracted the least attention commercially, economically, and strategically of all geographic realms.

At present, however, the arctic region is considered valuable as a possible future link in commercial aviation, and it possesses potentialities of tremendous but tragic significance as bases for operation in possible future wars. Nature has placed the Arctic Ocean squarely between the great civilization centers of North America and Eurasia (Fig. 216). Until recently, man was compelled to go around this sea with its huge grinding ice pack, and the North Pole remained a mystery until Robert Peary reached it on foot in 1909. Since then the North Pole or its vicinity has been crossed many times by air. Soon the Arctic Ocean will, in all probability, be crossed by a network of airplane routes since its ice-filled water lies athwart the shortest routes between the greatest industrial centers of the northern hemisphere. If any nation should be so foolish as to cause a third world war, the Arctic Ocean will be its strategic center according to some of the most noted military experts of our time. Certainly the borders of the Arctic Ocean will be of great strategic importance in any war in which the North American civilization is opposed to all or part of the Eurasian civilization.

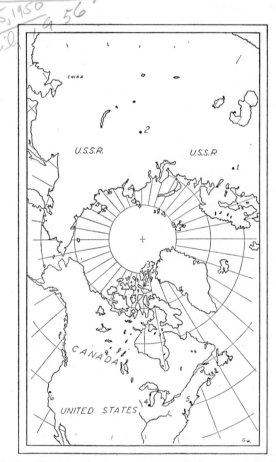

Fig. 216. The ice-filled Arctic Ocean lies directly between North America and most of Eurasia. Some of our leading military authorities believe that, should a third world war occur, the Arctic Ocean will be its strategic center. Places: (1) Moskva, (2) Tomsk, (3) Ellesmere Island, (4) Chicago, (5) New York City, (6) San Francisco.

Although the tundras and polar ice caps occupy more than 6,000,000 square miles, they normally support less than 100,000 people.[1] Even

[1] An unknown number of laborers are now stationed in the tundras building highways and air fields, searching for minerals, and in other ways preparing these near-waste lands as commercial, industrial, and military outposts of civilization.

the hot, dry deserts of the tropics are of greater economic value at present than the polar regions.

Nevertheless, these high latitudes have been of greater value and of more scientific interest than the present density of population indicates. These areas are the natural home of the reindeer, musk ox, caribou, polar bear, and other animals that are adapted to cold climates. The ice-laden waters of these regions have long been the source of valuable oils, furs, skins, and ivory. Radium, uranium, cryolite, nickel, mica, copper, gold, petroleum, and other minerals have been discovered in the tundras, and some of these minerals are being exploited. Although the tundras will never support a dense population, these desolate lands are believed to be capable of producing much larger quantities of food than at present.

For centuries high-latitude seas have supplied man with valuable products. But overproduction has already destroyed some of the fishing industries of these cold waters and, as we shall learn later in this chapter, threatens to destroy other resources of the seas.

POLAR CLIMATES AND MAN

"By their fruits shall ye know them" is an excellent principle on which to judge climates. The truth of this statement fits the polar regions with a nicety not found in many other parts of the world. The climates of these high latitudes are exacting, and only those plants and animals which are well adjusted to severe climatic conditions can survive. Human opportunities are also hedged about on every hand by climate. Social progress is and will long remain handicapped by sparsity of population, by the high degree of isolation, and by a lack of diversity of profitable occupations.

The climate of polar regions is severe and is characterized by monotonous and long-continued periods of cold and the absence of any season of warmth. The temperatures of the air over polar ice caps is always below freezing, and many records of mid-summer show temperatures well below zero Fahrenheit. The waters of high latitudes are always cold and most of the time filled with floating ice. Even the tundra has no season of reliable warmth in spite of the fact that temperatures of 90° F. or even 100° F. have been recorded. These high temperatures last only a few days and thaw scarcely more than a few feet of the surface ice before freezing temperatures are once more recorded.

In these high latitudes the winters are long and the summers short. For some months during the summer the sun never sets; at the same time it does not rise far above the horizon. In winter the sun never rises, although much of the time it is not far below the horizon; and, even though there is continual night for some months, yet during the noon period the sun comes so near the horizon that it makes a kind of twilight. Furthermore, the moon, stars, and at times the spectacular auroras give sufficient light for intermittent fishing and trapping.

The winter, however, is a season of little activity, the natives spending much of their time indoors. The appearance of the first feeble rays of the sun, after a long winter, is the occasion of great rejoicing. In Lapland the dawn is celebrated by feasts and merrymaking. In Siberia, the Samoyedes and Ostiaks celebrate the event with festivals which may last several days. Bonfires are made, reindeer killed, and there is general rejoicing.

As might be expected under such pronounced seasonal conditions, the yearly range of temperatures is extreme. A few summer days may be warm except on snow fields or highlands, but the winters are cold everywhere.

According to present records, the cold pole of the earth is just south of the tundra, near Verkhoyansk, where a minimum of $-93.6°$ F. has been recorded. This is $20°$ or $30°$ lower than the estimated minimum at the North Pole. It may be found, however, that the winter temperatures of Antarctica are even lower than those of Siberia. Roald Amundsen in his dash to the South Pole recorded a temperature of $-75°$ F. late in the spring, and temperatures as low as $-24°$ F. during mid-summer. On the afternoon of December 14, the temperature at the South Pole was $-10°$ F. It is probable that the temperatures of this high plateau are below zero during most of the summer months, and it may be found that the winter temperatures are the coldest on earth.

To add to the severity of the climate of Antarctica, the winds are persistent and strong. Amundsen, writing of this region, says, "At best the climate of Antarctica is about the worst in the world, chiefly because of the terrific intensity of the gales which blow almost incessantly. These gales are of almost unbelievable velocity." [2]

The winters of arctic North America are not so cold as those of central Siberia. The lowest temperature ever recorded on this con-

[2] Reprinted by permission from *My Life as an Explorer*, by Roald Amundsen, copyright 1927, Doubleday, Doran & Co., p. 67.

tinent is $-86°$ F., near the mouth of the Pelly River, about 100 miles
south of Dawson. But this station is remote from the coast. Along
the northern coast of Canada and Alaska the lowest temperature ever
recorded is only 54° below zero. Lower temperatures are occasionally experienced in Montana.

Although the winters of the tundra are cold, the summers are warm
and at times uncomfortably hot. In summer the sun is never very
high above the horizon, but for many days together it shines throughout all or most of the 24 hours. Along latitude 70° the sun shines
continuously for 73 days. Most of the tundra experiences a month or
more when the sun shines more than 20 hours each day, and therefore
the earth has but little time to cool during the exceedingly brief nights.

These long hours of sunshine quickly melt the small accumulation
of winter snow, except on the uplands, and thaw the surface of the
ground to a depth of several feet. Then the atmosphere is quickly
heated. Much of the low tundra has temperatures of 90° F. every
summer, and at Fort Yukon a shade temperature of 100° F. has been
recorded. These hot spells frequently cause much discomfort. Mr.
Stefansson reports that during the summer of 1918, while he was confined to the hospital at Fort Yukon, the temperature reached 97° F.,
and that because of the heat most of the patients moved out of the
upper stories of the hospital into the cooler cellar.

SOILS OF THE TUNDRAS

The soils of the tundras are largely the results of mechanical weathering associated with frost and water. The long winters with their exceedingly low temperatures reduce the chemical weathering and narrowly limit the annual period when the growth of plants and the
activities of animals affect the soils. As a result, most of the tundra has
no well-developed soil profile.

The soils of the tundra of the Soviet Union are typical of most
tundra soils. The soil survey of the Soviet Union classifies the tundra
soils under three heads, namely: (1) dry tundra soils, (2) bog tundra
soils, and (3) the podzolized soils. The dry tundra soils which commonly cover slopes are scarcely soils at all, but loose angular
rock fragments—"rock fields"—which have resulted from mechanical
weathering, with just enough chemical and biological activity to make
a bed of material in which tundra vegetation can live. The bog tundra
soils are situated on more level areas. Here the poor drainage, which
results from the frozen subsoil, keeps the fine particles from being

carried away by running water. Even though the chemical and biological weathering processes act slowly, they have played a larger part in bog soils than in dry soils. The bog soils are covered with partly decayed humus or peat, below which there is a sticky loam which may be so wet that it becomes semi-fluid during the summer. The nature of the podzolized soils has already been discussed in Chapter 3.

VEGETATION OF THE TUNDRA

During the brief but intensive summer vegetation grows with remarkable rapidity. The great variety and wealth of plant life during the summer are among the most surprising features of the scenery to those who visit the arctic regions for the first time. Flowering plants, grasses, mosses, and lichens, together with stunted willows, alders, and aspen, cover the surface except in the more forbidding places such as ice caps, glaciers, and moving moraines which may be complete deserts.

The arctic plants, as if aware of the fleeting opportunity for life, fairly leap through the various stages of growth to maturity. Flower buds not infrequently open before the snow is off the ground and, with the first warm days of summer, burst into bloom.

During the flowering season these plants are the most conspicuous part of the landscape. Orchids, violets, lilies, poppies, buttercups, and many other bright-colored flowers turn thousands of square miles of the vast arctic plains into nature's largest remaining primeval gardens. The abundance of these flowering plants is indicated by Mr. Stefansson, who says, "There can be no doubt that for every ton of mosses and lichens on the land beyond the Arctic Circle there are at least ten tons of flowering plants." [3]

This wealth of vegetation during the short summer must remain of little economic value. The number of animals which can be supported on the tundra bears little relation to the richness of the summer pasture, but it is limited by the scant supply of mosses, lichens, and stunted forest vegetation available for feed during the long cold winter. During this season, climate is a despotic master, and pastoral activities are pursued under some of the harshest conditions found anywhere. The summers are too short to permit any kind of agricultural crops to be grown for winter feed; the frozen subsoil during

[3] Reprinted by permission from *The Northward Course of Empire*, by Vilhjalmur Stefansson, Harcourt, Brace & Co., 1922, p. 52.

the summer prevents the moisture from sinking into the ground, making the soil too wet for the growth and curing of hay. The richness of summer vegetation is, therefore, merely a matter of scientific interest and of little economic value.

ANIMALS OF THE TUNDRA

The most notable animals of the tundra are the musk ox and caribou (American reindeer) of America, and the domestic reindeer, formerly of Eurasia, but now successfully introduced into the American tundra. Carnivorous animals such as wolves and foxes also roam over the tundra, preying on hares and lemmings or eating the scraps of meat left by the Eskimos and polar bears. During the brief summer the poorly drained tundra swarms with mosquitoes, flies, gnats, and other insects which torment both man and beast.

The Musk Ox. The musk ox combines characteristics of both the sheep and the ox. It has long, smooth, brown hair with a heavy undercoat of wool, excellent protection against the bitter cold of the arctic winter. It likes to feed on grass but can subsist on a diet of coarse shrubs on which most animals would starve.

Formerly, the musk ox had a wide range over the American arctic and its numbers reached several millions. Now, as a result of the introduction of modern rifles among the Eskimos and Indians, this shaggy animal has been exterminated over extensive areas. Accordingly the musk ox is now limited mainly to the uninhabited island archipelago north of Canada and to northwest Greenland.

Stefansson believes that the musk ox could be domesticated and bred for both meat and wool. But shearing might have disastrous results by leaving the animal a prey to the weather and to the attack of mosquitoes.

The Caribou. The caribou is the most valuable wild animal of arctic Canada today and was the most valuable animal of Alaska before the introduction of domestic reindeer from Europe. The caribou and his near relative, the reindeer, are to the tundra what the camel is to the desert. They seem to be as well adjusted to their harsh environment as the camel is to the desert. The skin of the caribou is thick and filled with air cells which afford excellent insulation against the loss of heat. The heavy fur is also warm so that the animal does not seem to suffer from the cold even during the worst arctic blizzards, provided that it can find food. The broad flat hoof of the caribou makes a good snow shovel with which to uncover the mosses and lichens.

The tundra presents only one climatic condition detrimental to the caribou. This is the winter thaw followed by a long spell of cold weather. Warm winds, known as the foehn in Norway and the chinook in the Rocky Mountain district of Canada, sometimes melt part of the snow, thus making it exceedingly moist. If these winds are followed by cold weather, a coating of ice may be formed over hundreds or even thousands of square miles of tundra, making it difficult or impossible for grazing animals to feed.

FIG. 217. The broad flat hoof of the reindeer makes a good snow shovel with which to uncover the mosses and lichens during the winter. (Courtesy U. S. Forest Service.)

Millions of caribou still range on the arctic slopes of Canada, and some range far south of the tundra. The chief foods of the caribou are shoots and leaves of willow, birch, and other shrubbery during the summer, and mosses and lichens during the winter. Where possible they migrate southward in summer, but they are quite capable, as in coastal Spitzbergen and Greenland (areas unaffected by chinook winds), of finding food in the Far North all the year round.

The caribou are gregarious and migratory. They sometimes graze in herds of thousands and even tens of thousands, and they may travel hundreds of miles within a few weeks. Consequently, it becomes necessary for those Eskimos and Indians who depend primarily upon them to lead a nomadic life.

Domestic Reindeer. The domestic reindeer are the great hope of the tundra. For many generations they have been the main resource of Lapland, the most highly developed and most densely populated tundra region of the world. To the Lapp, the reindeer are food, clothing, and shelter. They supply the power for transportation and constitute the basis of trade. Reindeer meat is the staple article of export, hundreds of tons being sold annually in Helsingfors (Helsinki), Stockholm, and Oslo (Christiana).

When the destruction of game threatened the Alaskan native with starvation, the U. S. Bureau of Education introduced reindeer from the Old World and taught the Eskimos to care for them (Figs. 217 and 218). In 1905 there were 10,000 deer; by 1929 the number had increased to 712,500. Since then the number has decreased so that in 1939 Alaska supported approximately 312,000 reindeer and in 1947 something less than 400,000. The U. S. Department of Agriculture estimates that Alaska, part of which lies outside the tundra, can support 3 to 4 million head. Stefansson estimates that the arctic pastures, including the Siberian tundra, are capable of supporting 100,000,000 reindeer, and Rudmose Brown believes that arctic Canada alone could support 30,000,000 reindeer and yield 10,000,000 carcasses of venison annually.[4] This exceeds the number of beef cattle slaughtered annually in the United States, but the average carcass of a deer would be only about one-third that of a fair-sized beef (Fig. 219).

Fig. 218. During the summer the reindeer usually graze on the scrub forest or other vegetation of the uplands where insect pests are less troublesome than in the low, wet tundra. (Courtesy Loman Reindeer Corporation, Seattle, Washington.)

Other Animals. In times gone by, the arctic foxes were the most common animals of the Far North. There are two varieties, the blue and the white fox. The fox obtains a living as readily from the sea as from the land and has been seen hundreds of miles from shore on the ice pack of the Arctic Sea. It feeds at bird rookeries, on hares, and on the scraps of seal left by the polar bear. The fox has been ruthlessly hunted for its winter coat. Two generations ago several

---

[4] J. Russell Smith estimates that arctic Canada could supply 3 to 4 million deer carcasses annually.

thousand fox skins were exported from Greenland annually; today the numbers have dwindled to a few score. The value placed upon the pelt of the white fox has been so great that hunters and trappers have practically exterminated this animal over large areas. Recently fox farming has been undertaken in the Mackenzie River Valley, with favorable results.

The wolf and the hare are almost as widely distributed as the fox except that the first two remain on land. The wolf feeds on hares,

Fig. 219. A reindeer corral in Alaska. Thousands of reindeer are slaughtered each year and the venison shipped to the industrial centers of the United States. (Courtesy Loman Reindeer Corporation, Seattle, Washington.)

foxes, lemmings, and even seals, with occasional meals of caribou and musk ox.

The white polar bear is the most characteristically polar of all arctic animals. Although it is an air breather, it is really a sea mammal and is seldom found far from sea ice. It commonly stays near the edge of the ice pack where seals are most numerous. During the last century the old whalers always brought home beautiful white skins as trophies. Such trophies are now rare and exceedingly valuable.

LIFE OF THE POLAR SEAS

Both the Arctic and Antarctic oceans abounded with life when the white man with his efficient methods of slaughter and insatiable greed first arrived in those waters. The variety of useful sea animals was even greater than that of the adjoining land. The seal, walrus, whale, sea elephant, together with many kinds of fish and birds have all contributed to the comfort and well-being of the natives who lived along the coasts of the polar seas, and also to the wealth of the European fisherman-hunter. The ruthless destruction of these animals by modern hunting and fishing equipment has all but exterminated some of

Fig. 220. Hunting seal in the frozen North. (Courtesy Finnish Foreign Office.)

them and has greatly depleted the numbers of all the sea mammals which were of value for their fur, oil, bone, or ivory (Fig. 220).

The exploitation of these resources was both romantic and lucrative. The whalers and seal hunters of New Bedford, Nantucket, Hull, and other New England and European ports were brave and daring men —men possessed of more than average ability and resourcefulness. Their love for adventure and desire for wealth sometimes induced them to make voyages of 20,000 or 30,000 miles through the most dangerous seas. Distances then, as measured by slowly moving sailing vessels, were much greater than today with our present facilities for rapid transportation. It took the New Bedford fleet almost a year to reach Bering Sea by way of the treacherous waters of Cape Horn. On these long journeys the fleet was away from the home port two or perhaps three years—many ships never returned at all.

THE FISHING INDUSTRIES

The Otary Seal. During the last half of the nineteenth century the fur of the otary seal was one of the most lucrative resources of the fishing industry, and it was the chief basis of many respectable fortunes. The center of this fur-seal fishing is the Pribilof Islands, where

Fig. 221. Fur seal, Pribilof Islands, Alaska. (Courtesy U. S. Bureau of Fisheries.)

formerly millons of seals gathered from distant seas during the mating season.[5] The Russians alone obtained approximately $100,000,000 worth of fur from the Bering Sea before the cession of Alaska to the United States.

The habits of the otary seals make them an easy prey for man. They are gregarious animals, and during the mating season they literally line the shores of some of the arctic islands (Fig. 221). Thousands of them could be seen from a single promontory as they gathered in the rookeries along the coast. The task of slaughter was a simple one. During the heyday of the sealing industry it was not uncommon for the crew of a single vessel to secure 20,000 seal skins in a season.

[5] It has been estimated that 3,000,000 seals formerly gathered on these islands annually.

Unfortunately it was impossible for any one country to make laws that would protect the seals. No country had jurisdiction over the sea or its products for a distance of more than three miles from shore. Therefore, when the seals went out to sea in search of food they were the legal prey of the fishermen of all nations. Since these animals swim much of the time at or near the surface, they are excellent targets for the hunters who in former times constantly scanned the waters in search of them (Figs. 222 and 223). Their numbers were rapidly depleted, and the industry was practically destroyed.

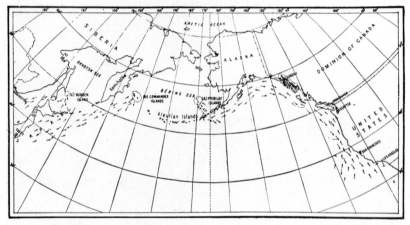

Fɪɢ. 222. Breeding grounds and routes of annual migration of fur seals. (Courtesy U. S. Bureau of Fisheries.)

In order to prevent the complete extinction of this valuable fur-bearing animal, the United States, Canada, and Japan entered into an agreement to stop pelagic sealing, and the United States passed laws to protect the herd on the reservations of the Pribilof Islands, now American territory. Consequently, the number of animals is slowly increasing. In 1939, the herd contained 2,020,438 animals, and more than 60,000 pelts are taken by the government each year.

Arctic Seal. The arctic seals, sought primarily for their oil and skins, are caught off the northeast coast of North America.[6] During the early spring large numbers of these animals drift southward with the Labrador Current to give birth to their young on the ice floes

---

[6] The seal skin makes a high-grade leather used in book binding and for the manufacture of handbags. The oil, formerly in demand as an illuminant, is now used in the manufacture of soap and other products of the chemical industry.

off the coast of eastern Canada. The sealing fleet drifts along the edge of the ice pack while the hunters take to the ice in search of the prey. Fifty years ago it was not uncommon for a single ship to take from 20,000 to 40,000 skins in a season, and the entire catch along this coast frequently exceeded 500,000 seals annually. The numbers of the herd are now greatly diminished, and the total catch by a fleet of less than a dozen ships sometimes scarcely exceeds 100,000 animals.

Fig. 223. When the seals migrate to their feeding grounds they swim much of the time at the surface of the water and are an easy prey to long-range rifles. (Courtesy U. S. Bureau of Fisheries.)

This type of sealing is one of the most dangerous industries of the sea. The sealing fleets leave port early in the spring—almost before winter is over. They operate in regions where stormy weather is the rule. Sometimes a severe storm breaks suddenly and without warning. Dense fogs or blinding blizzards may encompass the hunters while they are scattered on the ice floes, making it impossible for them to return to their ships. High winds may cause the ice floes to be broken up, leaving open water between the hunters and their ships, or the ice may be driven far out to sea. Those of the crew who are able to outlive the storm may be picked up, but when the rescue is delayed even the most hardy soon perish from exposure.

The Walrus—an Easy Prey to Man. The walrus was one of the earliest arctic animals known to Europe. Aside from its great size, the walrus is conspicuous for its two ivory tusks in the upper jaw. Those tusks are used to dig in the mud of the sea floor for clams, shellfish, and mussels—its favorite foods. Unlike other seals it does not feed on fish. Since its food is found in shallow water it is an animal of the coast and does not frequent the open sea far from land.

The walrus is valued chiefly for its ivory, but the tough hide also finds a ready market. Its flesh, like that of all seals, is good food and was formerly one of the major items in the diet of the natives who lived along the arctic shores. A love of gregariousness and the habit of remaining close to shore have proved to be fatal characteristics of the walrus. Hundreds and even thousands haul upon the beaches together and make the hunter's task all too easy. There is a record of more than a thousand of these animals being killed in Spitzbergen within a few hours. Now they are seldom seen in the waters north of Europe. In a similar manner over-hunting has greatly diminished their numbers in all arctic waters, and in many places they have virtually disappeared.

The Sealing Industry of Antarctica. A century ago the waters bordering the Antarctic continent supported millions of fur seal and sea elephants. The one is valued for its skin, the other for its oil. In 1800 the fur seal "swarmed" in the waters about South Orkney, South Georgia, and the Shetland Islands. At South Georgia a single vessel took 57,000 skins in one season, and hundreds of thousands were taken by other ships. In 1885 only 2 fur seals were killed in that region, and few have been seen there since. In a similar manner the fur seals have been practically exterminated in other antarctic waters.

The huge, ungainly sea elephant, another antarctic animal which has been of considerable commercial value, is still widely distributed about the antarctic islands and is now protected by law. Like other seals, the sea elephants are gregarious and spend much of their time ashore. These habits make them an easy prey for man, who has traced them to all their island haunts. The demand for oil has not been sufficiently great to threaten the extermination of the sea elephant. A few thousand of these animals are killed every year, but they are still plentiful about many of the antarctic islands.

Whaling. During the nineteenth century whaling was an important industry in both the Arctic and Antarctic seas. In 1820, Hull, England, sent 62 ships to the old Greenland whaling grounds, and the season's catch of oil and bone exceeded a million dollars in value. The price of the oil fell when mineral oil and gas were introduced as illuminants. But as the price of oil declined the value of bone (baleen) increased. By the end of the nineteenth century whalebone was selling for $10,000 a ton.[7] At such fabulous prices for bone a single whale might show a profit for a season's voyage. If the season had been especially successful and several whales had been caught the owner of the vessel returned home independently rich and the wages of the crew were correspondingly large. Occasionally a sick whale was caught which contained ambergris. Such whales were veritable gold mines.[8] Many respectable fortunes were made by New England and western European whalers within a few years.

The whaling fleet was not always successful. The industry was a dangerous one, especially in the Arctic Sea, and took a heavy toll of ships and human lives along the north coast of Alaska, Canada, and Siberia. Strong northern winds sometimes bring the ice down suddenly from the north, catching the ships and driving them ashore. R. N. Rudmose Brown, in writing of this subject, says that in 1876 36 ships were crushed off Point Belcher, and in 1879 several were caught and destroyed 40 miles off Point Barrow with great loss of life.

At the beginning of the twentieth century a cheap substitute was found for whalebone. The price of baleen dropped immediately, and within a few years it was selling for less than $500 a ton. At such prices a whaling voyage without the certainty of a "full ship" faced the prospect of financial disaster, and the whaler turned to some other type of fishing.

The whaling industry of the north polar seas is now of little importance; a romantic industry has all but disappeared. A few years ago 300 whaling vessels passed Bering Strait annually. Now the whaler seldom appears along the coast of Alaska.

The whaling grounds of the Antarctic Ocean were opened up in 1904 by the establishment of floating factories in that vast but slightly exploited sea. The floating factory has huge, jawlike gates in the ship, which when opened reveal a sloping "gullet" from the sea up

[7] A 60-ton whale yields 15 tons of bone—approximately 7.5 tons of baleen or flexible bone and 7.5 tons of bone of whale. The latter is of slight value.

[8] Ambergris is a secretion produced only in the intestines of a sperm whale. Presumably the squids upon which the beast feeds cause irritation in the intestines. Ambergris is found about these spots. Formerly, it sold for more than $200 a pound, and a single whale might produce hundreds of pounds. Ambergris is used as a base for the most delicate perfumes, not for its odor but as a fixative to make the perfume last. (Roy Chapman Andrews, *The Ends of the Earth*, Garden City Publishing Co., 1934.)

to the deck. A whale can be dragged up this slope to the deck, which is then turned into a factory. This pelagic whaler opened up a vast area in the Antarctic Ocean which hitherto had been beyond the limits of a factory. Consequently, the whaling industry was renewed on a larger scale than ever before. From 1930 to 1947 more than 90 per cent of the world's supply of whale oil was obtained from the Antarctic whaling grounds where the bulk of the oil is extracted on

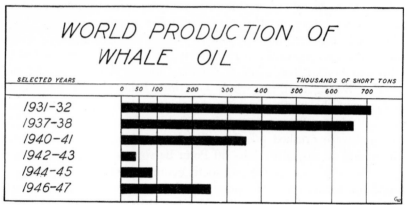

Fɪɢ. 224. The whale-oil industry will never be so important again as it was during the second and third decades of this century. The whaling grounds have already been greatly depleted and the catch is now limited by international agreement to approximately one-third (in oil take) of that of 1931-1932. (Courtesy *Foreign Commerce Weekly*, U. S. Department of Commerce, February 1946, p. 2.)

board the floating factories that are stationed along the edge of the ice field. In 1937–1938, Antarctic production reached a total of 541,000 tons of whale oil and more than 51,000 whales were killed. The catch is now limited by international agreement to 16,000 blue whale units a year. (A unit consists of one blue whale or two fin whales.) Such a catch provides about 250,000 tons of oil worth $450 a ton in 1947, as compared with approximately $150 a ton before World War II.

The whaling industry of every region has followed the same course —first a period of rapid development and profitable enterprise followed by collapse and final failure. By the fifteenth century the Basques had exterminated the whale in the Bay of Biscay. In the sixteenth century the Newfoundland fisheries rose and fell. Then the Greenland whale was discovered, and from the beginning of the seventeenth century to the middle of the last century a series of whale fisheries, one after another, flourished and then failed. In 1865, just when it seemed that whaling in the North Atlantic-Arctic was dead, Svend Foyn, a Norwegian, invented the modern harpoon gun. This opened a new fishery, that of the great rorqual whale which hitherto had been too fast and powerful to be attacked. Then history repeated itself, and for many years now only few whaling vessels have operated in the North Atlantic and adjoining Arctic. In a similar manner, but much more quickly, the whaling industry of the North Pacific-Arctic region rose and fell. In 1937–1938, the whaling industry of the Antarctic Ocean reached the peak of all times in the number of whales killed, but the output of oil was less than in 1931–1932 (Fig. 224).

International regulatory measures have been taken to preserve the whales that inhabit waters south of latitude 40° S. These measures will at least prolong the life of the whaling industry of the Antarctic Ocean. Whether the restrictions are sufficient to prevent the over-exploitation and the consequent undue decline of whaling remains an unanswered question.

BIRD LIFE OF HIGH LATITUDES

In addition to the mammals there is a rich bird life in both the arctic and antarctic regions. Practically all the birds obtain their food from the sea, and, except for the ptarmigan and white owl, all are summer visitors. Most widespread and loyal to the arctic is the ptarmigan, which varies its plumage so effectively with the season that it scarcely can be seen against either the stony banks in summer or the snow in winter.

Millions of migrant birds such as geese, ducks, and gulls visit the arctic region, where they nest during the summer on the rocky shores. When the weather is favorable the natives of northern Canada and Eurasia make visits to these islands in order to lay in supplies of duck meat and eggs.

The only arctic bird of commercial value is the eider duck, from which eider down is obtained for local use or for export. The Eskimos prize eider down for lining gloves or clothing and the eider skins for the manufacture of light and warm clothing.

The bird most common to Antarctica is the penguin, which gives life and animation to many lifeless and desolate coasts. The most remarkable species is the Emperor penguin, which stands, when full-grown, 3 feet high, and weighs more than 80 pounds. The Emperor is a rare bird, and only a few rookeries are known to exist.

The Adelaide penguin, which stands about 18 inches high, has been called "the population of Antarctica." We are told by Rudmose Brown, in his book *The Polar Regions*, that the Adelaide penguins are almost human in their behavior. The explorers of Antarctica always welcome their arrival, which is a sure sign that the long cold winter is over, and their "funny antics, strange conceits, and little foibles" are a source of entertainment about ships and at camps.

The number of these penguins is prodigious. Many an antarctic coast is alive for miles with nesting birds, and discordant with their ceaseless chatter. One estimate puts the number on Laurie Island, one of the South Orkney group with an area of only 30 square miles, at more than 5,000,000 during the nesting season.

Man has wrought some havoc among the penguins, but he has left many of their rookeries undisturbed. At the Falkland Islands there formerly was an industry of boiling down penguin oil. In 1868 a single ship load of oil represented the product from nearly 500,000 birds. The penguin is now protected by law and its numbers are increasing.

CONCLUSIONS ON POLAR SEA ANIMALS

Thus a study of the arctic and antarctic sea life indicates that, in spite of the relative inaccessibility of these waters, their most valuable animal resources have been overexploited and some of them almost exterminated. The habits of some of these animals made them an easy prey of the white man, and the great demand for their products, such as fur, oil, bone, and ivory, stimulated the search for them and set a premium upon their destruction. Since the high sea is international territory it was difficult to pass laws protecting these animals, and competition rather than cooperation was therefore unavoidable.

Fortunately the decreasing demand for oil and bone checked the slaughter of whales and of those seals and birds which were caught primarily for their oil products. Before the fur seals were completely exterminated the nations were able to agree upon a pelagic sealing law which has saved these animals from extermination. Of some of the mammals, such as the walrus and the antarctic fur seal, only a few remain—a precious seed which will increase in numbers if given sufficient protection.

PEOPLES OF THE TUNDRAS

As measured by population density the tundras may be classed among the most desolate deserts of the world. The permanent population of the Canadian tundras, covering approximately 1,000,000 square miles, is estimated at less than 6,000—one family for each 800 square miles.[9] The arctic slope of Alaska with its mining, fishing, and pastoral industries supports about 10,000 people, and the vast and desolate tundra of Siberia is the home of only a few thousand Samoyedes, Yakuts, and Eskimos, all of whom eke out a precarious living along one of the least accessible coasts of the world. Although the tundra of northern Europe is the most populous of all these sub-arctic regions and has the best developed civilization, yet even this land supports less than one person per square mile.

Tundra Culture

The environment of the tundra demands an amazing adaptation of man to his climate and meager resources. The chief occupations are hunting, fishing, and tending the reindeer. With few exceptions a nomadic or semi-nomadic life is imperative. The hunter must follow the caribou, seal, or other game from one feeding ground to another; the fisherman must be ever ready to migrate and perhaps to become a hunter when fish are not abundant; and even the pastoral tribes must constantly be seeking new grazing grounds.

Nomadic Culture

The Canadian Eskimo. The entire Eskimo race probably does not number 35,000, of which 16,200 live in Greenland. The Canadian Eskimos number approximately 6,000 and are among the most isolated peoples of the world. They are shut in between the eternal ice floes of the north polar sea and the barren "high tundras" to the south (Fig. 225). In places the Eskimo culture touches that of the forest Indian to the south, but there is little intermingling of the races. The red man is hostile to the Eskimo and treats him as an inferior.

[9] The total number of Eskimos in the entire Dominion of Canada is about 7,200, located mainly in the Northwest Territories, with approximately 1,780 in Quebec. *Canadian Year Book,* 1946, p. 1133, and 1947, p. 1163.

Although the Eskimo race is badly cut up into isolated groups by the broken character of the coast, the conditions of life are so much the same and the contacts frequent enough so that the peoples of the various groups are wonderfully alike both in appearance and in human activities. The major contrasts in human activities are those forced upon the Eskimos by the nature of the resources found in the various regions in which they live. The Eskimos living on the coast gain

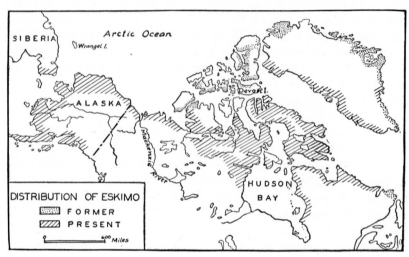

Fig. 225. The Eskimos live primarily along the coast.

most of their living from the sea and their chief occupation is fishing; the Eskimos who dwell in the interior are supported largely by wild game, and their chief occupation is hunting. Recently, the reindeer has been introduced into the tundra of Canada, and the number is increasing rapidly. Undoubtedly, within a few years the reindeer will play a much more important role in the life of the Eskimo than at present.

Coastal Peoples, a Fishing People. Most of the Eskimos are a coastal people whose food is obtained almost solely by hunting, chiefly in the sea. In summer the seal and other sea mammals are hunted in open water, in frail boats—the kayaks—made of skins stretched on frameworks of driftwood or bone, and sewn with sinews; in winter the seals are surprised and speared at holes in the ice where they come up to breathe. The weapons of the natives are made of the teeth or tusks of animals, and their clothing is made of skins. Even the sledges drawn by dog teams over the frozen snow are largely fashioned from the bones and skins of sea mammals.

Sometimes the Eskimos find seal and other sea mammals scarce. Then they migrate to find the nesting places of birds, or to seek new hunting or fishing grounds along the coast. Perchance they travel a little inland to follow the caribou or the musk ox, but that is the exception, not the rule. Wherever they go the quest for wild animals is their main object.

Dress. The men and women all dress alike. They wear boots, trousers, and hooded jackets made largely of seal skins; but the skins of foxes, caribou, bears, and other animals are also used. The skins of eider ducks are especially prized for clothing, but they are expensive. Several seals are exchanged for a single pair of eiderskin gloves.

Houses. Many of the coastal Eskimos live most of the time in log huts, or houses built of wood, peat, or stone, but tents and igloos are still common. In spring, summer, and autumn the Eskimos who do not have permanent houses and those who are forced to move in order to find better fishing or hunting grounds live in seal-skin or caribou-skin tents; in winter they build their snow houses, which require only the heat of a tallow lamp to give complete protection against the cold. George Binney in writing of the Eskimo dwellings says that tents and snow houses have the hygienic advantage of not being permanent establishments, and are therefore less likely to harbor the germs of disease. On the other hand, these dwellings have their unsatisfactory features. Winter sets in before there is sufficient snow for the building of snow houses, and likewise in the spring the igloos melt before the snow is off the ground. During these two transition periods tent life is extremely cold, and extremely wet, respectively. The exposure and the dampness thus encountered are allies of tuberculosis.

In Labrador and other places along the coast many of the Eskimos have abandoned tents and snow houses and are living in stone, peat, or wooden shacks. Such a change is of doubtful benefit among primitive peoples who know little about the laws of sanitation.

Eskimos of the Interior or "Caribou Eskimos." Parts of northern Canada are among the most isolated and inaccessible places in the world. This is especially the condition which exists in the "barren grounds," a large tract of untimbered land lying just west of the northern half of Hudson Bay. On the north there are ramifications of the Arctic Ocean permanently filled with ice and fog, which bar entrance; on the south and to some extent on the west lie great trackless forests, where travel is slow and difficult. It is because of this isolation that these "barren grounds" are still the home of the most primitive and uncivilized tribes of Eskimos to be found anywhere. The life of these people is a hard one—so hard, indeed, that they grow old before their time.

These interior Eskimos depend almost entirely upon caribou for their support. This hardy animal supplies them with food, clothing, summer shelter, and warm bedding for their winter homes. Since they must follow the caribou they are forced to lead a nomadic life, and any permanent houses of stone, wood, or peat would be inconsistent with their method of living. They therefore live in tents during the summer and in snow houses during the winter.

These interior Eskimos are distinctly handicapped because of a shortage of fuel supply. The caribou does not provide large quantities of fat for fuel, and the Eskimo's home remains unheated even though the temperature may often fall below $-50°$ F. A more serious result of fuel shortage is the fact that for days in succession they may have nothing to eat but frozen meat with not even a mouthful of hot soup to help it down.

Another serious difficulty is that of getting their footwear dry after a long day's hunting. If they have skins enough the wet things are thrown away and replaced by new ones; failing this the old wet clothing has to be dried at night by laying it next to the body.[10]

Unfortunately the life of the "caribou Eskimo" is made harder by the fact that the moving of the caribou during the summer and autumn comes at just those seasons when traveling is most difficult. The introduction of firearms probably aided the Eskimo for a time, but in the end these superior facilities defeat their purpose by making possible the excessive slaughter of caribou and thus unduly reducing their numbers. As a result, according to Knud Rasmussen, the inhabitants of some areas have been completely exterminated by starvation.

Semi-Nomadism

The Influence of Domestic Animals. The peoples who have domestic animals differ in many respects from those who live by hunting. In general their resources are more dependable, they have better tents or huts, better equipment, and a greater variety of utensils and weapons. Since their mode of life provides greater material resources,

[10] Knud Rasmussen, *Across Arctic America*, G. P. Putnam's Sons, 1927, p. 78.

they are able to purchase a greater abundance of articles from civilized peoples.

Progress in Arctic Alaska. The domestic reindeer has wrought great changes in the lives of the Laplanders and the Alaskan Eskimos. The reindeer of Alaska number about 500,000. Those of arctic Alaska number about 400,000 head, of which the Eskimos own about two-thirds. Along the coast of the Arctic Ocean huts have been replaced by houses, camps by villages, and barter by systematic trade. In short, the nomadic hunters are being transformed into a semi-nomadic class which is adopting civilized methods of life. Along this coast are villages such as Barrow and Point Hope with houses, schools, churches, and stores. It must be remembered, however, that these villages must forever remain small since the tundra can support only a few reindeer per square mile.

Culture in Lapland. The Lapps lead a semi-nomadic life. They depend in part upon hunting and fishing, but their most valuable resource is the domestic reindeer. Each group has a summer settlement and another settlement for winter. During the winter they live in villages usually located within the marginal zone of the northern forest where the herds of reindeer find some shelter from the winter storms. When the snow melts, some of the Lapps drive their herds to the mountains in order to find good pasture and, at the same time, to escape from the poorly drained tundra where swarms of mosquitoes and gnats torment both man and beast. Others go to the coast where they fish during the summer. They leave behind them all their winter necessities stored in wooden buildings ready for use again in the fall.

The Lapps produce a surplus of reindeer meat and hides which is sold in the coastal cities of Norway and other European countries. With the proceeds they purchase coffee, cloth for summer clothing, and machine-made utensils and weapons.

Civilization in Iceland. Iceland, bathed by the warming winds from the Gulf Stream and settled by European colonists, has developed the highest civilization found within the subarctic regions. Its area of 40,000 square miles, the size of Ohio, has habitable grounds of less than 10,000 square miles. Yet it supports about 100,000 people, mostly of Scandinavian descent. It has good public schools, a university, a national library, and publishes many newspapers and periodicals.

The pastoral activities represent the most important industry of the island. At present the pastures support more than 20,000 cattle, many thousand ponies, and more than 1,000,000 sheep. At times the annual exports from this small island reach $30 or $40 per capita.

The Yakuts. Even the pastoral peoples are compelled to live in extreme poverty in the harsher parts of the tundra. This is well illustrated by the Yakuts, who live in the northeastern part of Siberia, one of the coldest lands in the world. They tend their herds of cattle, hunt for seal along the shore, and fish in the streams and in the Arctic Ocean. They occupy several square miles of pasture per capita. Yet the majority of householders have only the bare necessities of existence, and the loss of a cow may leave a family immediately in serious circumstances.

Developments in Soviet Russia. During the decade 1930 to 1940, the Soviet Union made remarkable progress along the arctic shore of European Russia. Forty to fifty thousand people have gone into this cold land to live. Ports, cities, and airports are being developed, and the lumbering industry and trade are being promoted. The lumber industry is supported by the timber of the great northern forest which lies along the southern border of the tundra. The logs are floated down the northward-flowing rivers, either to the sawmills situated along the arctic shore or to ships for export to western European countries.

The Cultural Effect of a Change in Environment

According to Ellsworth Huntington the Samoyedes of northern Siberia appear to afford an interesting example of the way in which a change in environment causes a change in civilization. "The Samoyedes once lived much farther south than now, in the better part of Siberia, and were correspondingly more highly civilized. They were all acquainted with mining, for example, and sometimes dug shafts to a depth of fifty feet. They knew how to build furnaces wherein to melt copper, tin, and gold; they manufactured weapons of hard bronze and made great pots. The polished decorations of bronze and gold testify to a high development of artistic feeling and industrial skill. They were not nomads, but husbandmen who practiced irrigation and built canals whose ruins can still be seen. They kept domestic animals, including a few horses, together with sheep and goats." [11]

[11] Ellsworth Huntington, *The Human Habitat*, p. 66. Reprinted through courtesy of D. Van Nostrand Co.

The Turkish invasion of southern Siberia drove the Samoyedes farther north, where they have degenerated to a very low stage of civilization. "Today the Samoyedes of the lower Ob have no domestic animals and maintain themselves by hunting and fishing. They dress in skins, use implements of bone and stone, and eat carnivorous naimals including the wolf. Instead of finely made copper utensils they use the crudest earthenware. Their huts resemble the stone huts of the Eskimos; their graves are mere boxes left on the Tundra. Such a low stage of culture is almost essential because a higher stage can scarcely be maintained on such a slender environmental basis, but it by no means implies the absence of fine qualities. The Samoyedes are noted for their honesty and independence, and are highly courageous. But neither these qualities nor almost any other can compensate for the repressive effect of an environment where even the herding of reindeer is beset with great difficulties, and men of every race are forced to become nomadic hunters if they would procure the means of life." [12]

HYGIENIC CONDITIONS OF POLAR AND SUBPOLAR REGIONS

Most European explorers of high latitudes have enjoyed a relative degree of freedom from diseases, even when exposed to hardships which undermine the physical condition and leave the weakened body with less than normal resistance against disease germs. Both the Lapps and the Eskimos are relatively healthy peoples except when diseases new to them and against which they have developed little immunity are introduced by the explorers or fishermen. The healthfulness of high latitudes is probably related to the low atmospheric humidity, the chemical purity of the air, and the relative freedom from bacteria, especially during the winter months.

The tundra peoples seem to be healthiest during the winter and succumb to illness in the spring when tent life gives inadequate protection against the melting snow and damp ground.

Unfortunately the nomadic tribes of the tundra, like so many other primitive peoples, have shown little resistance to the white man's diseases. Diseases of the lungs, once introduced, are especially disastrous. Tuberculosis is now widespread among many of the Eskimo tribes scattered from Alaska to Greenland and is especially threatening among the tribes of Labrador who have abandoned the snow houses and tents to live in disease-infected shacks.

[12] *Op. cit.*, pp. 66–67. Reprinted through courtesy of D. Van Nostrand Co.

Another disease which has been especially disastrous among these northern peoples is influenza. It has been particularly virulent in Labrador, where, in 1918, it is said to have caused the death of one-third of the entire population. In 1928, an influenza epidemic spread throughout the whole of northern Canada, resulting in a heavy mortality among the natives.

FUTURE OF THE TUNDRA

The tundra must ever remain sparsely populated, and the standards of living are likely to remain low. The increase of pastoral activities and the conservation of valuable sea mammals and fish seem to afford the best opportunity to raise the standards of living and at the same time permit an increase in population density. Nevertheless it is pointed out by Huntington that these northern hunting and pastoral peoples are always poor according to our standards. Their wealth is largely in their reindeer and unreliable products of the sea. There are definite limits to the size of the herd which any one man can maintain, especially in the tundra, where the carrying capacity of the pasture is at best only a few animals per square mile. The average productive capacity of 100 square miles of tundra would scarcely equal that of a moderately good farm in the corn belt. Under such conditions a nomadic or semi-nomadic life seems best adapted to most of these vast areas. Only in favored places are the local resources sufficiently abundant and reliable for man to settle down.

No nomad can ever carry many goods or chattels with him; consequently he is deprived of most of the things which we consider necessities.

REFERENCES

AMUNDSEN, ROALD, *My Life as an Explorer*, Doubleday, Doran & Co., 1927.
The South Pole, Lee Keedick, 1929.
BROWN, RUDMOSE R. N., *The Polar Regions*, E. P. Dutton & Co., 1927.
BURWASH, L. T., "Across Arctic Canada," *Geographical Journal*, December 1929, pp. 553–568.
BUTLER, FRANK HEDGES, *Through Lapland with Skis and Reindeer*, Frederick A. Stokes Co., 1917.
BYRD, RICHARD E., *Exploring with Byrd*, G. P. Putnam's Sons, 1937.
Alone, G. P. Putnam's Sons, 1938.
Canadian Year Book, Dominion Bureau of Statistics, Ottawa, Canada, 1947, annual.
COLBY, MERLE, *A Guide to Alaska: Last American Frontier*, Federal Writers' Project, The Macmillan Co., 1939.

Cox, Leo, "The Golden North," *Canadian Geographical Journal*, Ottawa, Canada, April 1938, pp. 203–210.

Fisher, Clyde, "The Nomads of the Arctic Lapland," *National Geographic Magazine*, November 1939, pp. 641–676.

Greely, A. W., *The Polar Regions in the Twentieth Century*, Little, Brown & Co., 1928.

Hayes, J. Gordon, *Antarctica*, Richard Press, London, 1928.

Hobbs, William Herbert, *The North Pole of the Winds*, G. P. Putnam's Sons, 1930.

Höst, Per, "With the Norwegian Sealers," *Natural History*, January 1943, pp. 6–17.

Innis, Harold A., "Hudson Bay Railroad," *Geographical Review*, January 1930.

Kendrew, W. G., *Climate*, The Clarendon Press, 1930, pp. 109–114.

Kuelz, Walter N., "A Naturalist with Macmillan in the Arctic," *National Geographic Magazine*, March 1926, pp. 299–318.

O'Malley, Henry, "The Fur-Seal Industry of the Pribilof Islands," Alaska Department of Commerce, *Economic Circular* 71, May 1930.

Patton, Harold S., "Canada's Advance to Hudson Bay," *Economic Geography*, July 1929, pp. 215–235.

"Problems of Polar Research," A Series of Papers by Thirty-One Authors, American Geographical Society *Special Publication* 7, 1928.

Shaw, Sir Napier, "Arctic Weather of April 15–16, 1928," *Geographical Review*, October 1928, pp. 556–566.

Stefansson, Vilhjalmur, "Some Problems of Arctic Travel," *Geographical Journal*, November 1929, pp. 417–431.

The Northward Course of Empire, Harcourt, Brace & Co., 1922.

The Friendly Arctic, The Macmillan Co., 1921.

"The American Far North," *Foreign Affairs*, April 1939, pp. 509*ff.*

Taylor, Griffith, *Antarctic Adventure and Research*, D. Appleton & Co., 1930.

Wilkins, Sir Hubert, "The Flight from Alaska to Spitzbergen, 1928, and the Preliminary Flights of 1926–27," *Geographical Review*, October 1928, pp. 527–555.

Chapter 18

HIGHLANDS AND MAN

Regions of Sharp Contrasts. Mountainous areas and deeply dissected plateaus provide areas of violent contrasts, in both natural environment and cultural development. Marked differences in climates, soils, topography, resources, and accessibility exist within a few miles of each other. Accordingly, many types of natural environment may be found within a relatively small mountainous area. Each type is associated with its distinct problems of human adjustment.

Since highlands produce many types of natural environment, man's adjustments to each of these types cannot be explained in the narrow limits of a single chapter of this book. Nevertheless, certain worthwhile generalizations can be suggested about highlands in addition to those already given regarding climate, soil, topography, resources, and accessibility.

For example, highlands act as barriers. Wherever rugged highlands are thrown athwart man's path they increase the difficulty of travel and also the expense and effort of transporting goods. Highlands act as barriers not only to man but also to winds, plants, and animals. This generalization of highlands acting as barriers becomes somewhat meaningless except as man studies specific highlands as a barrier against some specific thing. The climatologist studies the influence of the Rocky Mountains as a climatic barrier; the botanist studies these mountains as a barrier to the spread of plants; and the civil engineer considers these highlands as a barrier to transportation.

Barriers may be few or many, long or short, high or low, steep or gentle, snow covered or dry, jungle covered or bare rock. Thus the Himalayas, Andes, and Pyrenees mountains are powerful barriers in many respects. They are high, long, and steep. The Alps, on the other hand, are high, but they are crossed by many passes at comparatively low elevations.

The Himalayas form a barrier difficult for man to cross. The Alps with their low passes are easily crossed in times of peace but the passes can be relatively easily held in times of war. Thus the importance of the Himalayas as a barrier to man is rather effective at all times, whereas the importance of the Alps as a barrier depends somewhat on political conditions.

Many generalizations have been made about highlands. Such generalizations should be studied with care before they are accepted as applying universally to all highlands. A study of the following generalizations indicates that some of them have universal application, whereas others apply only to certain mountainous regions. (1) Highlands influence rainfall. (2) Highlands influence temperature conditions. (3) Highland agriculture is difficult to develop. (4) Highlands act as barriers to man, plants, and animals. (5) Highlands act as a defense against enemies. (6) Highlands make good places of refuge. (7) Highlands tend to cause isolation and to retard human progress. (8) Highlands are used as political boundaries. (9) Some highlands have helped to preserve ancient customs, manners, and languages. (10) Highlanders are largely economically independent. (11) Highlands are important sources of water power, minerals, and forest products.[1]

A study of the above statements that have been selected from various sources will indicate something of the dangers of generalizing. Highlands have played a part in determining national boundaries; in protecting peoples from their enemies; and in preserving ancient customs, manners, and languages. Yet not all highlands have been useful in these respects.

For our special study the highlands of the world are divided into two groups as related to their influences upon cultural development. These groups are as follows: (1) highlands of low latitudes, and (2) highlands of middle and high latitudes.

Low-latitude highlands, because of their elevation, provide home sites that possess more comfortable, wholesome, and invigorating climates than the surrounding lowlands. Consequently, tropical highlands (not all tropical highland areas but the best of them) have become the centers of the most highly developed *native* civilization of many parts of the tropics. In recent years, the cultural development of both tropical lowlands and tropical highlands is largely the result of the initiative of energetic peoples from the temperate zones. That is, the progress is largely due to imported human energy rather than

---

[1] An excellent study of the influence of mountains on human activities may be found in *Mountain Geography* by Roderick Peattie, Harvard University Press, 1936.

to native energy. Yet even the white man can retain his health and energy in the tropical highlands longer than in the tropical lowlands.

Highlands of middle and high latitudes provide, on the whole, less favorable opportunities for cultural progress than the surrounding lowlands. Most highland climates of middle latitudes, when considered for the entire year, however, are no more invigorating than the climates of the neighboring lowlands. On the other hand, the rugged topography is a distinct handicap to cultural progress.

Thus, as a whole, highlands have favored the advancement of civilization within the tropics and have retarded progress in middle and higher latitudes. There are many exceptions to this general classification. These exceptions are not of sufficient importance to vitiate the general principle that has been stated. Its truth is indicated by the fact that in many tropical areas the highlands are more densely populated than the lowlands, in spite of the fact that the rugged topography of the highlands does not lend itself to ease of agricultural, industrial, or commercial development. Most highlands of middle and higher latitudes are, on the other hand, less densely populated than the surrounding lowlands.

HIGHLANDS IN LOW LATITUDES

The low-latitude highlands are widely scattered. In east-central Africa they occupy large sections of Abyssinia, Kenya, Tanganyika, Uganda, Rhodesia, and Nyasaland; in Asia they are scattered throughout the East Indies, the Philippines, and Ceylon, and they occupy parts of the southeastern peninsula of the continent; in America they are found in the West Indies, on the mainland from northern Mexico to southern Peru and Bolivia, and in eastern Brazil.

The plateaus and mountains of moderate elevations (5,000 to 10,000 feet near the equator and 2,000 to 7,000 feet near the tropics) possess the most agreeable and healthful climate of the low latitudes and in general support more highly developed native civilizations than the surrounding lowlands.

Climatic Zones of Low-Latitude Highlands

The climatic conditions found within a mountainous region vary almost as markedly as the relief. Places only a few miles apart may have striking contrasts in temperatures, precipitation, strength of winds, and other atmospheric conditions.

Since the temperature of the air decreases approximately 1° F., on the average, for every 330 feet of elevation,[2] high plateaus and mountains, even within the tropics, rise into the cool, upper layers of the air. Indeed, many low-latitude mountains rise so high that their summits are perpetually snow covered, and glaciers occupy their upper valleys.

The seasonal range in temperature is small in both the low-latitude lowlands and uplands, but the diurnal range is large, especially in the uplands.

Elevation and land forms have almost as marked an influence on precipitation as on temperatures. Mountains which lie athwart the path of moisture-bearing winds have an abundant rainfall on the slopes against which the winds blow (windward), while the opposite slopes (leeward) are relatively dry. This principle is well illustrated in Central America and Assam. The highlands of Costa Rica present a bold front to the trade winds. As these moist winds are forced up the steep eastern slopes the air is cooled rapidly and consequently the area is one of eternal clouds and showers, the atmosphere is damp, and the luxuriant vegetation is dripping wet. On the leeward side not far distant sunshine is much more abundant and the annual rainfall may be only a few inches. Similarly the Assam Highlands which lie directly across the path of the summer monsoons are rain drenched on the southern slopes but relatively dry on the northern side. Cherrapunji, situated on the southern slopes, receives an average annual rainfall of 458 inches, and during one exceptional year 905 inches fell. Shillong, located on the northern slope only 30 miles from Cherrapunji, has only 83 inches.

Classification of Tropical-Highland Climates. The highland climates are so varied that they do not readily fall into a few simple patterns which can be easily classified. Nevertheless, a few broad, yet significant, generalizations can be made. Three climatic zones based on differences of temperature are aptly designated by the Spanish terms *tierra caliente* (hot lands), *tierra templada* (temperate lands), and *tierra fria* (cold lands). A fourth zone that lies between the tierra fria and the permanent snow line is sometimes called the *páramos*. The altitude of each of these zones depends on the latitude. In general, each of the zones extends 2,000 to 3,000 feet higher at the equator than in latitude 20.

[2] The decrease in temperature with each 1,000 feet of elevation varies considerably from one place to another, and at the same place from one time to another, as a result of differences in exposure to sun and winds and of changes in atmospheric conditions.

The Tierra Caliente. Near the equator the tierra caliente lies between sea level and approximately 3,000 feet, while in latitude 20 it
scarcely extends above the 1,000-foot contour. Where this zone is
well watered throughout the year it has all the characteristics of the
rainy low latitudes and is so classified (Chapter 5). Where it is arid
it becomes a part of the desert or steppe (Chapter 8), and where the
rainfall is distinctly seasonal it is classified as low latitude wet and
dry (Chapter 7).

The Tierra Templada and Tierra Fria. The tierra templada and
tierra fria are the true highlands of the tropics. They are the lands of
hot sunshine and cool shade, of warm days and cool nights. It is not
uncommon in such altitudes for the diurnal range to exceed 25° or
even 30° F. At noon the temperature may be uncomfortably high; in
the evening light wraps are in demand; and the early mornings may
be disagreeably cold. Thus at Fort Hall, Kenya Colony, with an altitude of 4,410 feet, the mean annual maximum temperature is 80.5° F.,
but its mean minimum temperature is only 64.6° F. During the dry
months of January and February, when the atmosphere of this upland
is exceptionally clear, the diurnal range usually exceeds 30° F. and
occasionally 40° F.

On the high plateaus the diurnal range is even larger and causes
great discomfort among the natives. This condition is well illustrated
on the Bolivian Plateau, which exceeds 12,000 feet in height. Here
Kendrew, in The Climates of the Continents, tells us that, owing to
the clear dry atmosphere, the sun's rays are powerful during the day
and radiation is effective at night. During the dry season the shade
temperatures are about 25° higher at midday than before sunrise. But
this fact does not bring out the significant difference between day and
night, since the contrast between sunshine and shade is also great.
"Early in the morning and late in the evening when the sun is below
the horizon, the cold is liable to be intense even in September and one
suffers from almost frozen feet. In the winter when the winds blow
and the frosts are yet more severe, the dry cold is so trying that even
the natives cover up their faces in thick woolen masks, and wrap
shawls about their heads and ponchos over their bodies. But as soon
as the sun is a little way above the horizon, its direct rays scorch the
traveler with their great heat, so that he soon begins to pray for the
night, as the lesser evil of the two. . . . By day the burning sunshine
so envelops all the brown, dry, dusty ground that everything in view
seems to vanish in the brightness; and the eye unprotected by dark

glasses cannot gaze steadily in any direction. . . . When the sun is hottest little cyclones raise dust whirlwinds which dance along, often by scores at a time."

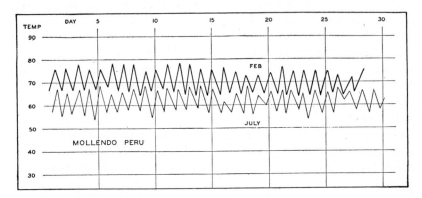

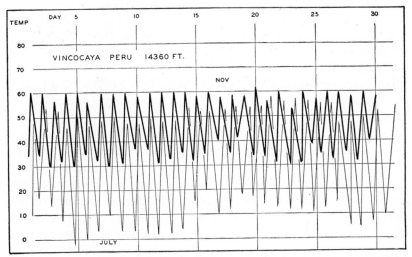

FIG. 226. Diurnal range of temperature for the coldest and the hottest months. (After Mark Jefferson, "Actual Temperatures of South America," *Geographical Review*, July 1926.)

Mark Jefferson has graphically illustrated the great diurnal range on the highlands of Peru (Fig. 226). It must be remembered, however, that these are shade temperatures, and the full effect of the powerful sun's rays in midday is not indicated here. On the other hand, the low temperatures of night are felt more keenly than in most parts of the world because of (1) the suddenness with which the temperatures drop, and (2) the strong winds that frequently accompany these wide and sudden fluctuations in temperatures.

These harsh climatic changes are not the only adverse atmospheric conditions which man encounters in high altitudes. The air pressure over the Andean Plateau of Ecuador, Peru, and Bolivia is only 20 to 22 inches of mercury, and visitors suffer much discomfort from mountain sickness. Even natives who travel from the coast to the plateau are not immune. The "soroche," as the complaint is called locally, causes breathlessness and palpitation and, sometimes, loss of appetite and nosebleeding. Colds are another very common complaint of these high altitudes.

During the winter cold gales sometimes sweep the plateau and cause much suffering and sickness. Because of the bronchial trouble which follows in their wake they are sometimes called "the harvest of death."

Man in the Low-Latitude Highlands

The highlands of moderate elevations are the most pleasant and healthful areas within the tropics. Accordingly the peoples are, for the most part, more active and progressive than the natives who live either in the hot lowlands or in the high plateaus which extend up into the dry, cold atmosphere where temperature changes are harsh and sudden.

Agricultural and Pastoral Industries the Major Activities. The tierra templada is suited to the cultivation, at one elevation or another, of a great variety of crops, including coffee, corn, wheat, sisal, millet, pasture, fruits, and vegetables. Coffee is the most important commercial crop. Since this zone grows more than 90 per cent of the world's supply, it has been called the coffee belt. Near the equator this zone extends from about 3,000 feet to 6,500 feet, but near the tropics it lies between the 1,000- and 4,000-foot contours.

The tierra fria has been designated as the hardy-cereal-pasture belt. Wheat, barley, oats, potatoes, and hardy vegetables mature throughout this climatic zone. Maize matures in altitudes up to 8,000 feet more or less, depending on the latitude.

Above the tierra fria are situated the treeless grasslands (called *páramos* in parts of Latin America) which are too cold for the maturing of crops. Grass may grow almost or quite to the snow line, and cattle, sheep, llama, and alpaca may be pastured at elevations up to 15,000 feet or slightly higher.

The Isolation of Low-Latitude Highlands. Isolation has been a retarding influence of major importance in the economic development of most low-latitude highlands. No navigable rivers afford easy access to the heart of these regions, nor can they be reached by railroad or highway except at a tremendous cost. They are usually approached across inhospitable lands of one kind or another. Swampy coastal belts, dense tropical forests, and rain-drenched mountain slopes make access difficult from the windward side; to the leeward, the highlands may be just as effectively isolated from the outside world by sandy or rocky stretches of desolate desert waste. In most of these plateaus and mountainous areas the effect of isolation is intensified by the ruggedness of the topography and the resultant difficulties of developing local trade. Such conditions must necessarily retard or even prevent the development of those economic activities which are dependent upon cheap and efficient transportation facilities.

Even where the highlands are close to the coast and the elevation not very great, the cost of transportation may be too high to permit the import or export of products other than those of relatively high value and small bulk. This condition is clearly illustrated in northern Venezuela. The railroad connecting La Guaira with Caracas winds along precipitous slopes mile after mile as it ascends from the lowlands to a summit level of more than 3,000 feet. The road is now electrified and represents the finest in engineering skill. It is an efficient but not a cheap system of transportation, and even today the two-wheeled mule cart competes for the traffic between La Guaira and Caracas.

The cost of building a railroad across the plateau is high also, and the upkeep is tremendously expensive. C. S. Cooper, in writing of the railway between Caracas and Valencia, says that in the course of its 111 miles there are 86 tunnels and 212 bridges, the road often coming out of a tunnel onto a bridge and immediately entering another tunnel. In times of revolution it is an easy matter to blow up some of the bridges or block some of the tunnels.

Some of the most spectacular results of engineering to be found anywhere are represented by the railroads extending from the Pacific and Atlantic coasts of South America to the Andean Plateau. The central railway of Peru is one of the most notable engineering achievements to be found in all South America. This railway ascends to a height of 15,865 feet above sea level, the highest point reached by any standard-gauge railway in the world. On several of these Andean roads the steepness of the grades is frightful and the cog-rail system is used. The cost of building and maintaining such roads is so great that freight

rates, as a consequence, are exceedingly high. In the highlands of
Bolivia the llamas are still cheaper carriers than railways (Fig. 227).
Thousands of them still carry ore from the mines to the mills and
frequently even transport goods between two points connected by
railway. In some parts of South America even the natives follow the
railway as a highway along which they carry their products to market
in competition with the railroad.

Similarly in southern Brazil, the Serra do Mar is a formidable barrier which separates the coastal cities from the fertile, well-watered

Fig. 227. A llama pack-train in Peru. (Courtesy Carnegie Institute, Washington,
D. C.)

plateau. The widely famed railway which extends from Santos to São
Paulo was built at a tremendous cost, and great engineering skill was
required to construct it on the steep, east-facing slopes of the Serra do
Mar. The gradient for part of the roadbed is 8 per cent, and it is necessary to pull the cars up the steep slope by cable. Fortunately this
road is profitable in spite of the great cost of original construction and
the high operating expenses, since more than one-half of the world's
coffee crop passes over it.

Effect of Isolation on Foreign Trade. The early trade, as might be
expected, was limited almost exclusively to products of relatively high
value as compared with the bulk. The exports of the Andean Highlands and the Mexican Plateau consisted largely of precious metals,
primarily gold and silver, which could stand the cost of shipment by
human carriers; from the highlands of eastern Brazil were obtained

diamonds and gold; from east-central Africa the daring and frequently unscrupulous trader obtained slaves and ivory. The slave trader solved his problems of transportation by compelling his unhappy victims to carry heavy loads of ivory across desert and through swampy coastal forest to some coastal city where both the slaves and their cargoes were sold at neighboring markets. The early import trade of these regions too frequently consisted merely of trinkets which were of little true value to the natives.

As previously indicated, the transportation facilities for most of the low-latitude highlands have been materially improved during the last few decades, and consequently the possibilities not only of foreign but also of domestic trade have been widened. A list of the agricultural and pastoral exports today includes coffee, tea, cotton, hides, wool, sisal fiber, and even wheat, corn, and millet; from the mines are obtained not only the precious metals, gold and silver, but also tin concentrates, copper, and lead.

The Influence of Elevation and Land Forms as Illustrated in Kenya Colony

Although crossed by the equator, the highlands of Kenya Colony support crops which are characteristic of every climatic zone from the equatorial lowlands to the polar ice caps. On those lower mountain slopes which are well watered, as around Lake Victoria, are found heat- and moisture-loving plants, such as coco palm, pineapple, rubber trees, and plantain, and on the drier eastern foothills the land is largely devoted to pasture. On the uplands of moderate elevation, 4,000 to 7,000 feet, coffee and sisal are the important commercial crops and supply the major exports of Kenya. On the high plateau above 7,000 feet most of the cultivable land is given to wheat and corn, but such crops as coffee, tea, fruits, and a great variety of those vegetables most commonly grown in Europe and America thrive in the lower parts of this zone. Throughout the highlands—except where irrigated—the drier areas which are sheltered by mountains from the moisture-bearing winds serve as pasture.

A Land Suited to European Colonization. Although all attempts at European colonization have failed in the hot, humid, tropical lowlands, the British are succeeding in establishing permanent settlements in the uplands not only of Kenya but also in other east African highlands. Here large tracts of cultivable land lie at altitudes of a mile or more above sea level, lands which are not unpleasantly hot except

for a few hours during the middle of the day. At Fort Hall, altitude
4,410 feet, the average annual temperature is only 64.6° F., whereas at

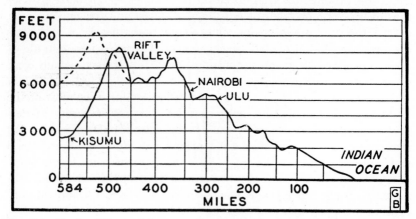

FIG. 228. Much of Kenya Colony consists of a highland well suited to colonization
by Europeans.

Mombasa, on the coast, it is 78.5° F. The average monthly minimum
temperature at Fort Hall never exceeds 58° F.; the mean monthly

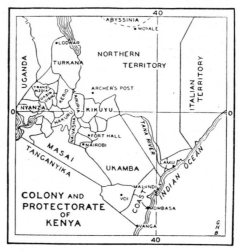

FIG. 229. Place map of Kenya Colony.

maximum temperature ranges from 75° to 88° F. The early morning
and late evening temperatures are always sufficiently cool and invigo-

rating to stimulate both mental and physical activities. The British have spoken of the uplands as an area of perpetual spring (Figs. 228 and 229).

EUROPEAN PLANTATION AGRICULTURE

Amazing tales of the pleasant temperate-zone climate of the Kenya Highlands were told with increasing frequency after 1885. Early travelers and traders also recorded the existence of large areas of fertile land well adapted to the cultivation of European crops and having mild temperatures suitable for the successful establishment of European colonies. Yet much of this land was totally unoccupied except for big game or was wastefully devoted to grazing. Rapid development of these lands was out of the question, however, because of poor transportation facilities. The only products which could be exported profitably were slaves who could walk to market, and ivory which could bear the high cost of transportation.[3]

The first requisite for the development of plantation agriculture was some improved method of transportation. The highlands lie 300 to 500 miles from the coast; no navigable rivers afforded a highway to the sea; and beasts of burden could not be used because of the ravages of the tsetse fly. Human portage was almost the only means of transportation, and that was costly. It was estimated that human portage in legitimate trade cost about 75 cents per ton per mile. Thus each ton transported from the highlands cost approximately $300 carrying charges alone—a cost prohibitive for most agricultural products.[4] Aside from the monetary expense, human portage in this part of Africa was extremely costly in life. In a single caravan, 2,000 natives died of dysentery while crossing Kenya from the Uganda border. In addition the caravans were the means of conveying epidemics all along the route and into the home villages of the porters. Under such conditions it was only natural that plantation agriculture should await the construction of a railway, which was completed across the highlands of Kenya to the Uganda border in 1901.

[3] The highlands of Kenya were seldom raided for slaves, partly because of the difficulty of crossing the desert back of the coast, and partly because of the fear of the fierce Masai who occupied part of this upland area. Occasionally, however, when traders found ivory difficult to obtain, they resorted to the slave traffic so as not to return to the coast empty handed. (W. McGregor Ross, *Kenya from Within*, George Allen & Unwin, London, 1927, p. 23.)

[4] Donald Fraser, *The New Africa*, Missionary Education Movement of the U. S. & Canada, New York, 1928, p. 68.

The Labor Problem of the Kenya Highlands

Since the completion of the railway, European settlement has been rapid and plantations have been expanded and developed with remarkable rapidity. Since cheap labor is needed to work these plantations the labor policy of the planter encourages the natives to work for European settlers even to the neglect of native agriculture. When the number of willing workers is not sufficient to meet the planter's needs, more are recruited, by coercion if necessary.

Such a policy is in sharp contrast to that followed in the equatorial lowlands where the heat and humidity prevent true European colonization. In these unhealthful and debilitating lowlands the natives are urged to till their own lands and to sell any surplus that they may produce to European middlemen.

The results of these divergent labor policies are forcefully indicated in the accompanying table, which shows that Kenya ranks first in the percentage of native laborers under European employment. This table is all the more impressive when due consideration is given to the fact that Kenya was one of the last sections of tropical Africa to be exploited by Europeans.

Percentage of Adult Male Population under European Employment *

Territory	Adult male population	Number continuously employed	Percentage of adult male population employed
Kenya	500,000	169,000	33.8
Belgian Congo	2,100,000	300,000	14.3
Gold Coast	495,000	25,000	5.4
Uganda	629,000	25,000	4.0
Nigeria	3,732,000	80,000	2.1

* Reprinted by permission from *The Native Problem in Africa*, Raymond L. Buell, The Macmillan Co., 1928, p. 346.

Crop Production

Coffee and Sisal the Major Commercial Crops. The southeastern section of the highlands, the Kikuyu Plateau, lies for the most part between the 4,000- and the 7,000-foot contours and may be designated as the *tierra templada*. The plantations situated within this area are given primarily to the production of coffee and sisal (Figs. 230 and

231), which together occupy practically the entire time and attention of the English settlers.

Almost immediately after the settlement of this area, coffee became the most important commercial crop and has remained in first position to the present time. The cultivation of coffee is limited almost exclusively to European plantations. The natives are effectively prevented from growing it by "The Coffee Plantation Registration Ordinance," which requires every coffee grower to secure an annual license costing

FIG. 230. A coffee plantation in Kenya. The large trees in the background are grown to shade the coffee trees and to protect them from the drying winds. (Courtesy U. S. Department of Agriculture.)

30 shillings.[5] Even if this sum were not prohibitive to natives, the district commission can refuse to issue a license.

The coffee plantations are all situated between 4,000 and 7,000 feet in altitude, the best results being obtained at altitudes ranging from 5,000 to 6,000 feet. The general tendency is for the lower altitudes to produce a heavy yield of low-quality coffee and the higher altitudes to produce a lighter yield of the better quality.[6] The area of most extensive cultivation and abundant production is situated on the southeastern border of the Kikuyu Plateau, at an altitude of 4,000 to 5,000 feet. It is near the Uganda Railway with only a short haul to the coast. The neighboring districts are densely populated with natives who supply most of the labor.

[5] Kenya Coffee Ordinance, 1918, p. 9.

[6] *Kenya, Its Industries, Trade, Sports, and Climate,* Kenya Empire Exhibition Council, 1924, p. 58.

The greatest fear of the coffee planter is adverse climatic conditions. Droughts are sometimes severe and seriously injure crops, as in 1921 and again in 1924. During these dry seasons hot winds from the north may almost destroy a crop within a few days. In order to reduce the exposure to these winds many of the plantations are situated on south-facing slopes. Throughout the highlands hailstorms are frequent and cause much damage, and on the higher elevations the crop is adversely affected by the low temperatures at night.[7]

Because of these adverse climatic conditions the acreage yield of coffee varies greatly from year to year, as is indicated by the following

Fig. 231. The background shows a field of mature sisal, in the center may be seen piles of leaves ready for the decortication plant, and the foreground shows the sisal fiber drying in the sun. (Courtesy U. S. Department of Agriculture.)

statement made by a resident of Kenya. "As long as I have lived in Kenya it has always been an abnormal year. In 1920 it rained in sheets, in 1921 my garden burnt to dust by the blazing sun, in 1923 we were marooned for weeks when floods and cloudbursts washed all our bridges away. Last year (1924) there was so little rain that people who had budgeted on a hundred tons of coffee, found themselves in great disfavor with their bank managers, and had only fifty tons to sell." [8]

In spite of climatic handicaps the coffee industry has prospered as the acreage and production have increased. The exports of coffee normally exceed $5,000,000 annually. In 1937, the exports of coffee exceeded $6,000,000. The area suited to the crop is still large, but the increasing shortage of labor is likely to be an effective check to continued and rapid expansion.

[7] Kenya Colony, Department of Agriculture, *Annual Report*, 1921, p. 183.

[8] Reprinted by permission from *Kenya Days*, by M. Aline Buxton, Edward Arnold & Co., London, 1927, p. 78.

Sisal. Sisal ranks second only to coffee as a commercial product of Kenya and is the most reliable of the major crops of the colony. It requires a tropical climate with moderate to light rainfall and can stand long periods of drought. During the years when the rainfall is much below normal, injuring the coffee and maize crops, sisal does exceptionally well.

Some sisal is grown along the coast, but the area of greatest production is on the uplands near Fort Hall. The rainfall is heavier than desired, but the land is hilly and well drained.

Since Kenya has two growing seasons (rainy seasons) each year, the sisal plant grows there more rapidly than in its original home, Yucatan. It also dies younger, but the number of leaves harvested from each plant before death is about the same in each country.

The methods of cultivating sisal in the uplands of Kenya differ markedly from those in the adjacent lowlands owing to the contrasts in climate, soils, and crop association in the two regions. In the lowlands the fields are not cultivated before planting. They are merely cleared of vegetation, after which holes are dug for the bulbils. This method is adopted partly because of the difficulty of keeping oxen in the hot, humid climate and partly because the coral land of the coast does not lend itself to cultivation. In the highlands the ground is thoroughly tilled in order that other crops such as maize, beans, and wheat may be grown along with sisal during the first two years.

Sisal production is primarily a corporation industry and consequently is entirely in the hands of the wealthy European planters. The manufacture (decortication) requires costly machinery; large expense is necessary to house and pay the laborers; and economical production requires the cultivation of an extensive area in order to supply sufficient raw materials (leaves) to keep a plant in steady operation throughout the season. Moreover, there is no financial return the first two or three years. These conditions have effectively prevented native production of sisal. Thus the two major commercial crops of the Kenya Highlands are grown almost exclusively on the plantations of European settlers, and under European management, but by native labor.

A Land of Agricultural Diversity. The western part of the highland contains large areas of cultivable land, which range from less than 4,000 feet near Lake Victoria to more than 8,000 feet in the higher parts of the Uasin Gishu Plateau. This area, at one level or another, is suited to plantain, coco palm, cotton, coffee, sugar cane, tea, wheat, barley, maize, pasture, and a great variety of fruits and vegetables.

The crop production is closely related to elevation, climate, topography, and transportation facilities. Where the land is exceedingly rugged and poorly suited to cultivation, it is left in the possession of the natives who tend their flocks and herds on the steep slopes and carry on a little primitive agriculture in the narrow valleys. Most of the land well suited to cultivation has been taken over by the English planters.

The cultivated land of the high plateau is largely given to maize, wheat, barley, and pasture, yet some coffee is grown for export, and

Fig. 232. The natives of Kenya Colony planting corn with sharpened sticks. Mr. L. W. Kephart, who took this picture, said it was the only large group of men that he saw working on native farms within Kenya. Most of the agricultural work is done by women. (Courtesy U. S. Department of Agriculture.)

fruits and vegetables for local consumption. Maize, which requires abundant moisture during the earing season, is well adapted to this upland. Maize is a crop well suited to primitive agricultural conditions since its production requires little machinery (Fig. 232). The maize which is intended for export must be grown close to the railroad in order that the cost of transportation will not be prohibitive. Maize is grown long distances from the railway, however, and marketed indirectly by feeding it to cattle, sheep, and hogs which can be driven to market.

Wheat is grown on relatively level land where large-scale machinery can be used. Thousands of tractors are in operation on this highland in spite of the fact that such machinery is necessarily expensive in an area so remote from manufacturing centers (Fig. 233). Consequently many thousand trained oxen are used on the farms of this upland, whereas human energy is still the major source of power for the farm in the coffee-sisal area of the Rift Valley where most of the land is cultivated by hand labor.

Tea is grown on the better-exposed slopes at altitudes of 6,000 to 7,000 feet where the precipitation is heaviest and the humidity greatest, for an abundance of moisture is necessary for rapid leaf development. But here, as in many other tropical uplands, the uncertainty of rainfall makes it quite impossible to rely on this source for tea cultivation. As a result the planter must resort to some artificial method of supplying moisture.

The Great Rift Valley and the drier parts of the adjoining highlands constitute the pastoral zone where approximately 80 per cent of the

Fig. 233.   Harvesting wheat in Kenya Colony.   (Courtesy U. S. Department of Agriculture.)

cattle, other than trained oxen, and 95 per cent of the sheep are raised. This shows a striking concentration of the pastoral industry within part of the highland having less than 40 inches of rainfall.

Although a railroad has been built across Kenya Colony, from the Atlantic Coast to Lake Victoria, the cost of transportation within the mountainous (most progressive) part of the country is still high. The chief exports are coffee, tea, sisal fiber, sesame seed, hides, skins, and wool. All these products are relatively non-perishable and of high value compared with their weight and bulk. Such commodities are best suited to stand the delays and expense involved in export.

Agriculture in Other Low-Latitude Highlands

The list of crops grown in other tropical highlands is similar to that of eastern Africa. However, the emphasis given to each crop varies greatly from one region to another, depending largely on the elevation, topography, climate, degree of isolation, and other environmental factors. Within the tierra templada, coffee is the major commercial crop and is grown to a considerable extent in almost every region. The most important of these highlands commercially is the plateau of southeastern Brazil.

The Plateau of Southeastern Brazil, the Major Coffee-Growing Region of the World

It has already been pointed out that tropical highlands have a great variety of climatic patterns. The plateau of southeastern Brazil might just as appropriately be considered with the tropical wet-and-dry realm, but since coffee is the major crop it is considered with the other important coffee-producing areas, all of which are tropical highlands.

The plateau of southeastern Brazil is sometimes called the land of four C's—coffee, corn, cattle, and cotton. Coffee is outstandingly the most important crop, and the plateau is the dominant coffee-growing area of the world. Here physical conditions are almost ideal for large-scale production; the area is easily accessible as it lies only 50 to 125 miles from excellent harbors; and the world demand has expanded with increased production. Consequently, the industry has grown until today coffee is a major factor in the economic and political life of Brazil, and it is the leading export not only of the nation but even of all South America.

The revenue from coffee furnishes a large part of the national income, and the profits from this crop have brought great wealth to the planters and have made São Paulo one of the richest and most influential of the Brazilian states.

The natural environment of this part of Brazil favors production of coffee. The deep residual soil of the plateau is rich in mineral fertilizers, especially iron and potash, essential to the production of high-grade coffee. The rolling topography insures excellent air drainage, and thus the coffee plants, which cover mile after mile of the hill slopes, are protected from the unseasonable frosts which frequently occur in the valleys.

The climate is almost ideal for coffee culture except during occasional winter seasons when frost, more severe than usual, occurs even on the best-protected slopes resulting in serious damage to the crop. The annual rainfall in the São Paulo district averages from 45 to 60 inches with the maximum precipitation coming during the summer when the tree and berries are growing. The autumn and winter are relatively dry and sunny, affording the most favorable conditions for harvesting and curing the crop. As a result, coffee has become the principal support of a large part of the population. Any failure in the crop or prolonged period of overproduction quickly brings on an economic crisis of the worst sort. The government has therefore encouraged the development of diversified agriculture in order to avoid the unpleasant economic consequences which might result from the one-crop system.

HIGHLANDS OF TROPICAL AMERICA OTHER THAN BRAZIL

Like southeastern Brazil, the uplands of Venezuela, Colombia, and Central America are best known to the outside world for their coffee. But on the high Andean Plateau only a few crops are grown, principally the hardy cereals and potatoes. The land is primarily given over to pasture, and the only export of consequence is wool.

The highlands of the Caribbean countries are also important producers of coffee, corn, and cattle, together with a few other subsistence crops. These areas are highly isolated, and consequently exports must be of high value and small bulk. Coffee is the agricultural product which meets these requirements best.

Not only are climatic conditions of these uplands suitable for coffee, but the cooler climate has attracted most of the population to these higher elevations, while few people live in the lowlands. Thus the European planter and promoter found an abundant labor supply for coffee growing. The planter needs laborers to plant and tend the orchards and to pick and cure the crop, and also to market the product. Since coffee may bring ten cents a pound or more, the native Indian may be able to carry several dollars' worth of the product to market in a single load. In many of these upland areas the traveler is likely to meet long lines of Indians trudging along towards the railway station with sacks of coffee on their backs. With the aid of this cheap and abundant labor supply the coffee production is rapidly increasing in several of these Caribbean countries and islands, which together with Brazil produce about 90 per cent of the world's commercial crop (Figs. 88 and 234).

Large numbers of cattle are pastured in small herds in all these countries. Although much beef is consumed locally, little is exported. But few of the highland areas have suitable facilities for the export of meat even if they had a surplus of cattle, which they do not now possess. Hides, however, are a general and important export, since they can stand the cost of transportation, will keep almost indefinitely even in this hot climate, and are injured little by the careless and rough handling incident to native methods of transportation.

Although coffee and hides are the principal commercial agricultural products, corn and beans are of even greater value to the natives them-

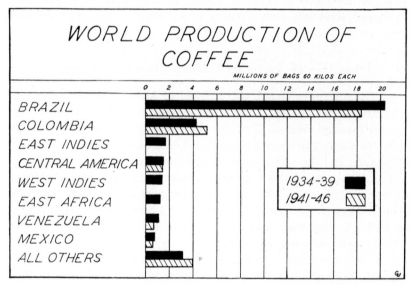

Fig. 234. Approximately three-fourths of the world's coffee is grown in Brazil and Colombia. A large part of the remainder is grown in the other highlands of tropical America. (*Foreign Crops and Markets*, U. S. Department of Agriculture, Vol. 53, No. 15, p. 209.)

selves. Millions of little fields are given largely to these two crops, together with a few squash, pumpkins, and perhaps a little tobacco.

Tierra Fria. The central plateau of Mexico and the high plateau of Bolivia and Peru are excellent representatives of the more populous regions of the tierra fria realm. The former, with an elevation of approximately 7,000 feet, has a climate that is much less severe than that of the latter, parts of which are more than 12,000 feet above sea level.

In the central plateau of Mexico, maize is the most important crop. The fertile soils of the lacustrine plains, the frequent summer showers, and the hot summer days are all well suited to this crop, but the cool nights and the indifferent methods of cultivation are ill suited to produce the abundant yield obtained in the American corn belt. Wheat, barley, and beans are also important crops of the better-watered portions of the plateau, while maguey, a drought-resistant crop, is grown on the drier mountain slopes. Since the area is largely of subsistence agriculture, thin corn cakes (*tortilla*) and beans are staple food of the ease-loving and unambitious peons.

Central Andean Plateau. As previously stated, the climate of very high tablelands is extreme to an unpleasant degree for man, and even hardy crops return a low and unreliable yield. In the central plateau of Peru and Bolivia the night temperatures are so low and the rainfall so light that both the variety and the yield of corn production are severely restricted. The higher levels yield a poor pasture of bunch grass and bushes suitable only for hardy animals such as the llama, alpaca, and sheep, which can live on this meager fare.

Very little land is given to agriculture, and few crops are grown. Potatoes, beans, barley, and a little hay, with occasional fields of wheat and oats, make up the list. The crop yield is so low that there is no inducement for Europeans to take an interest in agriculture, and the Indian cultivates such small patches of land that he could not afford modern implements even if he desired them, which at present he does not. The Indians have made little or no progress in their methods of farming during the last four centuries. Modern implements are practically unknown, and cultivation is carried on in a shiftless manner.

Few peoples in the world at present have a lower standard of living than the natives of the high central Andean Plateau. The very existence of many of these peoples is a continuous struggle against cold and hunger. Their mud or stone huts are almost without furniture; their diet, largely potatoes, barley, and corn, is exceedingly monotonous; and in general, the outlook on life is cheerless at best.

Above the habitable plateau lie the cold, misty, bleak *páramos* or moors. Above the moors is the zone of permanent ice and snow. Occasionally the Indians may drive their flocks and herds into the moors for a few days during the hottest season, but this zone will not support a permanent population. The areas of permanent snow are never visited except by daring adventurers or scientists who are willing to risk the dangers of mountain climbing at their worst. Storms are sudden and severe, snowslides are common, the air is rare, and breathing is difficult. Consequently, even experienced mountaineers must exercise great care in venturing into this zone of permanent snow and ice.

In the highlands of tropical Mexico and Central America, and in the Andean Highlands from northern Colombia to southern Bolivia, native food crops occup most of the cultivated land. Much of the cropped area is made up of small cultivated patches hidden away in narrow valleys, clinging to steep mountain slopes, or lying on wind-swept uplands. Maize, beans, and white potatoes are the chief crops. Wheat and barley are of minor importance. The potato and beans are especially important in the higher elevations that are unsuited to maize. Coffee, cotton, tobacco, and maguey de pulque (used for the manufacture of alcoholic beverages) are grown in scattered areas as commercial crops. Irrigation, frequently of ancient origin and practiced by laborious methods, is common. Since most of the land is poorly suited to cultivation, the grazing of livestock is an important adjunct to crop production. Most of the pasture is given to sheep and cattle, although many llama and alpaca are raised in the Andean Highlands of Peru and Bolivia. The llama and cattle are the draft animals, but the pastoral industries are carried on chiefly to supply wool, hides, and skins for local use and as a cash product.

Mineral Industries of the Tropics

For almost three hundred years after the Spanish conquest, minerals were the outstanding economic contribution of the uplands of tropical America to the outside world. As might be expected in such mountainous regions, the great crustal movements of the earth together with the agents of erosion have exposed outcrops of both igneous and metamorphic rocks of many geologic ages. In many places these various rock formations contain rich deposits of precious metals, gold and silver, as well as the baser metals, copper and tin.

The fabulous wealth taken from the highlands of Mexico caused that country to be known as "the treasure house of the world." Yet during the colonial days the output of gold and silver from Peru and Bolivia frequently surpassed that of Mexico. The mines of Potosí alone have yielded, according to estimate, more than $3,000,000,000 worth of silver, and for 300 years following 1550 Bolivia ranked among the leading gold-producing countries of the world. The constant flow of gold and silver far from the tropical American uplands lured many daring pirates to lie in wait along the major lines of shipment, where they hoped to gain unearned riches by the capture of some poorly guarded treasure ship.

The days of the pirates are gone, but the treasure ships are more numerous than ever before and the cargoes are more valuable than those captured by the famous buccaneers. The slow-moving sailing vessel laden with a few hundred pounds of silver and gold has been replaced by the great ocean steamship weighted with thousands of tons of copper and tin. The mountains of Bolivia and Peru have lost much of the glamour which allured the early explorer to risk all for fame and fortune, but the vast mineral wealth of these countries is as great a challenge to the world today as it was in early colonial times. Science is meeting this challenge now just as bravery and daring met it four centuries ago. The Spanish army entered the land equipped with the crossbow and arrow in order that they might conquer the natives and compel them to give up their treasures of silver and gold; the modern industrial army has equipped itself with railroads, power plants, electricity, steam shovels, vast smelters, and other industrial plants, in order that it may conquer the mountains and wrest from them their treasures of tin, copper, silver, and gold. The Spanish conquerors and their successors reduced the natives to a pitiable state of existence; the industrial conquest should relieve some of this misery by affording opportunity for profitable employment in mines, smelters, and on railways. Unfortunately, most of the economic gain goes to foreign capitalists, and the raw materials are used by the great industrial nations of the northern hemisphere. The present mining industry is largely an exploitive one, much as it was in colonial days, and most of the profits flow into foreign lands.

No other low-latitude highlands are so abundantly blessed with mineral wealth as those of tropical America. Nevertheless, the meager mineral resources of the highlands of central Africa have been a valuable asset in the development of the native civilization. Iron has been found in several places and for centuries has been used for the manufacture of spears, knives, machetes, and other simple tools and weapons; gold mining is carried on in numerous places, and the metal has been used for ornaments and for barter. In addition, valuable deposits of potash have been reported in northeastern Ethiopia (Abyssinia).

The rich mining centers of some of the low-latitude highlands have furnished markets for agricultural products, machinery, and railroad equipment, and in many other ways have contributed notably to the industrial development of these areas. This situation is especially true in the tropical Andean region. For example, most of the machinery entering Bolivia is used for mining or closely related purposes, and thousands of laborers have been employed in mines and metallurgical plants; many miles of railroad and highways were built primarily to tap rich mineral deposits, but they proved later to be an asset to the country in other ways also.

Peoples and Cultures

When the European explorers first arrived in the various tropical highlands, they found there a higher stage of civilization than had been attained by the natives of the surrounding lowlands.[9] This contrast in cultural achievements was largely a consequence of differences in climate. Since the highlands of moderate elevation possessed comparatively pleasant, healthful, and stimulating climates, it is only natural that the natives of these regions would progress more rapidly than those of the wet, hot, unhealthful, and debilitating lowlands. Thus the peoples of upland Peru, Bolivia, Ecuador, central Colombia, and Mexico had advanced to a state of semi-civilization while the natives of the surrounding lowlands were still steeped in ignorance and savagery.

When Pizarro landed in Peru, the Incas—centered in the Andean Highlands—controlled fully one-half of South America. Their possessions constituted the most extensive empire of the New World. Moreover, the remains of excellent stonework, pottery, masonry, and sculpture, together with the complex social system which they had developed, indicate that the semi-civilization of this region is extremely ancient. "We seem to look back upon a vista whose length it is impossible to conjecture, a vista of many ages during which this has been

---

[9] There are a few notable exceptions to the general rule that the native civilization of the tropical highlands was more advanced than that of the surrounding lowlands. In the highlands of western Burma the hill tribes could communicate with one another only by toiling up and down tortuous trails, often not wide enough for a pony or a mule. This condition helps to explain the backward state of these peoples, and the multiplicity of languages and the variety of customs found among them. Under such conditions tribal warfare is common. "Slavery, human sacrifice, and head hunting still survive, or did, until recently." Likewise the extreme isolation of the mountainous area of western Colombia, the Guiana Highlands, and the mountains of Taiwan has helped to preserve barbarism in parts of these areas until recent times.

On the other hand, the high stage of cultural development achieved by the Maya peoples of the hot, wet lowlands of Yucatan is a notable exception which has never been satisfactorily explained.

the home of peoples already emerged from such mere savagery as that in which the natives of the Amazon Valley still live." [10]

Similarly on the central plateau of Mexico, Cortez found the source and power of the great Aztec Empire, and the center of the most advanced civilization of North America. Primitive agriculture was well developed: the fertile plateau was intensively cultivated in maize and potatoes—both nourishing foods; and the ill effects of unreliable rainfall had been overcome, in part at least, by extensive irrigation from the reliable snow-fed mountain streams. The neighboring mountains, rich in precious metals, have been the seat of native mining industries for unknown centuries. The fabulous wealth of gold and silver accumulated during this long period surpassed the fondest dreams of Cortez and his men, astounded the Spanish Court back home, and whetted the insatiable greed of the conquistadors of all Europe.

The highland tribes of east-central Africa have no records of such an illustrious past as those found in America. Nevertheless, their cultural achievements have been distinctly greater than those of the lowland tribes. The Abyssinians, aided by the fortress character of their country and by the infiltration of capable and energetic peoples of Arabia and North Africa, have been able to maintain their political independence and to defend their country against the aggressions of European peoples, without the aid of any foreign power. The superior skill and training of the Abyssinian warriors have enabled them to enslave some of the backward lowland tribes, and domestic slavery is still a recognized institution of the country. For centuries, the pastoral industry of Abyssinia has been well developed, and although the agricultural methods were primitive, much of the land has been intensively cultivated.

Similarly some of the tribes of other east African highlands have made considerable progress in the agricultural and pastoral industries. Mr. Francis G. Hall, after whom Fort Hall is named, has given us an excellent description of the intensive agriculture of the Kikuyu Plateau —the eastern portion of the highland of Kenya—prior to the European colonization. In writing of this plateau he stated that every available piece of ground was under cultivation with the exception of a few small swamps and patches of grass which were kept for grazing purposes. Still earlier, explorers had reported the cultivation of the area as extensive with the whole countryside under tillage. These high-

[10] Reprinted by permission from *South America,* James Bryce, The Macmillan Co., 1921, p. 150.

land tribes had also learned the arts of self-defense, and some of them were such fierce, courageous, and capable warriors that slave traders did not venture into their territory.

In spite of the noteworthy achievements of these tropical highland peoples, they were still far down the ladder of civilization as measured by European standards.

This superiority of European culture was in part at least a response to their wider contacts with other peoples. We may reasonably assume that, in both Europe and the tropical highlands, the intermixture of different races and cultures made for achievement. But James Bryce points out that this great factor in the progress of mankind was far less conspicuously present in some of these highlands than in southern Europe. For centuries the Europeans had been schooled among the most advanced peoples of the world, whereas ideas filtered into these tropical highlands very slowly. Think of what Spain owed to Italy, Greece, Egypt, western Asia and to the influences radiating from the remote countries of China and India. This contact with a great variety of races and cultures was a vital part of the preparation of western Europe for her achievements during the colonial period. "How different was the lot of the Peruvians, shut in between an impassable ocean on the west, a desert on the south, and the savage tribes of a forest wilderness on the east. . . . They were out of contact even with other American peoples, such as those of Yucatan, Mexico, and Arizona, for there were vast spaces between, many shadowy mountains, dense jungles, and a resounding sea." [11] These peoples were no match, therefore, for their shrewd, wily, brave, and greedy conquerors from Europe.

As a result, a governing minority of temperate-zone peoples have thrust themselves upon the natives in all the tropical highlands except Abyssinia; and even there the ruling class is descendant from Arabs and North Africans who peacefully invaded the country and later intermarried with the natives and their slaves.

Isolation—lack of opportunities for trade and communication—still remains a major factor in retarding economic, educational, and political development of most of these uplands. With restricted opportunities for trade are associated limited possibilities for the accumulation of wealth, which in turn stunt the educational growth of the inhabitants. The ignorance of a people still invites interference in political

[11] Reprinted by permission from *South America*, James Bryce, The Macmillan Co., 1921, p. 151.

and economic affairs from more powerful nations whose motives, all too frequently, are born of greed rather than of service. Foreign rule or, as is most frequent, misrule is the result.

It is doubtful that the Mexican Indians were much better off at the close of the long Spanish regime than they were when Cortez took possession of the country. Practically all of them were still sunk in profound ignorance and constituted a menace to political or economic stability. Education of both the Indians and the *mestizos* (persons of mixed white and Indian ancestry) has been slow. Together they constitute the exploited and oppressed laboring class of Mexico, commonly spoken of as the peons, who because of their ignorance form one of the gravest problems of the country.

This condition exists in a land of great natural wealth. In some of the highlands where resources are less abundant, and the isolation more marked, the native occupies a still more humble position than that of the Mexican peon. On the bleak, inhospitable plateau of Peru and Bolivia the Indian has little chance to become acquainted with the products of civilization. There is scant opportunity to exchange the commodities of this dreary environment for those of the industrial world. He toils on with much the same equipment as his forefathers possessed (Fig. 235). Modern machinery is practically unknown, and existence is a constant struggle against cold and hunger. The Indians may work in the mines, but many of them dread to leave their home community and their own people to enter a world that seems so strange and in which the dangers are unknown. For centuries the white man has taken advantage of the Indians' ignorance to exploit both the people and their resources. It is not surprising then that the Indian is suspicious of the white man even when his motives are good.

Some progress is being made by the Peruvian Indian who works in mines and has the most frequent contact with the outside world, but the country-dwelling Indian lives in a miserable mud hut where his bed is a sheep pelt or the bare floor; his diet is potatoes, parched corn, a stew of vegetables and barley, and on feast days, meat; and his education consists in learning to do the same things in just the same way as his forefathers have done for hundreds of years. The hard struggle for existence leaves little room for a contented and happy home life, and there is little show of affection or any of the finer feelings which are apparent among the more enlightened and progressive peoples.

The mountainous region of southeastern Brazil, with its fertile soil, equable and reliable climate, and position close to the sea, has attracted true colonizers from Europe who are developing sound economic, political, and educational institutions similar to those of their home

FIG. 235. Winnowing. After being threshed under the hoofs of horses the wheat and chaff are tossed into the air where the chaff drifts off with the breeze while the grain falls in a pile. "Threshing floors" like the one shown are maintained by the Indians as common property and are never plowed up. In the course of years they become either bare and hard as pavement, or covered with smooth, dense turf, depending on the rainfall of the particular locality. Near Huancayo Magnetic Observatory, Peru, June 1923. (Courtesy Carnegie Institute, Washington, D. C.)

countries. Since this region had a sparse native population, the plantations have been worked largely by European laborers who were more intelligent and commanded more respect and better treatment than the Indians of Mexico and the Andean Highlands.

True European colonization is also taking place in parts of eastern Africa, but here the uneducated native population is sufficiently large to do all the manual labor. Consequently, a class system almost as bad as that of Mexico and Peru is being developed. In parts of Kenya and Tanganyika the power to rule is passing into the hands of wealthy European planters while the labor falls to the lot of the servile natives.

The remedy for these conditions lies in the education of the masses. Under intelligent guidance this process may proceed rather rapidly, especially in a region like the central plateau of Mexico which is easily opened to commerce and is rich in agricultural and industrial opportunities; but in a region such as the high plateau of Peru, which is highly isolated and poor in resources, the process is sure to be exceedingly slow.

HIGHLANDS IN MIDDLE AND HIGH LATITUDES

From the cultural point of view a few of the outstanding facts about highlands of middle and high latitudes may be listed as follows: (1) Many mountainous areas afford desirable recreation sites. (2) Mountains and plateaus supply man with many valuable minerals. (3) Mountain agriculture is normally developed with difficulty, and many mountain farmers are poor and backward. (4) In many high plateaus and mountains, summer pasture and hay are the major economic products. (5) Highlands afford opportunities of developing hydroelectric power. Many other subjects of interest might be suggested to students for study such as: (1) feuds among mountaineers, (2) ancient customs preserved in mountains, (3) marauding tendencies among mountaineers, (4) the difficulty of conquering mountain peoples, (5) plant and animal zones of mountains, and (6) avalanches, earthquakes, and volcanoes in mountain regions. These topics merely indicate some of the many ways in which man adjusts himself to highlands. Here we can only give a few examples of the way in which the highlands of middle and high latitudes influence human activities.

Highlands as Recreation Centers. In a prosperous country such as the United States, where a large part of the population can take a few weeks off from work each year for recreation, many highlands have become famous as tourist centers, or as summer or winter resorts. Yellowstone National Park, Glacier National Park, the Great Smoky Mountains, the White Mountains, Mt. Rainier, and many other highlands of North America are well-known recreational centers. Beautiful scenery, cool summer weather, opportunity for skiing or engaging in other winter sports, and the opportunity to get away from the crowded industrial centers are some of the attractions for tourists of mountainous areas.

Mountains and Minerals. It has already been pointed out that some of the great mining industries of the world have been developed in tropical mountains. Many of the important mining centers of middle and high latitudes are also found in highlands. The same processes that build and tear down mountains favor the formation and exposure of rich mineral deposits. Volcanism, hot flowing waters, faulting, and other processes may bring about the concentration of metals. Nearly all the minerals that occur in veins are found in disturbed land masses. On the other hand, erosion, which tears down mountains, may carry away the lighter minerals and leave behind rich deposits of gold, tin, and other heavy metals. Moreover, erosion tends to expose mineral deposits, thus making them easy to exploit. The pressure that causes the crust of the earth to be wrinkled into mountain chains may change low-grade coal into a high-grade product. The anthracite coal of the Appalachian Mountains of eastern Pennsylvania illustrates this fact. Thus the processes of mountain building and mountain destruction have in many ways favored the development of mineral industries.

Mountains and Agriculture. The agriculture of mountainous areas of middle latitudes is usually more backward than that of the surrounding lowlands. The rugged topography and steep slopes are associated with difficulties of cultivation and of the retention of soil and moisture. Large-scale farming cannot, therefore, be practiced in such areas. In sparsely populated areas mountain agriculture is normally confined to the narrow valleys and more gentle slopes, and to patches of land on steep slopes. The latter areas are cropped at great expense of human effort per acre cultivated. Terrace agriculture has been practiced for centuries on steep mountain slopes of Japan, China, Italy, Germany, and Sicily, where population pressure necessitates the use of all land that can be cultivated. On steep mountain slopes, even when terraced, the retention of the soil is a difficult problem. After each heavy rain in Japan, one may see farmers laboriously carrying the soil from lower terraces back to the higher ones from which it has been washed.

Many fertile valleys of mountainous areas are the sites of productive agriculture. But the farmers of such areas may be confronted with the problems of isolation and the resultant high cost of transportation. In highly isolated mountain regions, subsistence agriculture develops. The farmers produce everything they consume and consume all they produce. This procedure is made necessary because of the great expense of exporting and of importing goods.

Mountains and Isolation. Many mountain peoples are extremely isolated. Isolation, in turn, affects the homogeneity of peoples, retards their progress, and in many other ways affects their well-being. In some of the least accessible sections of the southern Appalachian Mountains, a few family names may include the entire population. Intermarriage of the same families has gone on for many generations, so that each individual finds that he is a blood relative of most of the other people in the community. Students of eugenics tell us that such intermarriage is likely to result in a community of backward people.

Isolation tends to preserve ancient customs and manners. Many of the more isolated communities of the southern Appalachian region, still use words that have been lost to other parts of the United States for more than a century. Many people still say "poke" for "bag," "tote" or "pack" for "carry," "you uns" for "you," "beast" for "animal," and "holp" or "holpen" for "help." Similarly, songs that have long been forgotten in other parts of the United States are still sung by those isolated mountaineers.

Isolation tends to result in poverty and ignorance, and may develop a disregard for law. Corn, beans, potatoes, pork, and other bulky agricultural products that are of low value per pound cannot be marketed profitably. Consequently the farmer's income is small. Where the topography is rugged and the roads are poor, manufactured products cannot be imported except at great cost. The great amount of labor involved in importing and exporting goods compels most of the people to go without refrigerators, screen doors, and a thousand other products that promote health, comfort, and happiness.

Because the farmers cannot export bulky products profitably, they may seek to export less bulky products even though the law may forbid. If corn cannot be exported with profit the farmer may change it into whiskey—a product of high value and small bulk that can stand the cost of transportation to market. Thousands of American farmers have felt persecuted at times because high taxes or prohibition prevented the sale of the one product that was best suited for export.

Wherever excellent transportation facilities have been developed within mountainous regions, the retarding influence of isolation is overcome but the disadvantages of topography for agricultural development still remain.

REFERENCES

BINGHAM, HIRAM, "The Wonderland of Peru," *National Geographic Magazine*, Vol. 24, 1913, pp. 387–574.

BOWMAN, ISAIAH, *The Andes of Southern Peru*, American Geographical Society, New York, 1916.

BUXTON, M. ALINE, *Kenya Days*, Arnold & Co., London, 1927.

CASE, EARL C., "The Pastoral and Agricultural Industries of Kenya Colony and Protectorate," *Economic Geography*, Vol. 6, 1930, pp. 244–256.

"Coffee Culture and Preparation in Brazil," *Tea and Coffee Trade Journal*, Vol. 56, 1929, pp. 41–48.

DE BARROS, N. O., "The Coffee Institute of São Paulo," *Tea and Coffee Trade Journal*, Vol. 56, 1929, pp. 75–80.

PEATTIE, RODERICK, *Mountain Geography*, Harvard University Press, 1936.

PLATT, ROBERT S., *Latin America*, McGraw-Hill Book Co., 1942. An excellent reference to highlands of Ecuador, Colombia, Brazil, and Venezuela. See Index for appropriate pages.

PART III

MINERALS AND MINERAL INDUSTRIES

Chapter 19

MINERALS—IRON AND STEEL

Minerals and Human Progress. The progress of the human race has been closely associated with minerals. The "Stone Age," the "Bronze Age," the "Iron Age," the "Steel Age," the "Alloy Age," and the "Atomic Age" are all terms indicative of the importance of minerals during the various stages of man's development. At the present time most of the iron that is used is alloyed with nickel, vanadium, tungsten, chromium, or some other mineral in the manufacture of alloys. These alloys are so numerous and have such varied uses that a single steel-manufacturing company has developed formulas for more than 10,000 different kinds of steel alloys. Each product differs from all others and is suited for a specific purpose. Thus, from the time of the cave man to the present, the various periods of human progress have been named after the minerals that were most useful to man.

Increasing Demand for Minerals. It was not until the advent of the industrial revolution, which began in Great Britain about two centuries ago, that the real exploitation of minerals began in a way to influence essentially our material civilization. Since then, at an ever-accelerating rate, minerals have become a fundamental basis of industrialism, until today they are ranked with climate, soil, land forms, and other major geographic factors in their influences on man's activities. More than a hundred minerals are now classed as "essentials," and other scores enter into the equipment which we use every day. As a consequence of this great demand the output of minerals during the last 35 years (1913–1948) has exceeded that for the entire preceding history of the world. During World War II, the annual output of minerals reached an all-time high. Since the end of the war the international struggle for minerals has been intensified and at times has threatened world peace.[1]

[1] Voskuil, Walter H., "Minerals and the Post War Politics of Europe," *University of Illinois Bulletin*, Vol. 41, 1944, pp. 1–10.

Minerals are used in the manufacture of almost every product made by man; they also enter into the composition of thousands of them. Without minerals our factories could not be operated, agriculture would be paralyzed, and the civilized world would be in darkness as soon as night comes. Every means of transportation—steam or electric railway, steamship, airplane, or automobile—depends upon our mineral industries; every means of long-distance communication—telephone, telegraph, cable, radio, television, and newspapers—depends absolutely upon the products of our mines. Something of this dependence is indicated by the fact that at least thirty-five metals enter into the manufacture of automobiles alone, and fourteen or more are required in the making of the telephone.

Accumulation of Mineral Products. The economic importance of minerals is much greater than the monetary value of the annual output would imply. The value of the total mineral output is small as compared with the annual production of either plants or animals. In fact, the value of the annual mineral output of the entire world is only a little greater than the income of American farms. However, the true value of minerals should not be compared with the value of agricultural products in terms of annual output. The minerals are accumulative, whereas the farm products are soon gone. Iron, stone, copper, aluminum, and other minerals may serve a useful purpose for decades or even for centuries; but meat, vegetables, fruits, cereals, and other foods are mostly consumed soon after they are produced. Even the more durable agricultural crops such as fibers used in clothing seldom last more than a few years.

Since mineral products accumulate, the total quantity in use increases each year. For example, the average annual steel production in the United States, during the decade 1938–1947, inclusive, was approximately 68,000,000 tons. Yet the amount of steel in use the first of January 1947 exceeded 1,400,000,000 tons. Thus the value of steel that is now serving a useful purpose in the United States is more than twice the average agricultural income of this great nation.

Just as steel produced fifty or even a hundred years ago is still being used, so copper, stone, nickel, and many other minerals that were mined or quarried several decades ago are still serving a useful purpose.

Not only is this accumulation of mineral products taking place in every part of the world but also it is now increasing at an accelerated rate. A large part of the steel that is made today is relatively rust and corrosion proof, and some of it will no doubt be valuable centuries hence. On the other hand, the agricultural products that are grown this year will soon be gone.   As a result of the durable nature of minerals in contrast to the perishable nature of agricultural products, the monetary value of the mineral goods possessed by this nation is several times the value of all the farm products which we possess at any given time.

Minerals and Standards of Living.   The extraordinary growth of the mineral industry and the ease of accumulating products made of minerals have been essential factors in raising the standards of living during the past century.   From 1840 to 1940, there was a remarkable increase in the per capita wealth of the industrial nations and a decrease in the hours of labor.   These achievements have been based largely on the substitution of machinery for human hands and of mechanical power for muscular energy.   Yet practically all machines, whether for use on the farm, in the factory, or in the transportation of goods, are made of minerals.   Similarly, most of the power for propelling this machinery is derived from minerals—coal, petroleum, and natural gas—or from water power.   Other factors such as progress in social organizations, the development of science and invention, and the opening up of new agricultural lands have played an important part in raising standards of living.   Yet without the large-scale utilization of minerals the notable industrial progress of the last century could not have been achieved.

Minerals and Power.   The large-scale use of minerals is indicative of power.   It gives power on the farm, in the factory, and in transportation.   This power may be utilized in production and thereby raise standards of living; or it may be devoted to destruction and thereby bring suffering, sorrow, and want.   The destructive potentialities of one mineral, uranium, has created fear for the entire world.   Also the bombing planes, tank cars, battleships, and other devices for destruction are still being kept in readiness for use in many countries.   This equipment may in the future be turned against mankind and thereby reduce the masses of people who are left after the carnage to want and poverty.

On the other hand it is conceded that the constructive potentialities of uranium are such that the metal can be of incalculable value to man if used wholly for peaceful purposes.   Similarly, other minerals used in the pursuits of destruction would be of great value if they were used only for construction.   Thus the power gained through the large-scale utilization of minerals may be used either to bless mankind or to blast the hopes of civilization.

The Outlook for the Mineral Industries. The prospects of the mineral industries of the future rest partly on the success of our social institutions and partly on the amount of minerals available. Wars, economic depressions, and other human relations will have their influences upon both the direction and the extent of the development of mineral industries. Under any circumstances the achievements of the world as a whole and particularly of the United States during the next century rest partly on the possibility of commanding ever-increasing supplies of minerals.[2]

Minerals and the Industrial Growth of Nations. With the growth of industrialism, the mineral production of a nation has become increasingly symbolic of its economic wealth and political power. The distribution of the most valuable mineral resources accordingly has become of growing importance, and the struggle for the control of these resources is the most potent international irritant of the present period.

A cursory survey of maps indicating the location of the known mineral reserves of the world might lead the layman to believe that these reserves are fairly well distributed over the earth. However, a careful study by one who understands the value of the various minerals to an industrial world indicates that nature has been especially generous with her gifts of minerals to those countries bordering the North Atlantic, while she has given but sparingly, either in amount or in combinations conducive to industrial growth, to most other parts of the world.

A well-balanced supply of major minerals—those required in large volume by the manufacturing plants of progressive nations—afford a firmer basis for industrial progress than the possession of one or two of them in very large quantities. Countries possessing only minor minerals—those required in only small quantities for industrial progress —must be given a lower ranking on the ground that no combination of these minerals will yield industrial power and that they will be tributary to the industry based on the more important group.

The United States and western Europe are the fortunate possessors of essential minerals both in amount and combinations necessary for industrial strength. At the same time they are favored with invigorating types of climate and with an abundance of good agricultural land. Accordingly, "it now appears that the industrial growth of the north

[2] Elmer W. Pherson, "The Mineral Position of the United States and the Outlook for the Future," *Mines and Metallurgy*, April 1945, pp. 204–214. An excellent review of the decreasing self-sufficiency of the United States in minerals.

Atlantic countries was not alone a matter of the superior enterprise of their people, but a response to unusually favorable environmental conditions affording the necessary raw materials for such development, and that there is little promise of similar growth elsewhere because of the deficiencies in the fundamental raw materials." [3]   The U.S.S.R. is now known to have a well-rounded supply of major minerals, but only in the Ukraine and perhaps in eastern Siberia have deposits of several of these major minerals been assembled by nature within a small area.   In most parts of the vast Russian domain, the problem of assembling the minerals necessary for modern industry creates a serious transportation problem.

As the United States and western European countries developed their resources they gained the experience, skill, scientific knowledge, wealth, and political power that are essential to expansion.   Consequently, it was only natural that they should protect their growing industries by gaining possession or control of mineral deposits in foreign lands to supplement their own reserves.   American and British organizations have been the leaders in this movement, so that as recently as 1931 fully three-fourths of the world's mineral production and reserves are controlled from these sources. [4]   After 1931, the United States and the British Empire lost part of this supremacy in the control of world minerals.   Yet, even in 1939, the capitalists of these two nations controlled close to 66 per cent of the world's output of minerals.   Since the close of World War II, the United States and Great Britain have once again become the dominant countries in the control both of mineral resources and of mineral output.

National Ownership of Minerals.   The United States and Russia are the only countries in the world that possess adequate resources of a large number of minerals, especially of those major minerals needed in large quantities for the development of modern industry along modern lines.   Other countries may possess large resources of one, two, or even three of the principal minerals, but they do not have a well-rounded supply of the many minerals needed in industry.   No country in the world possesses all the minerals it needs.   In fact, the interdependence of nations is increasing with respect to mineral supplies with the increase in the number of minerals that industry demands.

---

[3] Reprinted by permission from *World Minerals and World Politics*, C. K. Leith, McGraw-Hill Book Co., 1931, p. vii.

[4] *Op. cit.*, p. 15.

The United States represents the outstanding world power with respect to minerals. It is the largest owner, the largest producer, and the largest consumer. This country leads the world in the production of coal, petroleum, natural gas, iron ore, copper, lead, zinc, phosphates, gypsum, sulphur, and several minor minerals. At present more than 100 minerals are mined in this country, though some of them in insufficient quantities to supply our needs.

The supremacy of America in the commercial production of minerals is indicated by Fig. 236, which shows the position of the United

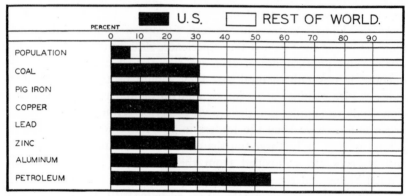

Fig. 236. The mineral resources of the United States compared with the resources of the remainder of the world. Although the United States contains only 6.5 per cent of the population of the world, this rich republic produces 20 to 55 per cent of each of the most important minerals used in industry.

States with respect to the world's population and production of some of the major minerals of industry. In addition, the United States has large commercial interests in foreign minerals: copper in Chile, Peru, Canada, and Rhodesia; iron in Cuba, Chile, and Brazil; oil in Mexico, Venezuela, and other South American countries; and large interests in many other minerals located in widely scattered parts of the world. Altogether, the United States has invested many million dollars in mineral industries located in more than a score of foreign countries. Most of this capital is engaged in producing those minerals needed to supplement our own tremendous resources in providing for the needs of American factories. Thus we see the most richly endowed nation of the earth drawing to its shores a steady flow of copper, oil, iron ore, zinc, asbestos, aluminum ore, gypsum, and scores of other minerals to be manufactured into useful articles and shipped to all parts of the United States and many foreign lands.

This worldwide production of minerals for the industrial plants of America gives this nation a vital interest in the political and economic stability of all parts of the world. Moreover, the worldwide movement of these minerals puts a premium on the freedom of the sea both in times of peace and of war.

The U.S.S.R. is second only to the United States in the possession of mineral resources. She will undoubtedly rank second also in the production and consumption of minerals in the relatively near future, provided her efforts are given to the peaceful development of her resources. The U.S.S.R. is handicapped by a lack of adequate transportation facilities and of modern machinery. She also suffers from a shortage of capital, managerial ability, and skilled labor. This backward industrial state of the U.S.S.R. is related to the fact that she has only recently become an industrial nation and also to the fact that her mineral resources are widely scattered over 8,000,000 square miles of land, most of which is undeveloped.

IRON ORE INDUSTRIES OF THE WORLD

Iron the Most Important Metal. Iron is by far the most useful of all metals. This metal, together with the minerals alloyed with it in the manufacture of steel, is essential to many phases of our industrial progress. The success of almost every industrial enterprise depends upon the extensive and efficient use of machinery and other economic equipment made wholly or in part from iron and its alloys. Thus practically every industry of farm, factory, mine, forest, and sea would be hopelessly crippled without iron. Even the economic and military strength of a nation is largely measured by the extent of its use of agricultural and industrial machinery; by the size of its navy and merchant marine, now made almost wholly from iron and steel; by the rapidity with which it can turn out high-grade ships, guns, locomotives, automobiles, and other material resources so essential to economic or military supremacy. Leadership, then, either in the peaceful pursuits of production and trade, or in the struggle between warring nations, demands an abundant and efficient use of mechanical equipment, which in turn necessitates a plentiful supply of iron and coal under the control of a capable and energetic people.

The relative importance of iron among the metals is indicated by the fact that in the decade 1937–1947 the average annual world consumption of pig iron exceeded 100,000,000 tons and represented more than 90 per cent of all metals used. This unique position of iron is

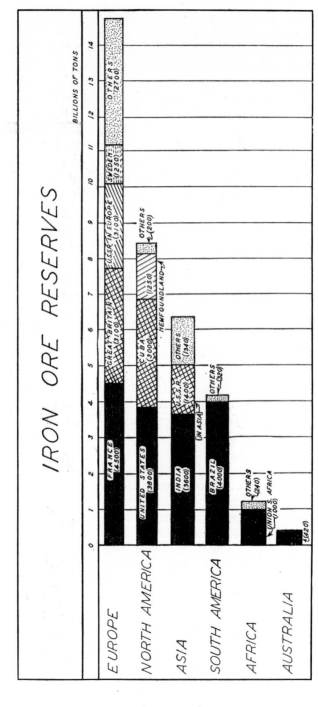

FIG. 237. Iron ore reserves of the world. Actual reserves are estimated at 35,240,000,000 tons and potential reserves at 164,800,000,000 tons. (Harry M. Mikami, "World Iron-Ore Map," *Economic Geology*, January-February 1944, pp. 1–24.)

due to its abundance, to the ease and cheapness of its recovery, and to the wide range of properties that can be imparted to it. It may be cast or hammered into any shape, it has great strength, and when protected from the weather it has great durability. By alloying it with smaller amounts of other metals and by special treatment in the furnace, iron may be given various qualities such as extreme hardness, toughness, elasticity, durability, brittleness, density, porosity, and resistance to oxidation or corrosion. No other metal has been adapted to so many uses, and none is so easily and cheaply produced.

Iron Ore Resources of the World. No doubt there are large deposits of iron ore which have not yet been discovered, and there are extensive known deposits which cannot be worked with profit at the present time. Moreover, progress is continually being made in the science of mining more cheaply and economically and of recovering metal profitably from low-grade ores. Any estimate of known reserves is likely, therefore, to need revision upward from time to time. Nevertheless, the known reserves of commercial value are the only ones that can support iron and steel industries at present. The most recent estimates of known iron ore reserves (actual reserves) range from 35 to 45 billion tons.[5] Potential reserves may exceed 160 billion tons (Fig. 237).[6]

Factors Affecting the Economic Value of Iron Ores

The value of an iron ore deposit depends not only on its richness in iron but also on its location, the ease or difficulty of mining, the nature òf competing ores, and the nature of the impurities as related to the specific use to be made of the ore. Some of the richest iron ore deposits of the world are at present of little economic value because of their remoteness from the great industrial centers and the resultant expense of transporting them to the places where they may be utilized. This is especially true of the great iron ore deposits of southern Brazil, which contain the largest reserves of iron ever discovered.

Ease or Difficulty of Mining. Open-Pit Method of Mesabi versus Deep-Shaft Mining in Lorraine. The value of the iron ore deposits

[5] Charles F. Park, "What to Do About Our Iron Ore Reserves," *Mining and Metallurgy*, April 1947, pp. 192–196.

[6] Harry M. Mikami, "World Iron-Ore Map," *Economic Geology*, January 1944, pp. 1–24. An excellent summary of the estimated actual and potential iron ore reserves of the world by continents and countries, with an accompanying map which shows the distribution of the iron ores.

of the Mesabi district is greatly increased because of the ease with which they can be exploited (Fig. 238). They are rich in iron and lie relatively near the surface, the deposits are thick, and the ore, being loosely cemented, can be easily scooped up with steam or electric shovels without preliminary blasting. These conditions favor the maxi-

FIG. 238. Open-pit mine near Virginia, Minnesota. Ten to thirty feet of the surface material is too lean in iron to be of commercial value and must be removed at great expense before the iron ore can be mined. Three or four bites of the great electric shovel fill a car. (Courtesy L. P. Gallagher, Duluth.)

mum use of mechanical power and machinery and result in a large output of ore per laborer. The ease of production within this district has been largely responsible for the rapid increase, during the last half century, in the yearly output of iron ore per worker employed at iron mines in the United States. Between 1870 and 1939, the annual output per laborer increased more than tenfold. In some of the deep mines of Lorraine where machinery and power cannot be used with the same facility, the annual output per laborer is less than a third that of the Mesabi district.

Vast Iron Ore Deposits of Brazil of Little Present Economic Value.[7] The iron ore deposits of Brazil alone are estimated at 4 billion tons of high-grade hematite, which is 60 to 70 per cent iron, and another 7 billion tons which contain 50 to 60 per cent iron, and which would be of great economic value if the location favored development.[8] But these deposits lie 250 to 350 miles from ports and are reached by only one railroad which is ill equipped to handle a large volume of ore. The region contains no coking coal, and electric smelting is expensive.

The only fuel thus far used and produced locally is charcoal, which is becoming scarce and very expensive with the destruction of the forests along the railroads and around the present steel plants. Some coal is mined along the coast of southeastern Brazil, but it is not suitable for metallurgical purposes. The geological formations of the region do not seem to favor the discovery of high-grade coal, and consequently it seems clear that any large-scale development of the iron and steel industry of southern Brazil can be accomplished only by means of imported fuel. Those companies which own the few iron and steel plants operated within the state of Minas Geraes have begun the planting of eucalyptus trees to insure a future supply of charcoal. Such fuel is expensive, and consequently this huge reserve remains of little present value.

Iron Ores of Lorraine Are of Vast Economic Value. Ores which are lean in metallic iron may be of great value provided that they are favorably located for the development of the industry. This fact is forcibly illustrated by the ores of Lorraine, which contain only 25 to 40 per cent iron, but which are of basic importance in the development of one of the major steel-producing regions of the world. The Lorraine ore beds are 60 to 110 feet thick and occur over considerable areas in almost horizontal strata at depths of 600 to 800 feet below the surface. Part of the ore contains sufficient lime to make it self-fluxing. Thus the ore is considered of fair grade in spite of the low iron content. The location of these mines near the heart of the greatest industrial region of the world (World War II) and close to

---

[7] In 1945, Brazil exported 299,994 tons of iron ore. In addition, an estimated 475,000 tons of iron ore were produced to supply the twenty-five charcoal blast furnaces located in Brazil. Thus in spite of her vast iron ore reserves and an unprecedented world demand for iron and steel, Brazil's iron ore production was small—less than 1 per cent of that of the United States.

[8] Newton B. Knox, "Factors Affecting Mining in South American Mining," *Mining and Metallurgy*, October 1945, p. 480.

large deposits of high-grade coking coal gives the Lorraine deposits great economic value.

Impurities and Their Effect upon Ore Production. The impurities of an iron ore may be either an asset or an injury, depending upon their nature and extent, and upon the use to which the ore is to be put. Each class of ore may be especially valuable for the manufacture of a special kind of iron or steel and poor for the manufacture of other kinds. Other properties being similar, a self-fluxing ore—one which contains 15 to 20 per cent calcium—is more valuable than one high in silica content. The latter ore is objectionable because of the additional lime that is required to neutralize the acid content, thereby decreasing the output of the furnace and increasing the cost of the iron. This disadvantage is well illustrated in the Mesabi deposits, where it is evident that the high-grade low-silica ores are being rapidly depleted.[9] However, the large iron ore producers on the Mesabi range are able to maintain the silica in their commercial ores at from 8 to 10 per cent by mixing ores of various grades, some assaying 4 per cent silica and some as much as 18 per cent silica. This mixing operation, however, can continue with profit only as long as high-grade ore is available. Consequently, in order to lengthen the life of the Mesabi deposits a large tonnage of ore is treated in beneficiation plants where part of the silica is removed before the ore is shipped to the furnace.[10]

Phosphorus, sulphur, and manganese are among the other most common impurities of iron ore. Sulphur is always objectionable in steel but it can be largely eliminated in the blast furnace. Phosphorus, on the other hand, is not subject to control in the blast furnace and must be removed in the steel-making processes. Since the acid Bessemer and the acid open-hearth processes, discussed later in the text, do not remove phosphorus, ores must be selected which contain less than 0.15 per cent of phosphorus or the pig iron must be treated in other types of furnaces. Usually the occurrence of manganese is not important and may be more or less desirable.

Physical Condition and Iron Ore Production. The physical condition of the ore is also of utmost importance. A very fine ore chokes the furnace, prevents the free passage of the gases, and leads to excessive dust losses. It is necessary, therefore, to sinter this fine material

[9] E. W. Davis, "Iron Ore Reserves of the Lake Superior District," *Mining and Metallurgy*, January 1947, pp. 15–18.

[10] E. W. Davis, "Concentration of the Mesabi Hematites," *Mining and Metallurgy*, November 1930, p. 518.

before it is used.   E. W. Davis estimates the cost of sintering to be $1 a ton, adding materially to the cost of the product.   On the other hand, very hard ores, such as some magnetites, are costly to smelt.

Each ore, then, must be considered in relation to its richness, chemical composition, and setting.   As a result, the actual production of

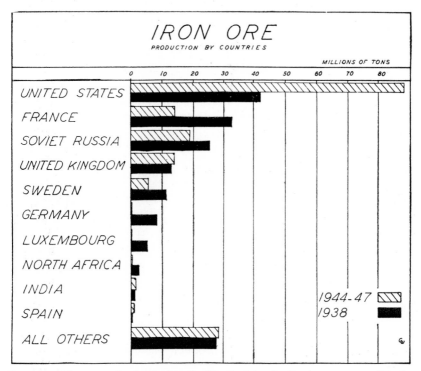

Fig. 239. The countries bordering the North Atlantic Ocean are responsible for most of the iron ore output of the world. Data obtained from the Statistical Office of the United Nations.

iron ore bears a closer relation to the present value of the various deposits than does the size of the resources (Fig. 239).   However, the vast and almost untouched resources of Brazil, Cuba, Newfoundland, and Labrador are a satisfying assurance to the great iron and steel industries of the United States.   Their location, remote from the industrial centers of the United States, creates a serious transportation problem which would be aggravated in times of war.[11]

[11] William O. Hotchkiss, "Iron Ore Supply for the Future," *Economic Geology*, May 1947, pp. 205–210.

Markets for Iron Ore. Although iron ore is widely distributed, it is mined in large quantities in only a few places, and large-scale production of pig iron is restricted to a few countries. The most productive iron mines in the world are those of the Lake Superior district. In 1945, this district shipped 74,821,000 tons of ore, or 85 per cent of the total iron ore mined in the United States and approximately 45 per cent of the metallic iron mined in the entire world.

While the market for Lake Superior ores is the largest for any single district, it is neither so complicated nor so widely competitive as that of the North Atlantic coasts of Europe and North America. The ore for this Atlantic trade comes from France, Sweden, Spain, Norway, Newfoundland, Cuba, and Brazil, situated on or near the Atlantic; and from Chile, southern Russia, northern Africa, and other widely separated areas.

PIG-IRON AND STEEL INDUSTRIES

Materials and Processes of Pig-Iron Production. Since the metallic iron ore is combined with other elements, the chief of which is oxygen, and is mixed with various other minerals called "gangue," separation of the metal from the other substances is necessary before it can be used. The process of extracting the iron from the ore is called "smelting." In this process the iron ore is mixed with coke and limestone in a blast furnace—a huge tower that may be 100 feet high—in which the mixture is heated by the burning of coke under a blast of air that has been previously heated by the burning of gas, a by-product of the coke ovens. The resultant product, pig iron, contains an abundance of carbon and is therefore brittle. Consequently, most of it is later converted into steel, a tougher, stronger product which can be given numerous properties by alloying it with other metals.

Most of the pig iron produced in the United States is converted into steel in the same plants in which it is smelted. An increasing amount of the pig iron is transferred directly from the furnace to the steel mill while it is still in the molten state and converted immediately into steel, thereby saving large quantities of fuel which would otherwise be needed to reheat the pig iron if it were permitted to cool.

Stages in the Development of the Iron and Steel Industry. The early development of the iron and steel industry was closely associated with forest areas where charcoal could be obtained for the smelting of the ore and the manufacture of steel. With the dawn of the industrial revolution the demand for iron and steel products increased rapidly. Consequently, there was a heavy drain on the forests of England, Germany, Spain, New Jersey, Maryland, and other parts of western Europe and eastern United States. Fortunately, before the forests were exhausted a substitute for charcoal had been found.

As early as 1735, Abraham Darby began the use of coke instead of charcoal in the reduction of iron ore. But improvement in the iron and steel industry was slow for another hundred years, and even in 1830 iron was still an industrial luxury.[12]

The modern iron and steel industry is therefore largely a development of the last century. The *Bessemer* furnace, invented in 1856, inaugurated a new epoch in the steel industry. The Bessemer process is so simple and efficient that many tons of steel can be produced within a few hours at a relatively low cost. For almost half a century this process dominated the manufacture of steel in all the important producing countries.

Bessemer steel sometimes breaks without warning and is therefore ill suited for the manufacture of steel rails, automobiles, and other mechanical equipment subject to great strain. A method of making a better-grade steel was invented in 1905, known as the *open-hearth process*. Open-hearth steel is slightly more expensive than Bessemer steel, but it is also of better quality. In 1945, more than 90 per cent of all the steel produced in the United States was made in open-hearth furnaces.

In 1909 a process of manufacturing steel in an electric furnace was discovered. The product is known as *electric steel*. The electric furnace is especially adapted to the manufacture of various kinds of steel in which metal alloys, such as nickel, tungsten, vanadium, and chromium are used. Because of the extremely high temperatures that can be speedily attained, many of the desired reactions can be brought about quickly and readily, and the steel made by this process is of uniform and high quality. Electric steel is expensive, but in a land of industrial wealth and expansion there is a large demand for high-grade steel, regardless of cost. Moreover, in this age of speed and industrial competition, where safety and efficiency are matters of major consideration, a high-priced steel may be more economical than a low-priced product. Thus because of its leadership in the steel industry, its abundance of cheap power, and its increasing demand for

[12] In 1883 the total pig-iron production of the United States was only 140,000 tons, whereas in 1945 it exceeded 53,000,000 tons.

the best grade of steel in many industries, it is only natural that the United States should have become the foremost producer of electric steel.

Location of Iron and Steel Industries

The Market Factor. The major factors affecting the location of steel plants are the relative location with respect to iron ore, coking coal, and markets for the finished products. Of these the market is the most important. The significance of the market factor is in part reflected in transportation costs. Thus whereas the tonnage of steel produced is usually less than one-half the iron ore and scrap used and less than one-half the coal required for its production, the unit cost of shipping steel as expressed in freight rates is commonly more than twice that of the raw materials. Moreover, the increasing amount of scrap used in making steel adds to the importance of the market factor, since the chief sources of scrap are obviously coincident with the consuming areas.[13] As a result of the importance of the market factor, all the large iron and steel industries have been developed in great industrial areas.

In 1946, the first full peace-time year since World War II, four industries—the automotive, construction, railroad, and container industries—accounted for the use of almost one-half the steel consumed within the United States. Steel mills centrally located with respect to these industries possess choice locations for the marketing of their products. Most great industrial areas are located on or near coal fields. Thus in most cases the iron ore can move to the market and to coal fields at the same time.

The Raw-Materials Factor—Coal and Iron. It is almost a truism that iron ore moves to coal. There are but few exceptions to this general rule. This movement results from the facts that (1) the coal consumed in the iron and steel industry is bulkier than the iron ore; (2) the coal deteriorates more rapidly in shipment than ore; and (3) the coal field begets industry and industry consumes steel.

The quantity of iron ore and coal consumed in the production of 100 tons of steel depends somewhat upon the grades of ore and coal and upon the efficiency of the plants. In the major districts of the United States it is approximately as follows: [14]

[13] Richard Hartshorne, "The Iron and Steel Industry of the United States," *Journal of Geography*, April 1929, p. 137.

[14] Richard Hartshorne, "Location Factors in the Iron and Steel Industry," *Economic Geography*, July 1928, p. 243.

District	Ore (tons)	Coal (tons)
Pennsylvania	193	291
Illinois-Indiana	212	222
Alabama	326	384

Additional fuel is required for heat and power in the further fabrication of steel, varying greatly in amount according to the nature of the product. Thus coal is the heaviest and by far the bulkiest raw material used in the iron and steel industry, with the exception of water which is usually cheap and plentiful wherever needed in the manufacture of iron and steel. It is only natural then that Pittsburgh; the Ruhr; Cleveland, England; Birmingham, England; Birmingham, Alabama; and the Saar, with their coal fields situated in great market areas, should be logical centers for the development of the iron and steel industry.

Although iron ore usually moves to coal, a notable exception is found in Lorraine, where, prior to World War I, about two-thirds of the iron ore was smelted in local blast furnaces with coke imported largely from the Ruhr. In 1913, slightly less than 6,000,000 tons of coal and coke were shipped from the Ruhr to Lorraine, whereas only 3,200,000 tons of iron ore and 600,000 tons of iron and steel went from Lorraine to the Ruhr.[15] The explanation for this exceptional situation is as follows: (1) the smelting of the low-grade Lorraine ores requires only one-half ton of coal per ton of ore; (2) the Lorraine is well situated with respect to the market of iron and steel products.

Limestone. Limestone for flux is used in large quantities (approximately 700 pounds for each ton of pig iron), but since it is widely distributed it exerts little influence on the general location of steel plants.

Cheap Land and an Abundance of Water Needed. The specific site for iron and steel plants must be chosen with reference to the cost of the land and the proximity of an abundance of water. Owing to the bulky and heavy nature of the commodities that are handled, all the processes of iron and steel manufacture are confined to one-story buildings. Consequently, a large area is required for a complete unit. It is not uncommon for a site to be chosen near swampy or marshy land fronting a river, lake, or other body of water. Such a situation permits the profitable disposal of the large amounts of waste, and land may be reclaimed as rapidly as the plant expands.

[15] Chauncy D. Harris, "The Ruhr Coal-Mining District," *Geographical Review*, April 1946, p. 205.

Iron and steel mills must always be close to an abundant supply of water. For example, a single steel plant at Buffalo, the Lackawanna plant, uses 150,000,000 gallons of water a day—an amount equal to that drawn for the entire city of Buffalo.

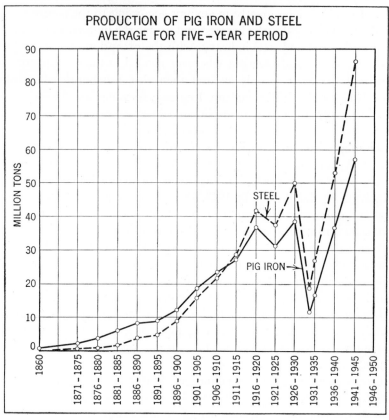

FIG. 240. Soon after the Civil War the demand for iron and steel began to increase rapidly and, with minor exceptions, continued to increase until 1929. During the next five years, due to a world-wide depression, the production fell off sharply. After 1934 the production increased once more to reach an all-time peak production of 89,641,000 tons of steel in 1944.

The Labor Factor. Although labor is obviously indispensable in the fabrication of iron and steel, it is not significant in the localization of the industry. Moreover, because of the extensive use of machinery, the labor cost is relatively low for the amount of work done. It is a rule in the iron and steel industry never to have a man perform a task that can be done as effectively and more cheaply by a machine. The development and adaptation of the all-but-human labor-saving devices, which perform most of the operations from the mining of the iron ore to the loading of the manufactured products for shipment, were inevitable in the United States where science in industry is empha-

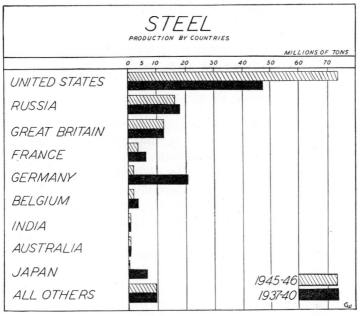

Fig. 241. The annual production of steel varies greatly from year to year as indicated by Fig. 240. During World War II, many steel mills in the war-torn areas of Europe were destroyed or were deprived of much-needed raw materials. At the same time the great demand for steel products caused the United States to increase its steel output greatly.

sized and where labor costs are several times those in many other parts of the world.

The United States is well suited to the production of iron and steel. It has an abundance of raw materials, a cheap and abundant supply of water in most places where needed, capable laborers, a plentiful supply of well-distributed power resources, excellent transportation facilities, and a large market for iron and steel products. However, the demand for steel products fluctuates violently. For that reason the steel industry is sometimes called the "prince or the pauper" industry. During the depression period of the early 1930's the demand

for steel products dropped to the level of thirty years earlier when
our steel industry was just entering its period of rapid expansion.
Then during the 1940's the demand jumped to an all-time high (Fig.
240). Because of the disarrangement of the iron and steel industry as
a result of World War II and of the political disturbances of the postwar period, recent data on world production of steel are somewhat
meaningless for some of the Eurasian countries (Fig. 241).

REGIONAL DEVELOPMENT OF THE IRON AND STEEL INDUSTRIES OF THE UNITED STATES

Regional Distribution of Iron Ores

Eastern United States possesses large reserves of fair-grade to high-
grade iron ore. The area east of the Mississippi River contains 4 to 6
billion tons of ore that are commercially available under present methods of mining and utilization.[16] In addition, several billion tons of
low-grade ore may become commercially valuable if science learns
how to improve these ores economically, or if the time comes when
the pig-iron producers are compelled to utilize a lower-grade product
than is acceptable at present.

Western United States is relatively poor in known reserves of iron
ore. Although small deposits of these ores have been discovered in
Utah, Idaho, Montana, California, Colorado, and several other states,
none of them compare favorably with the major deposits of eastern
United States.

The ancient rocks near the western end of Lake Superior contain
some of the finest iron ore deposits of the entire world. For several
decades, the iron mines of this district have been the most productive
ones in existence. The output of these mines represents approximately 85 per cent of all iron ore produced in the United States and 30
to 40 per cent of the world output. The ores of the Lake Superior
district are above the average in iron content. As a result, the mines
of this area account for approximately one-fourth of the metallic iron
output of the world (Fig. 242).

Although rich iron ores are widely scattered throughout northern
Minnesota, the upper peninsula of Michigan, and northern Wisconsin,
one small district in Minnesota, the Mesabi district, yields more iron

[16] Harry M. Mikami, "World Iron-Ore Map," *Economic Geology*, January-
February 1944, pp. 4–6.

than all of the Appalachian Mountain and Valley deposits which are scattered from Birmingham, Alabama, to Canada.

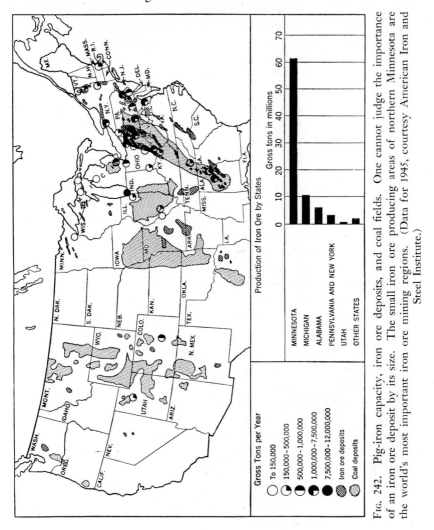

FIG. 242. Pig-iron capacity, iron ore deposits, and coal fields. One cannot judge the importance of an iron ore deposit by its size. The small iron ore producing areas of northern Minnesota are the world's most important iron ore mining regions. (Data for 1945, courtesy American Iron and Steel Institute.)

Regional Manufacture of Iron and Steel

The Northern Appalachian Region. The northern Appalachian region is the greatest iron- and steel-producing district of the United States and one of the two largest in the world. Western Pennsylvania, eastern Ohio, and northern West Virginia contain 43 per cent of the blast-furnace capacity of the country. This small area, with Pittsburgh as the center, produces more pig iron and steel than any foreign country in the world, except Germany and the Soviet Union, and, in 1938, the output was more than twice that of Asia, Africa, Australia, and South America combined.

The mills of this region are located almost exclusively in the narrow valleys of the headwaters of the Ohio River—a situation well suited to the assembling of raw materials and the marketing of the finished products. Good coking coal outcrops along the sides of neighboring hills, where it is cheaply mined and easily removed by the "slope" or "drift" methods. Natural gas, an important asset in steel making, is also produced locally. The streams supply the abundance of water required by the iron and steel mills; the rivers are natural highways for the transportation of part of the raw materials and finished products; and the deep valleys afford the most gentle gradients for the transportation lines which serve the area. Finally, this region, together with the lower lakes region, has the finest location in America for the marketing of its products. Lying between the Middle West and the Atlantic seaboard, it occupies a central position in the northeastern quarter of the United States—the most densely populated region of the continent and the one having the greatest industrial development and greatest railroad mileage. If one excludes the Pacific Coast and the scattered cities of the Rocky Mountains, the center of the industrial gravity of the United States must have been close to Pittsburgh during the latter part of the nineteenth century, and even today it is probably east of Columbus, Ohio.

The chief disadvantage of the northern Appalachian region is its remoteness from the source of practically all its iron ore, the Lake Superior district. However, this handicap cannot offset the advantages mentioned above.[17]

Iron and Steel Industry of the Lower Lakes Region. Although the lower lakes ports are several hundred miles from their coal supply, they have the advantage of eliminating one transshipment of the ore and have excellent transportation facilities both by water and by rail. The most rapid development of the iron and steel industry has occurred along the southern shore of Lake Michigan at South Chicago, Illinois; Gary, Indiana; and Indiana Harbor. This region has exceptional advantages with respect to the growing markets of the northern

[17] Richard Hartshorne, "The Iron and Steel Industry of the United States," *Journal of Geography,* April 1929, pp. 133–153.

interior of the United States and is close to Chicago, the greatest rail-road center of North America. The iron ore is brought from the Lake Superior region in large modern barges especially constructed for the transportation of iron ore, and consequently the freight rates to the lower lakes ports are among the lowest in the world.

Similarly the iron and steel industry is growing rapidly along the southern shore of Lake Erie from Detroit to Cleveland. At present the industry is expanding with remarkable rapidity in Detroit, where the automobile factories utilize a tremendous tonnage of high-grade steel. Buffalo, situated at the other end of Lake Erie, has an even better market location than Detroit. It is in position to compete with other steel centers for the business in the great Middle West; it has an excellent location with respect to the industrial area of Canada, which imports large quantities of iron and steel from the United States; and finally it has a superior position for shipping products to the eastern markets, since it is the terminus of many eastern railroads and also of the Erie Canal. Approximately one-fourth of the pig iron is shipped to the middle Atlantic seaboard and New England for fabrication in eastern plants.

Southern Appalachian Region. There are several places in the Valley of East Tennessee where iron ore, limestone, and coking coal are all found within the range of a few miles. Formerly the Valley supported an abundance of hardwood which afforded an excellent supply of charcoal for the iron and steel industry. The numerous small but rich deposits of iron ore were ideal for a primitive iron and steel industry, and nails, horseshoes, harrow teeth, wagon tires, and other articles needed by the pioneers were manufactured in many places.

Unfortunately, the iron ore deposits of the Valley are too small and unreliable to support modern iron and steel mills. Although the plateau to the west contains large deposits of iron ore, they are lean and expensive to mine, except for the small quantity near the surface which has already been exhausted. Consequently, the development of the iron and steel industry within the Valley has been slow and uncertain and the outlook for the future is not bright.

In northern Alabama, however, large deposits of iron ore, coking coal, and limestone are found in closer juxtaposition than in any other part of the world.[18] All lie within 15 miles of Birmingham, and the

[18] E. F. Burchard estimates the iron ore reserves of Alabama at 1,470 million tons of first-grade ore and 500 million tons of second-grade ore. He estimates the coking coal of the Warrior field at 3,366 million tons, or more than enough to smelt all the iron ores of Alabama. ("Alabama Ores Equal Lake Supply,"

cost of assembling them is cheaper than in any other iron and steel district of the United States. Moreover, the cost of living is less in Birmingham than in most iron and steel centers of America, and the cost of labor is correspondingly lower. Thus it is claimed that pig iron can be produced in the Birmingham district at a lower cost than anywhere else in the United States.[19]

MARKETS. The local markets of the Birmingham district are small as compared with those of the northern Appalachian and the lower lakes districts. Nevertheless, Birmingham is well situated to supply iron and steel products to the South and to the West Indies, Mexico, South America, and the Orient. Birmingham is the greatest railway center of the South, and it has been estimated that the railways radiating from the city give her a logical market area of approximately one-third of the country both in size and population. But it must be remembered that the per capita consumption of iron and steel in the agricultural South is much smaller than in the industrial North.

Birmingham's situation with respect to foreign trade has been improved recently by the construction of a canal which connects the city with the Gulf of Mexico. This waterway permits the transportation of iron and steel products *via* barge at 80 per cent of the cost by rail and gives Birmingham an all-water route to Latin America and the Orient. Since Birmingham can produce pig iron at low cost and can ship it to foreign markets by water, this area has had special advantages for the production and export of this valuable basic metal. As a result the blast-furnace industry of Alabama has increased rapidly during the last few years.

HANDICAPS OF THE BIRMINGHAM DISTRICT. Most of the Alabama ore lies at a considerable depth and must be mined underground where the use of machinery is somewhat restricted and the amount of human effort required is correspondingly large.[20] Under such conditions, mining is much more expensive than in the Mesabi Range. The Birmingham iron and steel industry is also handicapped by the fact that the ores are lean, carrying only 30 or 40 per cent metallic iron as against 52 per cent for Mesabi ores. This low content of iron is partly

Iron Age, March 24, 1927, pp. 847–853.) Less than 100,000 tons of this reserve was mined between 1927 and 1939.

[19] Langdon White, "The Iron and Steel Industry of the Birmingham, Alabama, District," *Economic Geography*, October 1928, p. 365.

[20] The Birmingham district contains a small reserve of brown ore, estimated at 15 million tons, which is high in iron content (39 to 50 per cent) and which is mined by the open-pit method.

offset by the high content of lime which the ores contain, making them self-fluxing.

WATER SUPPLY OF BIRMINGHAM. The iron and steel industry requires an abundance of water for cooling purposes. In this respect Birmingham is not so fortunate as Pittsburgh, Chicago, Cleveland, or Buffalo—cities that can obtain unlimited quantities of water from nearby lakes or rivers. For many years the lack of a cheap and abundant water supply for industrial purposes constituted a serious problem of the Birmingham district. Recently this handicap has been overcome, at least in part, by water obtained from the Cahaba River and from deep wells.[21]

Duluth. Duluth, like the lower lakes ports, has the advantage of cheap assembling of raw materials. The situation, however, differs from that of the lower lakes region in that the coal is brought up the lakes rather than the ore being taken down. Since the traffic down the lakes is much heavier than the return cargo, Duluth profits from the lower back-haul rates. Unfortunately, Duluth has only a small market for iron and steel.

Western United States. West of the Mississippi River the iron and steel industry is only slightly developed but it is growing.[22] The largest market for iron and steel products of this area is found in the Pacific states, but unfortunately these states lack resources of coking coal and are poor in iron ore resources. An iron and steel industry has been developed at Pueblo, Colorado, situated between the iron deposits of eastern Wyoming and the Trinity coal field in Colorado and New Mexico. Here the development has been slow since the local market is small. Colorado can scarcely compete with eastern mills for the Pacific trade, since the freight rates over the western mountains and deserts are higher than are the ocean freight rates from the middle Atlantic seaboard.

The Geneva steel plant in Utah was constructed during World War II at a cost of $180,000,000 to provide additional steel west of the Rocky Mountains. Coal is supplied from mines opened at Horse Canyon approximately 130 miles southeast of the plant. Iron ore is obtained from open-pit mines located at Iron Mountain, Iron County, Utah, about 255 miles southwest of Geneva. Limestone and dolomite are quarried near Payson, Utah, about 25 miles from the steel plant.

[21] Langdon White, "The Iron and Steel Industry of the Birmingham, Alabama, District," *Economic Geography*, 1928.

[22] H. Foster Bain, "Western Steel Problem," *Mining and Metallurgy*, July 1945, pp. 329–335.

Water is obtained from the near-by Wasatch Mountains, from arte-
sian wells, and from flowing springs on the plant site (Fig. 243).
Open-hearth furnaces, steel foundries, and rolling mills have been
developed at Pittsburg, California (near San Francisco), and at Tor-
rence, California.

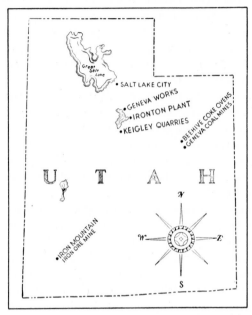

Fig. 243. The Geneva iron and steel plant is well situated with respect to major
raw materials, but the market of the region is normally small. (*U. S. Steel News*,
U. S. Steel Corporation, October 1943, p. 5.)

The Future of the Iron and Steel Industries of the United States

It is clear that the depletion of the high-grade iron ores of the Lake
Superior district would be a tremendous handicap to the iron and steel
industries of the Pittsburgh and lower lakes area—the most important
iron- and steel-producing area of its size in the world. The near
exhaustion of the high-grade ores of the Lake Superior district cannot
be delayed many decades. This will leave a vast tonnage of low-grade
ores that can be utilized. Already some of the low-grade ores are
being passed through beneficiation plants and the iron content increased
in order to reduce freight costs to the lower lakes district and, at the
same time, to increase the iron content of the ore so that it will be

acceptable to the pig-iron producers. Increasing quantities of low-grade ore will undoubtedly be used in the future.

Although our Lake Superior ores cannot last indefinitely, the Birmingham district contains 2 to 3 billion tons of commercial ore. Then, too, this country is relatively favorably situated for the importation of ores from Cuba, Newfoundland, Brazil, Chile, and other foreign countries.

THE IRON AND STEEL INDUSTRIES OF EUROPE

The greatest iron and steel manufacturing region in the world extends from northern France and the Saar, through Luxemburg, Belgium, and northward into the Ruhr district of Germany (Fig. 244).[23] This belt, approximately 400 miles long and less than 300 miles wide, normally produces most of the iron and steel output of western continental Europe. The natural conditions are almost ideal for the development of the iron and steel industries, but political conditions are less favorable. This area is centrally located in a region that, except for war and its aftermath, affords one of the finest markets in the world. Before the ravages of World War II, it was served by an excellent network of railroads, canals, and rivers, and was readily accessible to several of the great ocean trade routes. Much of the area is underlaid with coal, and near by are the vast iron reserves of Lorraine—the largest of all Europe, estimated at more than 5 billion tons.[24]

But for the political conditions existing in western Europe, the Lorraine iron ore reserves are well situated for the development of the iron and steel industry. There are six coal fields within 150 miles of the Lorraine iron ore district which have a known reserve of 86 billion tons of coal, of which about 34 billion tons, most of which is situated in Germany, is suitable for coking. The position of the Lorraine ore deposits along the drainage basins of the Meuse and Moselle rivers gives easy access by railroad to both the Rhine Valley and the lowlands of Belgium, which, in turn, have river or canal connections with tidewater.

[23] Eastern United States usually surpasses this European region in the output of iron and steel. However, the iron and steel industry of eastern United States is spread over an area that is many times as large as the European region that is mentioned above.

[24] "The Iron and Associated Industries of Lorraine, the Saar District, Luxemburg, and Belgium," *Bulletin* 703, U. S. Geological Survey, 1920, p. 18.

Unfortunately the national distribution of iron ore and coking coal reserves of continental Europe is unfavorable for the economic development of industry. The iron ore reserves lie near or across the boundaries of several countries, each one jealous of the military and economic strength of the others. This condition has caused bitter contests for the possession of these resources so essential to economic

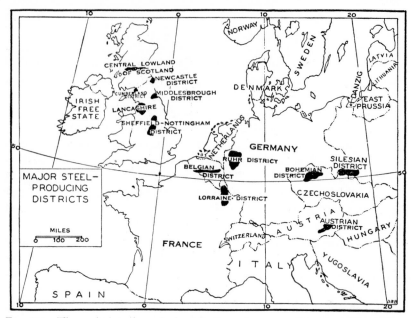

Fig. 244. The major steel-producing districts of western Europe are located on coal fields with the exception of the Lorraine district which is located near large iron ore deposits.

and military greatness. The better of these iron ore deposits were seized by Germany at the conclusion of the Franco-Prussian War in 1870 and were ceded back to France in the readjustment that followed World War I. They were taken over again by Germany during World War II but were returned to France after the defeat of Germany.

The Germany of the future is likely to be left with only low-grade iron ores. Recently 2 billion tons of low-grade iron ore were discovered south of Brunswick in the central part of the Germany of 1938. During World War II the German government began the manufacture of iron and steel from these ores. The development had a much broader scope than an average iron and steel plant; it was also a huge public utilities concern and manufactured many synthetic products. The cheap lignitic coals near Brunswick were used to generate gas which was piped to many industrial areas of Germany. One purpose of this development was to relieve other crowded industrial areas and to permit the expansion of population into a comparatively undeveloped area. The plant was closed down at the end of the war.[25] Whether these low-grade resources—iron ore and lignite—can be profitably developed during peacetime remains to be determined.

The most notable iron and steel center of Germany is that of Westphalia, located on or near the Ruhr coal field which is discussed in the next chapter. This center is so situated on the navigable Rhine and Ruhr that Swedish and Spanish ores can be cheaply imported to supplement Lorraine ores, and the finished products can be marketed over the great ocean highways to remote parts of the world.

Western continental Europe is by no means dependent upon Lorraine for her iron ore supplies. Northern Sweden, Spain, and western France possess large iron ore reserves, and many other smaller deposits of ore are scattered throughout western Europe (Fig. 245).

The British Isles. During most of the nineteenth century the British Isles led the world in the production of iron and steel. In 1850, the United Kingdom produced four times as much pig iron as the United States, and as late as 1875 her mines produced half of the world's output of iron ore. The location of the coal fields, ore deposits, and limestone beds near the coast of England, Scotland, and Wales, and close to good harbors gave the British easy access to the sea for export and aided in the distribution of the product for home consumption.

About a half century ago England found her higher-grade iron ore running low and began to depend more and more on imported ore, until, during the period 1928–1946, the imports represented almost 40 per cent of the total used.

The coastal location of many of the blast furnaces favors the importation of iron ore, most of which comes from Spain and northern Africa although an increasing amount is supplied by Sweden and France.

Other European Iron-Manufacturing Centers. Northern Sweden contains the largest deposits of high-grade iron ore of Europe. These

[25] Charles F. Park, Jr., "What to Do About Our Iron Ore Reserves," *Mining and Metallurgy*, April 1947, pp. 192–196.

deposits are located less than 100 miles by rail from an ice-free port, Narvik, Norway, through which the iron ore is exported during the winter; and almost as close to Swedish ports on the Gulf of Bothnia, through which the bulk of the export passes during the summer when

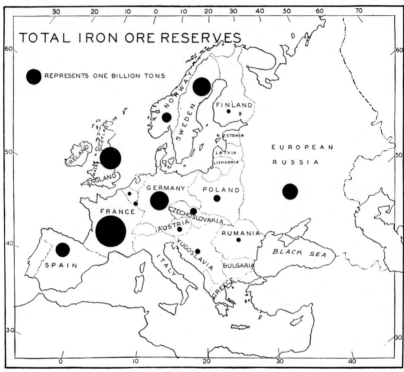

Fig. 245.   The chief iron ore reserves of Europe.   Circles drawn with respect to relative sizes of reserves.   The largest reserves, the iron ore reserves of France, are estimated at approximately 4.3 billion metric tons.   The iron ore reserves of Sweden and of Spain are high grade while most of those of Germany are low grade.

the Gulf is free from ice.   The ore, like that of the Lake Superior district, is near the surface and easily mined by the steam-shovel method.

Unfortunately, Sweden has no coking coal with which to smelt her ore.   Consequently, most of it is exported, primarily to Germany and England.   Recently the prospects have brightened for an increased use of iron ore at home.   During the present century new processes of smelting and steel manufacture have been developed—processes by which electric heat displaces a large part of the coke formerly required. Since Sweden can develop an abundance of hydroelectric power she is turning to these new processes of iron and steel making and is rapidly becoming one of the leaders in the field. The electric furnace is especially adapted for the making of the highest quality of various steels using metal alloys such as nickel, chromium, tungsten, and vanadium, all of which are becoming of increasing importance. The electric steel is higher in price than Bessemer and open-hearth, but it is also of better quality.

Czechoslovakia, Poland, Spain, and Italy all manufacture some iron and steel. Czechoslovakia has coking coal, some iron ore, and a fair local market; Poland has large stores of good coking coal, a small amount of iron ore, and, during peace times, she can easily obtain ore from Sweden. Spain, like Sweden, is without coking coal, but since the country exports several million tons of iron ore annually to other countries of Europe she can import fuel cheaply in vessels that are returning directly from the British coal fields for ore.

Soviet Russia (European and Asiatic). The iron and steel industry of Russia grew with phenomenal rapidity during the decade just prior to World War II. In 1929, Russia produced only 4,000,000 tons of steel and ranked fifth among the countries of the world in the manufacture of this commodity; in 1938, Russia produced 18,000,000 tons of steel and stood third among the nations in the output of this valuable product. Russia is known to possess several hundred million tons of high-grade iron ore. Some of the less-authenticated reports indicate that the iron ore reserves of Russia even surpass those of the United States. These iron ores are widely distributed throughout the vast Russian domain (Fig. 246).

The best of the known reserves are situated in the central and southern parts of the country and lie relatively close to both coal fields and transportation facilities where they can be developed to best advantage. In several areas one or more other important minerals such as copper, lead, zinc, chromium, manganese, or bauxite are situated close to coal fields, iron ore deposits, or oil fields (Fig. 247). As a result, conditions are favorable for the development of a series of iron and steel centers and also of industrial centers, which extend across Russia from Ukraine in the west to the Pacific Ocean on the east.

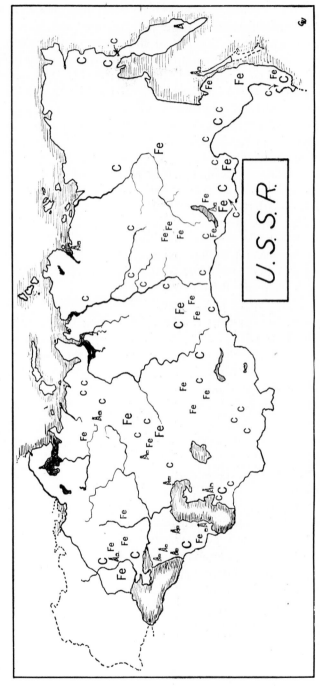

Fig. 246. The U.S.S.R. and the United States are the world's most highly mineralized nations. The U.S.S.R. is rich in coal, iron ore, and petroleum resources. The large letters represent major resources and the small letters represent smaller resources or unexplored resources of unknown extent. Minerals: C—coal, Fe—iron ore, and the diagram of an oil derrick represents petroleum resources.

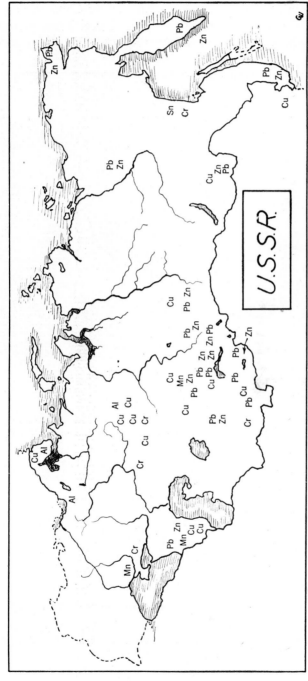

Fig. 247. The two maps, Figs. 246 and 247, indicate that several regions in the U.S.S.R. possess well-rounded supplies of minerals. Minerals: Cu–copper, Cr–chromium, Mn–manganese, Al–aluminum, Pb–lead, Zn–zinc, Sn–tin.

China. In spite of the meager iron reserves of China the country has sufficient ore to support a larger iron and steel industry than has yet been developed anywhere within the Orient.[26] The backward

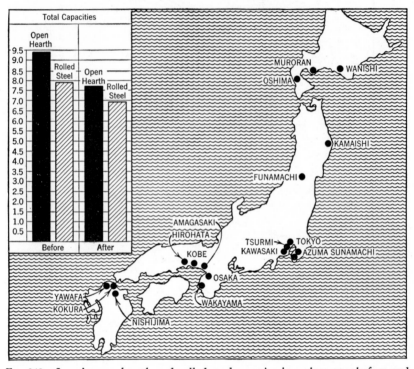

Fig. 248. Japan's open hearth and rolled steel capacity in major areas before and after war damage. Japan's iron and steel industries are widely scattered over the main islands. ("Summation No. 3," General Headquarters, Supreme Commander for the Allied Forces. Taken by permission from *Steel Facts,* American Iron and Steel Institute, April 1946, p. 2.)

state of this basic industry can scarcely be overcome until the transportation facilities of the country are improved.

Wars and civil strife together with the lack of railways and roads have been a greater handicap upon the mining industry of China than upon any other industry in the country, and their influence has been most marked in respect to iron. A good railroad system in China

[26] China possesses approximately 1,500,000,000 tons of known iron ore reserves. Vei Chow Juan, "Mineral Resources of China," *Economic Geology,* No. 4, Part 2, Supplement, June-July 1946, pp. 424–433.

would undoubtedly stimulate the mineral industries of that country. The output of iron, however, has made very little progress since 1916, owing to the fact that it was impossible to build new furnaces during World War I, and since 1937 war and political unrest have retarded industrial development. Thus during the period when the world demand for iron and steel products was almost insatiable, China was unable to profit by the situation and consequently lost one of her best opportunities to establish her iron and steel industry on a modern basis. By 1940, the war with Japan had demoralized the small iron and steel industry that had previously developed.

Japan. Although Japan has developed the largest iron and steel industry of the Orient, her total iron ore reserves of approximately 70,000,000 tons are insufficient to supply the American steel mills for one year.[27] If the reserves of Korea and Formosa are included, the total probably does not surpass 100,000,000 tons of ore economically available under present mining conditions. The Japanese coal supply is reasonably abundant and of fair quality, but most of it lies at considerable depth and is difficult and expensive to mine.

Since their own resources for the development of the iron and steel industry are small and expensive to develop, the Japanese have been compelled to turn to Manchuria, the Philippine Islands, southeastern Asia, and India for iron ore.

In 1943, the Japanese produced 9,656,000 tons of steel but only 8,616,000 tons came from plants on the home islands. During 1946, Japan produced less than 2,000,000 tons of steel. However, few of her plants were ruined by the war and her capacity for production has been reduced but little. Most of Japan's iron and steel industries have been developed in or near cities bordering her inland sea, and in cities situated near Tokyo Bay (Fig. 248).

OTHER IRON AND STEEL INDUSTRIES

Throughout the vast expanse of Africa, southern Asia, and Australia, iron ore deposits are known to exist in many places. Northwest Africa—Tunisia, Algeria, and Morocco—contains rather extensive deposits of iron ore and, between 1930 and 1945, 2 to 4 million tons of iron ore were exported annually to the industrial centers of Europe.

India possesses abundant resources of high-grade iron ore, vast resources of manganese and chrome ores, and moderate supplies of

[27] Harry M. Mikami, "World Iron-Ore Map," *Economic Geology*, January-February 1944, p. 22.

vanadium and tungsten ores. She also possesses a plentiful supply of fair-grade coking coal, and limestone suitable for fluxing materials outcrops in many areas. North and west of Calcutta, abundant sup-

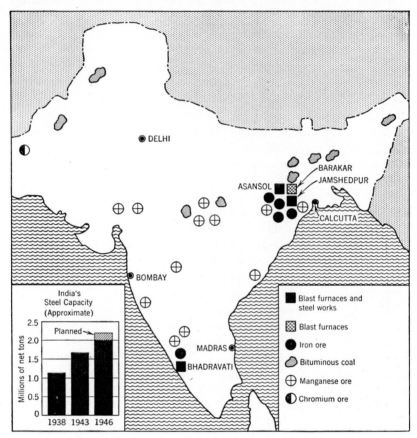

FIG. 249. India possesses an abundance of iron ore, coking coal, lime, manganese ore, and chromium ore—the major raw materials for the production of iron and steel. (Taken by permission from *Steel Facts*, American Iron and Steel Institute, October 1946, p. 2.)

plies of several of these raw materials have been discovered within a few miles of each other (Fig. 249). A prosperous and politically stable India could consume vast quantities of iron and steel products. However, this country needs a better supply of laborers with skill and especially with managerial ability—qualities that are acquired as industrialization progresses.

Australia emerged from World War II with a rapidly growing and fairly well-integrated iron and steel industry. The largest steel mills of the country have been developed near Sydney which lies close to large or moderate reserves of coal, iron ore, and manganese ore. Limestone is obtained from Tasmania.

REFERENCES

BAKER, JAMES S., "Brazil—Land of Great Potential Mineral Wealth," *Mining and Metallurgy*, May 1945, pp. 249–251.

BROOKS, A. H., and MORRIS F. LACROIX, "The Saar District and Belgium," *Bulletin 6*, U. S. Department of Commerce, 1922.

BURCHARD, E. F., "Alabama Ores Equal Lake Supply," *Iron Age*, March 24, 1927, pp. 847–853.

EMENY, BROOKS, *The Strategy of Raw Materials*, The Macmillan Co., 1934, pp. 42–85.

ERSELCUK, MUZAGGER, "Iron and Steel Industry in Japan," *Economic Geography*, April 1947, pp. 105–129.

GREGORY, JAMES J., and D. W. SHAVE, *The U.S.S.R.—A Geographical Survey*, John Wiley & Sons, 1944.

HARRIS, CHAUNCY D., "The Ruhr Coal-Mining District," *Geographical Review*, April 1946.

HARTSHORNE, RICHARD, "Location Factors in the Iron and Steel Industry," *Economic Geography*, July 1928, pp. 243–245.

HENRY, THOMAS R., "War's Wake in the Rhineland," *National Geographic Magazine*, July 1945, pp. 1–32.

HOTCHKISS, WILLIAM O., "Iron Ore Supply for the Future," *Economic Geology*, May 1947, pp. 205–210.

Imperial Mineral Resources Bureau, *The Mineral Industry of the British Empire and Foreign Countries* (1920–1922), London, 1924.

JOHNSSON, A., and A. WOHLBERG, "Development of the Swedish Iron Industry During the Last Thirty Years," *Journal of the Iron and Steel Institute*, No. 114, 1926, pp. 51–94.

JUAN, VEI CHOW, "Mineral Resources of China," *Economic Geology*, No. 4, Part 2, Supplement, June-July 1946, pp. 399–471. This is an excellent summary of all the important minerals of China with maps showing the distribution of each mineral.

KILLOUGH, HUGH B., *Raw Materials of Industrialism*, Thomas Y. Crowell Co., 1929, pp. 230–249.

LEITH, C. K., *World Minerals and World Politics*, McGraw-Hill Book Co., 1931.

MIKAMI, HARRY M., "World Iron-Ore Map," *Economic Geology*, January-February 1944, pp. 1–24.

MILLER, WILLARD E., "Some Aspects of the U. S. Mineral Self-Sufficiency," *Economic Geography*, April 1947, pp. 77–84.

PARK, CHARLES F., "What to Do About Our Iron Ore Reserves," *Mining and Metallurgy*, April 1947, pp. 192–196.

ROGERS, ALLAN, "The Manchurian Iron and Steel Industry and its Resource Base," *Geographical Review*, January 1948, pp. 41–54.

SCOTT, JOHN, "Magnetic City—Core of Valiant Russia's Industrial Might," *National Geographic Magazine*, May 1943, pp. 525–556.

VOSKUIL, WALTER H., "Minerals and the Post War Politics of Europe," *University of Illinois Bulletin*, Vol. 41, 1944, pp. 1–110.

Chapter 20

MINERAL FUELS AND WATER POWER

Mineral Fuels and World Industry. Our modern industrial civilization is based to a large extent upon mechanical power, most of which is derived from coal, petroleum, natural gas, and falling water. No full appreciation of the economic and industrial potentialities of regions or countries is possible without an evaluation of these important resources. For that reason it is necessary for a student to understand the nature, distribution, and uses of these products if he is to comprehend many of the pressing problems of the economic, industrial, and political world of today. These problems confront the individual, the community, and the nation. Newspaper headlines such as: "Russia Demands Oil Rights in Iran," "Lewis Calls Out Miners," "Nation Faces Coal Famine," and "Homes in Europe are Cold and Dark" indicate something of the broad scope of problems presented by our mineral fuels. These problems are general enough to affect each individual, and large enough to create serious international difficulties.

The problems presented by the *power-producing resources* of the world are not new. Man has ever sought to accomplish his purpose with a minimum expenditure of personal physical effort. This attribute has had a material influence on the progress of civilization. The strong and resourceful primitive man impressed the energy of his weaker fellow men to serve his needs. Later, animals were domesticated and taught to labor that man might accomplish more and at the same time increase his hours of leisure. Then the winds were harnessed that they might work for man. But this human desire to accomplish more work with less effort seems to be insatiable. Finally man learned how to use the energy of mineral fuels and falling water—discoveries that presaged the great industrial age which had its beginnings a little more than a century ago. Since then developments have been rapid until today it is a platitude to say that the whole structure of modern civilization is dependent upon this ability which man has acquired to control the energy of mineral fuels and water power to do his bidding. As on the sea, where fuel power has almost displaced that of the wind, so on land it has replaced the animal as a primitive motive force and has become the dominant power in transporting goods.

The steam engine, internal-combustion machines, and the electric devices have cut down distances and have furthered the development of communication to such a degree that a great nation has become a single community. But the influence does not stop with national boundaries. Locomotion on the land and sea and in the air has brought places that were distant, or even inaccessible, near and within the reach of the least adventurous spirit; the products of the remote parts of the world are brought to our doors; the earth is girdled with wire so that the doings of this evening may be known the world over by tomorrow morning,[1] and the important events of the day may be flashed to the entire radio audience of the world within a few minutes after they occur. All these developments have been accomplished within little more than a century, thus altering the whole social, economic, and political picture of the earth.

Similarly in industry, the use of power has made possible the production of goods on a gigantic scale. This has been accompanied by high wages, more leisure, and means for enjoying that leisure, and has thus resulted in higher standards for the masses. In the home, power has been the servant that has removed drudgery. By January 1, 1948, it had reached 65.1 per cent of the farms and had made practicable the pursuance of agricultural operations on an unprecedented scale.[2]

Mineral fuels are used not only for power development but also as basic raw materials in industry. At present the United States leads all other countries of the world not only in the total consumption of mineral fuels and water power, but also in the per capita consumption of these products.

Power and Industrial Development. So completely does modern industry depend upon power that the industrial position of a nation may be gauged by its consumption of power. At present the regions of great industrial development are the United States and western Europe, which accordingly produce and consume approximately 90 per cent of the world's power.

These countries bordering the North Atlantic not only are in possession of an abundance of fuel and water power, but they also are

---

[1] F. C. Lea, "Power Production, Past, Present, and Future," *Proceedings of American Institute of Mechanical Engineers*, No. 5, 1929, p. 1045.

[2] Estimate made by the Cincinnati Gas and Electric Company, June 1948.

blessed with the most complete and well-rounded resources, necessary for the development of industry, found anywhere in the world. These countries are especially fortunate in having an abundance of coal and iron. The coal acts as a key by which the iron is obtained, and the iron in turn is used to harness and control the energy of the coal. Moreover, the climates of these regions stimulate both mental and physical vigor. With such a fortunate combination of factors favoring its development, it is only natural that the industrial revolution should have had its beginnings and its most rapid growth along the borders of the North Atlantic.

After the countries of the North Atlantic had acquired industrial growth and strength of substantial proportions, it was only natural that they should assure themselves an abundant supply of resources by searching in other parts of the world for those raw materials which they considered the "key products" to industrial development. Consequently, the countries of the North Atlantic, already enriched and made powerful by the products of their factories, have sought out and gained control, in one way or another, of a preponderant percentage of the known mineral resources of the world. They have also brought under their control vast plantations within the tropics to provide fibers, gums, oils, and other products needed by industry. Most of these products are shipped, in the raw or semi-finished state, to the countries bordering the North Atlantic, to supplement their own resources, which, as stated above, are already the most abundant and well rounded to be found anywhere.

USES OF POWER IN AMERICA

America to a greater degree than any other nation has applied power to the fulfillments of man's needs and desires. The energy used per capita during the past sixty years has increased more than fourfold (Fig. 250). The output of energy in the United States from coal, petroleum, gas, and water power amounts to about one-half the world's total. Since the total power available from man and beast is insignificant in comparison, it is not far wrong to say that the United States today is actually doing nearly half the world's work.[3] For a long time in the early stages of the industrial revolution, Great Britain

[3] A person who drives a high-powered automobile is using lots of energy and is technically doing work. It may or may not be useful. Thus while the United States does about one-half of the work of the world it is not producing one-half of the necessities of life. Much of the energy is utilized for pleasure.

held a pre-eminent position in the output of energy. In 1870 it was releasing about three times as much energy as the United States. In recent years, the United States has been producing four to five times as much energy as Great Britain. As a result, in no other country in the world does the laboring man produce so much goods with such little physical effort. In no other country are living standards so high.

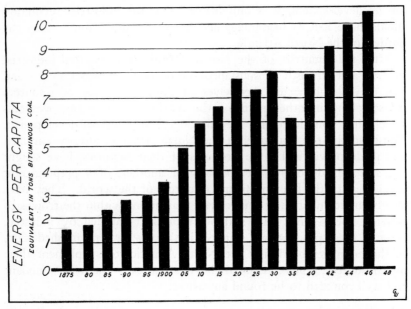

FIG. 250. One reason for the high standard of living in the United States is indicated in this graph. No other country in the world even approximates the United States in the per capita utilization of mechanical energy.

With minor setbacks, our standards of living are increasing continuously while the length of the work week for the average laborer is decreasing (Fig. 251).

Wherever power is not employed on a large scale women are still doing a great amount of heavy manual labor. Where industry has shifted the burden to mechanical shoulders women are the first to receive the benefits. In China, millions of women still engage in heavy masculine work, and in many other foreign countries where machinery is little used women are still compelled to toil in a way scarcely known to American women. In America and much of western Europe, "the round table of King Arthur has been superseded by the drafting board and the conference table.   The place of the knight who went forth to protect the women of the days of chivalry from molestation and oppression, has been taken by the engineer who has freed modern women from toil and drudgery." [4]

Mineral fuels are by far the most important of all mineral products both commercially and industrially.   Within the United States the value of the annual output of mineral fuels is almost three times that of all other primary minerals combined (Fig. 252).

COAL

Coal is the most important mineral product both commercially and industrially.   It is the greatest source of power for manufacturing, mining, and transportation; it is a major raw material in the manufacture of iron and steel, gas, and dyes; and it is the principal source of fuel for most of the industrial nations of the earth.   The production of coal constitutes the largest mining industry in the world and, in America alone, employs more than a half million men.

Uses of Coal for Heat and Power. Coal is only one source of heat and power, but it is the major one for the world as a whole.   However, in the United States it supplies only about 50 per cent of our total mechanical energy (Fig. 253).   During the last few decades other sources of heat and power have been increasing rapidly while that of coal has increased little.

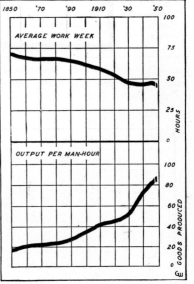

FIG. 251.   During the past century the average work week of the American laborer has decreased from more than sixty hours to something less than forty-eight hours, while the output of goods produced per man-hour has increased more than fivefold.   The fewer hours that the laborers work, the more time they have for the consumption of goods.

The energy developed from coal, like that from oil, gas, and water power, makes two major contributions to industrial progress: First,

4 P. L. Alford, "Progress in Manufacturing," *Mechanical Engineering*, April 1930, p. 403.

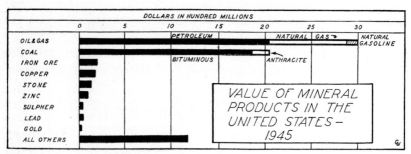

FIG. 252. Mineral fuels represent almost two-thirds of the total value of all minerals produced within the United States annually. (*Statistical Abstract of the United States*, U. S. Department of Commerce, 1947, pp. 731–735.)

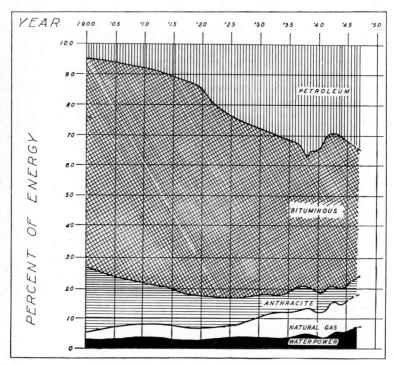

FIG. 253. In 1900, coal supplied approximately 90 per cent of the energy utilized in the United States; today it supplies barely 50 per cent.

when applied in the use of machinery, it increases the human power manyfold; and, second, it makes possible the concentration of power so that it can be used most effectively for industrial purposes.

Advantages of Mechanical Energy. In many respects mechanical energy is vastly superior to either man power or animal power. An automobile may have more than 100 horsepower, and an ordinary stationary engine may be capable of generating 20,000 horsepower or more. Recent developments in the electrical industry have changed the steam central station from a source of mere local distribution to one of electrical supply over large areas. This change has necessitated the development of huge power plants which may be far removed from the industrial community, involving sometimes single installation units of approximately 500,000 horsepower and turbine units as large as 70,000 horsepower.[5] It is inconceivable that 10,000 men could apply their power in pushing a train or that 3,500,000 men could apply their physical energies in any possible way so as to create the power in a form that could be quickly and easily distributed over thousands of square miles and applied in widely separated places in just the amount needed; yet the power of the great turbine can be applied with an equal degree of success to run a sewing machine, which uses but a minor fraction of a horsepower, or to turn the machinery of a great industrial plant which requires thousands of horsepower, and which perhaps is most effective if applied in some small space, inaccessible to man or beast.

This ability to concentrate power has been a major factor in the development of transportation facilities and consequently in the concentration of industrial centers and in the growth of cities. For, without rapid, cheap, and large-scale commerce, the concentration of peoples in large cities, far removed from the products which they must have every day, would be impossible. In 1945 the railroads of the United States had in operation 41,018 locomotives which pulled an aggregate of 10.5 billion loaded car miles and 4.8 billion empty car miles. In comparison with this, human labor used for transportation purposes could accomplish only insignificant results.[6]

Mechanical Energy versus Human Energy. The horsepower installed to run our factories, mills, and railroads, to light our homes, to operate our refrigerators, gas ranges, etc., plus the power installed in our automobiles was estimated (1938) by General Motors Corpora-

[5] A. D. Blake and P. W. Swain, "Fifty Years of Power," *Mechanical Engineering*, April 1930, pp. 321ff.

[6] Compiled from *Statistical Abstract of United States*, 1947, pp. 510–516.

tion as considerably more than 1.5 billion. Since then the energy consumption has increased sufficiently to indicate that, by 1945, this horsepower approximated 2 billion. Comparisons of human and mechanical power have their limitations, but it is estimated that the power of an ordinary man is $\frac{1}{10}$ horsepower. Reduced to human equivalent then, 20 billion mechanical slaves are ready to serve us at all times at a cost per slave of only a few dollars a year.

Coal Resources of the World

Coal is one of the most abundant of our industrial minerals. The reserves within 6,000 feet of the surface are estimated at approximately 8,000 billion tons, an amount large enough to last the world approximately 4,000 years at the present rate of consumption, assuming one-fourth of the coal to be lost because of poor methods of mining. With a supply sufficient to satisfy our present needs for more than 100 generations there seems to be little reason to worry about any probable future shortage (Fig. 254).

We have every reason to believe that the scientific world will not stand still and that as necessity arises other sources of energy will be found. There are probably more possible substitutes for coal than for any other important industrial commodity used by man. There are many sources of power, including petroleum, natural gas, water, tides, differences in temperature of sea water, the sun, and atomic energy, which are being used or may be used as substitutes for coal. It is now known that a few pounds of uranium will produce as much heat or energy as thousands of tons of coal or petroleum. Scientists differ as to how soon this heat and energy may be applied to the task of heating cities, or of propelling ships, airplanes, automobiles, and the thousands of other types of machines.

In the meantime coal, oil, natural gas, and water power are still indispensable. Science is, therefore, continuously endeavoring to discover methods of reducing the waste in the utilization of coal, thus lengthening the life of this valuable resource. At present, however, the energy which is lost in burning coal far exceeds that which is utilized. An ordinary steam engine will not convert 15 per cent of the heat of combustion into useful work; the steam locomotive utilizes less than 10 per cent of the energy; and domestic consumption is even more wasteful. Similarly there is great waste in the processes of mining and distributing coal. This may be reduced, thereby saving fuel and thus prolonging the life of the reserves.

Limited Supply of High-Grade Coal. While the complete exhaustion of our coal supply is so remote as to be of little concern at present, the danger of depleting our high-grade reserves merits more attention. The great bulk of coal, especially in the United States, is the low-rank bituminous, subbituminous, and lignite; and the high-grade coals are relatively scarce. The best coals are the ones that are being

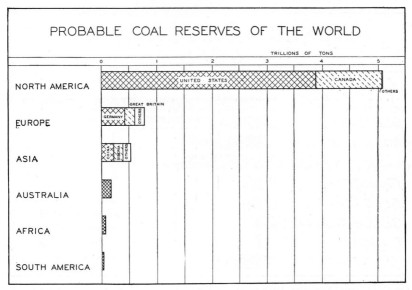

Fig. 254. North America, and particularly the United States, possesses vast reserves of coal. The total quantity of good-grade and readily mined bituminous coal in the United States is estimated at 1.4 trillion tons—enough to last the world at the present rate of consumption for about 1,000 years. The United States also possesses more than 2 trillion tons of low-grade coal.

drawn upon most extensively and will be the first to be exhausted. There is no immediate cause for alarm, however, as the reserves of easily mined high-grade coal of eastern United States and western Europe are sufficient to supply the needs of the industrial world for several generations to come. By the time these are gone, science may have solved the problem of securing heat and energy from other sources. It should not be forgotten, however, that mankind has lived on the earth for hundreds of thousands of years, and so far as we can foresee should be able to live here many more thousand years. Consequently a due regard for the rights of future generations demands that we do not wantonly waste such valuable resources as coal, oil, and gas until we are certain that their functions can be performed equally well by substitutes.

Although nature has supplied mankind with an abundance of coal, a study of Fig. 254 indicates that future political boundary lines were not considered when the coal beds were being formed. According to the present estimates, North America contains about two-thirds of the

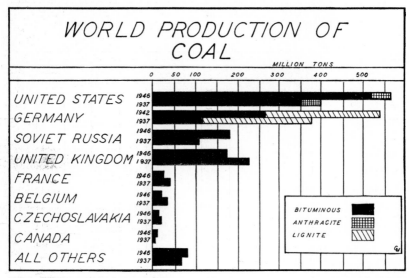

Fig. 255. Note that the dates of coal production for the various countries of the world are 1937 and 1946 except those for Germany which are 1937 and 1942. Since 1942, German coal production has declined sharply.

world's coal resources, and the United States alone contains more than half of the total known reserve. Among the continents, South America and Africa have fared worst, having small known deposits, most of which are of inferior grade.

Coal Production of the World

Most of the coal production of the world is concentrated within a few of the great industrial countries. The United States, Germany, Great Britain, and Soviet Russia are preponderantly the leaders in the industry. Although these four countries support only 21 per cent of the world's population they produce approximately 80 per cent of the world's output of coal. Most of the remaining fourth is mined in other European countries, more than 90 per cent of the world's output being mined in countries which drain to the North Atlantic (Fig. 255). All the South American countries combined produce less than 0.5 per cent of the output of the United States, and each of the continents of Africa and Australia produces less than 3 per cent of the amount mined in the United States alone. Asia, with more than half of the world's population, produces less than 8 per cent of the world's coal supply. This unequal distribution of coal production is more strikingly emphasized in the per capita consumption of coal in selected countries and continents. Although the United Kingdom and Germany both produce more coal per capita than the United States, the United States is distinctly the leader in the per capita consumption of mineral fuels, since it is the world's largest consumer of petroleum, the leading substitute for coal.

The approximate per capita coal and lignite consumption for selected countries prior to World War II is indicated below:

Germany	6 tons
United Kingdom	5.4 tons
United States	3.8 tons
Japan	0.6 ton
Africa	0.2 ton
China	0.1 ton

Trends of Coal Production in the United States

Coal has been mined in the United States since 1750, but in those early days wood was plentiful and the use of coal was so little understood that the demand for it was small. As late as 1822, the annual production had barely reached 54,000 tons. From this time on, the output gradually increased with only minor recessions until the peak of production was reached in 1918 when 678,000,000 tons were mined. Since then the curve of coal production has flattened out with a tendency to bend down except as stimulated by the great demand of World War II and its aftereffects.

This recent decrease (relative not actual) in the output of coal is largely the result of (1) the increasing use of competing fuels and water power, (2) the more efficient use of coal, and (3) the interruptions to the flow of coal because of strikes.

THE COAL FIELDS OF THE UNITED STATES

The Appalachian Coal Fields. Although coal is mined in more than thirty states, the Appalachian Highlands probably contain nine-tenths of the high-grade coal of the country and supply more than two-thirds of the total output of the nation. Nearly 60 per cent is mined in Pennsylvania and West Virginia, the foremost mining states of the Union (Fig. 256).

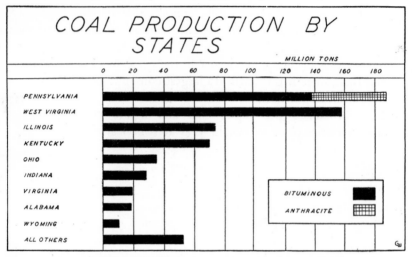

FIG. 256. Approximately three-fourths of the coal supply of the United States is mined in the Appalachian region. (Data for 1944–1947.)

The major fields of the Appalachian region are the anthracite field of eastern Pennsylvania and the northern, central, and southern fields of the Appalachian Plateau. These fields contain the greatest store of high-quality coal to be found in America, if not in the world, and constitute the foundation of the great industrial development of eastern United States. They have supplied most of the fuel for the blast furnaces and the great iron and steel mills not only of the Pittsburgh district but also of all the country east of the Rocky Mountains; they have provided most of the energy and part of the raw materials for the countless manufacturing enterprises of eastern United States; and they have supplied fuel to warm millions of homes, both within this country and in Canada. Each of the major Appalachian coal fields contains vast quantities of high-grade coal which is relatively easily mined, and each has contributed in a major way to the wealth of the nation. But the northern Appalachian field, which contains, among others, the famous Pittsburgh bed, ranks first in value and production not only among all the coal fields of the United States, but also of the world.

THE PITTSBURGH COAL BED. The Pittsburgh coal bed is probably the most valuable single mineral deposit in the world and undoubtedly stands first among all the mineral deposits of the United States in its contribution of wealth to this nation. Already it has contributed to Pennsylvania, alone, almost 3,000,000,000 tons of high-grade coal worth nearly $4,700,000,000.[7] And yet the vast amount of coal which remains in this bed is estimated at approximately ten times that which has already been mined. This bed averages about 7 feet in thickness and is remarkably persistent over large areas, covering approximately 5,729 square miles in Pennsylvania, West Virginia, Ohio, and Maryland.

In early times the long black bands, indicating the outcrop of this coal bed, circled the hills in the Pittsburgh area at an elevation of 400 feet above the waters of the Allegheny and Monongahela rivers, and extended up the valley sides of the Monongahela in an unbroken line for a distance of 200 miles.

The horizontal position of the coal bed, the thickness of the seam, and the outcrop of the seam along the valley walls are all factors which nature has provided to make mining an easy task. Consequently, the per capita output of coal is exceptionally large. The quality of the coal for a variety of purposes is almost unsurpassed, and the location near the head of several river systems has facilitated the marketing of the coal over a wide area. The plateau in which the coal bed is situated is deeply dissected by numerous streams, thus exposing the coal seams for hundreds of miles along the valley sides. The coal is accordingly easily mined by tunneling into the hillsides and is cheaply transported by the aid of gravity to the valley floor below (Fig. 257). In many places the downward-moving coal-laden cars haul the empty cars up to the mine so that little extra power is needed in the operation.

[7] "The Pittsburgh Coal Bed," *Transactions American Institute Mining Engineers*, April 1930, p. 482. Between 1930 and 1945 this bed produced almost a billion tons of coal worth more than 2 billion dollars. The exact data are not available, but the average price of bituminous coal per ton at the mine has jumped from $1.70 in 1930 to more than $3 in 1948.

In early days the coal became famous for its excellent qualities for the manufacture of gas and coke. It was used in a wide area extending from the Atlantic seaboard to Chicago, and from southern Canada to the Ohio River, for the manufacture of artificial gas. Coke, especially from the Connellsville district, served blast furnaces through much of the eastern United States, so that, quite aside from furnishing a foundation for the great iron and steel industry of the Pittsburgh district, this coal has supplied the wants of half a nation or more.[8]

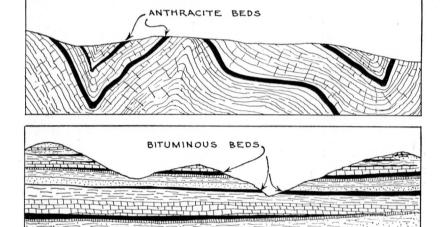

FIG. 257. Coal-mining machinery can be more easily and more efficiently used in the bituminous coal fields than in the anthracite.

The marketing of the coal over a wide area was facilitated, in early times, by the natural and artificial waterways which radiated from the region; more recently the field has been served by more than a score of railways which connect the region with all parts of the United States. The Potomac, with the Chesapeake and Potomac Canal, has afforded cheap transportation from the Pittsburgh-Maryland section of the bed to the eastern seaboard; the Youghiogheny, Monongahela, and Ohio rivers afforded cheap transportation for the coal of West Virginia, Pennsylvania, and Ohio to the broad Mississippi Valley both north and south; the Great Lakes gave an easy outlet to central Canada and to the far Northwest; and the Erie Canal opened a large market

[8] I. C. White, et al., "The Pittsburgh Coal Bed," *Transactions American Institute Mining Engineers*, Vol. 74, p. 482.

for Pittsburgh coal in central and eastern New York and New England.[9]

The reserves of the bed are still large, estimated at approximately 22 billion tons, which at the recent rate of recovery should last about 180 years.

THE MIDDLE APPALACHIAN COAL FIELD. About 500 miles south of Pittsburgh lies the middle Applachian field, second only to the north Appalachian field in the production of high-quality coal. Here, in southern West Virginia and eastern Kentucky, the plateau is even more deeply and intricately dissected than farther north. Consequently, the mines are easily opened in the walls of the valleys and the cost of mining is less than in any other American field.

The best known coal of this region is the Pocahontas coal, which is almost smokeless and, consequently, is used extensively for heating homes. The high quality of the coal, together with the low cost at which it can be delivered at the Atlantic seaboard, have resulted in its extensive use for bunkering ships.

THE SOUTHERN APPALACHIAN COAL FIELD. Near the southern end of the Appalachian Highland is situated the third major field of this physiographic province. Here the largest production of coal is in the Birmingham district, where a good grade of coking coal is produced to supply the iron and steel industries of the vicinity.[10] This coal field also supplies large quantities of fuel for southern railroads, and, with the industrialization of the South, the public utilities are consuming an increasing amount. Coal is also distributed throughout much of the South for domestic purposes, but, because of the mild winters in that part of the United States, the amount of fuel consumed in the homes is small.

INTERIOR COAL FIELDS. Coal underlies a large part of the interior plains of North America (Fig. 258). The eastern interior field, situated in Illinois and Indiana, is the only one in which coal is being extensively mined. It contains the highest-grade coal of the interior region and is favored by location which permits it to compete with Appalachian coal for the industrial markets of the Great Lakes region and a large part of the Mississippi Valley.

The other coal fields of the interior lowlands contain inferior grades of coal and under present conditions can scarcely compete with eastern fields. Consequently, they are of little importance at present. How-

[9] *Ibid.*

[10] R. Dawson Hall, "The Coal Fields that Underwrote Birmingham's Industrial Activity," *Coal Age*, Vol. 33, Oct. 1928, p. 587.

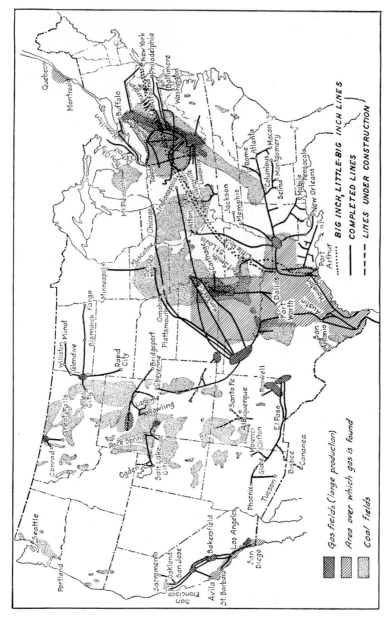

Fig. 258. The locations of Big Inch and of Little-Big Inch pipelines are only approximate. Big Inch does not enter New York City but the gas from it is piped to New York City. (*Mineral Industry*, McGraw-Hill Book Co., 1930. Modified to show major changes from 1930 to 1947.)

ever, their vast potential resources of fuel may become more important when our eastern coal fields are depleted; or, perhaps, they may become competitors of our eastern coal fields, provided that we learn how to use low-grade coal more efficiently.

Anthracite Coal. The first coal to be extensively mined in the United States was in the anthracite field of eastern Pennsylvania. This field of approximately 480 square miles, an area about the size of an average county of Ohio, plays an exceedingly important role in American life. It formerly produced 60 to 80 million tons of coal a year, but coke, petroleum, natural gas, and artificial gas are replacing the more expensive anthracite in many markets. Consequently, in recent years only 45 to 50 million tons have been produced annually. Reserves of anthracite, estimated at 21 billion tons, are sufficient to last at the present rate of consumption for several centuries.[11]

The anthracite field lies in the highly folded rocks of northeastern Pennsylvania. Indeed, the same series of geological activities which brought about this folding changed the vegetative accumulation of swamps and bogs into the finest grade of anthracite coal. These processes have left the beds tilted, in places at a high angle, making deep mining necessary and involving heavy expenditures for mining machinery. Under such conditions the amount of labor per ton required to mine anthracite coal is much greater than that needed in mining bituminous coal.

Anthracite is principally a domestic fuel. This hard, dense coal, with low volatile content, burns slowly with a low flame and little smoke, but with an intense heat. The heating of houses by public utility corporations has not yet become common, and as long as it remains in the hands of the householder, the manifest need of convenience and cleanliness gives anthracite a distinct advantage over bituminous coal. Since most of the coal is used in the home rather than in industry, the principal basis for the anthracite market is cold winters in a densely populated region. As a consequence the great outlets are in New England, the Atlantic states, and those sections of the Middle West which are connected with the anthracite mining district by water transportation. These areas take more than 90 per cent of the total domestic sizes, and with Canada they consume almost 97 per cent.[12]

[11] M. R. Campbell, "The Coal Fields of the United States," *Professional Paper* 100-A, U. S. Geological Survey, 1922, p. 24.

[12] Walter H. Voskuil, *Minerals in Modern Industry*, John Wiley & Sons, 1930, p. 44.

The struggle of transportation companies to secure a part of the freight created by the anthracite field has given the region excellent marketing facilities. During the early development, a canal was built along the Schuylkill River to connect the field with the populous Philadelphia region. Later almost every railroad company whose lines came within a few hundred miles of the field began to reach out for a share of the coal freight. Consequently, the region is now served by more than a dozen roads. Something of the amount of this freight is indicated by the fact that the tonnage of coal shipped from this small region is more than fifteen times that of the largest cotton crop ever grown in the cotton belt, and more than three times that of the entire wheat crop of the United States.

Coal Industry of Europe

For several years prior to World War II, Europe had been producing about one-half of the world's supply of coal and most of the world's lignite. The major producers of coal were Germany, Great Britain, the U.S.S.R., France, Belgium, Poland, and Czechoslovakia. During the years between the two world wars, the western European countries had greatly increased their capacity to produce coal by increasing the mechanization of the mines. World War II, together with the post-war political, economic, labor, and transportation problems have disrupted production so seriously in several countries that world statistics for 1940 to 1947 are not very meaningful.

The Importance of Coal to the United Kingdom. The United Kingdom was the first country in the world to use coal on a large scale, and, in the per capita production, she still holds a high place.

Coal from her mines supplies the power for her manufacturing industries upon which the masses of the population depend for their income; coal supplies a large part of the power for her merchant marine—the largest in the world—which brings to the country food for her industrial population, and raw materials for her factories; and, finally, coal is a major export—one of the very few raw materials which the United Kingdom produces in excess of her home needs.

The coal reserves of the United Kingdom are small in comparison with those of the United States (Fig. 254); they are large enough, however, to supply her probable needs for several more generations, and at the same time to permit her to produce large quantities for export. Moreover, the resources are almost ideally distributed over the United Kingdom for most effective development of industry at home and for export (Fig. 259).

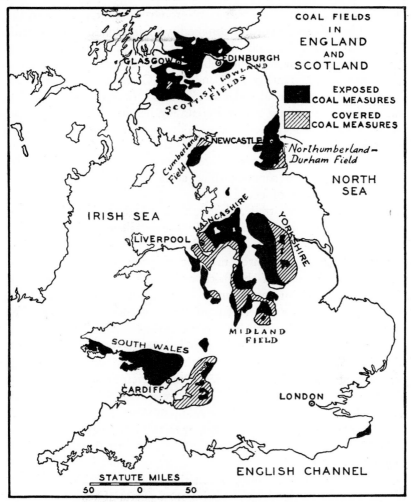

Fig. 259. Coal fields in England and Scotland. The Northumberland-Durham (in which Newcastle is located) and the South Wales fields are the most important in the coal export trade. (Reproduced by permission from Case and Bergsmark, *Modern World Geography*, J. B. Lippincott Company, 1938, p. 410.)

Each coal field supplies the fuel and power for industries particularly suited to the region. The cotton textile industry of Lancashire, the woolen industry of Bradford and Leeds, the iron and steel industry of Birmingham and Sheffield, and the shipbuilding of the Clyde and the Tyne are all dependent upon local coal fields for most of their fuel and power.

GREAT BRITAIN AN IMPORTANT COAL-EXPORTING COUNTRY. From the time coal became an important commodity of international trade until 1937, Great Britain always held first place in the export of coal except for a few years when disastrous labor strikes disrupted Britain's coal-mining industry.[13]   During 1937 and 1938, Germany was the leader in the exportation of coal and coke.   At that time Germany needed cash with which to buy raw materials for her industrial plants, and also with which to increase her stock piles of those raw materials that were needed by her munition plants.   Coal could be exchanged for cash balances in foreign lands.   Consequently, as a result of necessity plus great effort and some sacrifice at home, she surpassed Great Britain in the export of coal.

Britain's coal export trade, although disturbed at times by strikes or a labor shortage, has been favored by the excellent quality of British coal, by the location of the coal fields close to the coast, and by the close proximity of the three major coal-importing regions of the world—the borderlands of the Baltic and Mediterranean seas, and the industrial region of northern France.   The export of coal has also been favored by the nature and extent of British trade.   The British imports are mostly bulky raw materials collected from all parts of the world, used to feed her industrial population and to supply her great industrial plants; her exports, other than coal, are largely manufactured goods of a less bulky nature.   Coal, therefore, may be shipped to distant countries at surprisingly low freight rates in order to help balance the tonnage.   Thus, ships going to Argentina for wheat, to Brazil for coffee, to Chile for nitrates, or to any other part of the world for bulky raw materials may take coal, provided that the country is in need of this valuable fuel.

Other factors which have favored the export of British coal are: the vast expanse of the British Empire, many parts of which are without an adequate fuel supply; the vast foreign investments of British capital in mines, railroads, and other enterprises which require coal; and the wide distribution of British coaling stations.

---

[13] During 1926 a coal miners' strike in the United Kingdom caused a most disastrous interruption of the coal trade.   As a result British exports fell to 20,000,000 tons, while the exports of the United States jumped to almost 22,000,-000 tons and those of Germany to 38,000,000 tons.

The Coal Industry of the Continent of Europe. Although Europe does not possess such riches of coal as are found in the United States, the continent is well supplied with a fair to excellent grade of coal. Moreover, the distribution of the coal would not be particularly bad but for the fact that the continent is made up of many countries, a few of which possess most of the coal. Too frequently the easy and economic distribution of this valuable mineral to the various parts of the continent where it could be most economically used is checked by numerous international boundary lines. These boundaries divide countries between which there is intense national rivalry. This is well illustrated by the fact that, although France and the Netherlands are both poor in coal, the rich industrial sections of both of these countries are relatively close to the Ruhr coal field. Yet international complications sometimes prevent the ready flow of Ruhr coal to France or the Netherlands just when it is most needed. Thus France, in her attempt to develop her own coal resources rather than to depend entirely upon foreign countries, is mining low-grade coal from exceedingly deep mines. Some of the mines of France are more than 4,000 feet deep. If western Europe were all one country, so that coal could flow easily from one part of the continent to another, those beds would probably await some future time for development. Present-day mining, under such conditions, would be pushed more vigorously in fields where the grade of coal is better and where mining operations can be carried on more easily and with less cost per ton of coal.

IMPORTANCE OF GERMAN COAL INDUSTRIES. The most valuable coal field in all Europe, and normally the most productive, is that of the Ruhr district. Located in the lower Rhine Valley, the region has ready access to foreign raw materials and markets. Before World War II, this coal field was connected by an excellent network of railways, highways, rivers and canals to the abundant raw materials and vast markets of western Europe. As a result of these and other advantages, the Ruhr had become the greatest industrial center of all Europe and probably, for its size, of the world.

Based upon the coke-making plants of this field, the Ruhr became, prior to 1940, a leader in the manufacture of dyes, and other coal-tar products, and of natural gas. In 1939, the Ruhr produced 13 billion cubic feet of gas which was distributed through 1,500 miles of high-pressure gas mains. During World War II the synthetic petroleum industry was expanded in the Ruhr region and the estimated capacity of gasoline production exceeded 1,500,000 tons annually before hostilities ended. The Ruhr district probably surpassed any other area of equal size in the production of coal-tar products, chemicals, and armaments and munitions of war.

The Ruhr is a region of great cities. In 1939, three cities—Essen,

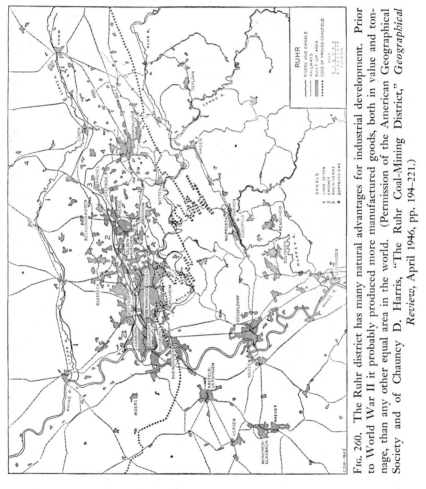

FIG. 260. The Ruhr district has many natural advantages for industrial development. Prior to World War II it probably produced more manufactured goods, both in value and tonnage, than any other equal area in the world. (Permission of the American Geographical Society and of Chauncy D. Harris, "The Ruhr Coal-Mining District," *Geographical Review*, April 1946, pp. 194–221.)

Dortmund, and Düsseldorf—each had a population of more than 500,-000. Twelve others had a population of 100,000 to 500,000 each, and the total population of the Ruhr district was approximately 10,000,000 (Fig. 260). The major industries of this region were (1) coal mining, (2) iron and steel manufacture, (3) production of metal goods, (4) manufacture of machinery, (5) chemical manufacture, and (6) the production of textiles (Fig. 261). In addition many other industries were developed within the Ruhr district. In fact, it is probable that no other area of equal size manufactured as great a variety of goods as the Ruhr.

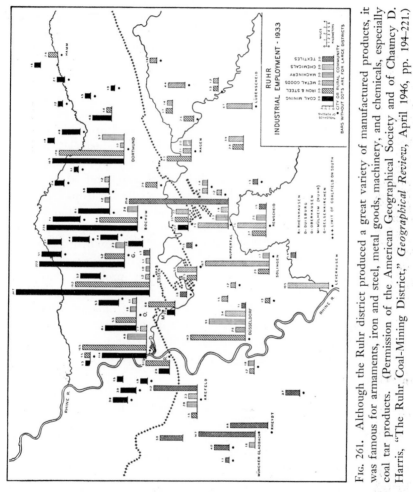

FIG. 261. Although the Ruhr district produced a great variety of manufactured products, it was famous for armaments, iron and steel, metal goods, machinery, and chemicals, especially coal tar products. (Permission of the American Geographical Society and of Chauncy D. Harris, "The Ruhr Coal-Mining District," *Geographical Review*, April 1946, pp. 194–221.)

Industry was first developed south of the Ruhr River. There the textile industry based on water power and soft water and the metal-working industry based on water power, local ores, and charcoal were developed long before the local coal mines were worked. Krefeld, München-Gladbach, Rheydt, Barmen, and Wuppertal are textile centers. Solingen and Remscheid are the leading cutlery and metal cen-. ters of Germany.

The central zone has developed coal mining and heavy industries. Duisburg, Essen, Bochum, Gelsenkirchen, and Dortmund are famed for their iron and steel industries. In the northern area coal mining is important but industry has not been extensively developed.[14]

Because of its great industrial importance and its large-scale armament production during World War II, the Ruhr was considered a necessary target for the bombing fleets of the United Nations. Postwar problems have retarded the rehabilitation of the region and the full redevelopment of peacetime industries. Consequently, the productive capacity of the district is greatly reduced. The burden that has resulted from this loss of production is not confined to the immediate area. It reaches every part of western Europe where the war-stricken peoples need the coal, iron and steel, chemicals, textiles, and other useful commodities which the region is well suited by nature to produce. It also reaches the United States and other remote countries that are called on to help support western Europe. Perhaps no other equal area of the world ever produced such vast quantities of armaments and munitions—implements of destruction; and perhaps in no other equal area of the world has the breakdown of peacetime industries caused so much and so widespread suffering.

LIGNITE PRODUCTION IN GERMANY. Germany produces more than 75 per cent of the world's total output of lignite. She has large lignite deposits which in several places can be worked from the surface by machinery operated by unskilled and cheaply paid laborers. Thus the German output of lignite, per laborer, is four or five times that of bituminous coal, which is mined from relatively deep seams and with inferior equipment.

Although the lignite possesses less than a fourth of the heat value of a good quality of coal, it can be mined so much more cheaply that it can compete successfully with coal both in heating homes and in supplying heat and power for certain types of industry. Most of the lignite is manufactured into briquettes before it is sold to the consumer, thereby reducing the moisture content of the fuel, increasing its calorific value, and making a product which is easier to handle and one better suited to the needs of industry. At the same time, the by-products of the briquette manufacture—oil, gas, and tar—are of considerable value and help to bear the cost of making the briquettes.

[14] Chauncy D. Harris, "The Ruhr Coal-Mining District," *Geographical Review*, April 1946, pp. 194–221.

The Coal Industry of Other European Countries. Coal is mined in more than a dozen other European countries, but the bulk of the output comes from the mines of Belgium, Russia, and France, and from Poland and Czechoslovakia. Underlying southwest Poland and the adjacent parts of Germany and Czechoslovakia is the famous Silesia-Moravia-Krakow coal basin which accounts for all the coal production of Poland and a fourth of that of Czechoslovakia. Moreover, the region is rich in zinc, lead, salt, and petroleum, and it contains some iron ore. It also lies in the heart of a great agricultural belt and has excellent connections with world markets and raw materials. Consequently, it has become one of the important industrial centers of Europe.

Coal beds underlie northeast France, the Saar Valley, and adjoining parts of Belgium, and the Netherlands. Most of these seams are deep, thin, of but medium grade, and expensive to mine. The demand for coal within this region is great, since the rich mineral and agricultural resources of the region, together with the excellent location, have favored great industrial development. Moreover, the desire to have as complete national independence as possible caused all these countries to put forth great effort to produce as much coal as possible during times of peace in order to reduce their dependence on other countries during times of war.

Coal Industry of the U.S.S.R. (European and Asiatic)

The U.S.S.R. is rapidly becoming a great industrial nation, and the opportunity for further industrial expansion, under good leadership, seems to be tremendous. The vast size of the country, her large population, and her rich resources of metals encourage the belief that under a strong form of government the country would become a great industrial power with need for an abundance of coal.

The coal resources of the U.S.S.R. are abundant and widespread. However, some regions that need power and fuel are remote from good coal fields. No good coal has been found near Leningrad, and, as a result, industrial development of that populous area is seriously handicapped. Industrial development in the Moscow (Moskva) Basin and in the southern Ural Mountain region has also been retarded because of a lack of easily available, high-grade coal. Since the early 1920's, both the Moscow Basin and the southern Ural region have become highly industrialized in spite of handicaps. The brown (low-grade) coal of the Moscow Basin is used in increasing quantities, coal has been imported from the Donetz Basin, petroleum has been brought in from the Caucasus, and hydroelectric plants have been developed near Moscow. The southern Ural region, as explained later, has succeeded in obtaining coal from Kuznetsk Basin situated 1,250 miles to the east.

The best coal field of European U.S.S.R. is situated in the Donetz Basin (Fig. 246). The quality of the Donetz coal is good and the field is well located to promote industrial development. It is centrally located in a populous region and is closely connected by railroad to the other densely populated areas of the country. The coal field is only 250 miles from the high-quality iron ore of the Krivoi Rog district, and only a little more remote from the abundant iron ores of the Kerch and Crimea peninsulas. Manganese, limestone (flux), chromium, copper, and petroleum are all found near by or in the Caucasus. The products of the Caucasus region may be shipped to southwest U.S.S.R. by cheap water transportation. The Donetz coal field is also centrally located in the Ukraine, an excellent agricultural region.

For several centuries Ukraine has been noted for its agricultural and pastoral activities. But with the development of modern industries, based largely on the coal and other minerals of the area, the Ukraine is rapidly becoming a region of cities and towns. Mining, aluminum manufacture, iron, steel, and machinery production, chemical industries, the building of railroad equipment, together with many other industries have developed rapidly. Phenomenal city growth in the region has necessarily been the result.

Eastward from the Donetz Basin, no large field of high-grade coal is found until Semipalatinsk, located in the Kuznetsk Basin, is reached. This field is approximately 1,250 miles east of the southern Urals. The southern Urals are rich in metals, especially iron ore; the Kuznetsk Basin is rich in coal. The formation of the "Ural-Kuznetsk Combine" has resulted in an exchange of raw materials between the two regions and the development of metallurgical industries in both centers. Iron ore and other metals are shipped from the Urals to the Kuznetsk Basin and the trains return loaded with coal. The result has been a striking industrial expansion in both areas.

Coal is mined in several places along the trans-Siberian railroad in south central Siberia. However, the largest producing field is located in eastern Siberia. Coal, iron ore, lead, zinc, and other minerals are mined near Svobodny (Svobodni) and have been used to develop metallurgical industries. Since the U.S.S.R. is in need of almost every kind of product made of iron—especially agricultural and industrial machinery, railroads and equipment—it seems likely that these coal and iron resources will be more extensively developed. In fact, the iron and steel industry which was almost destroyed by World War I grew very rapidly after 1921, as indicated by the table.

COAL AND PIG-IRON PRODUCTION IN RUSSIA

(Thousands of gross tons)

Commodity	1921	1925	1930	1935	1938
Pig iron	112	295	4,996	12,493	15,179
Coal	6,914	14,914	39,000	109,000	136,000

Coal Resources and Industries of Other Parts of the World

China has large reserves of high-grade coal.[15] Although the major part of this coal is found in the northern part of the country, mainly in Shansi and Shensi, smaller reserves are found in every one of the eighteen provinces. But little coal is being mined at present, owing to the backward state of the industrial development of China, the poor transportation facilities of the nation, her inadequate supply of some of the "key minerals," especially iron, and the political unrest. China and the U.S.S.R. possess the largest known coal reserves of Asia. Japan, with an output of 36,000,000 tons, ranks first in production among the countries of Asia, but no other world power has such small reserves. The actual known reserves are less than a billion tons, and, because of the difficulties of mining, the Japanese coal costs more than twice as much as coal in the United States.[16] However, the island empire has an abundant water supply which she is developing on a large scale to supplement her limited resources of coal.

The coal production of Africa, Australia, and South America, combined, scarcely equals that of a third-rate coal-producing center of the United States.

PETROLEUM INDUSTRIES

The story of the production and utilization of petroleum and its associated product, asphaltic pitch, extends over a period of many

[15] Vie Chow Juan, "Mineral Resources of China," *Economic Geology*, No. 4, Part 2, Supplement, June–July 1946, pp. 408–419.

[16] Boris P. Torgasheff, "The Mineral Industry of the Far East," Chahli Co., 1930, pp. 433–434.

thousand years. Yet, as recently as 1859, these products had few known uses, and the annual production of crude oil did not exceed a few thousand barrels.

Since 1859, the petroleum industries have been developed with amazing rapidity. Today, the products derived from this black fluid are essential to the progress of a score of industries, and as a source of lubricants it is a "key product" of industry considered indispensable to the operation of machinery throughout the world.

Petroleum stands second among the minerals in value of output, being surpassed only by coal. In 1945, the value of the petroleum produced in the United States was $2,093,300,000, only slightly less than the value of coal which was $2,101,000,000. The petroleum refining industry of the United States represents an investment of approximately $32,000,000,000 and ranks high in value among the industries of the United States.[17]

Causes of the Rapid Growth of the Petroleum Industries

Several factors combined to favor the rapid growth of the petroleum industries after oil was discovered in Pennsylvania in 1859. Chief among them were: (1) the best known whaling grounds had been rapidly depleted and a shortage of whale oil for illumination purposes threatened; (2) the method of distillation of kerosene from petroleum had already been discovered and could be rapidly and easily developed; (3) the principle of the lamp was already known, and as a consequence kerosene made a better illuminant than whale oil; (4) the facilities that had been used for the distribution of whale oil could now be utilized for the marketing of kerosene; and (5) easy methods of digging deep wells for the production of oil had already been discovered, and suitable machinery for this purpose had been devised.

As a result of the factors listed above the kerosene industry grew rapidly. The use of the automobile, the development of the industrial age, and the progress in transportation facilities caused a rapid increase in the demand for gasoline, lubricants, and fuel oil. The products of petroleum are now considered so essential to industrial progress and to the successful prosecution of modern war that all the major powers of the world are seeking to gain control of, or at least an interest in, one or more of the proved large oil fields and are searching diligently for possible reserves not yet discovered. During the last few years

[17] *Statistical Abstract of the United States,* U. S. Department of Commerce, 1947, pp. 731–735.

the struggle for the possession of petroleum has been so keen that the control of major oil fields causes more international concern than that of any other mineral.

Occurrence of Petroleum

The term "oil pool" may be misleading to the layman. Oil commonly occurs in a porous sandstone or cavernous limestone of such fine texture that in developing the field a large part of the oil, perhaps one-half to four-fifths in the sandstone, sticks to the walls of the pores and cannot be recovered. Since oil is lighter, it remains on top of the water and is pushed up through the pores of the enclosing bed until it is arrested by an impervious stratum called the "cap rock." Under such conditions, it is clear that wherever these strata are bowed upward the oil will be concentrated in the highest part of the porous or cavernous stratum, that is, in the "dome." Thus an "oil pool" is most commonly found in porous rock strata, usually of convex shape like an inverted basin, lying under the crest or dome of an impervious layer of rock.

The major task of determining where to drill for oil is usually allotted to oil geologists, who attempt to locate the oil dome or other favorable structure. This task is not a simple one. The dome may lie under thousands of feet of rock, may be small or large, and is frequently very irregular in shape. Moreover, some of the domes may contain oil though others do not. Consequently, the search for oil is characterized by many hazards. Every year thousands of wells are drilled which fail to strike oil. These wells are called "dry holes" or "dusters."

Developing an Oil Pool. The discovery of a great new pool usually results in feverish activity which rivals that of a "gold rush," especially if the pool is brought in with a gusher. Thousands of adventurers rush into the district to lease land and to prepare for the rapid exploitation which inevitably follows. Land values soar; banks, stores, hotels, and other places of business are built or enlarged to take care of the expanding business. "The boom is on." Towns or even cities spring up within a few weeks.

Frequently, scores of companies may have obtained rights in the pool before the development is many days old. Every one knows that the pool contains only a certain amount of oil and that this oil will readily flow from one leasehold to another. "First come first served" is the rule. Consequently those having an interest in the pool drill wells as quickly as possible in order that they may obtain their full share of the oil. As a result the number of wells drilled is unnecessarily large—a waste of both time and money (Fig. 262). Moreover, when several major oil pools are discovered within a few months,

FIG. 262. In many oil pools more wells are drilled than are economically advisable. This condition is frequently the result of keen competition of rival oil companies, each trying to get as much oil as possible before the pool is exhausted. (Courtesy The Los Angeles Chamber of Commerce.)

as happened several times between 1929 and 1940, overproduction and ruinous prices for petroleum are the natural consequences of such competitive methods.

Nature and Uses of Petroleum

Crude petroleum is a complex chemical substance from which many products are made to serve a wide and diverse range of usefulness. It is compact and can be easily handled; at present it can be quickly and cheaply obtained; and it is easily converted into light, heat, or power. In these respects it competes with other fuels and water power, but as a source of lubricants its function is unique.

EARLY USES OF PETROLEUM

Petroleum and its associated products have been used for many thousand years. Asphaltic pitch was used to waterproof the Ark of Noah, the cradle of Moses, and the cisterns and silos of ancient Egypt and Mesopotamia. Also it was used by the Egyptians in the process of mummification. Asphalt was used as a mortar in the construction of Nineveh and Babylon and also in the buried cities of Ur, as early as 4000 B.C. Oil from Sicily was used by the Romans to light the temple of Jupiter, and many centuries later flame throwers fed by naphtha were employed against the crusaders when they stormed the walls of Constantinople.

The early American Indians were familiar with natural petroleum seepage. They set their mosaics in asphaltum; they used it as an adhesive substance; they lined their baskets with it; and they had great faith in petroleum in performing all manner of cures.[18]

RECENT USES OF PETROLEUM

In recent years many new uses have been found for petroleum, and the volume of production has increased with great rapidity. Romania was the first country to keep a record of the output of crude petroleum. In 1857, that country produced 1,977 barrels and since then has had an unbroken record of production. In 1859, petroleum was discovered in Pennsylvania. Within less than a year the United States led the world in the output of crude oil and has held the leading position in all phases of the petroleum industry from that day to this.

Petroleum as an Illuminant. The discovery of petroleum in Pennsylvania afforded a cheap and abundant resource for artificial light that was superior to the fats of animals, principally whales, that had been previously used. For approximately fifty years after 1860, the use of kerosene expanded until this illuminant penetrated to the uttermost parts of the earth. The 5-gallon oil can was a symbol of light, not only in most of the highly civilized world but also in parts of

[18] Reprinted by permission from "Our Petroleum Supply," Hugh D. Miser, U. S. Geological Survey, *Journal of the Washington Academy of Sciences*, Vol. 29, March 15, 1939, p. 95.

China, India, central Africa, and other remote regions. It would be difficult to estimate the value of kerosene and the coal-oil lamp to the civilized world; but if one were able to list the agents of civilization in order of importance, kerosene would undoubtedly have to be given a prominent position. Kerosene is still more widely used in many backward areas than any other type of illuminant.

Petroleum as a Source of Power and Heat. During the last few decades the demand for petroleum products for the development of power and heat has become so great that the amount consumed in these industries dwarfs by comparison that used for light. Petroleum products have been a major factor in revolutionizing the transportation facilities of a large part of the world; they have given a new and convenient source of power to the farmers and industrialists of America; and, finally, they now provide the source of heat for millions of dwellings.

The numerous uses of petroleum result from the fact that it can be readily broken down into a group of fuels that are equally adaptable to (1) the light combustion engine of airplanes, automobiles, and tractors; (2) the heavier Diesel engines in merchant ships, naval vessels, and stationary engines; or (3) the ordinary hot-water or hot-air furnaces for heating buildings. For some of these uses there are, at present, no cheap and acceptable substitutes, whereas petroleum may be generally substituted for coal where heat and power are desired, except, of course, for the fact that petroleum may be more expensive than coal.

Gasoline. In the early years of the petroleum industry gasoline was a troublesome waste product. But with the development of the internal-combustion engine, and especially with the introduction and rapidly increasing use of the automobile, the demand for this volatile fuel grew rapidly, and soon it became the most profitable product of the industry. Consequently, the major efforts of the refiners have been to increase the percentage yield of gasoline from crude oil. Their success is indicated by the fact that the average yield of gasoline from a barrel of crude oil rose from 5.5 gallons in 1889 to 20.1 gallons in 1945.

More crude petroleum is now used for fuel than for any other purpose except the manufacture of gasoline. The largest use of fuel oil is for bunkering ships. During the last few years thousands of vessels have been remodeled so that oil fuel may be used as bunker instead of coal, and most of the ships recently constructed have been equipped to burn oil.

The extent of this change is indicated by the fact that, in 1914, the gross tonnage of all oil-burning vessels registered by Lloyds agencies was less than 3,000,000 tons, whereas by 1945 the total had leaped to 105,000,000.

It has been estimated that the largest modern trans-Atlantic liners, by burning oil instead of coal, save 5,000 tons of fuel on one round trip between Liverpool and New York and need only one-tenth as many stokers as would be required for a coal-burning ship of the same size. The additional freight which can be carried adds materially to the profits of the trip.

An increasing quantity of petroleum is being used as fuel for railroad locomotives, gas and electric power plants, and for the heating of buildings. Petroleum is replacing coal as a fuel in many homes because of its cleanliness and the ease with which it can be regulated by machinery.

Lubricants. The whole development of our machine civilization has been made possible only by petroleum lubricants. The lubricants derived from vegetable oils and animal fats met the needs of the slow-moving machinery of the pre-industrial age; but the high-speed, high-temperature machinery of today quickly decomposes these vegetable and animal oils so that they lose their lubricating properties. Only the lubricants of mineral oils are suited for modern machinery.

Petroleum Products Used in the Manufacture of Rubber. Butadiene is a gas which once existed only in insignificant quantities as a minor impurity of petroleum. Because science found ways of making it from petroleum in enormous quantities, the United States and its allies have had enough synthetic rubber to fight a global war. Butadiene is a gas under normal atmospheric conditions, but it can be liquefied under pressure. When liquefied it has the characteristic of being able to combine with itself and with other substances such as styrene, into a rubbery material suitable as a substitute for natural rubber.

Marketing Petroleum Products. Next to coal, petroleum is the heaviest and most bulky product of American commerce. It is carried from the field to the refining centers by tank cars, tank steamers, and pipelines, of which the last is by all means the most important. More than 113,000 miles of pipeline connect the fields with refineries located in more than thirty states. This pipeline system represents an investment of more than a billion dollars.

Although pipelines are used to transport the crude oil, most of the manufactured products have been shipped by rail. At present, however, pipelines are being used to transport gasoline, and it is probable that within a few years most of the largest markets will be served in this way.

The Petroleum Reserves of the World

Any attempt to estimate the world's reserves of petroleum is a hazardous undertaking. Men of high repute in the field of oil geology have made estimates which, as shown by subsequent production records, have fallen far from the mark. Prudent observers no longer make definite predictions, and leading oil refineries do not conduct their business without giving due consideration to the uncertainty of the reserves. Geologists are combing the earth in search for geological conditions which may indicate the presence of new pools; in the old pools the drillers are sinking wells to greater and greater depths in search of deep oil-bearing horizons; and constant study is being given to methods of recovery so that less oil will be left in the natural reservoirs.

The proved reserves of the world are estimated at approximately 63.5 billion barrels. The largest of these reserves are situated in the Middle East and in the United States. The reserves discovered in the Middle East are estimated at 26.8 billion barrels, and those of the United States are estimated at 21.5 billion barrels.[19]

Present Production and Outlook

The active development of petroleum resources is in progress in more than a score of countries, but seven of them produce more than 90 per cent of the world's output, and the United States alone produces approximately two-thirds of the total (Fig. 263).

Recently the production of petroleum has been increasing rapidly. The output during the last fifteen years, 1932–1946 inclusive, has exceeded the production of the entire preceding history of the world. The output of the United States now exceeds 1,800,000,000 barrels annually, although it did not cross the 100,000,000 mark until 1903 and the half-billion mark was not reached until 1922.

Although the petroleum resources of the United States are by no means on the eve of immediate exhaustion, we have certainly entered a stage of lavish expenditure of this precious fuel which can never be

[19] *Petroleum Times*, Brettenham House, Lancaster Place, London, June 1948, p. 4. This issue of *Petroleum Times*, pp. 4–115, gives an excellent review of the oil fields of the Middle East.

replaced and for which no cheap and adequate substitute has as yet been discovered.

The search for petroleum has been more intensive in the United States than in most other parts of the world. Although the domestic deposits are widely scattered, the major production comes from three districts, and about half of the total output comes from 2 per cent of the wells. Although many new pools may yet be discovered, the

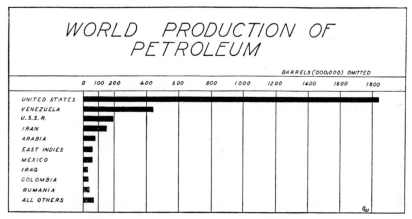

FIG. 263. E. G. Dahlgren, "Oil Output Hits New High in 1947," *Mining and Metallurgy*, American Institute of Mining and Metallurgical Engineers, February 1948, pp. 140–142.

general locations of the oil-bearing strata of this country are fairly well known, and, after considering the intensive work which has been done in these regions during the past few years, it seems inconceivable that we will long continue to discover new pools at the rate they have been found during the last few years.

Large oil companies and governments have become concerned over the future supply of petroleum, which is so essential to the welfare of nations. Consequently, commercial rivalry is keyed to a high pitch. The struggle for the control of the major oil fields of the world has been a bitter one in which a few countries have gained control of practically the entire known world supply.

Geologists are fairly well agreed that the fear of an oil shortage is not without foundation. The most optimistic estimates indicate that, if the rapid increase in production continues, a petroleum shortage is a possibility if not a probability within a few decades.

NATURAL GAS

Four billion dollars are invested in the natural gas industry of the United States. Gas is produced from more than 95,000 gas wells and distributed through 175,000 miles of pipelines to approximately one-fifth of the population of the country.

The period of rapid expansion in the natural gas industry began in 1920 (Fig. 264). Since then, there has been continued construction of

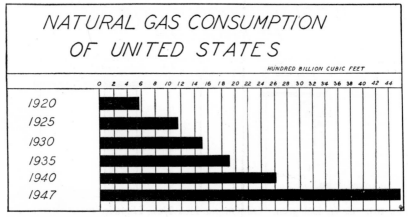

FIG. 264. Natural gas is the finest fuel produced by nature. Yet in spite of the fact that we possess limited supplies of this valuable fuel we are wasting it rapidly.

gas mains from the major producing centers to the populous industrial districts. Some of these mains are 20, 22, and even 24 inches in diameter and reach out hundreds or even a thousand miles from the wells.

Nature has provided the pressure which forces the gas to distant markets. In the western fields the pressure ranges from 450 pounds in the Texas Panhandle to nearly 2,000 pounds in the field near Oklahoma City. The major gas mains are built to carry only 400 to 900 pounds, and consequently the pressure of some of the fields must be stepped down before the gas is permitted to enter the pipelines.

The major regions of natural gas production are located west of the Mississippi River, but the most important potential consuming areas lie east of the Mississippi River. Gas mains have been constructed to connect the Amarillo Field in Texas to Minneapolis, Chicago, Indianapolis, and Terre Haute (Fig. 265). More recently the Big Inch and

Little-Big Inch pipelines have been constructed from Texas to the great urban centers of eastern United States (Fig. 258). These pipelines have cost hundreds of millions of dollars—a tremendous outlay of capital, especially since the length of life of any given gas field is still somewhat problematical. However, all these major mains cross fields of workable coal, and, should the natural gas play out earlier

Fig. 265. Machinery now does most of the work of laying gas mains from the field to distant markets.

than expected, the lines may be used to carry artificial gas from the coal field to the industrial centers.

Natural gas is already a strong competitor of coal. During the last decade it has had a bad effect on the coal market of Colorado and Utah and also on the coal fields of the Mississippi Valley. At present more than 75 per cent of the natural gas consumed in the United States is used by industrial plants.

Natural gas is an extremely valuable fuel which is definitely limited in quantity. Yet no other resource has been so carelessly used and so recklessly wasted by the American people. It has been uneconomically used for the generation of power through steam, even though its efficiency is much higher as a fuel for the internal-combustion engine. But this and other similar wasteful methods of consumption, common during the early part of this century, have now been largely discarded and the general industrial use is becoming increasingly efficient.

One of the chief industrial applications of natural gas is in the manufacture of carbon black. Although 1,000 cubic feet of gas weighs about 44 pounds, 75 per cent of it being carbon, the average commercial yield of carbon is only about 1.3 to 1.4 pounds, or 3 per cent of the possible yield. Yet the loss of gas through its uneconomical use has been unimportant as compared with the absolute waste, which has been going on ever since the first discovery of the product.

WATER POWER

Early Uses and Limitations. Many centuries ago man contrived methods of converting falling water into useful mechanical energy. During the early stages of manufacturing development the steam engine had not been invented, and water power was the most important source of mechanical energy. The early use of water power, however, required that the industry dependent upon it be located at the site of power. Thus scores of cities in eastern United States and in western Europe owe their locations to waterfalls.

The old water wheel could be just as easily installed and was as efficient in small streams, where the water flowed over ledges only a few feet high, as in large and turbulent rivers with falls of vast proportions. Thus New England and the Mohawk Valley, with their numerous small falls, were ideally suited to the type of manufacturing developments of early times, and the tremendous power resources of the Niagara and the St. Lawrence rivers were of little or no value.

Rivalry of Steam Power. The application of steam power freed industry from the restriction of geographical location and permitted it to migrate to the centers of population, to bulky raw materials, or to areas where other natural or social environmental conditions were suited to industrial development. This step was so significant that it deserves the name "Industrial Revolution." Recent developments in the long-distance transmission of electricity reinstate water power and permit it once more to become a major source of mechanical energy. Moreover, the electric turbine permits the efficient utilization of waterfalls and makes it possible to utilize almost the entire energy produced by our mightiest falls and most turbulent rapids.

Although more electric energy is produced from steam than from water power, water has the advantage of being more widely distributed than either coal or oil and affords a source of power that is inexhaustible. The relative importance of steam-electric and hydro-electric energy differs greatly from one region to another, depending upon the supply of each and the relative ease and cheapness of installing hydroelectric and steam-electric turbines. Thus in Norway, where there is an abundance of water power but a scarcity of fuel, practically

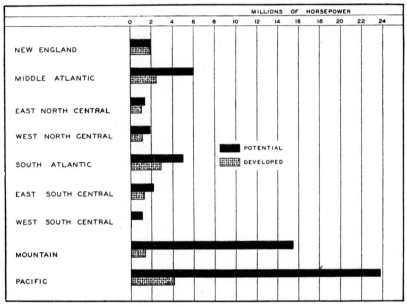

FIG. 266. Western United States possesses tremendous water-power resources. Since the West is poor in coal the water-power resources are very valuable. The greatest development of water power has, however, taken place in the industrial East.

all the electric energy is produced from falling water, whereas in northern Germany, where coal is abundant and easily mined, steam is the major source of electric energy. Similarly, in those parts of the United States where fuel is abundant, steam-electric power predominates, except in such areas as the southern Appalachian region, where water power is also abundant and cheaply developed; but in north-western United States, where fuel is scarce and water power abundant, hydroelectric power predominates (Fig. 266).

The Electric Industry Largely a Development of the Present Century. It was not until 1900 that new inventions and improvements in the methods of producing and transmitting electricity made it possible for electric energy to compete in a large way with steam power. In fact, the most rapid progress has been made since 1915. In 1917, the electric power production of the world was only 55 billion kilowatt-hours; in 1937 it totaled 230 to 240 billion kilowatt-hours. Within the United States the output of electricity has increased from 70 to 150 per cent every five years since 1902. Approximately one-third of this energy is supplied by falling water.

Distribution of Water Power as Related to Utilization

The Vast Unused Water-Power Resources of Africa and Asia. Although electricity may be transmitted several hundred miles, the cost increases rapidly with added distance from the source of power. Transmission lines are expensive and the upkeep high, so that the extreme limits to which this form of power can be transported for ordinary industrial uses are 400 to 600 miles. Unfortunately, the largest water-power resources of the world are remote from the great industrial centers where most of the power is needed.

Africa, the most backward of all continents and the one that has made the least industrial progress, possesses the greatest potential power resources of any continent, approximating 40 per cent of the world's total (Fig. 267). So far as can be seen now, this resource can never be transported to other continents to add to the wealth of the great industrial nations, as could be done with many other products of Africa. A steady stream of copper, iron ore, tin, and industrial crops flows from the "dark continent" to enrich the great industrial powers, and during past centuries even the natives were an item of lucrative commerce. But, so far as can be seen now, if the vast water-power resources of central Africa are ever developed, they will have to be devoted to the promotion of home industries.

It is probable that several generations may pass before any considerable amount of these vast potential water-power reserves will be developed. Yet it is not inconceivable that some day part of it will be employed to cool the homes within the hot, steaming forest lands of equatorial Africa, just as fuel has been burned for many centuries to heat the homes of middle and higher latitudes. Some day this power may be taken advantage of on a large scale to exploit the copper, iron ore, phosphate, tin, and other mineral resources of the continent and to produce fertilizers for the relatively infertile lands of the humid forest regions.

If this vast resource is ever fully utilized, it will represent the equivalent of several hundred million mechanical men working for peoples who, in the past, have been only too willing to impress their fellow men to serve their needs.

Asia ranks second only to Africa in her potential water-power resources and resembles her in her retarded development. China, with

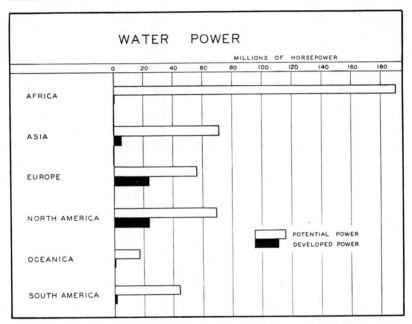

FIG. 267. Africa, the most backward of all continents, possesses the greatest potential power resources of any continent, whereas the United States and western Europe have developed their power resources more completely.

a population of more than 400,000,000, has not, as yet, developed the water-power resources within her vast domain, and the total turbine installation of the entire continent of Asia is less than that of either Norway or Italy. Yet this continent contains almost a third of the land area of the globe and supports more than half of the total population. Millions of women and children are toiling under conditions of which the women and children of America have no conception.

Utilization of Water Power in North America and Europe. More than 95 per cent of the world's output of hydroelectric power is produced in North America and Europe, the United States and Canada accounting for approximately half of the total. Turbine installations are widely scattered over these continents, but they are by no means uniformly distributed.

Importance in the United States. The United States has a commanding position in the production of hydroelectric power, just as it has in the development of power from coal, oil, and gas. In the competition between cheap fuel and water power the low cost of installing steam plants has given fuel the advantage in most parts of the United States. However, in the mountain and Pacific states, where coal is less abundant and water power plentiful and easily developed, fuel plays a less important role in the electrical industry.

In no other section of the United States has water power played such a significant part as in New England. Here the natural environment favors easy water-power development, and the demand for power is large. Precipitation is heavy and relatively uniform; the glacier threw dams across practically all the larger streams, causing hundreds of waterfalls of varying height; and the lakes, forests, and glacial débris all tend to regulate the flow of water, giving it remarkable uniformity throughout the year. Moreover, during the early period of manufacturing in New England, water power represented practically the only source of mechanical energy, for the steam engine had not then been invented. Later the absence of coal, oil, and natural gas within the region was a distinct handicap to the development of steam power. Consequently, the water-power resources of New England have been more completely utilized than those of any other part of the United States (Fig. 266).

Canada and Norway the Most Lavish Users of Hydroelectric Power in the World. Canada has a turbine installation of more than $\frac{1}{2}$ horsepower per capita or approximately four and one-half times that of the United States. The capital invested in the hydroelectric industry represents one-sixth of the total investment of the manufacturing industry of the nation, and the rate of growth is more rapid than that of most other industries. The major development has occurred in southern Ontario and Quebec, where the demand for power is rapidly expanding and where natural conditions favor the economic installation of turbines.

Ontario and Quebec lack coal and oil reserves, but they have a potential water-power resource of approximately 18,000,000 horsepower—60 per cent of the total for the entire country. Moreover, there are few regions where water power can be developed more easily than in the southern part of these provinces. Ontario shares with New York the vast resources of Niagara, and the southern parts of both Ontario and Quebec are drained by rivers whose waters tumble over many cataracts and falls as they descend from the lake-dotted forests of the Laurentian Plateau to the St. Lawrence Valley.

Much of this power is situated near the heart of a great industrial area where the demand for power is large. Even the frontier industries, forestry and mining, which are gradually pushing into the land of the frozen north, demand an abundance of power. Power is needed for almost every process of paper and pulp manufacture, and these industries consume 15 to 20 per cent of the output of the country. Electric power is being used in increasing amounts in the mining operations such as drilling, shaft mining, and the concentration of ores. Recently there has been a growing demand for electric power in the development of electrochemical industries, such as the recovery of gold and silver, the production of aluminum pig, and the manufacture of fertilizers.

In many respects the water-power industry of Norway parallels that of Canada. Environmental conditions favor the easy and cheap installation of turbines, while the scarcity of fuels retards the development of steam power; the location, close to great industrial markets and in an invigorating climate, promotes the growth of manufacturing; and finally, the local raw materials, especially forest products, require an abundance of power for manufacturing processes. Power in Norway, as in Canada, is used chiefly in the manufacture of wood pulp, paper, and chemicals, and in the smelting, refining, and alloying of metals.

REFERENCES

ALFORD, L. P., "Progress in Manufacturing," *Mechanical Engineering*, April 1930, pp. 401–403.

BALLERT, ALBERT G., "The Coal Trade of the Great Lakes and the Port of Toledo," *Geographical Review*, April 1948, pp. 194–206.

BLAKE, A. D., and P. W. SWAIN, "Fifty Years of Power," *Mechanical Engineering*, April 1930, pp. 321–323.

BRANDT, KARL, "The Fuel Crisis in Europe," *Foreign Affairs*, January 1946, pp. 337–340.

CAMPBELL, M. R., "The Coal Fields of the United States," *Professional Paper* 100-A, U. S. Geological Survey, 1922.

COLLISON, N. H., *A Medical Survey of the Bituminous-Coal Industry*, U. S. Department of the Interior, 1947.

CRONE, G. R., "Inland Waterways of Germany," *Geographical Journal*, April 1939, pp. 333–339.

HALL, R. DAWSON, "The Coal Fields that Underwrote Birmingham's Industrial Activity," *Coal Age*, Vol. 33, October 1928, pp. 587–589, 599.

HARRIS, CHAUNCY D., "The Cities of the Soviet Union," *Geographical Review*, January 1945, pp. 107–121.

JUAN, VEI CHOW, "Mineral Resources of China," *Economic Geology*, No. 4, Part 2, *Supplement*, June-July 1946, pp. 399–471.

KILLOUGH, HUGH B., *Raw Materials of Industrialism*, Thomas Y. Crowell Co., 1929, Part 5.

LEITH, C. K., *World Minerals and World Politics*, McGraw-Hill Book Co., 1931.

LIPPINCOTT, ISAAC, *Economic Resources and Industries of the World*, D. Appleton & Co., 1929, pp. 127–170.

LOGAN, L. J., "Need For Synthetic Fuel Industry," *World Oil*, The Gulf Publishing Company, March 1948, pp. 37–38.

Mineral Industry, McGraw-Hill Book Co., Annual.

MISER, HUGH D., "Our Petroleum Supply," *Journal of the Washington Academy of Sciences*, Vol. 29, March 15, 1939.

Petroleum Times, Brettenham House, London, June 1948, p. 4.

PHERSON, ELMER W., "Mineral Position of the United States and the Outlook for the Future," *Mining and Metallurgy*, April 1945, pp. 204–210.

STAMP, L. DUDLEY, "Britain's Coal Crisis," *Geographical Review*, April 1948, pp. 179–193.

STOUGHTON and BUTTS, *Engineering Metallurgy*, McGraw-Hill Book Co., 1930, pp. 146–163.

The Coal Resources of the World, Morang & Co., Toronto, Canada, 1913.

TORGASHEFF, BORIS P., *The Mineral Industries of the Far East*, Chali Co., Shanghai, 1930, pp. 421–441.

VAN HISE and HAVEMEYER, *Conservation of Our Natural Resources*, The Macmillan Co., 1930, pp. 23–59, 175–192.

VOSKUIL, WALTER H., *Minerals in Modern Industry*, John Wiley & Sons, 1930, pp. 24–170.

WHITE, I. C., *et al.*, "The Pittsburgh Coal Bed," *Transactions, American Institute Mining Engineers*, Vol. 74.

WOOD, ALBERT C., "Industrial Power," *Mechanical Engineering*, Vol. 52, No. 4, April 1930, pp. 340–346.

Chapter 21

OTHER MINERAL INDUSTRIES

Although iron and mineral fuels represent the very foundations of our great industrial development, literally scores of other minerals are absolute requirements if we are to maintain present high standards of living and to retain present strength in the economic, commercial, industrial, and naval affairs. In a basic textbook in world geography, space does not permit a discussion of the usefulness of all the minerals. Yet special reports on such minerals as vanadium, chromium, tungsten, helium, platinum, and other minerals that cannot be discussed here will add richness to the study of mineral industries. Some of these minor minerals are of such vital significance to the industrial world that their present distribution, national ownership, or commercial control create serious national and international problems.

COPPER

Early Uses of Copper. Copper was one of the first elements to be used in the metallic form; its use preceded that of iron in the development of civilization. Prehistoric remains reveal the fact that tools, implements, weapons, and ornaments were made of copper or of bronze—an alloy of copper and tin—before the time of recorded history. But owing to the changes which have taken place in art, science, and industry, the copper and bronze tools, weapons, and machinery have been almost wholly replaced by those made of steel, aluminum, and other metals or alloys better suited to the manufacture of such products; the copper ornaments have been largely replaced by those of gold, silver, and other precious metals and stones.

Although copper has been replaced by other metals for many of its former uses, new needs have arisen during the past century which have increased the demand for this copper manyfold. As late as 1850, the total world production of fine copper was only 52,000 tons,[1]

[1] *Minerals Yearbook,* U. S. Department of the Interior, 1939, p. 115.

whereas the average annual production for the five-year period, 1941–1945, reached the impressive total of 2,600,000 tons.[2]   Indeed, copper has become one of our most valuable industrial minerals (Fig. 252).

Present Uses of Copper.   The phenomenal growth of the copper industry is closely associated with the rapid increase in the use of electricity and the development of the automobile industry.   With the exception of silver, copper is the best known conductor of electricity.   It is abundant, cheaply produced, and resistant to corrosion. Moreover, it can be easily drawn into wire; it can be hammered into any shape; and, by alloying it with other metals, it can be given many specific properties, such as hardness or toughness, to meet specific demands.

Since the telegraph was the only outstanding electrical device used before 1860, the demand for copper in this field had not yet become large.   After this date, however, new phases of the electrical industry were developed in rapid succession.   The use of the telephone was increasing rapidly before 1870; the trolley wire was introduced before 1880; and rapid strides were being made in the use of hydroelectric power before 1900.   During the present century there has been a tremendous expansion in the use of copper for the production of all of these electrical conveniences, while at the same time there has been a growing demand for copper in the manufacture of automobiles, refrigerators, and plumbing equipment.

Copper Resources.   Copper ore is much more irregular in occurrence, and more widely scattered, than iron ore.   It is therefore impossible to make even as accurate an estimate of copper resources as is made of iron ore.   Moreover, improvements in the methods of mining and refining copper ore have been more rapid than for iron.   Only a few decades ago the minimum limit of copper in ore, of economic value, was 2 to 3 per cent, whereas now immense quantities of ore which contain less than 1 per cent copper are worked profitably.

Technology Increases Reserves.   Our copper reserves have been greatly increased during the last few decades by the discovery of tremendous deposits of fairly rich copper ore.   Yet our *economic* reserves have been increasing even more rapidly as a result of the invention of means of greater efficiency in using low-grade deposits that formerly could not be utilized.[3]

[2] *Minerals Yearbook*, U. S. Department of the Interior, 1945, p. 145.

[3] C. K. Leith, *Second Report of the Science Advisory Board*, 1935, National Research Council, p. 362.

Almost every mining industry of the United States affords numerous examples of the aid of technology. One of the best examples is found in the copper industry. Before 1907 the ores of Bingham, Utah, could not be mined profitably unless they contained at least 3 per cent copper. This left tremendous deposits that were so lean that they could not be economically exploited. With later advances in the technology of ore recovery, the copper companies were able to mine with profit ores that contain but slightly more than 0.5 per cent copper. Similarly a few decades ago the largest known copper deposits in the world, the famous Chuquicamata deposits of northern Chile, could not be mined profitably. Recently this has become one of the greatest copper-mining centers in the world. Such achievements as those mentioned above have greatly enlarged the estimates of copper ore reserves of the world. Thus, billions of tons of low-grade ore have been added to our reserves, and enough ore has been developed, or at least proved, to last several generations.

Copper Smelting and Refining. Copper sometimes occurs in the native state, that is, in the form of masses of pure copper embedded in the rock. Such is the nature of the copper ore of the Lake Superior district, where the masses of copper that are of commercial value vary in size from minute particles to many cubic feet. Most of the ore now being mined in this district is less than 3 or even 2 per cent copper, and the particles of the metal are small. However, bodies of pure copper are found occasionally that are too large to be handled by the mining machinery and must be cut into pieces before being removed from the parent rock. These native ores need only mechanical separation and melting. Consequently, the richer ores were exceedingly profitable in the early days of development, and for many years Michigan was the foremost producer of copper in the world. But the surface ore of the region has long since been exhausted, and some of the mines are more than a mile deep. The resultant increase in the cost of mining is a distinct handicap to the industry, and the output is scarcely holding steady.

In most of the ore bodies the copper is chemically combined with other elements and is somewhat uniformly distributed through the ore body. Such ores must be reduced by a chemical process called "smelting." Since only a small percentage of the ore consists of metallic copper, it is evident that the smelting must be done near the mines. This necessity is clearly indicated by the fact that in a recent year the Utah Copper Company milled 14,000,000 tons of copper ore which contained only 117,000 tons of the metal. Great concentration and smelting plants, which are located close to the mines, eliminate most of this rock waste and produce "copper matte" which contains 35 to 50 per cent copper, and "blister copper" which is approximately 95 per cent pure. These products can bear the cost of long-distance transportation.

The final stages of refining are usually completed near the great market centers and at sites suited to utilize the copper from several mining districts. The profitable production of refined copper requires a large and expensive plant which can handle the output of several mines. The refineries situated on the eastern coast of the United States have the largest output of any district in the world. In 1945, eleven plants produced the entire United States output of refined copper. Only three of these refineries were located west of the Great Lakes: one at Great Falls, Montana; one at Tacoma, Washington; and one at El Paso, Texas. Three small plants were located on the Great Lakes and five large ones were situated near the Atlantic seaboard.

The Atlantic refineries are located near the greatest American markets; they are close to coal fields which supply cheap fuel needed for electrical refining and for manufacturing copper into wire, bearings, brushes, and numerous other products; they have port facilities for handling the ores of the South American, Congo, and other foreign copper mines; and, finally, they are well situated for the export of the finished product to all parts of the world.

The refineries of the Great Lakes are centrally situated in the large and rapidly expanding markets of central North America; the refineries of Montana and Puget Sound were established close to great water-power sites where electric current could be produced cheaply. These refineries are also well located to supply the growing demand for copper in the West and the Orient.

Distribution of World Production of Copper

Most of the copper supply of the world is produced in the United States, western South America, central Africa, and Canada. Smaller quantities are mined in widely scattered parts of the world (Fig. 268). Our supremacy in the copper industry is indicated by the fact that in recent years more than one-third of the world's supply of copper comes from American mines and approximately 40 per cent is refined in American plants.

This commanding position in the copper industry has been favored both by our huge supplies of domestic ores and by the large demand

for the red metal in the development of our home industries. With
large reserves of raw materials [4] and rapidly expanding markets at
home, it was only natural that science should be called on to find methods of producing and distributing the product as cheaply as possible.
The larger the industry grew, the greater the reward for reducing the
cost of mining, smelting, refining, fabricating, and marketing the metal.

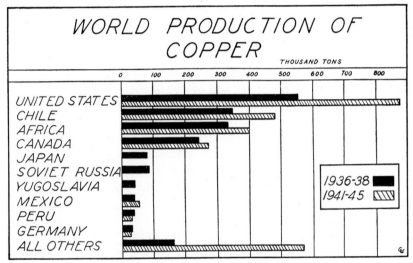

FIG. 268. Munition manufacturers use lots of copper. During World War II, the
copper output of the world went to an all-time high. (*Minerals Yearbook*, U. S.
Department of the Interior, 1945, pp. 143–145.)

The promoters of the industry turned to the American universities
for aid. They secured the services of hundreds of chemists, geologists,
mining engineers, and metallurgists to aid them in the solution of their
problems. American leadership in the industry has been the result.

Copper Production within the United States

Before 1845 most of the copper output of the United States was
produced from small and unreliable deposits situated in Connecticut,
New Jersey, and Pennsylvania. These mines could not supply the

[4] The estimated copper content of the copper ore reserves of the United States
exceeds 20,000,000 tons, or enough to last this country a generation, at the present
rate of production. (*Mineral Industries*, U. S. Department of the Interior, 1930,
p. 226.)

home market, and for many years copper was imported from Chile. The opening of our large reserves in Michigan, soon after 1845, made the United States independent of foreign resources and provided a surplus for export. Cheap lake transportation aided the mining industry, and Michigan soon became the foremost copper producer of the Union, a position which it held until the beginning of the present century.

Something of the vast copper resources of the Rocky Mountain states had been known for years, but the mining of low-grade ores in regions so remote from markets had to await the building of railroads. With the opening of the West, particularly after 1880, expansion of mining was rapid. Butte, Montana, soon became the greatest copper producer of the United States and of the world.

Later, vast deposits of copper ore were discovered in Arizona, and, by 1910, the desert about Bisbee, Globe, and Jerome was an area of feverish activity, witnessing the development of one of the greatest industrial programs ever undertaken in such an arid land. The towns of this region are practically dependent on the output of this red metal. When the demand for copper is large and the price high, prosperity is felt by all; when the copper industry is depressed these cities are most affected, and many of the laborers go elsewhere for work. As soon as the copper has been mined out, the industry will cease and the towns will be deserted—mute evidence of the impermanency of certain types of mineral exploitation.

During recent years deposits of copper ore have been developed in the desert of Utah and Nevada. These ores are of low grade but the deposits are enormous, representing at present the largest known reserves of the Republic, and are easily mined (Fig. 269).[5]

The importance of Arizona, Montana, and Utah as copper producers is indicated by the fact that from January 1, 1935, to January 1, 1946, these three states were responsible for more than two-thirds of this nation's output of the red metal. The totals for each state, 1941–1945, were as follows: Arizona, 33.48 per cent; Montana, 20.26 per cent; and Utah, 19.93 per cent.

Foreign Copper Production

South America. The Pacific coastal area of South America contains some of the richest and most extensive copper deposits of the world.

[5] A. B. Parsons, "Utah Copper—Biggest Excavation," *Mining and Metallurgy*, February 1947, p. 47.

Some of these mines have been worked by the Indians and Spaniards for centuries, and the output of copper from this region (Chile and Peru) is second only to that of the United States.

In the early days, the industry depended upon small, shallow veins of high-grade carbonate and oxide deposits (ores easily smelted) that

Fig. 269. The world's largest open-cut copper mine, Bingham, Utah. (Courtesy Union Pacific Railway Co.)

were situated close to the coast, or upon the small but rich veins that were found within the Chuquicamata deposit. The ores were smelted in small, inefficient, charcoal furnaces; the product was necessarily expensive, and the output small.

During recent decades, these rich but small and unreliable deposits have been exhausted or greatly depleted, and the mining industry has been shifted to the large deposits of low-grade ores situated high on the Andean slopes. Something of the vastness of these ore resources had been known for more than a century, but large-scale, economic exploitation awaited improvement in the processes of mining and smelting, and the development of modern transportation facilities.

Many problems had to be solved before the large-scale production of copper could be put on a paying basis. Before copper could be produced it was necessary to build railroads through the desert, lay pipelines to carry potable water to the laborers, erect high-tension lines for the transmission of power to the mines, and build different types of metallurgical plants for the treatment of oxide and sulphide ores. Moreover, the desert conditions made it necessary to import laborers, to build homes for them, and to make provision for their food and other necessaries of life. Since all the equipment for mine development must be imported and all the product exported, it was necessary to provide port facilities to handle these products. Thus a tremendous outlay of capital and labor was required before a ton of ore was mined. The fact is illustrated by the Patillos mines; it required approximately $80,000,000 and more than ten years of constructive effort to place the property in a position to produce revenue.

Prior to 1915, the output of copper had grown slowly but steadily. The way, however, had been paved for rapid expansion to meet any sudden increase in demand. With the outbreak of war, the industry suddenly leaped into vigorous activity, and within twelve years the output of copper had increased approximately 400 per cent.

The reserves are enormous.[6] Those of Chuquicamata district alone are estimated at 700,000,000 tons of ore averaging 2.12 per cent copper—the largest known reserves of the world. The Teniento mines, 40 miles from Rancagua, have known reserves of 176,000,000 tons of 2.45 per cent copper and large reserves of lower-grade ore.

African Output Increasing Rapidly. Africa has recently become an important source of copper. At the beginning of the present century, phenomenally rich ores were discovered in Katanga, situated in the heart of Africa. A little later, other deposits were discovered in Belgian Congo and in northern Rhodesia. Some of the surface ores contained 30 per cent copper and were easily mined by means of the steam shovel. Vast quantities of 7 per cent copper ore have been proved. Because of the isolation of the area, development was slow and the first mining operations were not started until 1911. During the five-year period, 1941–1945, the production of central Africa averaged approximately 400,000 tons annually, giving the area third place among the copper-producing regions of the world.[7]

---

[6] William J. Waylett, "Chilex Mine Model Revised," *Mining and Metallurgy*, January 1948, pp. 19–21.

[7] *Minerals Yearbook*, U. S. Department of the Interior, 1945, p. 145.

The chief obstacle to rapid expansion of operation in central Africa is inadequate transportation facilities. The major copper mines are situated in a wooded plateau in the heart of savage Africa, thousands of feet higher than the place where the Congo becomes navigable. The main railroad reaches the sea at Beira, on the east coast. This single-track line is 1,600 miles long, and its limited capacity was quickly overtaxed. A shorter and more direct railway has now been constructed to Benguela, on the west coast. This railway traverses 250 miles of territory in which there are more than 100 ore deposits that have hitherto been remote from modern transportation facilities. The road, which is 750 kilometers shorter than the Beira route, opens up large resources, reduces the cost of importing machinery and exporting the mineral products, and puts the district in position for rapid expansion when the demand for copper increases.

This copper-mining industry of the Belgian Congo is bringing about industrial development in the heart of Africa undreamed of by the natives of a few generations ago. It also offers opportunity to thousands of natives to secure the products of civilization in ever-increasing quantities. In 1937, the mines were employing 40,000 workers, and it was estimated that the mines and metallurgical industries would soon require 80,000 men, or 3 per cent of the adult males of the country.

Spain. Although the western hemisphere and Africa are now the major sources of copper, with an output in 1928 of approximately 90 per cent of the world's total, the dominant position was held by Spain and Portugal for such a long period that the Iberian Peninsula will always deserve honorable mention in any treatise on copper. The copper district of southwestern Spain, which also extends into Portugal, has been an important source of the world's supply since Phoenician times, and was the most important source during much of the Bronze Age. It still contains one of the world's largest deposits, and, in spite of the fact that it has been productive for perhaps 3,000 years, the present rate of output can be maintained for many years to come. The ore is pyritic and valuable as a source of sulphur as well as of copper. Some of the ore is smelted locally, some is leached of part of its copper content and shipped as sulphur ore, and pyrite containing copper is exported.

The Soviet Union. During recent years (1923–1942) the U.S.S.R. has increased its copper output with remarkable rapidity. In 1923, the production approximated 3,000 tons, whereas in 1942 the output was estimated at 160,000 tons,[8] and at present Soviet Russia probably stands fifth among the nations of the world in this respect. Copper ores are widespread in Russia but some of the largest reserves are located in the southern Ural Mountains and in the Caucasus Mountains (Fig. 247). According to official Soviet estimates, the Soviet Union contains 17 million tons of copper or about one-sixth of the world's resources. Because of these vast copper resources of Soviet Russia, and the rapid industrial development that is taking place within the country, the output of copper may be expected to increase very rapidly.

Marketing Copper

Copper ore exists in such large quantities and in such widely scattered areas that the resources cannot be monopolized. Likewise, the mining industry has been developed by many companies—some high-cost producers, other low-cost producers—so that the price fixing is a difficult task. Therefore, copper is sold in a highly competitive market, and the price is normally governed by uncontrolled supply and demand. All attempts to maintain an artificial price level have failed, and sometimes such attempts have reacted on the producers with such violence that many companies have been compelled to suspend mining operations.

The basic reason for this situation is not difficult to understand. When the price of copper is high the low-grade ores may be mined with profit and, at times, even under inefficient mining conditions. As a result, mines are opened that normally could not be operated with profit, and all low-cost producers are worked at capacity in orders to secure the full benefits of the high-priced metal. This increase in mining activity results in overproduction, stocks of copper mount, and, in an attempt to dispose of the surplus, prices fall until the high-cost producers are compelled to suspend operation. Output then decreases and the stocks of copper dwindle to such an extent that any unlooked-for increase in demand results in an acute copper shortage. Then the prices soar again until the high-cost producers are once more operating at full capacity, and the cycle is started all over again.

An organization known as the Secretan Syndicate tried to maintain copper prices years ago by withholding copper from the market. The supply simply mounted, buyers held off, and the syndicate exploded with an accompanying downfall in the price as the accumulated cop-

[8] *Minerals Yearbook*, U. S. Department of the Interior, 1945, p. 145.

per was dumped on the market. Early in 1907, another attempt to hold up the price of copper ended disastrously; and again in 1920 those who tried to bolster up the price, contrary to the law of supply and demand, found the task an impossible one. The experience of 1929 is still fresh in our memory. For months the majority of producers refused to quote copper below 20 cents a pound, despite the fact that huge stocks had been accumulated and the demand was poor. Of course, a few low-cost producers cut under the maintained price level just enough to market their current production. Their numbers gradually increased, and soon the prices crashed down to 6 cents or less, the lowest price in history.

Between 1929 and 1939 further attempts were made to regulate the price of copper by artificial means. One of the latest was made in May 1937 in London. Discussions were opened there in an attempt to restrict production. But it was not until October of that year that an agreement was finally reached. This agreement was to have expired June 1938, but new agreements were reached to curtail output for an indefinite period. Obviously the difficulty is found in the fact that the productive capacity of the mines far exceeds the consumption requirements of the world in normal times.

In 1932, a tariff of 4 cents a pound was placed on imported copper. This tariff resulted from the fact that large quantities of foreign copper were being imported at prices below the cost of production at home. This tariff is defended largely on the theory that it is advisable to protect home industry and to provide work for American laborers even though this protection results in increasing the price of copper to the ultimate consumer.

In 1947 and 1948, the price of copper once more soared to more than 21 cents a pound, and American manufacturers found it difficult to supply their needs even at such a price. Consequently, the 4-cent tariff on copper was removed. This action will encourage copper mining in many parts of the world; overproduction will almost certainly result; and prices will again decline to the point where the high-cost producer will be compelled to suspend operations.

LEAD AND ITS MANIFOLD USES

Uses of Lead. Lead is exceeded in quantity of production by iron and copper, but in diversity of usefulness and application it is exceeded by only one metal—iron. As a metal, an alloying agent, an ingredient of manufactured goods, and an agent in industrial operations, the range of lead's usefulness is almost as wide as the field of industry itself. It is present in the home in paint, plumbing materials, glassware, and musical instruments; in the office it is used in typewriters and calculating machines; in transportation large quantities are required in the manufacture of automobiles, airplanes, and locomotives. It is valuable in the building trade, communication by wire, the printing industry, the sportsman's rifle, and the chemical laboratory.

Ever since the introduction of firearms, lead has supplied the materials for shot and bullets. But with the progress of science and the development of industry, the principal use of lead is no longer for the destruction of life and property, but rather to add to the fullness of life and to give protection to property. Although the modern manufacturer of munitions still uses large quantities of lead, amounting in 1938 to 31,000 tons in the United States alone, other industries use more than seventeen times as much.

Since 1880, the demand for lead in the manufacture of electrical equipment, primarily batteries and cable covering, has expanded so rapidly that, during the years 1929 to 1945, 300,000 tons were required annually for these purposes—approximately ten times as much as was needed to supply the munition plants of our country.

Lead is also one of the most important products used in the manufacture of paints. It may be easily worked with oil, it mixes readily with other pigments to form any color desired, and it can be uniformly spread over a surface, giving complete protection against weathering.

Lead is resistant to the action of sulphuric acid and is, therefore, suitable for lining tanks and other apparatus for the manufacture and transportation of this widely and extensively used chemical.

Lead is soft, pliable, ductile, and blends readily with other metals. These properties make it valuable for the manufacture of lead foil, bearing metal, solder, pewter, type-metal, castings, and for a score of products used in the building trade.

Consumption of Lead. The consumption of lead in the United States is centered principally in the industrial area of the Northeast, where the major industrial development has been concentrated. The area would be included by a line drawn around St. Louis, Louisville, Cincinnati, Baltimore, Philadelphia, New York, Boston, Detroit, and Chicago. The industrial section of northwest Europe is the second largest consuming center, but the per capita consumption is much less than in America.

Part of the overwhelming predominance of the United States as a consumer is due (1) to the large domestic use in paints, a use that is strictly prohibited by law in many foreign countries,[9] and (2) to the supremacy of the electrical and automotive industry in America.

American Markets. The two major markets for lead are New York and St. Louis. Through the St. Louis gateway, most of the Missouri and Oklahoma product reaches the eastern market. Through the New York gateway, lead enters from the west coast and foreign countries by water. Most of it is mined in Idaho, Utah, and Colorado, and goes *via* the Pacific coast ports and Panama Canal to the eastern market. At times a large tonnage of lead enters New York from Spain, Mexico, and other foreign countries.

St. Louis is close to the lead mines, and normally the price of the metal in this western market is $2 to $5 a ton below the New York price. At times, however, in spite of the tariff on imports, foreign lead is sold in New York in sufficient quantities to depress the eastern market price and for brief periods may bring the New York price below that of St. Louis.

LEAD PRODUCTION OF WORLD IN TONS

	1934–1938	1941–1945
United States (refined)	398,000	450,000
Australia	217,000	186,000
Mexico	197,000	188,000
Canada	163,000	181,000
Germany and Austria	151,000	157,000
Belgium	77,000	9,800
Burma	75,000	
Spain	49,000	36,000
U.S.S.R.	47,000	112,000*
Italy	40,000	
Tunisia	24,000	
Poland	16,000	
Peru	12,000	42,000
All other countries	37,000	

* 1942 and 1943 only.

Production of Lead. The increase in the output of lead during the last century was even more phenomenal than that of copper. In 1825, the total production of lead in the United States was only 1,500 tons, whereas, during the years 1925 to 1929, the average annual production

[9] Walter H. Voskuil, *Minerals in Modern Industry*, John Wiley & Sons, 1930, p. 242.

was 664,000 tons from domestic ores, and the American consumption during that same period was approximately 900,000 tons or almost one-half of the total for the world. During recent years lead production has sharply declined, partly as a result of the fact that some of our best lead mines are being depleted. During 1945, the mine production of lead in the United States was only 390,000 tons, while our consumption was 637,000 tons. For more than two decades our domestic consumption has exceeded domestic production, and we have been compelled to draw a considerable part of our supplies from Canada, Mexico, Australia and other foreign sources (see the table on page 701).

Losses of Lead. The losses of lead are unfortunately high in production and through consumption. The losses in mining have been estimated at 15 per cent, even with the best mining practices for exploiting this metal. Moreover, only the high-grade ores are mined, and the low-grade ores may be left in such condition as to prohibit their future recovery. Milling and smelting losses are high also, ranging from 5 per cent up to three times that amount with difficult ores and poor practices. Finally, the bulk of the lead goes into paints and other uses where recovery is impossible or unprofitable. Unfortunately the world resources are not known to be large and there is danger of a lead shortage in the next few decades.[10]

ZINC

Zinc production within the United States is largely a development of the last century. There was a small commercial production as early as 1860, but the industry did not make much progress until the late 1880's. Since 1925 the domestic production has usually ranged between 600,000 and 800,000 tons, and world production in prosperous years has surpassed 1,600,000 tons.

Zinc is used primarily for the galvanizing of iron and steel—a process which protects these products from decomposition when exposed to the weather. The galvanizing industry utilizes 30 to 50 per cent of the total zinc output.

Brass making provides the second largest use of zinc, accounting for approximately 30 per cent of the total American consumption during the period 1934 to 1946. Brass is an important industrial

[10] A. B. Parsons, "Metals and Minerals: Has the World Enough," *Mining and Metallurgy*, April 1945, pp. 195–196.

material. From it are made worm wheels, gears, propellers, bearings, steam fittings, tubings, non-corrosive castings, valves and valve stems, automobile parts, and scores of other products of the metal industries.

Rolled Zinc. Zinc, resistant to acids and rust, is used in the manufacture of battery cans, glass jar tops, photoengraving sheets, boiler plates, and brake linings.

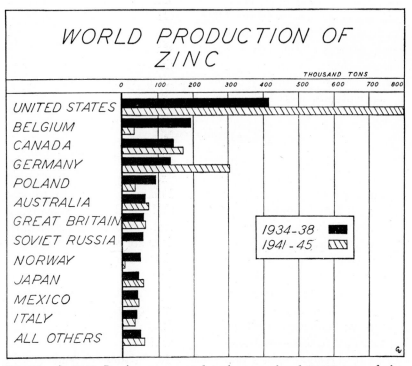

Fig. 270. In 1940, Russia was reported to have produced 85,000 tons of zinc. (*Minerals Yearbook*, U. S. Department of the Interior, 1945, p. 195.)

Zinc Dust. Commercial production of zinc dust in the United States began about 1910, and the output approximates 10,000 tons a year. In Europe the production of zinc dust is normally much larger than in this country. Originally, zinc dust served chiefly for the manufacture of a gray paint for protecting iron against rust. More recently, it has been used almost exclusively for plant painting in the industrial districts of France, Belgium, and western Germany. It is also used extensively in marine paints both here and abroad. Just prior to World War II, an entirely different use was discovered for zinc dust. The United States Navy found that it makes a most effective smoke screen.

World Production of Zinc. The United States now leads all other countries in zinc production, western and central Europe and Canada producing most of the remainder (Fig. 270). In this country 40 to 50 per cent of the total output is produced in the tristate area—a small area situated within fifty miles of the point where Missouri, Kansas, and Oklahoma come together. Oklahoma leads the states with approximately one-fourth of the total output.

Any estimate of zinc reserves are at best unreliable. In most of the mining regions, the known supply is sufficient to last a few decades at most, and the prospective output of known resources will probably fall short of future needs.[11]

ALUMINUM

Aluminum is the most abundant of the metallic elements of the earth's crust, but unfortunately there are relatively few places where it exists in a form that permits of easy and cheap extraction by present methods. The commercial product is obtained from bauxite, a weathered rock of high aluminum content. Scores of commercial deposits are being exploited, but eight nations are responsible for most of the world's output since the mines of Italy, formerly a large producer, have been almost idle most of the time since the close of World War II (Fig. 271). Important bauxite deposits, as yet undeveloped, have been discovered in other countries and the resources of known deposits are sufficient to last many decades.

The largest reserves of bauxite found within the United States are located in Arkansas which produced 6,036,000 tons of crude ore in 1943, when the demand for aluminum for the manufacture of airplanes was at its height. By 1945, production had decreased to less than 1,200,000 tons. Georgia, Alabama, and Virginia produced 196,-393 tons in 1943, but the output dropped to 70,000 tons in 1945. However peacetime needs of aluminum are growing rapidly as new uses for the metal are discovered.

Prior to World War II, more bauxite was imported into the United States than was produced locally. However, during the war, when shipping space was at a premium, the United States produced more

[11] A. B. Parsons, "Metals and Minerals: Has the World Enough," *Mining and Metallurgy*, April 1945, p. 195.

than 75 per cent of its domestic requirements. Most of the remainder
came from British Guiana and Surinam.

In Europe the known deposits of fair to high-grade bauxite are so
widespread that no country need transport this product long distances
unless shipping conditions make the long haul inexpensive. Likewise
Asiatic countries and Australia either possess large supplies of bauxite
or have easy access to them.

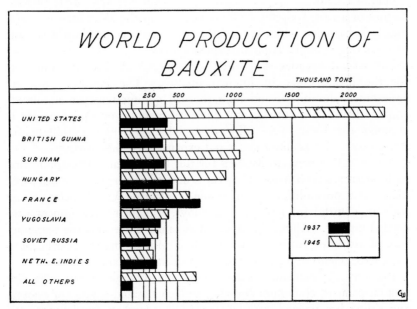

FIG. 271. The aluminum industry is relatively young. Aluminum is used in the
manufacture of hundreds of products, but the manufacture of airplanes required
many thousand tons of aluminum during World War II. During the eight-year
period, 1937–1945, the bauxite requirements increased more than 100 per cent.

Properties of Aluminum. Aluminum has numerous properties
which make it desirable for a wide variety of commercial purposes.
It is a light metal having only one-third of the specific weight of iron.
It is resistant to corrosion, is malleable and ductile, is a fairly good
conductor of electricity, and has high thermal conductivity. For its
weight, aluminum has high tensile strength and is of special value
where both lightness and strength are desired. Compared with iron
and steel, it is still expensive.

Uses of Aluminum. Aluminum for commercial purposes is a product of the last half century. More than one hundred years ago, 1831,

the first metallic aluminum was produced by the ingenious application of chemistry. This metal, however, was almost priceless, and another 60 years of labor were required before a cheap and convenient method of producing it was discovered. The reduction in the price of aluminum from a value of $204 a pound in 1854, when it was worth almost its weight in gold, to less than 20 cents a pound in less than a century is "magic money."

One of the earliest uses of aluminum in America was for the manufacture of a cast, weighing 100 ounces, to cap the Washington monument. It has been subject to weathering since 1884 and is still capable of reflecting sunlight from its exposed surface.

For several decades the largest commercial use of aluminum was for the manufacture of kitchen utensils. The lightness, pleasing appearance, durability, and high thermal conductivity of aluminum, and the harmless nature of any chemical reaction of the container in cooking the food, were all factors which favored aluminum for kitchenware and resulted in a rapid expansion of this market.

About 1912 a new era dawned for this light metal. The application of modern research methods to the study of aluminum alloys showed many new possibilities. As a result of World War I there was an insistent demand for strong, light alloys, and their development proceeded rapidly. Aluminum or its alloys now enter into the manufacture of airplanes, furniture, automobiles, railroad and street cars, optical goods, scientific instruments, camp equipment, and paint.

Recently the demand for aluminum abrasives, aluminum salts, aluminum cement, aluminum shingles, and corrugated sheets for roofing and siding has opened new and expanding markets for bauxite, and the production increased more than tenfold between 1919 and 1943. The peak of the World War II demand for this light but strong metal was reached in 1943. Except for temporary setbacks, the demand for aluminum will probably increase. There is now a strong tendency to substitute aluminum for steel in an increasing number of industries. Because of its great strength and lightness, aluminum is now replacing steel in the manufacture of bulkheads for dams. Many thousand aluminum cables (steel reinforced) are in use in the United States and Canada alone. Airplanes, passenger cars, dining cars, engine cables, tank cars, lifeboats, trucks, and trailers are being made wholly or in part of aluminum and of aluminum alloys. Among the new uses, according to the Aluminum Company of America, perhaps the aluminum roofing sheets have the greatest possibilities for immediate expansion. Maritime construction companies are using additional quantities of aluminum in ships.

Aluminum Manufacture. Cheap power is an absolute essential for the concentration and the smelting of aluminum ore on a commercial scale. The bauxite which contains 30 to 60 per cent aluminum, therefore, moves to centers where cheap power is available.

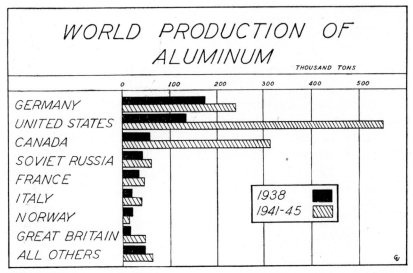

Fig. 272. No other major mineral industry has had such a phenomenal growth during recent years as aluminum. The aluminum industry is still expanding rapidly in several parts of the world. In 1947 the United States produced approximately 600,000 tons. (*Minerals Yearbook*, U. S. Department of the Interior, 1938, p. 647, and 1946, p. 697.)

The major aluminum factories of the world are situated near cheap and abundant power resources. Most of the American aluminum industries are located close to the Appalachian coal fields, or near the cheap and abundant water power resources of Niagara Falls, of the southern Appalachian region, or of northwestern United States. Recently the cheap power of the Saguenay River has attracted to itself one of the largest aluminum plants in the world. The Saguenay River Basin collects enough water to produce 2,000,000 horsepower of electrical energy the year round and has an installed power capacity of 2,050,000 horsepower. The aluminum works at Arvida, Quebec, has a capacity of 80,000 tons of aluminum pig annually, and its total output was needed during World War II.[12]

Since the late 1930's the aluminum industry has been growing rapidly in many parts of the world. Prior to World War II, Germany had built up her aluminum industry to the point where she led all the nations of the world in the output of this light, strong metal that is so useful in times of war. Today the United States and Canada are the leaders in production and in peacetime uses (Fig. 272).

TIN

Tin, one of the rarest and most indispensable of the base metals, was among the first used by man. Prehistoric remains reveal great quantities of tools, implements, weapons, and ornaments made from bronze, an alloy of copper and tin. Its chief application at present is as a coating for other metals, but its other uses are multitudinous. "It accompanies man in every walk of life, literally from the cradle to the grave—from the time his childish hands receive their first baby rattle until his virtues are immortalized in imperishable bronze. It is a necessary ingredient of solder, and is a component of babbitt and most other anti-friction metals, without which manufacture and transportation would be impossible. As foil, it wraps alike the workingman's tobacco and the school girl's confections. It accounts for the rustle and luster of silk so dear to the feminine heart, while the tin dinner pail has a place in politics and is celebrated in song and story. Without the humble tin can the world could no longer be properly fed." [13] No complete substitute has ever been found for tin. In most manufactured articles only a small percentage is tin, about 2 per cent in tin plate, so that its price has very little influence on total costs.

At present the most essential use of tin is for the manufacture of containers, making possible the utilization of food products out of season and in places remote from the centers of production. The rapid growth of the canning industry has called for an ever-increasing tonnage of tin, which has been met by a gradual increase in world production. The rapid expansion and improvement of transportation, especially by automobile, has increased the demand for babbitt-bearing

[12] W. M. Goodwin, "Low-Cost Power on the Saguenay," *Compressed Air Magazine*, December 1946, pp. 326–329.

[13] Reprinted by permission from Spurr and Wormser's *Marketing of Metals and Minerals*, McGraw-Hill Book Co., 1925, pp. 181–182.

metals. These industries together with the manufacture of solder, brass, and bronze account for the major uses of tin.

World Production of Tin

For centuries the world obtained most of its tin from Cornwall, England. But the supply of England was depleted just when the

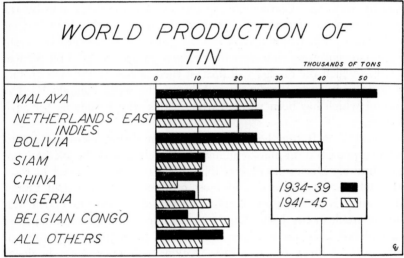

Fɪɢ. 273. The world production of tin for 1941–1945 clearly shows the influence of World War II on tin mining. In countries situated within the war zones, production decreased notably; in most other countries output increased.

demand was increasing. Consequently, this semi-precious metal was sought elsewhere, and the Cornish miners have spread the knowledge of the best tin-mining practices to many parts of the world.

Fortunately, rather abundant deposits of tin have been discovered as rapidly as needed. In 1938, the total production of tin was 147,000 tons. The chief source of supply, 45 per cent of the total, was produced in the Straits Settlements and the two neighboring islands of the Netherlands East Indies, Banka and Belitong. Bolivia is the only other region with a large known reserve and large production (Fig. 273).

Malaya and the Netherlands East Indies. Chinese records show that tin was mined in Malaya as early as the fifteenth century. Later the faction fight among the various clans of Chinese led to British interference and eventually to British administration of the peninsular tin mines.

Nearly all the tin mined in Malaya and the Netherlands East Indies is alluvial tin. The richest deposits are found in the valleys of western Malaya. Since the tin is heavier than the gravel it is usually found concentrated in the deeper layers of the alluvial deposits. Usually a thick useless overburden of sand and gravel has to be removed before the tin-bearing gravel is uncovered. The heavy tin can be removed then by washing. Considerable quantities of tin are still won by the age-old method of panning. Most of the work of this kind is done by women. The major part of the tin, however, is obtained by washing in concentrating sluices or by dredge. In dredging, "a pit is excavated in which the dredge will float; it then eats away the rich ground in front of it, sorts out the tin and dumps the waste behind." [14] The ground which has been worked over in this way is suitable for agriculture.

World War II together with the postwar disturbances has practically stopped the tin-mining industry of Malaya and the Netherlands East Indies. During 1945, less than 3,000 tons were mined in these areas which were formerly the most productive in the world. Since the mining is mostly done in alluvium silt, sand, and gravel, the war did not result in any lasting injury to the mines, and after the Japanese surrendered, even the dredges and smelters were found to be in fair condition. Sooner or later these regions will once again be listed among the most important tin-mining regions of the world.

Bolivia. Bolivia now ranks first among the countries of the world in the output of tin. And yet, perhaps, no other important mining region in the world suffers from more colossal handicaps than those which nature has thrown about the tin mines of Bolivia. Most of the mines are situated at elevations of 14,000 to 19,000 feet, and the higher ones are not far from the zone of perpetual snow. The inadequate supply of oxygen renders the European incapable of hard and sustained effort, and the native, accustomed to the rare atmosphere, is inefficient. Moreover, these cold, bleak lands support no forests and contain no coal or oil. Fuel is accordingly scarce, and the cost of importing it is almost prohibitive. The mines are difficult of access; until a few decades ago almost all food, fuel, and materials of construction were brought in on the backs of llamas, and the tin ore or concentrates were exported by the same method.

[14] For further information concerning tin mining in the Malay States see *Mining in Malaya*, Malay States Information Agency, London, 1924.

Some of the mines now have railroad connection with the outside world, but many of the mineralized areas lie at considerable distances from railways and must still depend upon pack trains of mules, burros, and llamas for the importation of machinery and other equipment for the mines and for the exportation of tin ore. Even those mines situated near railways are handicapped by excessively high freight rates. This condition is unavoidable because of the tremendous cost of constructing, maintaining, and operating trans-Andean railroads, which in places have frightfully steep gradients and which reach unparalleled heights for railway construction. In addition to the foregoing handicaps, the tin-mining industry presents difficult problems of ore production and concentration.

In contrast to the alluvial deposits of Malaya, the Bolivian tin is found in lodes or mineral veins. These veins vary in thickness from a few inches to 10, 15, or 20 feet. The richer ores carry 6, 8, or even 15 per cent tin. Although the Bolivian ores are richer than the placers of Malaya, they are also more difficult and expensive to mine. Moreover, the ores must be mechanically concentrated, often by the cheap labor of women and children, before they are shipped to the tin smelters.

The high cost of fuel, power, and imported machinery prevents the smelting and refining in Bolivia. Most of the concentrates, therefore, move to the British Isles for smelting, but some of them are shipped to the smelters at Perth Amboy, New Jersey.

In spite of the many handicaps faced by the mining companies of Bolivia, the development of tin ores has become the dominant economic activity of the republic. Tin not only supplies 75 to 90 per cent of the exports, but also serves as "trade key to the quantity and quality of imports." Most of the machinery entering Bolivia goes for mining or closely related purposes; and a large part of the textile and food imports is consumed in the mining centers.

The known reserves are sufficient to last for half a century, and since the region has been but poorly prospected it is not unlikely that new reserves will be added by discoveries.

China. The Chinese production of tin is relatively small, and yet, from the standpoint of value, tin is the most important metal produced in China. Eighty per cent of the tin comes from the Kotchin district near Mingtze, Yunnan. Although the supply comes from lodes in limestone, the veins have been deeply oxidized, and in early times the mining was conducted in the same manner as though the ores were placer. Later, lode mining was developed, and at present these lodes supply most of the tin output of the country.

Until recently, lode mining was in a backward state of development, and little machinery was used. Consequently, the amount of human effort required to produce a few tons of tin each day would be considered appalling in America. For years the ore has been carried from mines on the backs of men. Long lines of laborers, heavily laden with ore, trudge up the steep slopes of the mine shaft, which in some places rise a vertical distance of 1,000 to 1,500 feet. Recently, vertical shafts, equipped with hoisting machinery, have superseded the slope in some of the deeper mines.

Recent studies have indicated that the mineralized area of Yunnan is large and the veins well defined; consequently it is expected that the production from this region will increase.[15]

Nigeria. For many years the natives of Nigeria have been obtaining tin of excellent quality by panning the gravel of the river beds. But, because of the resistance of the natives, it was not until 1902 that it became profitable for Europeans to prospect for tin. For almost another decade the country was in an extremely unsettled condition, and until 1909 the British had to maintain garrisons to protect life and property. Nevertheless, the production of tin has steadily increased until the output is now approximately 12,000 tons.

Future of Tin

Tin seems to be a very scarce metal. The original deposits of tin in hard rock are commonly of very low grade, and it is only the occurrence of placer or stream deposits of tin ore which have kept the price of tin within its past range. At present there are no deposits of tin in sight which give promise of affording largely increased tin supplies at reasonable prices.[16]

Since 1914 the annual production and price of tin have fluctuated violently. The tin industry, like that of petroleum, often suffers from overproduction, and there is danger that the resources will be seriously depleted in the near future. Any greatly enlarged demand would undoubtedly create an acute tin famine. This danger has gradually stimulated research in an effort to find suitable substitutes for the metal. The National Canners' Association has been experimenting

[15] *Mineral Resources of the United States,* U. S. Geological Survey, 1927, p. 149.

[16] E. C. Eckel, "Coal, Iron, and War," Henry Holt & Co., 1920, p. 171.

with the "tinless can," consisting of sheet steel coated with various lacquers that are resistant to fruit and vegetable acids; the Bell Telephone Company has been gradually substituting antimony for tin in lead cable sheetings; nickel is being substituted for tin in brass and bronze; and roller bearings for railway cars and heavy mechanical equipment may be considered a substitute for babbitt and other bearing metals.[17]

MANGANESE

Little manganese is mined in the United States in spite of the fact that the industry is favored by a high protective tariff. In 1945, the domestic output of manganese amounted to only 212,000 tons (metal content) compared with 633,000 tons imported.[18] This country has large deposits of low-grade ores, located mostly in Montana and New Mexico, which as yet cannot be developed except at a high cost per ton of metal.

Manganese is indispensable to the manufacture of steel. Inasmuch as steel is basic to industry and to mechanized warfare, any shortage of this valuable mineral would cripple industry and handicap our defense organizations. The dangers resulting from a shortage were well illustrated during World War I. In 1914, the domestic price of manganese ore was $14 a ton. By 1918, owing to increasing demand for the metal and to a shortage of transportation facilities, the price rose to $68.50 a ton. In the early 1940's, when similar conditions prevailed, the price exceeded $70 a ton.

There is no need to run the risk of having this situation arise again. Since manganese is non-perishable, a supply should be imported and stored to be resorted to only in emergencies.

The largest and best-known deposits of manganese ore are situated in Brazil, the Gold Coast of Africa, the Soviet Union, India, Egypt, the Union of South Africa, and Cuba. None of these countries needs large quantities of manganese and consequently they are all glad of the opportunity to sell the ore.

NICKEL, GOLD, AND SILVER

Nickel. The annual world production of nickel rose from 46,000 tons in 1933 to approximately 143,000 tons in 1945. This phenomenal

[17] *Mineral Resources of the United States*, U. S. Geological Survey, 1926, pp. 39–40.

[18] *Minerals Yearbook*, U. S. Department of the Interior, 1945, pp. 594–596.

growth was the result of the increasing importance of the metal both in industry and in preparation for war. Nickel is used primarily as an alloy with iron in the manufacture of steel, and as a coating for other metals to improve their appearance and to prevent corrosion. Sixty to seventy-five per cent of the world's output of this metal is now used in the manufacture of nickel-steel, which, because of its toughness and strength, is in great demand for the construction of battleships. After the late 1920's the demand for nickel-steel in the manufacture of armor plate increased rapidly until the close of World War II.

The use of nickel-chromium steel is rapidly expanding. The largest application of this product is found in the manufacture of automo-

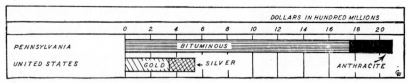

Fig. 274. Coal has been our most valuable mineral product except occasionally when its value has been surpassed by that of petroleum.

biles. This industry also demands large quantities of nickel in plating metals. A film of chromium, superimposed upon a film of nickel and highly polished, gives a fine silvery effect, superior in this respect to silver alone.

Canada is the chief source of nickel. In 1945, that country produced 110,000 tons. Russia ranked second in production with an estimated output of 13,400 tons, while Cuba and New Caledonia produced 10,900 tons and 4,328 tons, respectively.

Gold and Silver. We are accustomed to think of gold and silver as standards by which other economic products are evaluated. These metals, however, have many essential industrial uses. Yet the combined value of all the gold and silver annually produced in the world is not sufficient, in normal years, to buy the agricultural products of Illinois, Indiana, and Ohio, and would not pay for one-half of the coal mined annually in the United States (Fig. 274).

Gold is one of the few metals that is found at times in such a state that it can be mined with great profit by the poor man who has little or no financial backing. This fact accounts for the lure of the newly discovered placer gold fields. Thousands of adventurers have entered placer gold fields with little or no equipment except pans, shovels, food, or ammunition with which to secure food, and resourcefulness; and have quit the "diggings" a few months later as wealthy men. Usually, however, where thousands succeed, tens of thousands fail. Yet there are always plenty of men who are willing to take the chance when a new placer deposit is discovered.

Unfortunately, most of the great placer gold discoveries have been made in regions accessible in the early stages of development only to hardy, daring, and resourceful men. Thus the "forty-niner" who rushed to the gold field in California had to brave the dangers of the Great American Desert, the dreaded diseases of the Isthmus of Panama, or the stormy waters of the Strait of Magellan, as determined by the route taken. Those who rushed to the Klondike in 1897–1898 endured many dangers and privations both en route and during the long cold winters that followed. Many of the placer mines of Australia and the United States were located in deserts where great hardships had to be endured in order to secure the coveted gold.

Perhaps the placer gold field of California afforded the finest opportunity ever discovered for development by the hardy pioneer. The land belonged to the United States Government, and a claim could be staked out by any American citizen. The climate was mild, and water for panning could be obtained the year round. The only equipment needed was a pan and shovel.

At present most of the gold and silver output is produced from mother-lode ores which require expensive machinery for mining operations.

WORLD PRODUCTION OF GOLD AND SILVER IN MILLIONS OF OUNCES FOR SELECTED YEARS

(Note that the rapid increase in production started about 1860)

Years	Silver	Gold
1493–1520	4.8	0.5
1581–1600	17.6	0.5
1661–1680	16.3	0.6
1761–1780	22.1	0.7
1861–1870	39.7	2.1
1871–1880	85.2	6.0
1881–1890	100.0	5.1
1891–1900	160.0	10.1
1901–1910	194.2	21.6
1911–1920	242.1	19.8
1939–1945	242.2	34.1

The tremendous increase in gold production after 1890 was largely a result of the discovery and development of exceedingly rich gold fields in the Union of South Africa (see the preceding table). Also the act of the United States Government in 1933, which raised the price of gold from $20.67 to $35 an ounce, has caused the gold-mining industries to boom in many parts of the world. Then, too, an increasing percentage of the output of precious metals, especially of silver, is produced as a by-product of copper, lead, and zinc ores. The tremendous developments in the mining of these baser metals have naturally caused an increase in the production of precious metals.

BUILDING MATERIALS

The character of rural dwellings in all climes is normally determined by the materials available, their abundance, and ease of handling. In countries of advanced civilization, where transportation is highly developed, the esthetic sense of the people may, it is true, cause the bringing of the materials, such as wood, bricks, or stone, from distant points for use in dwellings. In less advanced countries, however, especially where building materials cannot be brought from the outside without great difficulty and expense, it is inevitable that most of the building materials must be obtained locally.[19]

In many parts of the world where timber is scarce man has turned to the minerals for construction materials. In fact, man used minerals for this purpose long before he used wood. In the early stages of man's development he sometimes made his home in natural rock caves which he probably altered very little. Later he improved these caves or carved out a home in the face of a cliff.

As time went on he learned to use an ever-increasing number of minerals in the building of his home until today the modern dwelling may contain scores of minerals in its construction.

Loess Dwellings. The distinctive characters of the building materials available have given rise to types of dwellings of like distinctiveness. Thus the loess deposits of North China, soft and easily excavated, have given rise to peculiar artificial loess cave dwellings and to the more common constructional buildings whose walls consist of loess frequently mixed with rice or millet straw as binder.

The loess cave dwellings consist of a chamber or chambers of arched-tunnel form excavated within the mass of any thick accumulation of loess. The length is ordinarily about 30 feet, the width 12 feet, and

[19] Myron L. Fuller and Frederick G. Clapp, "Loess and Rock Dwellings of Shensi, China," *Geographical Review*, Vol. 14, p. 215.

Fig. 275. Cliff dwellings in Shensi and western Honan, carved not in rock but in the strange loess formation, which is easily cut and withstands action of rains and frosts.

Fig. 276. Loess cave dwellings of North China.

the height 14 or 15 feet. The width varies with the coherency of the loess at the particular locality (Figs. 275 and 276).

When the loess is wet, there is likelihood of flowage; when dry, it crumbles and caves. The best time for excavating loess dwellings is, therefore, some days or weeks after a period of rain, when the loess is still moist but no longer wet. At such times it is easily cut and shaped. After the completion of the excavation the inner walls are surfaced with plaster of loess mud which prevents the loess from caving.[20]

Clay as a Building Material. Clayey soil, which can be molded, and can absorb substances which solidify and harden it when dried in the sun or baked in the fire, is a material which is easily shaped and which lends itself to many uses. For purposes of construction it is commonly used in the form of bricks. When combined with steel these bricks meet the requirements of quick and easy construction and great strength.

The utilization of bricks did not originate in the regions of great industrial development where they are most popular today, but in the arid regions of the Old World. The great Chaldean and Assyrian palaces, and even those which succeeded them in western Asia and Iran up to the time of Alexander, were built almost exclusively of clay. In regions so arid that sun-dried bricks can be used it has always maintained its supremacy.

In much of the Nile Valley only the roof and stockade are made of thatch, the hut being of earth. Many of the Sudanese villages and most of the dwellings of Saharan oases are made of sun-dried bricks, and some of them are surrounded by mud walls.[21]

At present, the greatest brick-manufacturing regions are western Europe and eastern North America, where brick is extensively used in the construction both of dwellings and of industrial plants. The value of the brick and tile output of the United States alone usually exceeds a quarter of a billion dollars annually; clay is the most valuable mineral used for construction purposes.

Distribution of Brick-Manufacturing Plants. The low value and great bulk of bricks make them relatively expensive to transport. Since clay suitable for their manufacture is widespread, the industry can usually be located near the market. Thus, in 1938 every state in

[20] *Op. cit.*, pp. 215–226.

[21] P. Vidal de la Blache, *Principles of Human Geography*, Henry Holt & Co., 1926, pp. 238–270. An excellent treatment of building materials.

the Union had brick kilns in operation, and in each of twenty-eight states the value of the output exceeded a million dollars. The leaders in the industry were Ohio, Illinois, and New York, which together produced approximately a third of the national output.

Fig. 277. Limestone quarry. (Courtesy Indiana Limestone Company.)

Building Stone. The geographical significance of stone consists primarily in its usefulness as building materials. Vidal de la Blache in his *Principles of Human Geography* says:

> The building stone par excellence is that which can be chiseled, cut in even blocks and fitted, thus lending itself to the construction of all the different shapes and combinations of shapes which the skill of the architect can imagine or devise. Limestone and, to a lesser degree, sandstone have supplied the materials for a varied artistic development [Fig. 277]. A relationship exists between stone and edifice. Mayan construction cannot be thought of apart from the limestone of Yucatan, just as the sandstones hemming in the Valley of the Ganges on the south bring up images of the innumerable monuments in the cities between Delhi and Benares, or sandstones of the Vosges the cathedrals and the castles of the Rhine Valley.[22]

[22] Reprinted by permission from P. Vidal de la Blache's *Principles of Human Geography*, Henry Holt & Co., 1926, pp. 248–249.

In a similar manner many cities of the British Isles and of countries bordering the Mediterranean Sea are closely related to the building stone available near by.

Although marble and granite make good building materials their occurrence is less common than that of limestone and sandstone. Moreover, they are more expensive to quarry and more difficult to shape. But because of the varied colors of marble and the excellent finish which it will take it is in great demand for decorative purposes.

Cement. Cement has been known since Roman times, but its extensive use is a development of the last few decades. At present it is one of the most valuable construction materials produced within the United States. It is made primarily from limestone and clay—minerals widely distributed throughout the United States. It is a product which fits nicely into the present machine age. It can be made quickly and cheaply by large-scale machinery; it can be mixed by steam power and poured by means of machinery and unskilled labor. Moreover, it makes a durable structure and when reinforced by steel it has great strength and is suited for the building of bridges, skyscrapers, and other structures which must withstand great weight or strain. As a result, the growth of the industry has been rapid.

Cement is now produced in thirty-five states, but during the last few years Pennsylvania and California have manufactured more than one-fourth of the total output of the nation, while a dozen other states have produced more than a million barrels each. Since materials for the manufacture of cement are widely distributed, the cement is usually produced relatively close to the areas of consumption. The greatest cement-manufacturing district of the United States is the Lehigh Valley in eastern Pennsylvania. Here the limestone, shale, and anthracite coal—the major raw materials for manufacturing cement—are found close together; the district is near the greatest urban centers of the United States; and the region has excellent transportation facilities, both water and rail. Moreover, the early start and the good name of the product of the region are factors which have aided in the development of the industry.

REFERENCES

COLLIER, JAMES E., "The Aluminum Industry of the Western Hemisphere," *Economic Geography*, October 1944, pp. 229–257.

EMENY, BROOKS, *The Strategy of Raw Materials*, The Macmillan Co., 1934, pp. 85–132.

FULLER, MYRON L., and FREDERICK G. CLAPP, "Loess and Rock Dwellings of Shensi, China," *Geographical Review*, Vol. 14.

JUAN, VEI CHOW, "Mineral Resources of China," *Economic Geology*, No. 4, Part 2, Supplement, pp. 399–471.

KENNEDY, E. V. N., "Canada's Aluminum Industry," *Canadian Geographical Journal*, November 1938, pp. 249–269.

LOVERING, J. S., *Minerals in World Affairs*, Prentice-Hall Inc., 1944.

Mineral Industry, McGraw-Hill Book Co., Annual.

Mineral Resources of the United States, U. S. Geological Survey, Annual.

Minerals Yearbook, U. S. Government Printing Office, 1947.

PARSONS, A. B., "Metals and Minerals: Has the World Enough," *Mining and Metallurgy*, April 1945, pp. 195–196.

"Utah Copper—Biggest Excavation," *Mining and Metallurgy*, February 1947, pp. 47–48.

TORGASHEFF, BORIS P., *The Mineral Industries of the Far East*, Chali Co., Shanghai, 1930.

TRYON, F. G., and MARGARET H. SCHOENFELD, "Comparison of Physical Conditions in British and American Coal Mines," reprinted from *Coal and Coal Trade Journal*, 1926.

VOSKUIL, WALTER H., *Minerals in Modern Industry*, John Wiley & Sons, 1930.

World Atlas of Commercial Geology, U. S. Geological Survey, 1921, Part I.

WANG, KUNG-PING, "Mineral Resources of China," *Geographical Review*, October 1944, pp. 621–635.

PART IV

TRADE AND TRANSPORTATION

Chapter 22

FUNDAMENTALS OF TRADE AND

TRANSPORTATION

TRADE ROUTES AND TRADE CENTERS

The Importance of Trade and Transportation. Trade and transportation go hand in hand. Neither one could be developed without the other, and taken together they are indispensable to industrial progress. Without them civilization could never have progressed beyond the subsistence stage of primitive peoples.

Primitive peoples first bartered a few products with their neighbors. They lived mainly unto themselves in their respective communities. They grew their own food and feed and manufactured their own clothing and implements. Even though such commodities could be produced more cheaply elsewhere, the cost of transportation was likely to prohibit their importation. Then as man's knowledge of other peoples and their products increased and as transportation facilities were improved, the scope of his trading grew in the volume and variety of goods traded and in the distances that the goods for exchange could be economically transported.

Specialization Dependent upon Trade and Transportation. Specialization had to await the time when the necessary raw materials could be cheaply delivered to the factory and the finished product cheaply distributed to the consumers. With the growth of cheap and rapid transportation a man could give his entire time to the type of work which he liked or for which he was best fitted. Also the production of each type of goods tended to develop at those centers where conditions were most propitious. Thus in our own country cotton-growing developed in the South; corn was grown chiefly in the corn belt; and the citrus fruit industry was developed in California, Florida, and Texas. Similarly each of our major manufacturing industries grew most rapidly in areas that possessed natural advantages for its development.

Inventions, discoveries, transportation facilities, personal desires, and other human or man-made factors had their influences on the distribution of production. Yet fundamentally trade rests on the natural bases of the irregular distribution of natural resources and land forms. Trade is also influenced by less permanent factors such as population distribution, stages of civilization, and man-made highways, railways, and transportation equipment. Wars, psychology of nations, tariffs, and foreign investments also influence trade, but they are changeable and uncertain factors. However, over long periods of time each industry tends to develop in regions that have natural advantages for its growth. Thus civilization has developed not only personal but also regional specialization. One need only mention such places as Pittsburgh, Pennsylvania; Akron, Ohio; Detroit, Michigan; Ivorydale, Cincinnati; and New Castle, England, to illustrate both personal and regional specialization.

Trade is a Fundamental of All Economic Progress. Without trade there could be no urban or industrial development. Without trade cities could not be fed, clothed, or housed; and factories could not obtain raw materials or distribute manufactured goods. Each farmer would be compelled to produce his own machinery, build his home, manufacture his clothing, and raise all his own food. Each hunter would be compelled to manufacture his own weapons and ammunition, and each fisherman would have to make his own nets, lines, boats, and other equipment.

Transportation and Urban Development. Urban development shows a marked relationship to transportation facilities, as is indicated in a study of the largest cities of the world. Most of these cities not only are favored in their location by access to various parts of the land, but also they commonly occupy a marginal position between land and sea or inland waterways and land routes. Thus New York, on the eastern seaboard of the United States, is favored by situation with respect to the only low break in the eastern highlands giving access to the rich interior of our country. The Erie Canal, the Hudson River, trunk line railways, and seaboard location all have played a part in the development of the metropolitan area of New York. Similarly, London, located on the Thames and in the heart of England where railway lines extend to various parts of that country, has become one of the five greatest entrepôts of the world and the chief distributing center for the great variety of goods found among the

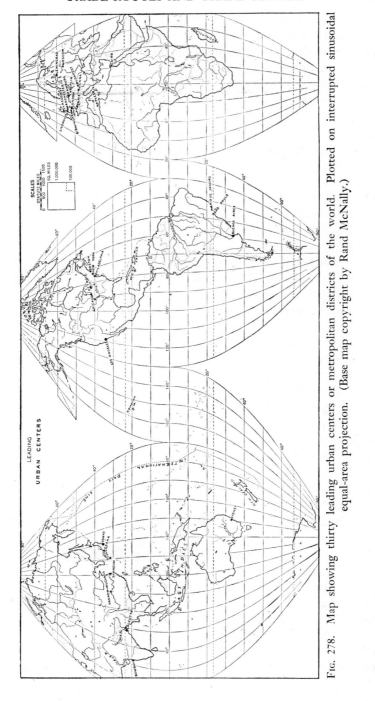

FIG. 278. Map showing thirty leading urban centers or metropolitan districts of the world. Plotted on interrupted sinusoidal equal-area projection. (Base map copyright by Rand McNally.)

imports of the British Isles. A study of Paris, Tokyo, Berlin, Chicago, Shanghai, Buenos Aires, and most of the other leading urban centers of the world shows forcibly the influence that favorable transportation has had upon their development (Fig. 278).

A few centuries ago the great majority of the people lived almost entirely upon domestic products. To a considerable extent foreign imports were luxuries, enjoyed by relatively few people, and did not figure prominently in the life of the masses. At the present time, on the other hand, even people with only moderate means satisfy their varied wants by purchasing commodities that have come from widely separated areas. Thus the average laborer of many lands wears garments made from raw materials originating in southern United States, Egypt, or India. His coffee and tea come from tropical highlands; and the mutton and beef which he eats may have been imported from remote semi-arid lands.

The commercial world has, therefore, broken over the limited confines of political units into which it was divided. For most of these units national economic self-sufficiency and independence are impossible. In many ways nations are bound together with visible as well as invisible ties, most of which are reflections of the intricate fabric of international trade—the exchange of goods and services of one country for those of another. Such exchange performs an invaluable function in the national economy of leading industrial countries. Thus it is not difficult to visualize what the effect would be upon the British textile industry—the greatest industry of that nation— if the United Kingdom were immediately cut off from all foreign supplies of cotton and wool.

Recent Growth of World Trade. The most marked development in world trade has taken place in but little more than a century. As late as the year 1810 the value of the combined imports and exports of all the leading countries amounted to less than 5 billion dollars.

For several years after the close of World War II, the United States alone had a foreign trade almost four times that of the entire world in 1910. Instead of the spices and precious stones of India and the rare luxuries of China, which filled the tiny holds of early sailing vessels, the cargoes of today consist of millions of tons of economic goods obtained in widely separated regions, and include bulky, low-priced commodities as well as those which are high in value and small in bulk.

Importance of Foreign Trade. Although in many countries the foreign trade is very small in comparison with the total domestic business, it is, nevertheless, an essential factor in their economic progress.

Thus although the foreign trade of the United States may be placed at 10 per cent of its total trade, a loss of this 10 per cent would have a far-reaching effect on domestic business. In other words, the overwhelming importance of the home market does not necessarily mean that the foreign market should be neglected. Variations of 5 to 15 per cent in operating ratios in some lines of business may cover the range from reasonable profits to ruinous losses. The percentage of our products absorbed by foreign trade may indeed be the difference between success and failure. Reduction in foreign demand may depress prices to a considerable extent, and unforeseen price changes may play havoc with profits. Moreover, the cumulative buying capacity upon which American industry prospers depends in large measure upon the profitable sale of products whose prices are determined in international markets. Our interest, therefore, in foreign trade and in foreign economic conditions exceeds by far the relative importance suggested by the 10 or 15 per cent which our foreign trade bears to our total trade.

International trade cannot prosper long unless both the importer and the exporter profit by the exchange of goods. These profits need be neither continuous nor immediate. Thus it may be good business, as well as a humanitarian act, to export goods to a region temporarily in distress even though the exporter loses money on the immediate transaction. Peoples stricken by earthquakes, famines, or wars may become prosperous again and also profitable customers much more quickly if they receive outside aid than if they are compelled to depend wholly on themselves for their rehabilitation. This principle is well illustrated in the trade of the United States with Europe and Asia after World War II. In 1946 we sent Europe more than 45 million tons of goods valued at 4,098 million dollars and received in return less than 2½ million tons of goods valued at 796 million dollars. This ill-balanced trade was carried on at great immediate sacrifice and financial loss to the people of the United States. However, one of the several purposes of this trade was to hasten the rehabilitation of Europe and help restore prosperity to that war-torn continent. In turn, a prosperous Europe can once again build up a trade that will be profitable to both the United States and Europe.

TRADE AND NATIONAL INTERDEPENDENCE

Development of Worldwide Trade. Foreign trade and domestic trade are essentially alike. Both consist of an exchange of goods and services, and in both there is an exchange of values. In foreign trade, however, financial exchanges usually become much more complicated than in trade within the boundaries of a country. In domestic trade the same monetary unit is usually employed by both buyers and sellers, whereas various kinds of units are commonly employed in the transactions of foreign trade. In addition, trade within a single country is ordinarily quite free from the obstruction of differences in languages, customs, commercial laws, and tariff barriers. The development of worldwide trade on a large scale had to await improved methods of transportation and is mainly a development of the past century. Such development has practically coincided with the period of most rapid exploitation of iron and coal and other basic minerals, and it has therefore swelled to tremendous proportions since the industrial revolution.

People learned comparatively early that they could best satisfy their varied wants by reaching out to distant lands, and by drawing upon foreign countries for some of their food, clothing, and luxuries. It was, indeed, the search for the products of world trade that ultimately brought about the discovery of America, and such trade was a fundamental factor in the maritime development of Portugal, Spain, Holland, and the British Isles.

Foreign Trade Necessary to a Well-Rounded Economic Development. No one nation possesses all the raw materials necessary for a high standard of living. Thus if the United States could not import such products as manganese, tin, quartz crystal, rubber, coffee, tea, jute, hemp, and literally scores of other raw materials, our industrial development would become disrupted within a few weeks. If England's supply of cotton were cut off, one of her largest industries would be paralyzed immediately. Moreover, as standards of living rise in a nation its dependence on the outside world increases. The subsistence farmer in central China is not influenced much by imported goods, but the ordinary American citizen would find his standards of living materially lowered without the use of imported products. Your telephone contains raw materials from three or four continents; your automobile is made of raw materials gathered from many parts of the world; and the food on your table probably comes from several widely scattered countries.

Foreign trade is also important because the demand of the combined markets of the world is greater than the demand of the markets of a single country. Thus foreign demand, because of its worldwide distribution, is less likely than domestic demand to be affected at one and the same time by adverse conditions. Foreign trade insures a more favorable continuity of demand and a more complete and steady utilization of a country's industrial equipment. For example, manufacturers of summer wearing apparel can make such goods for markets in the southern hemisphere during our winters.

International trade has certain advantages in bringing about a better social understanding among peoples. Trade between two countries should and often does lead to a close relationship in other than purely economic lines. Through the business contacts established there may develop a better mutual understanding and an appreciation of the culture and civilization of various peoples, and international economic relations tend to militate against provincialism.

MODES OF TRANSPORTATION

Within a large part of the world the modes of transportation have been revolutionized during the last century. One hundred years ago man was still transporting goods in most parts of the world by much the same methods that he had been following for thousands of years. On land, man and animals supplied the motive power; on water, the energy for transport was still supplied by the currents, winds, and humans. Within the brief span of a century the revolution in methods of transport has been almost complete within an ever-widening portion of the earth. Yet, in spite of these changes, more than half of the world's population still transport a large part of their goods by primitive methods.

Human and Animal Carriers

Still Important in Many Parts of the World. There are still hundreds of millions of people who depend largely upon human energy as the major motive power in the local transportation of goods. Within a large part of China the ever-squeaking wheelbarrow, pushed by man or pulled by the donkey, takes the place occupied by the freight train and motor truck of America. Within the vast tropical forests where roads are difficult to build and maintain, in parts of the uplands of east Africa where the tsetse fly makes animal transportation impossible, and in certain highly isolated regions of central Asia, man is still the chief carrier.

In some regions where the environmental conditions are distinctly unfavorable for modern methods of land transportation, animals have largely replaced man as carriers. Thus the North American Eskimos use the dog, and many people living in northern Eurasia depend mainly upon the reindeer to draw them from place to place over vast barren tracts of snow and ice.   In many arid lands the camel, an animal well adapted to the desert environment, is the most practicable carrier (Fig. 279).   The horse is widely used in southwest Asia, especially Arabia, central Asia, western Eurasia, and in North America.   In various Andean countries the llama and donkey are used in areas of rugged relief and in some regions successfully compete with the rail-

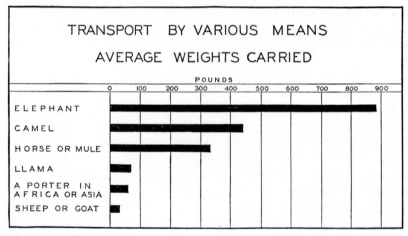

FIG. 279.   The approximate weights carried by various means of transport.

ways that have been constructed.   In Burma and Siam the elephant is trained not only to carry passengers and cargo, but also to pile teak logs in the monsoon forests.

Animals are also utilized to drag vehicles and are thereby capable of transporting larger loads than they can carry.   Thus a horse that is capable of carrying 300 pounds can draw a wagon load of more than 1 ton over a hard-surface road, and a team of horses can draw from 8 to 10 tons on a sled over a compacted, snow-covered surface. An African or Asiatic porter, capable of carrying from 55 to 66 pounds, can ordinarily push 250 pounds of goods in a wheelbarrow.

Human and Animal Carriers versus Improved Methods of Transportation.   The cost of transportation by primitive methods is never cheap, as is indicated in a comparative analysis of human transport and the modern freight train.   For example, a modern locomotive, hauling a train at the rate of 40 miles an hour, can do the work of more than

65,000 coolies transporting goods in wheelbarrows. By reason of the low cost at which railways transport commodities from place to place, they have become the most important carriers for long-distance transportation by land. Every continent, with the exception of Africa, has now at least one railway line across it.

Motor vehicles are competing to an ever-increasing extent with the railroads, especially for rapid, short-distance transportation. Still more rapid transport is by airplane, the newest and fastest mode of carriage. This method is employed mainly for the rapid transport of mail, articles of high value in small bulk, or passengers who find the saving in time worth the relatively higher rates that are charged.

As the railways are the principal means of carrying passengers and commodities long distances by land, so the modern steamship is the major carrier of people and goods over the ocean highways. The modern steamship, however, transports a much larger cargo than an average freight train, the proportion being approximately 5 to 1; and the cost per ton-mile of ocean transportation is lower than that of either the railway or the highway.

Ocean Transportation

The fact that water covers approximately three-fourths of the surface of the earth is of major significance in the study of transportation. The vast expanses of connected ocean have made possible permanent communication at regular intervals between widely separated regions. Sea lanes or definite routes of travel have been established, and these, unlike roads, railroads, and canals, cost nothing to maintain. Long-distance transportation of economic goods and people is therefore achieved at a relatively low rate.

Development of Ocean Transportation. Although the oceans have long been used in transporting commodities and people, it was not until the beginning of the fifteenth century that the oceans were widely navigated, in part because of the discoveries of nautical instruments and the improvement of sailing vessels and in part by reason of the urgent desire to obtain the commercial products of distant lands. Prior to the fifteenth century, water transportation was confined mainly to rivers, coastal areas, and inclosed shallow embayments. It was well developed in the quiet waters of the Mediterranean, where Genoese, Phœnicians, and Carthaginians were guided by numerous promontories and found shelter in the many embayments of that region. It was only logical that Spain and Portugal, located at the junction of the Mediterranean Sea and the open Atlantic, should be the first in the development of ocean navigation, especially at a time when the Turks took possession of the eastern portals of the Mediterranean Basin.

Although the last four centuries have witnessed an ever-widening utilization of ocean lanes, it was not until the last century that the large oceangoing vessels were developed. The small sailing vessel has given way to the large coal- and oil-consuming steamer. Ships have increased so much in size that a modern tramp steamer carries approximately as much as is hauled by 200 railroad cars. There has also been an increasing production of large passenger liners, because of (1) their ability to maintain high speed in rough weather, (2) greater steadiness and comfort to passengers, (3) better and more spacious passenger accommodations, and (4) the business attraction incident to having the largest, fastest, and finest vessels.[1]

Liners and Tramps. A ship that plies regularly between foreign ports is called a liner. It usually carries approximately the same kinds of products from time to time, and it is therefore possible to adapt the type of the vessel to the nature of the trade. This results in specialization of service. Although liners carry a great variety of goods, they normally tend to transport commodities that are relatively high in value and for which it is desirable to have regular, speedy service. Liners therefore, because of their advantage of speed and regularity, have attracted a large percentage of the world's shipping; and normally more than 80 per cent of the shipping space for cargoes is available in liners.[2]

The drab general cargo ships, on the other hand, are the tramps. They usually carry goods that do not require speed. Lacking in fixed routes or regular sailing schedules, tramps go from port to port wherever cargoes are offered at sufficiently attractive rates. Sometimes tramp vessels are out several years before they return with cargoes to the home port. These vessels carry commodities that are comparatively great in bulk and low in value, especially timber, ores, coal, fiber, and grain.

Periods of warfare greatly interfere with the liner and tramp traffic of the world. Thus, during the first and second world wars, many ships were forced to depart from regular schedules and routes. The convoy system was often used by belligerent nations. British and

[1] *Scientific American*, S. 76, 1913, p. 166.
[2] E. S. Gregg, "Ocean Trade Routes," *Geographical Review*, Vol. 16, p. 295.

French warships and bombing planes would frequently accompany the cargo vessels. Yet great numbers of unprotected vessels were sunk by submarines, mines, and enemy aircraft.

Ports and Coaling Stations. The increase in number and size of steamships has been matched by a development of coaling stations and ports. Large ships require deep, spacious harbors. Most of the successful ocean ports have (1) an approach channel of ample dimensions, (2) a good harbor, (3) a large consuming and producing hinterland affording trade and traffic possibilities, (4) freight-handling machinery and large warehouse space, and (5) low port charges.

Of the various physical factors favoring the development of a good port, the harbor is one of the most noteworthy. It should not only have sufficient depth for the largest of oceangoing vessels, but it must also be protected from destructive winds and waves. A large anchorage, straight channel, and freedom from ice, fog, and shifting sand are other characteristics of a good harbor.

Fueling stations are necessary on the long ocean lanes of the world. Bunker fuel is bulky, and if a ship is compelled to go long distances without refueling a large amount of space must be given to the fuel—space that could otherwise be used for profitable cargo. These stations are most numerous in the northern hemisphere, especially in the North Atlantic. It has been estimated that approximately 80 per cent of the coaling stations of the world serve the North Atlantic and Mediterranean trade routes. Coal for these stations is obtained mainly from the British Isles (Cardiff), Germany, and eastern United States.

Increasing Use of Oil as Fuel. Oil is being used on the larger oceangoing vessels to an ever-increasing extent, and in 1930 approximately one-fourth of the large ships were consuming oil as a source of power. Among the various reasons for this relatively greater increase of oil, mainly at the expense of coal, as a source of power are: (1) less fuel space required per horsepower, (2) greater ease of loading oil, (3) saving in boiler upkeep, and (4) greater cruising radius. On some of the larger ships the crew has been reduced by more than 200 men when a change has been made from coal to oil as a source of power. Moreover, the extra space available (if oil is substituted for coal) makes it possible for large ships to carry additional profitable cargoes of 4,000 or 5,000 tons, especially if these ships are compelled to go long distances without refueling.

Ocean Trade Routes. Although the oceans cover approximately three-fourths of the surface of the earth, they are crossed only in certain places by the major routes of commerce. This concentration of traffic along well-defined lanes is due to several factors: (1) In connecting commercial regions, ocean routes follow the shortest lane, which, owing to the sphericity of the earth, is the arc of a great circle. (2) The presence of land makes it necessary at certain places to depart from the great circle route. (3) Ocean currents and winds influence the direction of the route, and especially of sailing vessels. (4) On long ocean lanes coaling stations further modify the course of the route.

Of all the oceans the North Atlantic has the greatest amount of traffic. Studies made by the U. S. Department of Commerce disclose the fact that approximately half the shipping of the world is engaged regularly in the North Atlantic. During normal times about two-thirds of the foreign trade of the United States passes over the Atlantic (Fig. 280).[3] This ocean contains approximately half the total number of coaling stations in the world, fuel for bunkerage purposes being available in large quantities on both the North American and European sides of this ocean. Here numerous steamship routes cross and recross one another, but there is a tendency of concentration of traffic along one major route, the North Atlantic.

NORTH ATLANTIC TRADE ROUTE. Just as the North Atlantic is the busiest ocean, so the North Atlantic trade route is the chief ocean highway. This route serves the two leading commercial regions of the world—eastern North America and western Europe. From numerous ports along the Atlantic Coast of the United States and Canada ocean lines converge into this major route, which, owing to the sphericity of the earth, follows as closely as possible the arc of a great circle. In following this course it passes close to Newfoundland and then curves northward and eastward across the Atlantic, and on the European side of the ocean splits into separate units which extend like gaping fingers to the various ports of western Europe (Fig. 280). Chief among these ports in the trade with the United States are those located in the United Kingdom and between Le Havre and Hamburg on the continent.

From the colonial period to the present day the traffic over this route has consisted mainly of raw materials eastbound and manufactures and passengers westbound. During the early period of American history large quantities of tobacco, wood products, and furs were exported to Europe. The traffic between tidewater Virginia and England was indeed so unbalanced that considerable ballast was necessary

[3] A. L. Crecher, *Ocean Routes in United States Foreign Trade,* Commerce Reports, December 23, 1929, p. 708.

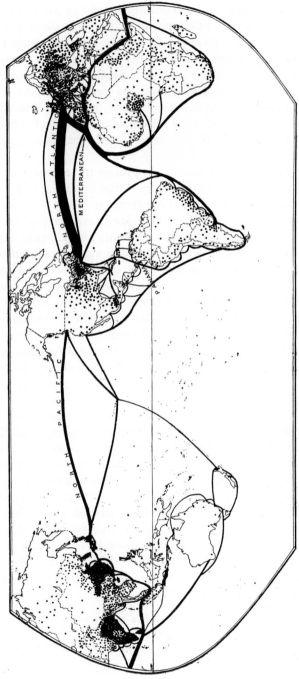

Fig. 280. Major trade routes and the world's population. Thickness of line drawn in proportion to volume of trade. Note that the important trade routes such as the North Atlantic, the Mediterranean, and the North Pacific connect the large population areas. Each dot represents 500,000 people.

on the westward voyage, and this consisted chiefly of stone and brick. Such trade accounts for the development of the large stone and brick mansions in tidewater Virginia even during the first half of the seventeenth century. Today the volume of eastbound traffic is swelled to immense proportions by items such as Canadian wheat, paper, and pulpwood, as well as cotton, food, and machinery from the United States. This unbalanced traffic, however, is gradually disappearing with the increasing exportation of manufactured products from the United States and the relative decrease of crude materials, especially cotton.

THE MEDITERRANEAN TRADE ROUTE. As a major trade route, the Mediterranean ranks second only to the North Atlantic in value and volume of traffic that passes over it. This route connects North Atlantic lands with the Orient, and extends through the Mediterranean Sea, the Suez Canal, and the Red Sea. It therefore touches lands which contrast strikingly in their economic activities, and a variety of commercial products are exchanged on various parts of this route. Thus the eastern basin of the Mediterranean region trades with the western basin, and this whole region in turn trades with North Atlantic lands and the Orient. In addition, there is a large amount of through traffic between the Orient and North Atlantic countries, especially western Europe. Important commercial products carried in this trade include silk, rubber, tea, jute, sugar, and tin westbound, and a great variety of manufactured goods, especially cotton goods and machinery, moving in the opposite direction.

Before the completion of the Suez Canal in 1869, commodities entering the ocean trade between North Atlantic countries and the Orient were carried in sailing vessels around the Cape of Good Hope, or had to be transported by land across southwestern Asia or northeastern Africa. Such commerce was small in comparison with that passing through the Suez Canal at the present time.[4] With the opening of the canal, and especially with the development of vessels receiving their power from coal and oil, the time required for this journey has been reduced greatly. The saving in distance to be traveled is strikingly indicated by the fact that the distance between New York and Calcutta, India, is 2,500 miles shorter by way of the Suez Canal than around the southern tip of Africa.[5]

---

[4] Two thousand to six thousand vessels with a total capacity of 10 to 30 million tons passed through this canal each year.

[5] Since 1935 the annual amount of goods passing through the Suez Canal has fluctuated between 7 and 35 million tons.

THE SOUTH AFRICAN ROUTE. It was mainly hope of reaching the Orient by means of a route around Africa which led the intrepid Portuguese explorers and navigators to advance farther and farther southward along the west coast of Africa during the fifteenth century until Vasco da Gama finally passed the Cape of Good Hope and reached India in 1497. From that time until the opening of the Suez Canal the South African route was the chief ocean lane connecting countries bordering the North Atlantic with the Orient. At present a large share of the shipping on this route calls at Durban for coal and at Cape Town, the most important center of the South African trade. The greatest volume of traffic over this South African route is carried by a number of freight steamers plying between northwestern Europe and Australia. Although passenger and mail steamers take the Mediterranean route from northwestern Europe to Australia, the distance saved as compared with the South African route (1,000 miles) is not sufficient to cause freight steamers to abandon the latter route.

THE PACIFIC ROUTES. During the last century the ocean trade over the Pacific has been increasing rapidly. The gold rush to California in the middle of the last century; the acquisition by the United States of Alaska, the Hawaiian Islands, and the Philippines; the opening of the Panama Canal and World War II—these are among the outstanding events that have played a conspicuous role in the development of Pacific trade. Since the opening of Japanese ports to foreign commerce, the trade of the United States with that country has increased rapidly. Equally striking has been the development of our trade with the Philippine Islands.

One of the striking features of our west coast trade with eastern Asia is the preponderance of goods moving to Asia. In this trade the tonnage westbound was three to four times as large as the eastbound tonnage. This unbalanced traffic was the result of our large exports of bulky commodities and our imports of commodities that are relatively small in bulk and high in value—a condition characteristic also of our trade with western Europe. In 1937 the United States exported more than 558,000,000 pounds of raw cotton to Japan, whereas she imported only 50,000,000 pounds of silk. Our trade with China indicates the same type of unbalanced traffic. Chief among our normal exports to China are kerosene, tobacco leaf, and raw cotton; silk is our leading import from China.

Although the vast expanses of the Pacific are crossed in a number of places by ocean lanes, the trade between the west coast of the

United States follows mainly two ocean trunk lines.   One passes westward from the Puget Sound region and San Francisco and follows as
closely as possible the great-circle route.   It therefore swerves to the
northward toward the Aleutian Islands.   The other route extends southward to the Hawaiian Islands, then westward to eastern Asia.   It is
approximately 700 miles longer than the direct route between such
ports as San Francisco and Manila, but it affords possibilities of handling
passengers, mail, and cargoes for the Hawaiian Islands.

SOUTH AMERICAN ROUTES.   Before the completion of the Panama
Canal, large quantities of goods were taken around the southern tip
of South America.   At present this traffic is small in comparison with
that of the east and west coasts.[6]   "Sailing vessels may continue to sail
around the Horn between Atlantic and Pacific ports, for the calms of
Panama Bay discourage their use of the Panama Canal, but they will
find greater difficulty in competing against their self-propelled rivals."[7]

Of all South American traffic, that of the east coast is most important.   Here the chief termini include the coffee-exporting ports of
southeastern Brazil and the grain-, hide-, meat-, and quebracho-ex-
porting ports of the River Plate lands.   "Various ships ply back and
forth between Europe and Brazil and the mouth of the Plata, and
some also between the United States and those sections of South America; but a considerable share of the imports of hides, wool, coffee, and
rubber from eastern South America has been brought to the United
States in vessels that take cargoes from Europe to South America, and
load there for the United States, where cargo for Europe is readily
obtained.   This is but one of the many triangular routes followed by
ocean shipping; it is, however, one of the most important."[8]

THE PANAMA CANAL.   Since the opening of the Panama Canal in
1915 it has been used to an increasing extent by oceangoing vessels
(Fig. 281).   In many of the trades served by the Panama Canal the
saving of distance, and hence of time, by the use of the canal is so
great that shipping cannot afford to take any other route.   The greatest possible distances that can be saved by using this waterway include
voyages between points on opposite sides of the Isthmus of Panama,
or in general between Atlantic and Pacific ports of countries near the
canal.   Thus the distance between Cristobal and Balboa is 10,500
nautical miles by way of the Strait of Magellan, but only 44 miles by

[6] E. S. Gregg, "Ocean Trade Routes," *Geographical Review*, Vol. 16, p. 293.

[7] Reprinted by permission from *Principles of Ocean Transportation*, by E. R.
Johnson and G. G. Huebner, D. Appleton & Co., 1920, pp. 62, 63.

[8] *Op. cit.*, p. 62.

way of the canal. For voyages between New York and San Francisco the canal reduces the distance by 7,873 miles.

Between some centers the distance saved as a result of choosing the
Panama Canal instead of the Suez is noteworthy, the distance being
3,357 miles shorter from New York to Yokohama via the former
route. Steamers loading in the United States with full cargoes for
eastern Asia normally proceed to their destination by the shorter

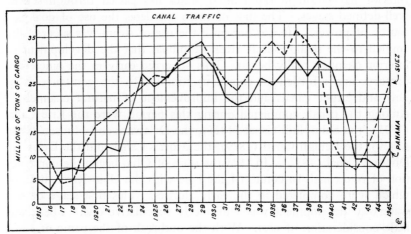

Fig. 281. The volume of traffic that passes through the Suez and Panama canals.
Note the depression slump that followed 1929, reaching a low in 1932, and a
second slump caused by the interruption of trade by World War II.

route, and the return voyage is governed by cargo offerings. A
steamer leaving New York harbor via the Panama Canal for Yokohama might find it necessary to continue to Singapore or Batavia for
a cargo consigned for either Europe or the United States, in which
event the return voyage would be by way of the Suez Canal.

Inland Waterways

Early Transportation by Water. Inland waterway transportation
has been an important factor in the lives of human beings since the
beginning of historic time. Even artificial waterways (canals) were
constructed many centuries before the time of Christ. The large rivers
of the Orient have long provided access to inland regions, and some
of them even at present are the chief highways of the countries
through which they flow. In the early history of the United States

our colonists used the natural waterways as practically their only means of communication with the interior. By way of the rivers, tobacco reached the seaboard in the area of tidewater Virginia, and by way of the Mississippi and its tributaries large quantities of corn, lard, bacon, whiskey, and other "western produce" were sent to the southern plantations and to New Orleans for export.

Stages of Inland Waterway Transportation in the United States. Interior navigation in the United States has passed through several well-defined stages. The first of these antedates the use of coal as a source of power. "It was not until the use of steam was successfully applied to the shallow-draft river steamboat that the development of interior channels really began. This occurred early in the nineteenth century, and afforded an enormous stimulus to the construction of new and larger canals and the improvement of natural channels." [9] Among the canals completed during this period were the Erie Canal (1825), the Schuylkill Canal (1825), the Delaware and Hudson Canal (1829), the Lehigh Canal (1829), the Morris Canal, and the Delaware Division Canal (1832). In 1825 the state of Ohio began the construction of two canals to connect Lake Erie with the Ohio River, both of which were completed in the early thirties. This first stage of our waterway development was a distinctly speculative one. There was little consideration of cost. With the outbreak of the panic of 1837, this marked movement of canal building received a severe blow, and by 1840 it came practically to an end.

In addition to the economic status of the country, there were various physical causes for the decline of river and canal transportation: (1) the channels of most of the rivers were crooked, shallow, and shifting; (2) the depth of water varies much from place to place and even from time to time; (3) the use of these waterways forced freight to take long, roundabout courses; and (4) the waterways were closed to navigation because of cold winters.

The second period in the history of interior navigation coincides with the period of first marked development of railways, and these expanded at a rapid rate after the construction of the first section of the Baltimore and Ohio in 1830. During the next ten years approximately 3,000 miles of railroad line (double track) had been laid, and by 1880 the mileage had increased to 93,300. These railways entered into vigorous competition with the rivers and canals. Indeed, the

[9] Reprinted by permission from "Natural Waterways in the United States," by W. W. Harts, *Annual Report of the Smithsonian Institution*, 1916, p. 545.

period during which our inland water routes were at their lowest ebb in the tide of our commercial transport is the time of the intensive development of railway transportation and facilities. The ability of the railway to move traffic directly between origin and destination without breaking bulk is an advantage which must be recognized. As long as no effective coordination existed between rail and water routes, it was natural for inland shippers to prefer the rail routes, even where the rates were more favorable by the water.

The third period in the history of interior waterways began during the latter part of the nineteenth century, "when the industrial development of the areas adjacent to streams and the increase in population had provided more than sufficient commerce for the existing railways." [10] One of the most important steps taken in the revival of water transportation was the passage of the transportation act of 1920. Section 500 of that act declared it "to be the policy of Congress to promote, encourage, and develop water transportation, service, and facilities in connection with the commerce of the United States, and to foster and preserve in full vigor both rail and water transportation."

Inland Waterway Divisions of the United States. From the standpoint of inland waterway transportation, four major divisions may be recognized within the United States. The most significant of these is the lake system along our northern border. The other three divisions practically coincide with (1) the Atlantic coastal plain, (2) the Mississippi River Basin, and (3) the Pacific lowlands. Both the Atlantic and Pacific lowlands contain few large rivers. In the central part of the country, however, the Mississippi and its tributaries constitute a large system for inland navigation.

Lake System of Interior Waterways. Along our northern border the Great Lakes constitute the most important system of interior natural waterways of this country or of the world. No other inland waterway carries as much traffic as the Great Lakes—188,000,000 tons in 1944. The great commercial importance of these lakes is due to a number of factors: (1) the east-west extent of the lakes, giving cheap transportation along the direction of greatest movement of commodities in the United States; (2) the excellent location with respect to abundant reserves of iron ore, coal, and timber, as well as the spring-wheat lands of the United States and Canada; and (3) the low cost of transportation on the lakes mainly because of deep natural channels and their great extent, together with an excellent adaptation

[10] *Op. cit.,* p. 546.

of shipping facilities to meet the needs of these bulky and heavy commodities.

Located between America's largest reserves of high-grade coal and iron ore, the Great Lakes constitute an important highway in the transportation of these commodities. Approximately four-fifths of all the traffic through the Sault Sainte Marie consists of iron eastbound and coal westbound, the other important items in lake traffic being grain, lumber, and flour.

The St. Lawrence Waterway. The St. Lawrence River is an important channel in the movement of Canadian and United States grain. But owing to a number of rapids in the upper part of the river, it was necessary to construct six canals each with a depth of 14 feet, thereby providing transportation around the rapids for vessels drawing approximately 13 feet or less of water (Fig. 282). Further deepening of the St. Lawrence has been considered by the governments of the United States and Canada, but no definite plan of progress has been reached.

It has been suggested that, although the project—making lake ports open to moderate-size ocean-going vessels—will cost approximately $250,000,000, it will be to the advantage of the wheat growers of the United States and Canada, and that it will convert lake ports into ocean ports. In addition, hydroelectric-power development will be facilitated. On the other hand, there are several objections to the deepening of this river: (1) The St. Lawrence, because of its location in an area of low winter temperatures, is closed for five months of the year. (2) Frequent fogs at the mouth of the river constitute a source of danger to shipping. (3) Although there will be an eastbound traffic in grain there will be but little return cargo. Moreover, local opposition to this project has been experienced in both Montreal and New York. Montreal, located at the head of navigation for oceangoing vessels, is favored by the necessity for a break in cargoes at that point. New York claims that she would lose much of the trade which otherwise reaches her by rail and the Erie Canal.

The Mississippi River System. Second in importance to the Great Lakes, the Mississippi River system of waterways serves a large area, and it has long been the route by which an extensive traffic from the central West found its way to the seaboard. Indeed, the Mississippi, with its several important tributaries, during the early years of the nineteenth century supplied the only means of moving freight in commercial quantities between the eastern seaboard and the cental West, and for many years it constituted the main trunk-line transportation route west of the Alleghenies for both freight and passengers. Although river-borne traffic declined during the early part of this century, it is now increasing. In 1944, the river-borne freight of the United States exceeded 450,000,000 tons and that of the Mississippi River exceeded 44,000,000 tons.

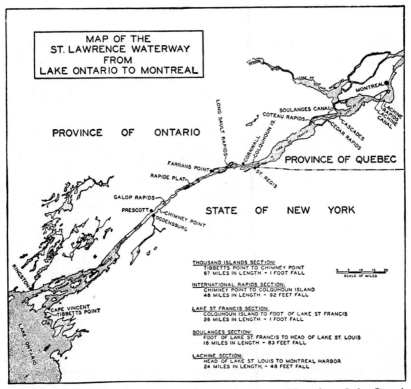

FIG. 282. Map showing five sections of the St. Lawrence River from Lake Ontario to Montreal, with the rapids, canals, and amount of fall in each section. (Based on map drawn by Corps of U. S. Army Engineers and U. S. Bureau of Railway Economics.)

The Ohio River. Of all the members of the Mississippi River system, the Ohio River is most important. This river, formed by the confluence of the Allegheny and Monongahela rivers at Pittsburgh, flows southwestward and empties into the Mississippi at Cairo, Illinois. In its original condition, it was obstructed for navigation not only by the falls at Louisville, but also by snags, rocks, and bars in various parts of its course. The minimum depth over bars at extreme low water was approximately 1 foot in the upper section and 2 feet in the lower part. It was therefore necessary to deepen the channel before modern barge service could be realized.

Various projects have marked the development of this channel until at present the navigable depth of the river is 9 feet. Such depth has been realized by means of constructing 50 low-lift dams, each with a lock chamber 110 feet wide.

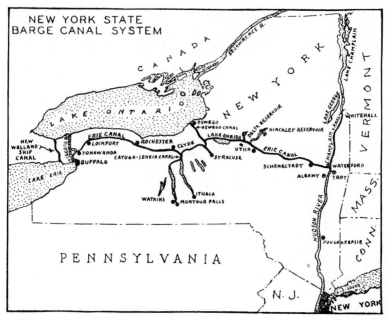

Fig. 283. Map showing New York State Barge Canal system. (According to the New York State Survey and Engineer and the Bureau of Railway Economics.)

The Ohio River system drains a region rich in natural resources. Near the river banks are enormous deposits of minerals, such as coal, fire clay, limestone, sand, and gravel. The traffic on the Ohio River consists mainly of low-priced, bulky commodities, such as sand, gravel, coal, and iron and steel products.

The Erie Canal. The most important waterway connecting the Atlantic slope with the interior of the country is the Erie Canal (Fig. 283). It extends from Waterford, New York, to Buffalo on Lake Erie. Together with the Hudson River it provides a through route from the Atlantic to the Great Lakes or the New York Barge Canal. For nearly a half century after its completion in 1825 it constituted the most important single route of trade between the Atlantic seaboard and the area west of the Appalachian Highlands. This canal practically revolutionized the carrying business, and in time the cost of transportation was reduced to one-tenth the former figure. Since its completion in 1825 the Erie Canal has been enlarged three times, and at present it has a 12-foot channel, but it is carrying only 10 to 15 per cent of its traffic capacity.

Economic Aspects of Inland Water Transportation. Inland waterways, though a worthwhile adjunct of the transportation facilities of the nation, are often developed at a tremendous cost.[11] In fact, even the total cost of enlarging the Erie Canal was estimated at approximately $330,000 per mile, whereas the capitalization of an average railway in the United States is less than $60,000 per mile.[12] In spite of comparatively high cost of construction, however, the waterways provide cheap transportation, and this mainly because of financial aid from the federal government or the state in the construction and maintenance of the channel. The burden therefore is carried by the taxpayer.

Railway Transportation

Importance of Railways. The modern railway constitutes the most important means of long-distance transportation on land. It has made possible the modern city and the geographical division of labor (Fig. 284). It constitutes the backbone of the transportation system of all the leading industrial nations of the world, and this mainly because of the ability of extending railway lines to all parts of a country, even into mountainous regions, and because of the low *real cost* of transportation by rail. In addition, the railway has the advantages of speed, capacity, regularity, and dependability of service.

Railway Location. In choosing the location of a railway, physical as well as economic factors must be considered. Chief among the physical factors are grades, curves, and distance. It is a well-recognized fact that steep grades have a marked effect upon operating costs. Where railroad lines are forced to ascend steep slopes a "pusher" service is often necessary. In planning the location of railway lines, it is the objective of the engineer to avoid grades wherever possible, and therefore the lowland stretches are often utilized. In areas of rugged relief the railway route is sometimes forced to make sharp

[11] This sometimes for advancement for pork-barrel politicians.
[12] H. G. Moulton, "Economic Aspects of Water Transportation," *Journal of Geography*, Vol. 15, p. 78.

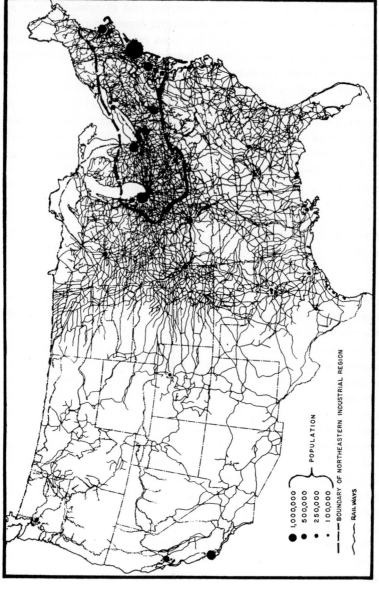

FIG. 284. Map showing railways, chief metropolitan districts (according to McKenzie), and limits of the northeastern industrial region.

curves. Although such curves generally affect the operating cost of a railway less than grades, they nevertheless constitute an important factor, mainly by decreasing speed and trainload, by increasing wear and tear of both rail and rolling stock, and by increasing accidents. In any given region the element of distance within reasonable limits is probably less important than the grades or curves, because cost of shipment does not increase in proportion to mileage.

Development of Railways. In the history of mankind, railway transportation is a recent development. It began in the United States and England about a century ago. In fact, by the end of 1830 the United States had only 23 miles of railway line.[13] Beginning slowly, railways have spread over much of the earth's surface until in 1939 there were almost 800,000 miles of railway line—a distance thirty-three times the circumference of the earth. The magnitude of this type of transportation is further reflected in the fact that the railways of the world carry almost 4 billion metric tons of freight and about 10 billion passengers a year.

The early railway development was marked by considerable hesitancy. By 1840, the railway mileage had not reached 4,740 miles. The figures for the United States—the leading country in railway mileage—are illuminating. Here the total, which in 1840 was only 2,818 miles, and which even in 1860, twenty years later, amounted to only 30,622 miles, had risen in 1900 to 193,300 miles. Several factors account for this early hesitancy in railway development. One factor was the belief that railways could not compete with the waterways but should be supplemental to them. In fact, a necessary section of what is now the main line of the Pennsylvania Railroad was built originally, as a means of hauling canal boats over the Allegheny Mountains, and the earliest railroads in the Middle West were mainly short lines connecting with the waterways. Moreover, in early days the railroads were not properly equipped to handle freight. For example, the Baltimore and Ohio in 1831 carried 81,905 passengers and only 593 tons of freight. As the era of railroad building proceeded, however, it became apparent that the railroad had important advantages in speed and in ability to go where the steamboat could not go.[14]

The marked development of railways in recent decades was associated with a realization of certain advantages of this type of trans-

[13] E. R. Johnson and T. W. Van Metre, *Principles of Railroad Transportation,* D. Appleton & Co., 1920, p. 26.

[14] F. H. Farwell, "Early Transportation by Water," *Congressional Record,* p. 1038.

portation, with its speed, capacity, regularity of service and dependability. In addition it was found (1) that an increase in traffic does not involve a corresponding increase in the cost of transportation, and (2) that cost does not increase in proportion to mileage.[15] Large profits were therefore realized by extending lines and by obtaining additional traffic. An increase in traffic was often obtained by undercutting the rates of competing lines. Indeed, during the last quarter of the nineteenth century veritable rate wars were waged among various of the railway lines in the United States. Railways even advanced their rates in areas where competition was lacking so that they could secure competitive traffic—an example of local discrimination.[16] It therefore became necessary to establish the Interstate Commerce Commission, which was given the power to establish such level of rates as would enable the railroads to earn a fair return on their property.[17]

Highway and Air Transportation

After the introduction of the automobile, the construction of all-weather highways proceeded rapidly. Thus today more than 30,000,-000 passenger cars and motor trucks are being used in the United States to carry passengers and freight in competition with other types of transportation facilities. In 1945, more than 108,000,000 tons of revenue freight were carried by inter-city motor vehicles and 131,-000,000 passengers were carried by inter-city motor carriers. These data leave out of consideration the local transportation of many million tons of freight and of hundreds of millions of passengers.

Transportation by air is increasing very rapidly. As late as 1926, transportation of goods and passengers by the United States systems of air lines was relatively unimportant. Twenty years later, 1946, the air lines of the United States carried 12,591,251 passengers more than 6 billion passenger-miles. In addition they carried 64 million ton-miles of mail and large quantities of freight and express.

From the United States important air routes have been extended through the West Indies and along the greater part of coastal South America. Still other routes cross the Pacific by way of the Hawaiian Islands. One of the Pacific routes that is under United States control

[15] P. Vidal de la Blache, *Principles of Human Geography*, Henry Holt & Co., 1926, p. 395.

[16] E. Jones, *Principles of Railway Transportation*, The Macmillan Co., 1925, p. 93.

[17] *Op. cit.*, p. 275.

connects Hawaii with the Philippines and coastal China; another extends from Hawaii to Samoa and New Zealand. Air transport has also been developed between American and European centers. When World War II started in Europe in 1939 approximately 10,000 persons were anxious to use the Pan American Airways in order to reach their native countries. The Pan American Airways, however, has centered much attention on the carrying of mail, and at England's request the service of this company was also extended to Bermuda because shipping was called off at that point.

This remarkable development of aviation within recent years has been due largely to improvements in the comforts, speed, and safety of air travel. Huge transport planes have been constructed, which have comforts that rival the best trains and steamers. On the airways of the United States rotating electric beacons have been placed at 10- to 15-mile intervals. The radio range beacons give directional guidance while the radar is used to determine the exact location of the plane, its altitude above the surface, and its proximity to other objects. Weather broadcasting stations give information with respect to atmospheric conditions.

FUNDAMENTAL AND BASIC FACTORS UNDERLYING FOREIGN TRADE

International trade is the result of a variety of factors, some of which are geographic in character, others non-geographic. From an economic standpoint, a nation specializes in the production or exchange of those goods in which it has a comparative advantage. That is, a nation specializes in producing those commodities whose cost of production is less than in other countries, and if the cost is less for several lines of commodities specialization tends to take place in those lines which show the greatest cost differential. But this difference in cost is based on certain fundamental factors, among which are differences in soils, in climate, in topography, and in forest and mineral resources. Even such non-geographical factors as stage of economic development and racial characteristics play an important part.

Differences in Natural Environment. Climatic differences are fundamental to trade, and the basic characteristic of this factor is reflected also in its influence on both the vegetation and soil. It is mainly because of climate that the low latitudes produce tropical fruits; Brazil, coffee; Ceylon, tea; and the East Indies, rubber.

The relief of the land is closely related to other factors of the environment. High altitudes give tropical peoples environmental conditions similar to those of the temperate zone. In addition, the relief of the land affects the flow of international trade. Thus high mountains often act as barriers to the free flow of goods, whereas the extensive plain facilitates the interdependence of peoples.

The study of natural resources is obviously fundamental to an understanding of the basic facts of foreign trade. Abundant reserves of high-grade coking coal and iron ore have given some areas a comparative advantage in the production of iron and steel, and the plentiful supply of fuel and power has been a basic factor in the industrial growth of the United States and countries of western Europe. The United States produces more iron, copper, petroleum, coal, and cotton —basic raw materials needed in modern manufacturing—than any other nation. Since our country produces more than it needs for home consumption, foreign trade is essential to our economic progress.

The differences between natural resources of various countries are likely to become increasingly important in the future development of international trade. Today, the trend of world trade is along the parallels of latitude. In other words, it flows chiefly from east to west and to a lesser extent from north to south. This is because today, except for the results of wars and their aftermaths, foreign trade is still largely the result of differences between the stages of development of various countries and continents in the temperate zone. But the more the process of leveling and assimilation proceeds, the more prominent will become the differences in natural resources and climatic conditions. These natural elements tend to influence trade to move between different zones—that is, north and south. Long after we have ceased shipping wheat to Liverpool and Rotterdam, we shall still be getting coffee from Brazil, hides from Argentina, sugar from Cuba, and wool from South Africa. The quantity of this country's imports from Europe has not grown as rapidly during the last fifty years as the imports of tropical products, like cacao, coffee, fibers, rubber, olive oil, rice, sugar, and tea.

Differences in Stage of Economic Development. Every young and developing nation passes through at least three stages of evolution. At first it has to rely upon the importation of machinery and other manufactured goods for the development of its natural resources. Since it is unable to pay for this foreign capital brought in on credit for the exploitation of its resources, it becomes indebted to other countries by an amount approximately as large as the excess of imports over exports. As the development of the land proceeds and increasing quantities of raw materials are exported, the country gradually gains a position where it is able to pay, in the form of commodities, not only for its exports, but also interest on foreign obligations. Its production has increased at a more rapid rate than the population, and the visible exports may exceed the imports by a considerable margin.[18] The third stage is that already reached by the great manufacturing nations of Europe. In this stage of development the country is relatively densely populated, and its imports may exceed its exports. But then invisible exports pay for the additional commodities imported. In other words, the excess of imports over exports represents largely the payment of interest on capital invested in foreign countries.

The relative conditions of industrial development in different countries have a marked effect upon foreign trade. China possesses a large, diverse, geographical base and contains advantages in natural resources superior in some respects to those of nations in western Europe, yet she is not so far developed industrially as the western world, and her per capita foreign trade is lower than that of any other country listed in the *Commerce Yearbook of the United States*. Many factors account for her retarded industrial growth, among which are: (1) long isolation from important centers of civilization, (2) the importance of the family rather than the individual as the working industrial unit, (3) the meager development of transportation, (4) the frequent political disturbances, and (5) the paucity of local capital. Similar conditions retard industrial development also in other lands.

Secondary Factors Influencing International Trade. A number of secondary factors influence the volume and direction of international trade. The wealth of a nation has much to do with the nature and volume of its imports. Thus rubber, sugar, coffee, silk, liquor, newspaper print, cacao, and furs are all listed among our major imports. Yet in a country of poor people the per capita consumption of most of these products would be small, especially if they had to be imported.

Tariffs. High tariffs tend to retard the flow of commodities between countries, and differential tariffs may help to determine the sources of imports. Duties may be placed high enough on some commodities to stop completely their importation. Such duties may be levied in order to protect industrial and agricultural products against

---

[18] There are not only visible but also invisible exports. The invisible items of foreign trade include services of a merchant marine, of banks or insurance companies, services to tourists, and interest payment on foreign loans.

foreign competition and to increase the use of labor at home. Regardless of the merits of high tariffs, it is an accepted fact that they retard the international flow of goods.

Foreign Investments. Wealthy countries have billions of dollars invested in foreign countries. For many decades Great Britain led the world in this respect. She owned railroads, oil fields, mines, and plantations in many countries. In many cases this capital invested in foreign lands was producing goods to be shipped directly to the United Kingdom. Similarly Americans have billions of dollars invested in foreign lands. Some of this capital is used primarily for the purpose of supplying home industries with needed raw materials.

Other factors such as customs, manners, language, friendship, political alliances, and philosophies of government tend to influence the volume and direction of trade.

The future trend of international trade will depend upon many factors. Chief among these will be the degree of business recovery of Eurasia; the degree of friendship among nations; and the extent to which tariff barriers are maintained, raised, or lowered. Other factors such as war, war psychology, and nationalism will also play a role in international trade. However, assuming that the nations of the world can restore peace and friendship, the future of world trade will be determined largely by two basic factors: (1) differences in environmental conditions; and (2) differences in the stages of economic development.

REFERENCES

ARTHUR, PAUL, and others, *World Trade*, Office of International Affairs, May 1946.

BAYLEY, W. S., "Geographical Effects of the Proposed Great Lakes-St. Lawrence Waterway," *Economic Geography*, Vol. 1, 1925, pp. 236–246.

BLANCHARD, W. O., "The Panama Canal as Related to the Intercontinental Trade of South America," *Transactions of the Illinois Academy of Science*, Vol. 18, 1925, pp. 335–350.

BROWN, R. M., "Our Waterway Requirements," *Geographical Review*, Vol. 5, 1918, pp. 119–126.

CLAY, HENRY, "Britain's Declining Role in World Trade," *Foreign Affairs*, April 1946, pp. 411–428.

CLERK, SIR GEORGE, "The Geography of Post-War Air Routes," *Geographical Journal*, March 1944, pp. 89–100.

CORMIE, J. A., "The Hudson Bay Railroad," *Geographical Review*, Vol. 4, 1917, pp. 26–40.

ELY, EDWARD J., and others, *Summary of Foreign Commerce of the United States*, Bureau of Census, 1946.

GREGG, E. S., "Ocean Trade Routes," *Geographical Review*, Vol. 16, p. 295.

HARTS, W. W., "Natural Waterways in the United States," *Annual Report of the Smithsonian Institution*, 1916, pp. 545–578.

HUNTINGTON, E., "The Distribution of Domestic Animals," *Economic Geography*, Vol. 1, 1925, pp. 143–172.

JOHNSON, E. R., and T. W. VAN METRE, *Principles of Railway Transportation*, D. Appleton & Co., 1920.

JONES, E., *Principles of Railway Transportation*, The Macmillan Co., 1925, p. 93.

MOULTON, H. G., "Economic Aspects of Inland Waterway Transportation," *Journal of Geography*, Vol. 15, 1916, pp. 73–78, 112–116.

PARKINS, A. E., "A Comparison of the Trans-Appalachian Railroads," *Journal of Geography*, Vol. 9, 1911, pp. 113–118.

THAYER, W., "Transportation on the Great Lakes," *Annals of the American Academy of Political and Social Science*, Vol. 31, pp. 126–138.

WHITBECK, FLORENCE, "New York Barge Canal. Expectations and Realizations," *Economic Geography*, Vol. 4, 1928, pp. 196–206.

WHITBECK, R. H., "The St. Lawrence River and Its Part in the Making of Canada," *Bulletin of the American Geographical Society*, Vol. 47, 1915, pp. 584–593.

WOHL, PAUL, "Transportation in the Development of Soviet Policy," *Foreign Affairs*, April 1946, pp. 466–483.

Chapter 23

WORLD COMMERCIAL REGIONS AND

UNITED STATES FOREIGN TRADE

MAJOR REGIONS OF WORLD TRADE

Three regions—west-central Europe, eastern North America, and southeastern Asia—normally account for more than two-thirds of the international trade of the world. In the first two of these regions, agriculture, mining, and manufacture have reached a higher stage of development than in other parts of the world, and they contain well-rounded supplies of major resources for the development of modern industry. In addition, these areas have economic control over distant lands and resources from which they are able to obtain large quantities of raw materials that are lacking at home. The third region listed above is the most densely populated portion of the earth and although the per capita trade is relatively small its total trade is large.

West-Central Europe. The greatest hub of international trade is located in west-central Europe. A great variety and vast quantities of raw materials normally move into the major industrial areas of Great Britain, Germany, Belgium, France, Netherlands, and the Scandinavian countries. Iron ore, copper or copper ore, bauxite, manganese, tin, and a variety of other minerals are imported by some or all of these countries. In addition cotton, jute, rubber, copra, and palm oil together with many other vegetable raw materials are imported. In return, literally thousands of manufactured products are exported to all parts of the world. Although this region produced large quantities of foods, additional food supplies must be imported to help feed the millions of workers normally employed in factories or engaged in trade, services, and professions. Normally Europe takes more than one-half of our exports but since 1925 she has accounted for only 15 to 20 per cent of our imports (Figs. 285 and 286).

756

Eastern North America. The second most important hub of international trade is situated in eastern North America. This region, like

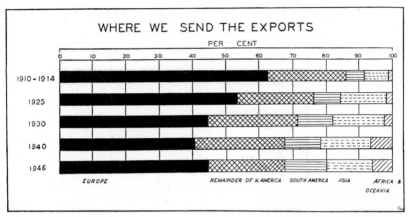

FIG. 285. Europe has been our best customer for export products from the time of the early colonization of America to the present.

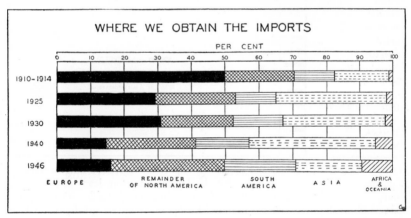

FIG. 286. The United States import trade by continents. Note that since 1925 we have obtained more goods from Asia than from any other continent except when that trade was disrupted by World War II. Rubber, oils, silk, tin, and a great variety of other minerals are obtained from Asia. As our industrialization has progressed, our imports from Europe have decreased.

that of west-central Europe is a great industrial area which imports needed raw materials from many parts of the world and exports finished or semi-finished products to a worldwide market. This area is also a large exporter of raw materials.

Normally in the trade between eastern North America and west-central Europe, the tonnage and value of eastbound goods greatly exceeds that of the westbound (Fig. 287). Thus in the trade between the United States and the United Kingdom our country normally

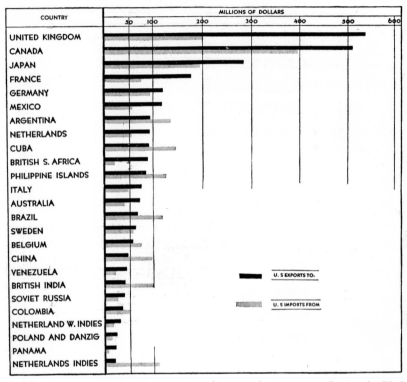

FIG. 287. Our chief markets and sources of imports in 1937, according to the U. S. Department of Commerce. Note that the United Kingdom leads in buying our goods. Yet Canada leads in the total of export and import trade with the United States. Normally our exports to most European countries greatly exceed the imports.

exports more than twice as many tons of goods as it imports; whereas in our trade with continental Europe our exports normally exceed our imports by more than 1,000,000 tons. In 1946 and 1947 most of the goods went east; little came west. In 1946 the United States sent to Europe 45,000,000 tons of goods valued at more than $4,000,000,000. We received in return less than 2,500,000 tons of goods valued at

$796,000,000.[1] In 1947, the volume of eastbound traffic from Canada
and the United States to hungry, cold, poorly clad, and poorly
equipped Europe was swelled to immense proportions by items such
as wheat, meat, cotton, coal, paper, wood pulp, and machinery;

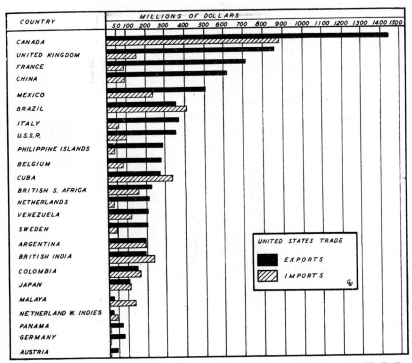

Fig. 288. Our major markets and suppliers in 1946, according to the U. S. Department of Commerce. Prior to World War II, the countries of western Europe
taken together had long been our chief source of imports and also led in buying
our goods. After World War II, poverty-stricken Europe could send us little,
but their need for U. S. goods was unprecedented. Our exports to Europe were
measured primarily by our capacity to produce the goods that they needed.

whereas Europe, struggling with post-war problems, sent us little in
return. This unhealthy trade condition is one of the tragic aftermaths of World War II (Fig. 288).

Southeastern Asia. This area, although densely populated, is still
able to sell vast quantities of products of the soil. Silk, rubber, coco-

[1] *Summary of Foreign Commerce of the United States,* U. S. Department of
Commerce, 1946, p. 4.

nut products, tea, sugar, hemp, jute, sisal, soybean oil, coffee, and timber represent some of the major exports of the region. Tin, manganese, chromium, gold, and other minerals are also exported. In return the region purchases almost every type of manufactured product that is made in the great industrial centers of the world.

MINOR REGIONS OF WORLD TRADE

Although more than two-thirds of the international trade is concentrated in the three regions already discussed, six other areas play an important role in international trade. They are (1) the borderlands of the Mediterranean Sea, (2) eastern Europe, (3) east-central South America, (4) the Caribbean region, (5) southeastern Australia and New Zealand, and (6) South Africa.

The Borderlands of the Mediterranean Sea. The Mediterranean region normally secures 6 to 10 per cent of the world trade. These subtropical countries send out both raw materials and manufactured products. Their fruits, nuts, wines, silk and cotton goods, olive oil, cork, tobacco, and perfumes are sent to all parts of the world, while iron ore and phosphates are shipped from North Africa to the industrial nations bordering the North Atlantic Ocean. Recently petroleum from Iran and Iraq has been piped or shipped in tank cars to ports of the eastern Mediterranean Sea for export. The volume and value of this trade is now increasing rapidly and gives promise of becoming a major export of this region. In return the Mediterranean region imports large quantities of coal and coke and a great variety of manufactured products.

Eastern Europe. This area normally secures 4 to 6 per cent of the world trade. Since it is industrially backward, its exports are composed primarily of raw materials or semi-finished products. Wheat, petroleum, manganese, chromium, corn, flax, lumber, and dairy products represent major exports. Its chief imports are manufactured goods, especially machinery, machine tools, automobiles, and woolen and cotton goods.

East-Central South America, Southern Australia, and New Zealand. Agricultural and pastoral products represent the major exports of these regions. Coffee, wheat, wool, dairy products, meat, flax, corn, hides and skins represent the most notable exports from one or more of these regions.

The Caribbean Region. This region is especially noted for its exports of bananas, the most important fruit of international trade. It is also the largest sugar-exporting region in the world. Cacao, coffee, pineapples, sisal, tobacco, iron ore, chromium, petroleum, gold, silver, and platinum are also important exports of the region. Its imports are chiefly manufactured products.

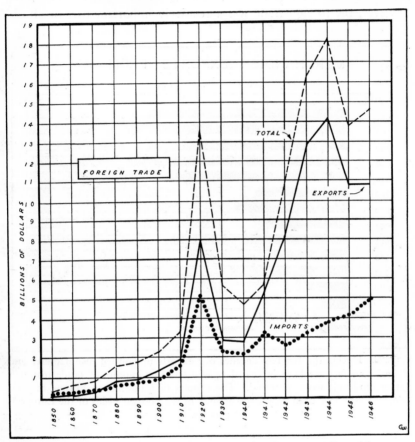

FIG. 289. Trends of American foreign trade by decades, 1850–1940, and by years, 1941–1946.

South Africa. This region is fortunate in possessing some of the most richly mineralized areas in the world and is famous for its production and export of diamonds and gold. It is also an exporter of wool and subtropical fruits. It purchases in return a great variety of manufactured goods.

Foreign Trade of the United States

Growth of Foreign Trade. From the time that the United States became an independent nation until 1850 foreign trade was small and practically stationary (Fig. 289). During the first part of this period, however, the foreign trade was a relatively important part of all our

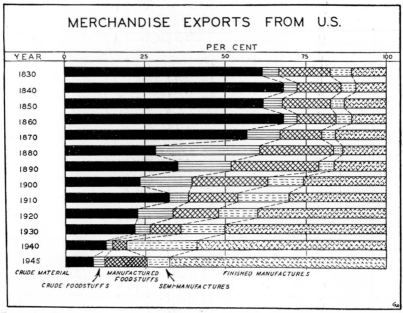

FIG. 290. During the last few decades our exports of finished manufactures and of semi-manufactures have increased rapidly and our imports of crude materials and of foodstuffs have decreased. The exports of foodstuffs to Europe in 1945, 1946, and 1947 have been very large because of the postwar needs of the European peoples.

trade (domestic and foreign) and held this comparatively prominent place mainly because of wars and commercial rivalries among European countries at that time. With the cessation of hostilities in Europe we turned more and more to domestic trade, as the population was moving westward into the Mississippi Valley.

From 1850 to 1870 there was a gradual increase in our foreign trade —an increase that may be explained in part by the development of the cotton industry. After 1870, however, with the development of cheap transportation, and with the production of large quantities of food-stuffs and crude materials, the Middle West began to affect the foreign trade of the country to a considerable extent, and the exports surpassed imports in value in the year 1873.

The foreign trade more than doubled between 1870 and 1900, and from the beginning of this period the large quantity of cheap grain

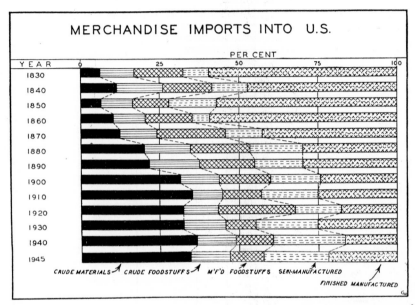

Fig. 291. A century ago manufactured goods represented more than 50 per cent of our total import trade; the imports of crude materials were relatively unimportant. Today crude materials represent approximately one-third of our total imports and the importation of manufactured goods is becoming relatively less important.

exported from America was creating a major problem in the agricultural districts of western Europe. Countries such as Denmark, for example, unable to compete in grain production with America's black prairies, turned to dairying and other types of more intensive utilization of the land.

Another period of rapid growth in American foreign trade began in 1900, when finished manufactures were becoming increasingly more important among our exports (Fig. 289). The foreign trade of the country swelled to tremendous proportions during and after World War I. The worldwide depression that followed caused our foreign trade to slump to less than one-fourth of its peak in 1920. World

War II and its aftermath have resulted in our foreign trade soaring to new heights in spite of the fact that it is largely a one-way trade—in 1946, exports represented 64 per cent in value whereas imports represented only 34 per cent.

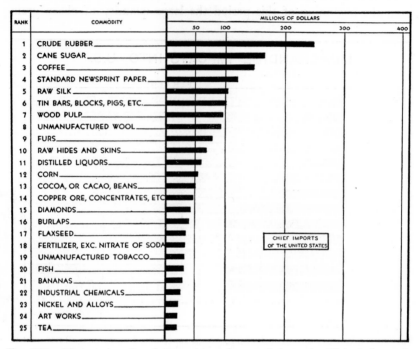

FIG. 292. The twenty-five leading items imported into the United States in 1937. In a general way, the pattern of imports indicated here had prevailed during most of the period between World War I and World War II. It may, therefore, be designated as our normal pattern of imports for recent times. (U. S. Department of Commerce.)

Kinds of Commodities Exported and Imported. The trade during our colonial period consisted chiefly of raw materials such as tobacco from tidewater Virginia, pine and oak timber, and furs exported to England in exchange for finished commodities. This was consequently an unbalanced traffic, a movement of bulky products to Europe in exchange for goods that were relatively high in value and small in bulk. Additional ballast was frequently required (in the westward voyage), which sometimes consisted of bricks, and gave rise to the early construction of brick mansions in tidewater Virginia.

The nineteenth century witnessed a period of rapid expansion in agricultural production and the export of such commodities. This development of agricultural exports was most marked during the second and third quarters of the nineteenth century, especially after

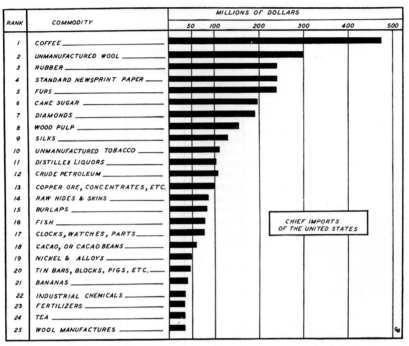

FIG. 293. The twenty-five leading items imported into the United States in 1946. After World War II our imports were quickly adjusted to fit, in a general way, the normal prewar pattern. Compare Figures 292 and 293. Of the twenty-five leading imports in 1937, twenty-two were listed among the leading imports of 1946. The order of importance has changed somewhat, but in general our most important imports of 1937 were also our most important imports in 1946. (U. S. Department of Commerce.)

the settlement of large stretches of fertile land in the West and the expansion of cotton growing in the South. But in the tremendous expansion of our exports which followed the revival of prosperity in 1896 there was a distinct and clearly defined change in the types of our imports and exports. For the first time in its history the United States began the export of manufactured products in large quantities.

During the years preceding World War I the foreign trade of the United States was in a decided state of transition (Figs. 290 and 291).

The exportation of foodstuffs was declining, both relatively and absolutely; home consumption required a larger percentage of our food production; and imports of crude materials and food products were increasing. These, however, were made up chiefly of tropical products, luxuries, and semi-manufactures. World War I and postwar

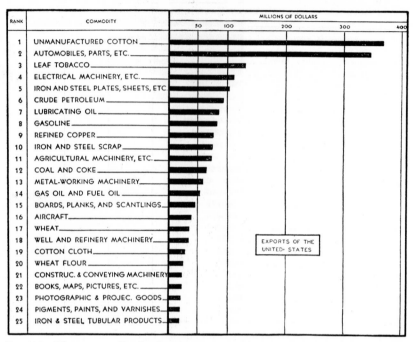

FIG. 294. The twenty-five leading items exported from the United States in 1937. (U. S. Department of Commerce.)

periods marked the definite triumph of machine industry. The export of manufactured goods increased on the one hand while exports of raw materials and foodstuffs, except for the actual period of the war, decreased sharply. This pattern was not changed greatly by World War II except for the great increase in the exports of foods.

After World War II our imports were quickly adjusted to fit, in a general way, the normal prewar pattern (Figs. 292 and 293). Our exports on the other hand were adjusted to fit the needs of the hungry, cold, ill-clothed, and ill-equipped masses of Eurasia. Food exports soared to an all-time high; exports of cotton goods to Europe were unprecedented; and our coal exports surpassed all previous records.

Some of this coal went to Germany and Great Britain, countries that normally lead the world in coal exports. Large quantities of industrial machinery and machine tools were sent to the devastated countries

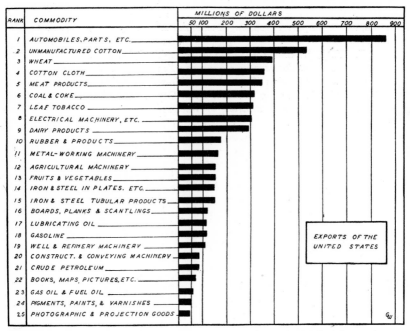

Fig. 295. The twenty-five leading items exported from the United States in 1946. After World War II our exports were adjusted to fit the needs of a war-devastated Eurasia. Our exports of food, coal, cotton goods, industrial machinery, and machine tools soared to an all-time high. (U. S. Department of Commerce.)

of Europe and Asia in order to hasten the rehabilitation of those areas (Figs. 294 and 295).

REFERENCES

Arthur, Paul, and others, *World Trade*, Office of International Affairs, May 1946.

Bishop, A. L., *Outlines of American Foreign Trade*, Ginn & Co., 1923.

Brown, H., *International Trade*, The Macmillan Co., 1915.

Cooper, C. S., *Foreign Trade Markets and Methods*, D. Appleton & Co., 1922.

Ely, Edward J., and others, *Summary of Foreign Commerce of the United States*, Bureau of Census, December 1946.

Fisk, G. M., and P. S. Peirce, *International Commercial Policies*, The Macmillan Co., 1923.

Fraser, H. F., *Foreign Trade and World Politics*, The Crofts Co., 1926.

GRIFFIN, C. E., *Principles of Foreign Trade*, The Macmillan Co., 1928.

KILLOUGH, H. B., *International Trade*, McGraw-Hill Book Co., 1938.

LIPPINCOTT, I., *The Development of Modern World Trade*, Appleton-Century, 1936.

LITMAN, S., *Essentials of International Trade*, John Wiley & Sons, 1923.

MEIRET, G., *Trade, Transport, and Finance*, The Macmillan Co., 1923.

ROORBACH, G. B., *Import Purchasing, Principles and Problems*, A. W. Shaw Co., 1927.

TAUSSIG, F. W., *International Trade*, The Macmillan Co., 1928.

U. S. DEPARTMENT OF COMMERCE: *Commerce Yearbooks*, 2 Vols. Annual.

WITHEROW, G. A., "Foreign Trade of the United States in 1930," *Commerce Reports*, Feb. 23, 1931, pp. 477–481, U. S. Department of Commerce.

WOLFE, A. J., *Theory and Practice of International Commerce*, International Publishing Co., 1919.

INDEX

Belgium, 126, 410, 633, 662, 669
Bellingham, Washington, 400
Benares, India, 719
Bengal, India, 234
Beni River, Bolivia, 193
Beograd (Belgrad), Rumania, 356
Bergen, Norway, 125, 386
Beriberi, 212
Bering Sea, 417, 554, 555
Bering Strait, 559
Berlin, Germany, 155, 728
Bern, Switzerland, 141
Berries, 411
Bihar, India, 157, 255, 256
Birch, 441
Birmingham, Alabama, 623; iron ore, 629–631; water supply, 631
Birmingham, England, 623, 664
Bisbee, Arizona, 694
Black Forest of Germany, 540
Black Sea, 158
Bluegrass, 428
Boa Vista, 167
Bochum, Germany, 668
Bolivia, 47, 149, 574, 578, 580, 594, 595; tin, 710–711
Bombay, India, 230, 231, 251
Borax, 297, 298
Bordeaux, France, 356
Borneo, 16, 168, 187, 192
Bosnia, 141
Bosporus Strait, 6
Boston, 454
Bradford, England, 663
Brahmaputra Delta, 255
Brahmaputra River, 72
Brahmaputra Valley, 248, 265
Brazil, 55, 86, 155, 192, 249, 251, 259, 313, 574, 580, 619, 620, 664, 713, 751; bananas, 210, 211; cacao, 197, 200; climate, 170, 171, 172; cotton, 254, 326; iron ore, 617, 619; maté, 265–266; oranges, 338, 372, 373, 375; plantation agriculture, 189; sugar, 262; timber, 179
Breadfruit, 221
Breezes: valley, 66; mountain, 66
Brest, 356
Bricks, 718–719

Briquettes, 668
Brisbane, Australia, 308
British Columbia, 390, 393, 394, 396, 397, 416
British East Indies, 8
British Empire, 15, 202
British Guiana, 705
British Isles, 5, 11, 386, 408; forest industries, 401; textile manufacture, 11
British Malaya, 192, 205
Brown, R. N. Rudmose, 559
Brownerths, 425
Brunhes, Jean, 293
Buckwheat, 333
Bucuresti (Bucharest), Rumania, 356
Budapest, Hungary, 356, 423
Buenos Aires, South America, 308, 338, 728
Building materials: bricks, 718–719; clay, 718–719; cement, 720; loess, 716–718; stone, 359, 719–720
Burma, 75, 128, 229, 238, 246, 257–267
Butadiene, 677
Butte, Montana, 694

Cacao, 165, 208, 214, 221, 244, 247; environmental requirements, 197; native versus foreign plantation, 201–202
Cadiz, Spain, 356
Cairo, Egypt, 277
Calabria, Italy, 157
Calamar, Colombia, 243, 244
Calcutta, India, 72, 249, 738
California, 46, 112, 154, 347, 358, 359, 382, 391, 395, 396, 397, 416, 417, 418, 540, 626, 725; agriculture, 361, 363, 365–366, 376; citrus fruits, 338, 361, 372; climate, 348, 349, 350, 351, 368; earthquakes, 151, 157; forests, 391, 395, 396, 397, 399; grapes, 378, 379; lumber, 395; map, 398; salmon fisheries, 416–419
Camel, 281, 282, 284, 357
Cameroon Mountains, 168
Campos of Brazil, 240, 242, 244–245
Campos of Venezuela, 177

To a possible May Day Queen.
I hope you luck, you have my vote.
Always—
Jerry Gaskins